Gluten-Free

GROCERY SHOPPING GUIDE

2011/2012 EDITION

W9-BON-433

Dr. Mara Matison
Dainis Matison

khP
Kal-Haven Publishing

Cecelia's Marketplace
Gluten-Free Grocery Shopping Guide

by Dr. Mara Matison & Dainis Matison

Kal-Haven Publishing
P.O. Box 20383
Kalamazoo, MI 49019 U.S.A.

ISBN 978-0-9794094-8-6

2011 / 2012 Edition

Printed in the United States of America
Cover illustration: Lilita Austrins

Making Gluten-Free Living Easy!

Cecelia's Marketplace
Kalamazoo, Michigan

www.CeceliasMarketplace.com

CONTENTS

About the Authors

The co-author of this book, Dr. Mara Matison, received her Doctor of Dental Surgery degree from University of Detroit Mercy, and her Bachelor of Arts degree in Psychology from Villanova University. Her husband and co-author, Dainis Matison, received his Master of Science degree in Information Technology and Bachelor of Arts degree in Finance from Ball State University. They are both members of Celiac Disease Foundation, Celiac Sprue Association, Gluten Intolerance Group, and supporters of Talk About Curing Autism and Generation Rescue. These are nationwide organizations that support people with celiac disease, gluten intolerance, gluten sensitivitiy and autism.

Cecelia's Marketplace was established by both Mara and Dainis in 2006, soon after Mara was diagnosed with celiac disease. The couple struggled with Mara's huge lifestyle change, which included adhering to a strict gluten-free diet. Shopping trips to the grocery store were very frustrating. Spending time calling food manufacturers to find out if products were gluten-free seemed like a daily routine. They knew there had to be an easier way, so they decided to compile a gluten-free grocery shopping guide. Since then, Mara has also been diagnosed with a casein and soy intolerance, which brought about the need for the *Gluten/Casein Free Grocery Shopping Guide* and the *Gluten/Casein/Soy Free Grocery Shopping Guide*. Her latest achievement is the newly released *Cecelia's Marketplace International Classics Gluten-Free Mexican* cookbook.

Thanks to all three of Cecelia's Marketplace Grocery Shopping Guides and the Gluten-Free Mexican cookbook, gluten-free living has now become easier not only for the authors, but also their families, friends and thousands of celiacs nationwide.

Preface - Note to the Reader

Cecelia's Marketplace Gluten-Free Grocery Shopping Guide has been written to help people that are in search of gluten-free products. Whether you are on a gluten-free diet, prepare gluten-free meals for yourself or others, or just enjoy eating gluten-free foods, this book is for you. It will help guide you to easy grocery shopping and eliminate the frustration and headaches that you've experienced trying to find gluten-free products. This guide is also great for restaurant owners, chefs, dieticians, family members, friends, and others that shop for, or prepare gluten-free foods. For those that are not familiar with gluten-free cooking, we have included two special sections in the front of the book: *What is Gluten? and Gluten-Free Kitchen Tips*.

We have alphabetized our *Gluten-Free Grocery Shopping Guide* to help you quickly find brand names of the products you are looking for. The guide is easy to use: just pick a product, look it up, and you'll have gluten-free brands at your fingertips. The book is small enough so that it can be carried with you to the grocery store when searching for products. Use it anytime, anywhere. In addition to the Gluten-Free Grocery Shopping Guide, there is a section in the back of the book that lists gluten-free over the counter (OTC) medications. Gluten-free shopping has never been easier. Treasure this book and enjoy all the gluten-free foods that are available!

Due to periodic changes in ingredients and new products, *Cecelia's Marketplace Gluten-Free Grocery Shopping Guide* is updated annually. Product alerts are posted on our website throughout the year at www.CeceliasMarketplace.com.

A percentage of our proceeds are donated to nationwide nonprofit organizations that support people with celiac disease, gluten intolerance and other gluten sensitivities.

Dr. Mara Matison & Dainis Matison

Acknowledgments

There are many people that have contributed to the creation of this book. The support from our family and friends has made this journey more enjoyable. Lilita A. for editing, cover illustration, and all the gluten-free meals that kept us going; Mik for editing, critiquing and successful business strategies; Ray for the reference materials and guidance to becoming successful entrepreneurs; Ligita for supporting us and all the delicious gluten-free recipes along the way; Lija for packaging & shipping; Lilita M. for showing us 'The Secret'; Liana, Velta, Ilga, Ryan and Matiss for believing in us; Our meticulous data collection and editing team of Annette Hensley, Caroline Aasen, Jessica Hensley, Jessica Rector, Jessica Schmidt, John Williamson, Lauma Matison, Melissa Al-Azzawi and Sarah Gregor; Jonnie Bryant for all the publishing advice and knowledge; Dr. Heidi Gjersoe for the diagnosis and support; Tracy Clupper for data entry & document styling; Natural Health Center for the wonderful gluten-free book signing events; Dr. Arnis Pone, Dr. Jason Ham, Kal-Haven Publishing, McNaughton & Gunn, and all our fellow "celiacs" for all the support.

Warning - Disclaimer

What is Gluten?

Gluten is a protein that is most commonly found in wheat, rye, and barley. It is comprised of two main protein groups: gliadins and gluteins. Gluten is found in most cereals, breads, pastas, soups, and pizza crusts. It may also be hidden in foods such as seasonings, salad dressings, sauces, additives and natural flavors. People that have celiac disease, gluten intolerance, or gluten sensitivity may suffer from chronic digestive problems when ingesting foods that contain gluten. Symptoms vary from person to person and may include diarrhea, bloating, weight loss and abdominal pain. Maintaining a strict gluten-free diet is the only way to alleviate these symptoms and treat the disease. If these conditions are left untreated, it may lead to serious health complications. After gluten is eliminated from the diet, the digestive tract begins to heal and the symptoms normally start to disappear after a few weeks.

Celiac disease, gluten intolerance and gluten sensitivity are diagnosed using various testing methods. These may include a blood test, a biopsy of the small intestine lining and/or a stool sample test. Approximately 3 million Americans are affected by celiac disease (1 in 133 people).[1]

[1]University of Maryland Medical Center, Dr. Alessio Fasano, 2003 Archives of Internal Medicine

Gluten-Free Kitchen Tips

It is very important prior to preparing a gluten-free meal, to clean the cooking area including, kitchen surfaces, pots, pans, utensils and any other items being used. Bread crumbs, flour particles or other gluten containing foods left in the cooking area can potentially contaminate a gluten-free meal.

Here are some tips to help prevent gluten contamination:

- Use an uncontaminated sponge to wash all working surfaces with soap and water.
- Clean and inspect pots, pans, utensils, cutting boards and other kitchenware for gluten residue.
- Use clean kitchen hand towels.
- If grilling, place aluminum foil over the grilling surface.
- Use squeeze bottle mayonnaise, mustard, ketchup, peanut butter, jelly/jam, butter/margarine and other condiments to prevent cross-contamination.
- Avoid using wooden utensils. Gluten residue can stay embedded in wooden utensils and cutting boards.
- Use a separate toaster for gluten-free bread, rice cakes, etc..
- Do not deep fry foods in contaminated oil (e.g. from breaded chicken wings, breaded chicken tenders, mozzarella sticks).
- In commercial kitchens, if using latex/rubber gloves, make sure the gloves are not coated with powder (starch).

Our Data Collection

The product information in this book was collected between August 2010 - November 2010. The information was received from product manufacturers and major supermarkets via internet, e-mail, phone, mail, or product labels.

The Food and Drug Administration (FDA) has proposed to define the term "gluten-free" as containing less than 20 parts per million (ppm) gluten. A final rule on this proposal will be issued no later than four years after the law's enactment date of August 2008. For further information on this regulation please visit www.fda.gov.

Some food manufacturers test their products for the presence of gluten. Those products that have not passed this test have been excluded from this book. Currently, not all companies test their products, therefore, we cannot guarantee that all the products listed in our book are less than 20 ppm gluten.

Those products that have been manufactured in the same facility or on shared equipment with gluten, but follow strict cross-contamination control guidelines, have been included. We have tried our best not to include products from manufacturers that do not take measures to prevent cross-contamination.

Symbols

There are some companies that manufacture their products in a dedicated gluten-free facility or environment. Some products also go through strict guidelines and vigorous testing by either the Celiac Sprue Association (CSA) Recognition Seal Program or the Gluten Intolerance Group (GIG) Gluten-Free Certification Organization to be verified as gluten-free. In this guide we have marked these manufacturers and products with the following symbols:

▲ - manufactured in a dedicated gluten-free facility or environment

● - verfied, tested, or certified gluten-free by either the CSA Recognition Seal Program or the GIG Gluten-Free Certification Organization

Celiac Spruce Association®

Certified
GF ™
Gluten-Free

There are also some manufacturers that label their gluten-free products as being manufactured in the same facility or on shared equipment with gluten. In this guide we have labeled those products with following symbols:

! - manufactured in the same facility as other products containing gluten

!! - manufactured on shared equipment as other products containing gluten

Other Products Available
by Cecelia's Marketplace

Grocery Shopping Guides:
Gluten/Casein Free
Gluten/Casein/Soy Free

Cookbooks:
Gluten-Free Mexican

Other Products:
Gluten-Free Dining Out Cards

FREE Email Newsletter:
Gluten-Free Product of the Day

For **Product Alerts** or more information about our products please visit us online:

www.CeceliasMarketplace.com

This book is dedicated to:

All those in search of gluten-free products.

Gluten-Free
Grocery Shopping Guide (A-Z)

A A

Alfredo Sauce
> **Bertolli** - Mushroom, Regular
> **Classico** - All Varieties
> **Food Club Brand** - Alfredo Sauce Seasoning Mix
> **Full Flavor Foods ▲** - Alfredo Sauce Mix ●
> **Mayacamas** - Chicken Fettuccine, Regular
> **Ragu** - Cheesy (Classic Alfredo, Light Parmesan Alfredo)
> **Safeway Select** - Regular, Roasted Garlic, Sundried Tomato

Almond Beverages ... see Nut Beverages

Almonds... see Nuts

Amaranth
> **Arrowhead Mills** - Whole Grain
> **Bob's Red Mill ▲** - Organic Flour
> **Gluty Free** - Organic ●
> **Nu-World Foods** - Amaranth Side Serve (Garlic Herb ●, Savory Herb ●, Spanish Tomato ●), Bread Crumbs ●, Flour ●, Pre Gel Powder ●, Puffed ●, Seed ●, Starch ●, Toasted Bran Flour ●

Anchovies
> **Crown Prince** - Flat In Olive Oil, Natural (Anchovy Paste, Fillet Anchovies In Olive Oil), Rolled w/Capers In Olive Oil
> **Star** - Fillets Of Anchovies

Angel Hair Pasta... see Pasta

Animal Crackers... see Cookies

Apple Butter
> **Bramley's**
> **Eden Organic** - Apple, Apple Cherry, Cherry
> **Fischer & Wieser** - Pecan
> **Lucky Leaf**
> **Manischewitz**
> **Musselman's**

Apple Cider... see Cider/Cider Mix

Apple Rings
> **Lucky Leaf** - Spiced
> **Musselman's** - Spiced

Apples

... *All Fresh Fruits & Vegetables Are Gluten-Free

Ceres Kitchen ▲ - Caramel Apple

Dole - All Fruits Bowls *(Except Fruit Crisps)*

Earthbound Farm - Organic Sliced

Food Club Brand - Fried Apples (Regular, w/Cinnamon)

Giant Eagle Brand - Caramel Cinnamon Side Dish

Gluty Free - Dried (Cinnamon ●, Organic ●, Regular ●)

Lucky Leaf - Fried, Sliced

Musselman's - Sliced

Nuts Online - Dried Apples (Cinnamon Wedges ●, Diced Fuji ●, Dried ●, Infused Dried Wedges ●, Organic Chips ●, Organic Dried●, Simply Organic ●)

Trader Joe's - Chunky Spiced Apples

Applesauce

Albertsons - Cinnamon, Natural, Original

Apple Time - Regular

Beech-Nut - Applesauce (Stage 1 Fruits, Stage 2 Fruits)

Eden Organic - Organic Apple (Cherry, Cinnamon, Regular, Strawberry)

Food Club Brand - Applesauce (Chunky, Cinnamon, Natural, Original, Strawberry)

Full Circle - Organic (No Sugar Added, Sweetened)

Giant Brand - Canned (Chunky, Cinnamon, Mixed Berry, Natural, Strawberry)

Great Value Brand (Wal-Mart) -
Applesauce Glass Jar (Cinnamon, Regular, Unsweetened),
Applesauce Plastic Cups (Cinnamon, Light, Natural, No Sugar Added, Regular, Strawberry)

Hy-Vee -
Cinnamon
Light (w/Mixed Berry, w/Strawberry)
Natural
Unsweetened

Kroger Brand - Flavored, Plain

A

Lucky Leaf - Cherry Fruit 'N Sauce, Cinnamon, Natural, Regular, Strawberry Fruit 'N Sauce

Meijer Brand - Chunky, Cinnamon, Mixed Berry, Natural, Organic (Cinnamon, Sweetened, Unsweetened), Original, Strawberry

Midwest Country Fare - Home Style, Natural w/(Cinnamon, Peaches, Raspberries, Strawberries)

Momma's Old-Fashioned Applesauce - No Sugar Added, Original Flavor

Mott's - Chunky, Cinnamon, Homestyle, Natural No Sugar Added, Original

Musselman's - Chunky, Cinnamon (Lite, Regular), Golden Delicious, Healthy Picks (Blueberry Pomegranate, Granny Smith, Raspberry Acai), Homestyle (Cinnamon, Regular), Lite Fruit 'N Sauce (Cherry, Grape, Orange Mango, Peach, Raspberry, Strawberry), McIntosh Apple, Organic (Regular, Unsweetened), Regular, Totally Fruit (Apple, Mixed Berry, Peach, Strawberry), Unsweetened

Nature's Goodness Baby Food - Stage 1, Stage 2

O Organics

Publix - Chunky, Cinnamon, Old Fashioned, Unsweetened

Publix GreenWise Market - Organic Unsweetened

Safeway Brand - Cups, Natural, Sweetened

Santa Cruz - Fruit Sauces (All Varieties)

Spartan Brand - Cinnamon, Natural, Peach, Raspberry, Regular, Strawberry

Stop & Shop Brand - Chunky, Cinnamon, Mixed Berry, Natural, Strawberry

Tree Top - Cinnamon, Naturally Sweetened, No Sugar Added Natural, Organic, Raspberry, Strawberry

Wegmans Brand - Chunky, Cinnamon, McIntosh, Mixed Berry, Natural (Chunky, No Sugar Added), No Sugar Added, Peach Mango, Regular

Winn Dixie - Cinnamon, Sweetened, Unsweetened

Woodstock Farms - Organic Applesauce (Apricot, Blueberry, Cinnamon, Mango, Regular)

Apricots
... *All Fresh Fruits & Vegetables Are Gluten-Free*

Albertsons - Canned

Del Monte - Canned/Jarred Fruit (All Varieties), Fruit Snack Cups (Metal, Plastic)

Giant Brand - Canned (In Heavy Syrup, Island In Light Syrup)

Gluty Free - Dried (California ●, Diced ●, Organic Turkish ●, Pluots ●, Turkish ●)

Gordon Food Service - Halves (Peeled, Unpealed (In Juice, Regular))

Hy-Vee - Lite Unpeeled Halves Sweetened w/Splenda, Unpeeled Halves

Nuts Online - Dried Fruit (California ●, Diced ●, Dried ●, Organic California ●, Organic Turkish ●, Pluots ●)

Publix - Canned Halves Unpeeled (In Heavy Syrup, Water & Artificial Sweetener)

S&W - All Canned/Jarred Fruits

Stop & Shop Brand - Heavy Syrup, Island Apricots (In Light Syrup, w/Splenda)

Winn Dixie - Unpeeled Halves In Heavy Syrup ●

Artichokes
... *All Fresh Fruits & Vegetables Are Gluten-Free*

Birds Eye - All Plain Frozen Vegetables

C & W - All Plain Frozen Vegetables

Cara Mia - In Water, Marinated, Salad

Kirkland Signature - Hearts

Mezzetta - Grilled, Marinated Hearts

Native Forest - Artichoke Hearts (Marinated, Quartered, Whole)

Private Selections - Hearts

Reese - Marinated, Regular

Safeway Select - Marinated Artichoke

Spartan Brand - Hearts

Trader Joe's - Artichoke Antipasto, Artichoke Hearts In Water, Artichoke Red Pepper Tapenade **!!**, Frozen Artichoke Hearts

A   **Wegmans Brand** - Artichoke Hearts (Halves & Quarters, In Brine, Marinated Quartered), Marinated Long Stemmed

B   **Asparagus**

... *All Fresh Fruits & Vegetables Are Gluten-Free*

Albertsons - Cuts & Tips, No Salt Spears, Whole Spears

Birds Eye - All Plain Frozen Vegetables

Cara Mia - Marinated Green

Del Monte - All Canned Varieties

Food Club Brand - Canned Cuts & Tips

Great Value Brand (Wal-Mart) - Canned (All Green Asparagus Spears, Extra Long)

Green Giant - Canned Spears, Cut Asparagus

Hannaford Brand - Cuts & Tips, Whole Tall

Hy-Vee - Cut Spears

Kroger Brand - All Plain Vegetables (Canned, Frozen)

Laura Lynn - Cut Asparagus

Meijer Brand - Canned Cuts & Tips

Native Forest - Green (Cuts & Tips, Spears)

Nuts Online - Simply Asparagus Freeze Dried Vegetables ●

S&W - All Canned Vegetables

Safeway Brand - Canned Cut

Spartan Brand - Cut

Stop & Shop Brand - Asparagus (Spears, Tips & Cuts)

Trader Joe's - Frozen (Grilled Spears, Spears)

Wegmans Brand - Cleaned & Cut Tips, Cut Spears & Tips

Woodstock Farms - Organic Frozen Whole Baby Asparagus

Avocado

... *All Fresh Fruits & Vegetables Are Gluten-Free*

B

Baby Food

Baby Mum-Mum ▲ - Rice Rusks (Banana, Organic Original, Original, Vegetable), Biscuits (Banana Rice, Organic Original Rice, Original Rice, Vegetable Rice)

Beech-Nut -
Cereals (DHA Plus Rice, Rice)
Stage 1 Fruits (Applesauce, Chiquita Bananas, Peaches, Pears),
Stage 1 Meats (Beef & Beef Broth, Chicken & Chicken Broth,
Turkey & Turkey Broth)
Stage 1 Vegetables (Butternut Squash, Tender Golden Sweet
Potatoes, Tender Sweet Carrots, Tender Sweet Peas, Tender
Young Green Beans)
Stage 2 Desserts (Banana Apple Yogurt, DHA Plus Apple Delight)
Stage 2 Dinners (Apples & Chicken, Chicken & Rice, Chicken
Noodle, Macaroni & Beef w/Vegetables, Pineapple Glazed
Ham, Sweet Potatoes & Chicken, Turkey Rice, Vegetables &
Chicken)
Stage 2 Dinners Good Evening (Creamy Chicken Noodle, Ham &
Pineapple & Rice, Hearty Vegetable Stew, Sweet Potato & Turkey,
Turkey Tetrazzini)
Stage 2 Fruits (Apples & Bananas, Apples & Blueberries, Apples
& Cherries, Apples, Applesauce, Apricots w/Pears & Apples,
Chiquita Bananas, Chiquita Bananas & Strawberries, DHA Plus
Apple Delight, DHA Plus Apple w/Pomegranate Juice, DHA
Plus Banana Supreme, Mango, Mango & Kiwi, Peaches, Pears,
Pears & Bananas, Pears & Pineapples, Pears & Raspberries)
Stage 2 Rice Cereal Apples w/Cinnamon
Stage 2 Vegetables (Butternut Squash, Corn & Sweet Potatoes,
Country Garden Vegetables, DHA Plus Butternut Squash w/
Corn, DHA Plus Sweet Potatoes, Mixed Vegetables, Sweet Corn
Casserole, Sweet Potatoes & Apples, Tender (Golden Sweet
Potatoes, Sweet Carrots, Sweet Peas, Young Green Beans)
Stage 3 Dinners Country Vegetables & Chicken
Stage 3 Fruits (Apples & Bananas, Chiquita Bananas, Homestyle
Apples Cherries Plums, Homestyle Cinnamon Raisins & Pears,
Homestyle Peaches Apples & Bananas, Homestyle Pears &
Blueberries)
Stage 3 Rice Cereal & Pears

B

Stage 3 Turkey Rice Dinner

Stage 3 Vegetables (Corn & Rice, Green Beans, Sweet Potatoes)

Bright Beginnings - Pediatric Soy Vanilla Drink

Earth's Best Organic Baby Food -

1st Beginner First Foods (Apples, Bananas, Carrots, Pears, Peas, Prunes, Squash, Sweet Potatoes)

2nd Antioxidant Blends (Apple Butternut Squash, Banana Mango, Carrot Tomato, Sweet Potato Apricot)

2nd Dinners (Rice & Lentil, Summer Vegetable, Sweet Potatoes & Chicken)

2nd Fruits (Apples, Apples & Apricots, Apples & Bananas, Apples & Blueberries, Apples & Plums, Bananas, Bananas & Peaches & Raspberries, Pears, Pears & Mangos, Pears & Raspberries, Plum Banana Brown Rice Fruit & Whole Grain Combination)

2nd Gourmet Meals (Creamy Chicken Apple Compote, Sweet Pea Turkey Wild Rice)

2nd Seasonal Harvest (Pumpkin Apple, Sweet Potato Cinnamon)

2nd Vegetables (Carrots, Corn & Butternut Squash, Garden Vegetables, Green Beans & Rice, Peas & Brown Rice, Sweet Potatoes, Winter Squash)

3rd Dinners Vegetable Beef Pilaf

3rd Fruits (Banana & Strawberries, Chunky Orchard Fruit)

3rd Vegetable Medleys (Sweet Corn & Carrot, Sweet Peas & Creamed Spinach)

Whole Grain Rice Cereal Apples

Ella's Kitchen -

Smoothie Fruits (The Green One, The Purple One, The Red One, The Yellow One)

Stage 1 Baby Food (Apples & Bananas, Broccoli Pears & Peas, Butternut Squash Carrots Apples & Prunes, Carrots Apples & Parsnips, Peaches & Bananas, Spinach Apples & Rutabaga, Strawberries & Apples, Sweet Potatoes Pumpkin Apples & Blueberries)

B

Gerber Baby Food -

    1st Foods Fruits & Vegetables (Applesauce, Bananas, Carrots, Green Beans, Peaches, Pears, Peas, Prunes, Squash, Sweet Potatoes)

    2nd Foods Dinners (Apples & Chicken, Beef & Beef Gravy, Chicken & Chicken Gravy, Chicken & Rice, Ham & Ham Gravy, Sweet Potatoes & Turkey, Turkey & Turkey Gravy, Veal & Veal Gravy, Vegetable Beef, Vegetable Chicken)

    2nd Foods Fruits & Vegetables (Apple Blueberry, Apple Strawberry Banana, Apples & Cherries, Applesauce, Apricots w/Mixed Fruit, Banana Mixed Berry, Banana Orange Medley, Banana Plum Grape, Banana w/Apples & Pears, Bananas, Butternut Squash & Corn, Carrots, Green Beans, Peaches, Pear Pineapples, Pears, Peas, Prunes w/Apples, Sweet Potatoes)

    2nd Foods Smoothies (Banana Yogurt, Fruit Medley, Hawaiian Delight, Mango, Peach Cobbler)

    3rd Foods Dinners (Mixed Vegetables & Beef, Mixed Vegetables & Chicken, Mixed Vegetables & Turkey, Turkey Rice & Vegetables)

    3rd Foods Fruits & Vegetables (Apples, Banana Strawberry, Bananas, Broccoli & Carrots w/Cheese, Green Beans w/Rice, Peaches, Pears, Squash, Sweet Potatoes)

    3rd Foods Smoothies Fruit Medley

    Graduates Finger Foods (Apple Wagon Wheels, Cheesy Carrot Wagon Wheels)

    Graduates Fruit Diced Apples

    Graduates Fruit Splashers (Grape, Strawberry Kiwi, Tropical Fruit)

    Graduates Fruit Strips (Strawberry, Wildberry)

    Graduates Fruit Twists (Apple & Strawberry, Cherry Berry, Strawberry & Grape)

    Graduates Healthy Meals For Preschoolers Chicken & Rice

    Graduates Lil' Entrees (Rice & Turkey In Gravy w/Green Beans & Carrots, White Turkey Stew w/Rice & Vegetables)

    Graduates Lil' Sticks (Chicken, Meat, Turkey)

    Graduates Smart Sips (Plain, Strawberry, Vanilla)

B

Graduates Mini Fruit Snacks Apple
Graduates Vegetables Diced Carrots
Graduates Yogurt Melts (Mixed Strawberry, Peach, Strawberry)
  Rice Cereal (DHA, Single Grain, w/Apples, w/Mixed Fruit)
Gerber Organic Baby Food -
  1st Foods (Applesauce, Bananas, Carrots, Pears, Sweet Peas, Sweet
    Potatoes)
  2nd Foods (Apple Strawberry, Applesauce, Bananas, Butternut
    Squash & Carrots, Butternut Squash & Corn, Carrots, Corn,
    Green Beans, Pear & Wildberry, Sweet Potatoes)
Homemade Baby - Baby Tex Mex ●, Just (Apples ●, Green Beans ●,
  Pears ●, Peas ●, Squash ●, Sweet Potatoes ●), Piwi ●, Squapples ●,
  Yummy Yammies ●
Kroger Brand - Comforts For Baby (Organic Baby Formula,
  Pediatric Electrolyte)
Meijer Brand -
  DND (Chocolate, Strawberry, Vanilla)
  Gluco Burst (Arctic Cherry, Chocolate Diabetic Nutritional Drink,
    Strawberry DND, Vanilla DND)
  Little Fruit (Apple, Strawberry/Banana)
  Little Veggies Corn
  PND (Bright Beginnings Vanilla Soy, Chocolate, Strawberry, Vanilla
    Soy, Vanilla w/Fiber)
  Term Formula (Regular, Soy)
  Vanilla Pediatric Nutritional Drink
  w/DHA (Follow On, Gentle Protein, Lactose Free, Milk, Soy)
Nature's Goodness Baby Food -
  Stage 1 Fruits & Vegetables (Applesauce, Bananas, Carrots, Green
    Beans, Peaches, Pears, Peas, Prunes, Squash, Sweet Potatoes)
  Stage 2 Desserts (Banana Pudding, Dutch Apple, Fruit Dessert,
    Tutti Frutti)
  Stage 2 Dinners (Apples & Chicken, Apples & Chicken, Apples &
    Ham, Beef & Beef Gravy, Broccoli & Chicken, Chicken &
    Chicken Gravy, Green Beans & Turkey, Sweet Potato & Turkey,

Turkey & Turkey Gravy, Turkey Rice Dinner, Vegetable Dinner (Chicken, Ham))

Stage 2 Fruits & Vegetables (Apples & Blueberries, Apples & Pears, Apples Strawberries & Bananas, Applesauce, Apricots w/Pears & Apples, Bananas, Bananas w/Apples & Pears, Bananas w/Mixed Berries, Carrots, Corn & Sweet Potatoes, Green Beans, Mixed Vegetables, Peaches, Pears, Plums w/Apples, Pumpkins w/Pears, Squash, Sweet Peas, Sweet Potatoes)

Stage 2 Rice Cereal (w/Applesauce, w/Peaches & Bananas)

Stage 3 Desserts (Bananas & Strawberries w/Tapioca, Bananas w/Tapioca)

Stage 3 Dinners (Green Beans & Rice, Turkey Rice)

Stage 3 Rice Cereal w/Apples & Bananas

Stage 3 Vegetable Sweet Potatoes

O Organics -

Stage 1 (Applesauce, Bananas, Carrots, Pears, Peas, Sweet Potatoes)

Stage 2 (Apple Apricot, Apple Banana, Apple Wild Blueberry, Applesauce, Bananas, Carrots, Mixed Vegetables, Peach Rice Banana, Pear Raspberry, Pears, Peas and Brown Rice, Prunes, Squash, Summer Vegetables, Sweet Potatoes)

Stage 3 (Sweet Potato Chicken Dinner, Vegetable Chicken Dinner, Vegetable Lentil Dinner)

Baby Formula

Bright Beginnings - Baby Formulas (Gentle Baby, Organic Baby, Premium, Soy)

Earth's Best - Organic Infant Formula w/DHA & ARA *(Except Soy Infant Formula)*

Enfamil - All Varieties

Hy-Vee - Baby Formula (Regular, Gentle, Milk Based, Soy), Pediatric Electrolyte (Fruit, Grape, Regular)

Neocate - Infant (DHA & ARA, Regular), Junior (Chocolate, Tropical, Unflavored, w/Prebiotics), Nutra, One +

Nestle Good Start - Good Start (2 Gentle Plus, 2 Protect Plus, 2 Soy Plus, Gentle Plus, Protect Plus, Ready To Feed Convenience Packs, Soy Plus)

B

 Nutramigen - All Varieties
 Pregestimil
 Private Selections - Organic Infant Formula
 Publix - Infant Formula (Milk, Soy)
 Similac - All Varieties
Bacon
 Applegate Farms - Natural (Canadian, Dry Cured, Peppered, Sunday, Turkey), Organic (Sunday, Turkey)
 Busseto - Pancetta, Prosciutto
 Butcher's Cut - Hickory Smoked (Regular Sliced, Sliced Center Cut, Thick Sliced)
 Butterball - Turkey Bacon (Lower Sodium, Regular, Thin & Crispy)
 Dietz & Watson ▲ - Canadian Style ●, Gourmet Imported ●
 Dorothy Lane Market - All Varieties (Uncured)
 Eckrich - Fresh Hickory Smoked Bacon, Fully Cooked Ready To Crisp Bacon
 Farmer John - Classic, Old Fashion Maple Table Brand, Premium (Applewood, Low Sodium, Old Fashioned Maple, Thick Cut)
 Five Star Brand - Canadian
 Garrett County Farms - Classic Sliced (Dry Rubbed!, Turkey!), Sliced (Applewood!, Canadian Style!), Thick Sliced Dry Rubbed!, Turkey Peppered!
 Giant Brand - Sliced (Regular, Thick)
 Global Gourmet - Irish Bacon
 Gordon Food Service - Cooked (Crumbles, Slices, Whole Muscle), Fresh
 Great Value Brand (Wal-Mart) - Hickory Smoked, Low Sodium
 Hannaford Brand - Fully Cooked, Lower Sodium, Maple Flavored, Premium Cut, Regular
 Hertel's - All Varieties
 Honeysuckle White - Smoked Turkey Bacon
 Hormel - Black Label Bacon (Center Cut, Lower Sodium, Maple, Mesquite, Original), Canadian Style, Fully Cooked, Microwave, Natural Choice (Canadian, Original)

bacon

B

Hy-Vee - Double Smoked, Fully Cooked Turkey Bacon, Hickory, Hickory Smoked Fully Cooked, Lower Sodium

Jennie-O Turkey Store - Bacon (Extra Lean Turkey, Turkey)

Jimmy Dean - Fully Cooked Slices Maple, Fully Cooked Slices Hickory Smoked, Thick Sliced (Hickory Smoked, Maple), Premium Bacon (Lower Sodium, Original, Thick Slice)

Jones Dairy Farm - Canadian ●, Cherry Hardwood Smoked Regular Sliced ●, Old Fashioned Slab ●, Sliced (Regular ●, Thick ●)

Kirkland Signature - Bacon, Crumbled

Kroger Brand - Bac N Buds, Canadian, Hardwood Smoked (No Sugar, Sugar Cured), Hickory Smoked, Turkey

Kroger Value - Hickory Smoked

Meijer Brand - Lower Sodium, Regular

Member's Mark - Turkey Bacon

Nature's Basket - Regular

Old Smokehouse - Applewood, Maple Peppered, Original

Organic Prairie - Hardwood Smoked Turkey Bacon

Oscar Mayer - America's Favorite, Center Cut, Fully Cooked (Bacon, Thick Cut), Hearty Thick Cut, Lower Sodium, Natural Smoked Uncured

Publix - All Varieties

Pure Market Express ▲ - Bac'un ●

Range Brand

Safeway Brand - Fully Cooked, Hickory Smoked

Safeway Select - 40% Less Sodium, Regular Sliced, Thick Sliced

Smithfield - Brown Sugar, Center Cut 40% Lower Fat, Cracked Peppercorn, Maple, Natural Hickory Smoked, Natural Hickory Smoked Thick Sliced

Stop & Shop Brand - Bacon (Center Cut Sliced, Lower Sodium, Maple Flavored, Regular Sliced)

Tom & Ted's - Thick Sliced Sugar Cured

Trader Joe's - Turkey, Uncured

Wegmans Brand - Fully Cooked Naturally Smoked, Uncured Applewood Smoked

B

Wellshire Farms - Bacon (Applewood Smoked!!, Beef!!, Bulk Maple Dry Rubbed!, Classic Sliced Dry Rubbed!, Classic Sliced Turkey!, Dry Rubbed Applewood!!, Fully Cooked Hickory Smoked!!, Natural!!, Sliced Canadian Brand Turkey!!, Sliced Canadian Style!!, Sliced Dry Rubbed!!, Sliced Maple!!, Sliced Panchetta!!, Sliced Peppered Dry Rubbed!!, Sliced Peppered Turkey!!, Thick Sliced Dry Rubbed!!, Whole Panchetta!!)

Wellshire Organic - Organic Bacon (Dry Rubbed, Turkey)

Winn Dixie - Hickory Sweet Sliced Bacon (Hardwood Smoked, Lower Sodium, Thick, Thin, Turkey)

Bacon Bits

Garrett County Farms - Salt Cured Bacon Bits!

Great Value Brand (Wal-Mart) - Imitation, Real Bacon Pieces

Hormel - Bacon (Bits, Crumbles, Pieces)

Laura Lynn - Bacon Chips

Oscar Mayer - Real Bacon Bits

Publix - Bits, Pieces

Spartan Brand - Bacon Chips

Wellshire Farms - Salt Cured Bacon Bits!!

Bagels

Against The Grain Gourmet - Sesame, Sun Dried Tomato/Basil

Ceres Kitchen ▲ - Regular

Enjoy Life ▲ - Bagels (Cinnamon Raisin ●, Classic Original ●)

Gluten-Free Creations ▲ - Berry ●, Cinnamon Raisin ●, Everything ●, Jalapeno Cheese ●, Onion ●, Plain ●

Glutino ▲ - Premium (Cinnamon & Raisin, Multi Grain, Plain, Poppy Seed, Sesame)

Kinnikinnick ▲ - Tapioca Rice (Cinnamon Raisin, New York Style Plain, Sesame)

Rose's Bakery ▲ - Salted

The Grainless Baker ▲ - Cinnamon Raisin, Onion, Plain

Trader Joe's - Gluten Free Bagels

Udi's Gluten Free Foods ▲ - Gluten Free Plain

Baguettes... see Bread

Baked Apples
   Lucky Leaf - Dutch
   Musselman's - Dutch
Baking Bars
   Baker's - Bittersweet, German's Sweet, Select (Bittersweet, Semi Sweet), Semi Sweet, Unsweetened, White
   Dagoba - Semi Sweet, Unsweetened
   Trader Joe's - Unsweetened Belgium Baking Chocolate
Baking Chips
   Albertsons - Milk Chocolate, Mini Semi Sweet, Semi Sweet
   Andes - Crème De Menthe, Peppermint Crunch
   Cause You're Special ▲ - Chocolate Chips
   Chocolate Dream - Semi Sweet
   Ener-G ▲ - Chocolate Chips
   Enjoy Life ▲ - Semi Sweet Chocolate Chips ●
   Food Club Brand - Baking Chips (Butterscotch, Milk Chocolate, Peanut Butter, Semi Sweet, Vanilla)
   Ghirardelli - Chocolate Chips (60% Bittersweet, Milk Chocolate, Semi Sweet)
   Giant Brand - Semi Sweet Chocolate
   Ginger Evans - Semi Sweet Chocolate
   Gordon Food Service - Semi Sweet Chocolate
   Hannaford Brand - Semi Sweet Chocolate Chips
   Hershey's - Chocolate Chips (Milk, Semi Sweet, Special Dark), Cinnamon Chips
   Hy-Vee - Chips (Butterscotch, Milk Chocolate, Mini Semi Sweet, Peanut Butter, Semi Sweet Chocolate, Vanilla Flavored White)
   Kroger Brand - Butterscotch Morsels, Chips (Milk Chocolate, Peanut Butter, Semi Sweet), Chocolate Chunks
   Kroger Value - Semi Sweet
   Manischewitz - Chocolate Morsels
   Meijer Brand - Butterscotch Chips, Chocolate Chips Semi Sweet, Milk Chocolate Chips, Peanut Butter Chips, White Baking Chips
   Midwest Country Fare - Chocolate Flavored Chips

B

Nestle - Milk Chocolate & Peanut Butter Swirled Morsels, Milk Chocolate Morsels, Peanut Butter & Milk Chocolate Morsels, Premier White Morsels, Semi Sweet Chocolate (& Premier White Swirled Morsels, Chunks, Mini Morsels, Morsels)

NoNuttin' Foods ▲ - Semi Sweet Mini Chocolate Chips ●

O Organics - Semi Sweet

Private Selections - Dark Chocolate Chunks, Milk Chocolate, Organic Semi Sweet, White Chocolate

Publix - Morsels (Butterscotch, Milk Chocolate, Semi Sweet Chocolate)

Safeway Brand - Butterscotch, Milk Chocolate, Semi Sweet

Spartan Brand - Baking Chips (Butterscotch, Chocolate Semi Sweet, Milk Chocolate, White Chocolate)

Stop & Shop Brand - Semi Sweet Chocolate Chips

Trader Joe's - Chocolate Chips Semi Sweet, Milk Chocolate Peanut Butter Chips, Milk Chocolate Peanut Butter, White Chocolate

Tropical Source - Semi Sweet Chocolate Chips

Wegmans Brand - Chocolate Morsels Semi Sweet

Winn Dixie - Milk Chocolate, Semi Sweet

Woodstock Farms - Organic Dark Chocolate Chips w/Evaporated Cane Juice

Baking Cocoa

Dagoba - Organic

Hy-Vee

Kroger Brand

Spartan Brand

Stop & Shop Brand

Watkins

Baking Decorations & Frostings

Betty Crocker - Cookie Icing (Blue, Green, Red, White), Decorating Decors (All Sugars, Chocolate Sprinkles, Nonpareils, Rainbow Mix Sprinkles, Red White & Blue Sprinkles, Stars), Decorating Gels All Colors, Decorating Icing All Colors, Easy Flow Icing All Colors,

baking decorations & frostings

B

Easy Squeeze All Decorating Icing, Rich & Creamy Frosting (Butter Cream, Cherry, Chocolate, Coconut Pecan, Cream Cheese, Creamy White, Dark Chocolate, Lemon, Milk Chocolate, Rainbow Chip, Triple Chocolate Fudge Chip, Vanilla), Whipped Frosting (Butter Cream, Chocolate, Cream Cheese, Fluffy White, Milk Chocolate, Strawberry Mist, Vanilla, Whipped Cream)

Cake Mate - Decorating Gels All Colors, Decorating Icing All Colors

Cherrybrook Kitchen - Gluten Free Frosting Mix (Chocolate, Vanilla) *(Box Must Say Gluten Free)*, Ready To Spread Vanilla Frosting

Dagoba - All Varieties

Duncan Hines - Frosting (Coconut Supreme *(Coconut Pecan is Not Gluten-Free)*, Creamy Home Style (Buttercream, Caramel, Chocolate Buttercream, Classic Chocolate, Classic Vanilla, Cream Cheese, Dark Chocolate Fudge, French Vanilla, Lemon Supreme, Milk Chocolate, Strawberries 'N Cream), Whipped (Cream Cheese, Fluffy White, Vanilla)), White Chocolate Almond)

Earthly Treats ▲ - Sugar Sprinkles ●

Food Tek Fast & Fresh ▲ - Dairy Free Chocolate Flavored Icing, Dairy Free Vanilla Flavored Icing

Gluten-Free Creations ▲ - Frosting Mix (Chocolate ●, White ●)

Gluten-Free Essentials ▲ - Frosting Mix (Lemon Glaze ●, Supreme Chocolate ●, Vanilla Royal ●)

Katy Sweet ▲ - Crumbles (Praline ●, Toffee ●)

Kinnikinnick ▲ - Icing Sugar

Kroger Brand - Rainbow Sprinkles, Sugar Sprinkles, White & Chocolate Bark Coating

Laura Lynn - Sprinkles Toppings (Chocolate, Rainbow)

Let's Do...Sprinkelz - All Varieties

Namaste Foods ▲ - Frosting Mix (Chocolate Fudge, Toffee Vanilla)

Nuts Online - Butterscotch Crunch ●, Filling (Almond ●, Chocolate●, Cinnamon ●, Poppy Seed ●), Macaroon Crunch ●, Marzipan ●, Nutty Crunch ●, Paste (Hazelnut Praline ●, Pistachio Nut ●)

B

    Pamela's Products ▲ - Frosting Mix (Chocolate Chunk, Confetti, Dark Chocolate, Vanilla)

    Whole Foods Market Gluten Free Bakehouse ▲ - Frosting (Chocolate, Vanilla)

Baking Mix... see Bread Mix

Baking Powder

    Barkat

    Bob's Red Mill ▲

    Cause You're Special ▲ - Double Acting Baking Powder

    Clabber Girl

    Davis

    Durkee

    Ener-G ▲ - Double Acting, Regular

    Ginger Evans - Regular

    Hain Pure Foods

    Hannaford Brand

    Hearth Club

    Hilltop Mills

    Hy-Vee - Double Acting

    KC

    Kinnikinnick ▲ - KinnActive

    Kraft - Calumet

    Kroger Brand

    Laura Lynn

    Nuts Online - Double Active ●

    Really Great Food Company ▲ - Baking Powder Aluminum Free/ Double Acting

    Royal

    Rumford

    Safeway Brand

    Spartan Brand

    Spice Islands

    Tones

    Watkins

    Wegmans Brand - Double Acting

Baking Soda
 Albertsons
 Arm & Hammer
 Bob's Red Mill ▲
 Durkee
 Ener-G ▲ - Calcium Carbonate Baking Soda Substitute
 Food Club Brand
 Ginger Evans - Regular
 Gordon Food Service
 Hannaford Brand
 Hilltop Mills
 Hy-Vee
 Kroger Brand
 Laura Lynn
 Lowes Foods Brand
 Meijer Brand
 Nuts Online - Arm & Hammer Baking Soda ●
 Spartan Brand
 Spice Islands
 Tones

Bamboo Shoots
 Native Forest - Organic Sliced

Banana Chips
 Brothers All Natural ▲ - Crisps (Banana, Strawberry Banana)
 Full Circle - Sweetened
 Gluty Free - Chips ●, Freeze Dried ●, Organic Chips ●
 Nuts Online - Dried Fruit (Chips ●, Organic Chips ●)
 Woodstock Farms - Regular, Sweetened

Bananas
 ... *All Fresh Fruits & Vegetables Are Gluten-Free
 Chiquita
 Dole
 Nuts Online - Dried Fruit (Organic Simply ●, Simply ●)
 Woodstock Farms - Organic Frozen Bananas

B Barbeque Sauce

Albertsons - Hickory, Original

Annie's Naturals - Organic (Hot Chipotle **! !**, Original **! !**, Smokey Maple **! !**, Sweet & Spicy **! !**)

Bone Suckin' Sauce - Habanero, Original

Cattlemen's - Kansas City Classic, Memphis Sweet, Mississippi Honey BBQ

Daddy Sam's - Bar B Que Sawce (Medium Ginger Jalapeno, Original)

Dorothy Lane Market - Original

Fischer & Wieser - Elly May's Wild Mountain Honey, Plum Chipotle Grilling Sauce

Food Club Brand - BBQ Sauce (Hickory, Honey, Traditional)

Frontera - Original Sweet & Smoky, Roasted Chipotle Pineapple, Texas Black Pepper

Giant Brand - Hickory Smoke, Honey, Original

Gordon Food Service - Dip Cup, Original, Pit Style, Sweet

Hannaford Brand - Honey, Kansas City Style, Original, Sweet & Zesty

Heinz - Chicken & Rib, Garlic, Honey Garlic, Original

Hy-Vee - Hickory, Honey Smoke, Original

Isaly's - All Varieties

Jack Daniel's - Hickory Brown Sugar, Honey Smokehouse, Masterblend, Original No.7 Recipe, Rich Honey, Smooth Original, Spicy Original

Kroger Brand - All Varieties

Kurtz - Hickory, Honey, KC Style, Original

Lowes Foods Brand - Hickory, Honey, Regular

Midwest Country Fare - Hickory, Honey, Original

Mr. Spice Organic - Honey BBQ

Mrs. Renfro's - Barbecue Sauce

Naturally Delicious - Regular

Organicville - Organic BBQ Sauce (Original ●, Tangy ●)

Publix - Hickory, Honey, Original

Royal Food Products - Garden Fresh, Gourmet Choice (Baby Back

Rib, Chipotle, South Texas), Royal Deluxe (Santa Fe, Texas Style)

Safeway Brand - Hickory Smoked, Honey (Mustard, Smoked), Original

San-J - Gluten Free Asian BBQ ●

Saz's - Original, Sassy, Vidalia Onion

Spartan Brand - Hickory & Brown Sugar, Honey, Original

Steels Gourmet - Agave (Chipotle, Regular)

Sweet Baby Ray's - Hickory & Brown Sugar, Honey, Honey Chipotle, Original, Sweet 'N Spicy, Sweet Vadalia Onion

Taste Of Inspiration - Maple Chipotle **!**, Spicy Mango **!**, Wild Maine Blueberry **!**

Trader Joe's - All Natural, Kansas City **! !**

Walden Farms - Hickory Smoked, Honey, Original, Thick & Spicy

Wegmans Brand - Brown Sugar, Kansas City Style, Memphis Style

Western Prime - All Varieties

Winn Dixie - Hickory, Honey, Original

Bars... (includes Breakfast, Energy, Fruit, Protein, etc.)

1-2-3 Gluten Free ▲ - Sweet Goodness Pan Bars ●

AllerEnergy ▲ - Nutrition Bars (Apple Cinnamon, Cherry Blossom, Chocolate Chip, Wild Blueberry)

Alpsnack - Apricots & Cranberries, Coconut/Mango & Pineapple, Fair Trade (Dark Chocolate, Espresso Chocolate), Plums & Currants

Arico - Cookie Bars (Almond Cranberry, Chocolate Chunk, Double Chocolate, Peanut Butter)

Attune Foods - Chocolate Probiotic Wellness (Almond Milk Chocolate ●, Blueberry Vanilla ●, Chocolate Crisp ●, Coffee Bean Dark Chocolate ●, Dark Chocolate ●, Mint Chocolate ●, Raspberry Dark Chocolate ●)

Bakery On Main - Granola Bars (Cranberry Maple Nut ●, Extreme Trail Mix ●, Peanut Butter Chocolate Chip ●)

Boomi Bar - Almond Protein Plus, Apricot Cashew, Cashew (Almond, Protein Plus), Cranberry Apple, Fruit & Nut, Healthy Hazel, Macadamia Paradise, Maple Pecan, Perfect Pumpkin, Pineapple Ginger, Pistachio Pineapple, Walnut Date

B

Breakaway Bakery ▲ - Organic Lemon Bar Dough & Topping ●, Shortbread Crumble & Bar Dough ●

Bumble Bar - Awesome Apricot, Chai w/Almonds, Cherry Chocolate, Chocolate Crisp, Chunky Cherry, Lushus Lemon, Original Flavor, Original Flavor w/(Almonds, Cashews, Hazelnuts, Mixed Nuts), Tasty Tropical

Carb Safe - Sugar Free Chocolate Bars Dark

Clif Nectar - Organic (Cherry Pomegranate, Cranberry Apricot Almond, Dark Chocolate Walnut, Lemon Vanilla Cashew)

Crenu - Nutrition Bars (Almond, Banana Nut, Blueberry, Cherry, Cherry Chocolate, Chocolate Chip, Lemon Chia, Orange Cranberry)

Crispy Cat - Candy Bars (Chocolate Sundae, Mint Coconut, Toasted Almond)

Dagoba - All Chocolate Bars

Eat Natural -
   100% Organic Brazils Hazelnuts & Sultans
   Almonds Apricots & Yoghurt Coating
   Blackcurrants Walnuts Mango & Dark Chocolate
   Blueberries Pistachios & Yoghurt Coating
   Brazils Sultanas Almonds & Hazelnuts
   Cherries Almonds & Yoghurt Coating
   Cranberries Apricots & Yoghurt Coating
   Cranberries Macadamias & Dark Chocolate
   Dark 70% Chocolate Brazils & Apricots
   Dates Walnuts & Pumpkin Seeds
   Macadamias Brazils & Apricots
   Peanuts Almonds & Hazelnuts
   Peanuts Cranberries Pistachios & Milk Chocolate

Ener-G ▲ - Snack Bar Chocolate Chip

Enjoy Life ▲ - Boom Choco Boom (Dairy Free Rice Milk Bar ●, Dairy Free Rice Milk w/Crispy Rice Bar ●, Dark Chocolate Bar ●), Caramel Apple ●, Cocoa Loco ●, Sunbutter Crunch ●, Very Berry ●

EnviroKidz Organic - Crispy Rice Bars (Berry Blast, Chocolate, Fruity Burst, Peanut Butter, Peanut Choco Drizzle)

Glenny's - Cashew & Almond ●, Classic Fruit & Nut ●, Classic Nut Mix ●, Cranberry & Almond ●

Gluten Free Cafe - Chocolate Sesame ●, Cinnamon Sesame ●, Lemon Sesame ●

Glutino ▲ - Breakfast Bars (Apple, Blueberry, Cherry, Strawberry), Candy Bars (Chocolate Peanut Butter, Dark Chocolate, Milk Chocolate), Organic Bars (Chocolate Banana, Chocolate Peanut Butter, Wildberry)

Gopal's - Happy Herb w/Maca, Rawma (Apple Delicious, Carob Quinoa, Pineapple Nut, Pumpkin Agave, Sesame Mango, Walnut Fig)

Goraw ▲ - Organic (Banana Bread Flax ●, Live Granola ●, Live Pumpkin ●, Real Live Flax ●, Spirulina Energy ●)

Gorge Delights ▲ - Acai Fruit Bars (Acai Apple Cherry, Acai Apple Raspberry, Acai Pear Cranberry, Acai Pear Strawberry), Just Fruit Bar (Apple, Apple Blueberry, Apple Cherry, Apple Raspberry, Blueberry Pear, Pear, Pear Cranberry, Pear Strawberry)

Grandma Ferdon's ▲ - Lemon ●, Pumpkin ●

Ian's - Wheat Free Gluten Free Go Bars (Apple Pie, Cinnamon Bun)

Jennies ▲ - Omega 3 Energy Bar (Coconut, Coconut Almond, Coconut Chocolate)

Jungle Grub - Berry Bamboozle! ●, Chocolate Chip Cookie Dough! ●, Peanut Butter Groove! ●

Larabar -

    Apple Pie ●

    Banana Bread ●

    Carrot Cake ●

    Cashew Cookie ●

    Cherry Pie ●

    Chocolate Chip Brownie ●

    Chocolate Chip Cookie Dough ●

    Chocolate Coconut ●

B

Cinnamon Roll ●
Coconut Cream Pie ●
Ginger Snap ●
Jocalat Chocolate (Original ●, Cherry ●, Coffee ●, Hazelnut ●,
    Mint ●, Orange ●, German Cake ●)
Key Lime Pie ●
Lemon Bar ●
Peanut Butter & Jelly ●
Peanut Butter Chocolate Chip ●
Peanut Butter Cookie ●
Pecan Pie ●
Tropical Fruit Tart ●

Manischewitz - Raspberry Jell Bars

Mareblu Naturals ▲ - Crunch (Almond ●, Cashew ●), Trail Mix
    Crunch (BlueCran Pomegranate ●, Mango Pomegranate ●,
    Pistachio ●, Strawberry Pomegranate ●)

Meijer Brand - Xtreme Snack Bars

Mixes From The Heartland ▲ - Coffee Bars Mix (Apple Cinnamon●,
    Cranberry ●, Tropical ●)

Mrs. May's Naturals - Trio (Blueberry ●, Cranberry ●, Strawberry ●,
    Tropical ●)

Nature Valley - Roasted Nut Crunch (Almond, Peanut)

Necco - Clark Bar, Skybar

NoNuttin' Foods ▲ - Granola Bars (Apple Cinnamon ●, Chocolate
    Chip ●, Double Chocolate Chunk ●, Raisin ●)

NuGO Free - Gluten Free Bars (Carrot Cake ●, Dark Chocolate
    Crunch ●, Dark Chocolate Trail Mix ●)

Nutiva - Organic (Flax & Raisin, Flax Chocolate, Hempseed Original)

Omega Smart Bars ▲ - Banana Chocolate Chip, Organic (Apricot
    & Almond, Carrot Cake, Chocolate Nut, Cinnamon Apple, Raisin
    Spice), Pomegranate Strawberry Colada, Pumpkin Spice, Youth
    In A Bar (Dark Chocolate Cherry, Organic Almond Macaroon,
    Organic Wild Blueberry w/Orange Essence, Yummy Cherry Berry)

Organic Food Bar - Organic Food Bar (Active Greens, Active Greens Chocolate, Chocolate Chip, Cranberry, Omega 3 Flax, Original, Protein, Vegan, Wild Blueberry), Organic Food Bar Kids Keerunch Chocolate Brownie Crunch, Raw Organic Food Bar (Chocolate Coconut, Chocolatey Chocolate Chip, Cinnamon Raisin, Fiber Chocolate Delite)

Orgran ▲ - Fruit Bars Fruit Medley, Fruit Filled Bar (Apricot, Blueberry)

Oskri Organics -
Coconut Bar (Almond, Cherry, Mango, Original, Pineapple, Strawberry)
Dark Chocolate (Almond Cranberry Granola, Nut Free Granola Raisin, Organic Coconut, Organic Sesame)
Date Fruit
Fiber Bar (Almond Cranberry, Cashew Cranberry, Pecan Raisin)
Fig Fruit
Honey Bar (Cashew, Desert Date, Flaxseed, Granola, Mixed Nuts, Muesli, Turkish Delight)
Mini Bars Coconut (Original w/Dark Chocolate, Original w/Milk Chocolate)
Sesame Bar (Black Sesame, Date Syrup & (Black Cumin, Fennel, Regular), Molasses & (Black Cumin, Fennel, Regular),Quinoa)

Prana - Apricot Goji, Apricot Pumpkin, Cashew Almond, Cinnamon Apple, Coconut Acai, Pear Ginseng, Supercharger (Blueberry Coconut, Goldenberry Goji, Mango Maca, Raspberry Pomegranate)

Private Selections - Frozen Premium Fruit Bars (Regular, Sugar Free)

PURE Bar - Organic (Apple Cinnamon ●, Cherry Cashew ●, Chocolate Brownie ●, Cranberry Orange ●, Trailmix ●, Wild Blueberry ●)

PureFit - Chocolate Brownie, Crunch (Almond, Berry Almond, Granola, Peanut Butter)

Quejos ▲ - Cranberry Raisin

Quest Bar - Peanut Butter Supreme, Vanilla Almond Crunch

B

Raw Revolution ▲ - Apple Cinnamon, Cashews & Agave, Chocolate & Cashews, Chocolate & Coconut, Chocolate Chip Cookie Dough, Coconut & Agave, Hazelnut & Chocolate, Raisin & Chocolate, Raspberry & Chocolate, Spiruluna & Cashew, Tropical Mango

Ruth's Hemp Power - Cranberry Trail HempPower, CranNut Flax Power, Ginger Almond MacaPower, Hemp & Trail HempPower, VeryBerry Flax Power, Vote Hemp/Blueberry Bar

Salba - Whole Fruit Bars (Cranberry Nut ●, Mixed Berry ●, Tropical Fruit ●)

Seitenbacher - Banana Cranberry, Choco Apricot, Energy, Fitness, Natural (Energizer, Sports), Sweet Romance, Xtra Fiber

Shakti Bar - Organic (Blueberry Chia, Goldenberry Goji, Mango Maca)

Taste Of Nature -
Exotics (Caribbean Ginger Island ●, Himalayan Goji Summit ●, Persian Pomegranate Garden ●)
Regular (Argentina Peanut Plains ●, Brazilian Nut Fiesta ●, California Almond Valley ●, Niagara Apple Country ●, Nova Scotia Blueberry Fields ●, Quebec Cranberry Carnival ●)

thinkThin - Brownie Crunch, Chocolate (Fudge, Mudslide), Chocolate Covered Strawberries, Crunch Bars (Mixed Nuts, Mixed Nuts & Chocolate, Mixed Nuts & White Chocolate), Dark Chocolate, Lemon Cream Pie, Peanut Butter (Chunky, Creamy), Tangerine Cremesicle, White Chocolate Chip

Tiger's Milk - Peanut Butter, Peanut Butter & Honey, Protein Rich

Trader Joe's - Fiberful Fruit

Wegmans Brand - Fruit Flats (Cherry, Grape, Raspberry, Strawberry)

Basmati Rice... see Rice

Beans

... *All Fresh Fruits & Vegetables Are Gluten-Free

Albertsons - All Dried, Canned Black, Blackeye, Chili, Dark Red Kidney, Garbanzo, Great Northern, Green (Cut, French Style, Whole), Pinto, Pork & Beans, Refried (Fat Free, Regular, w/

Tomatoes & Green Chile)

Amy's - Organic Light In Sodium (Black**!**, Traditional**!**), Organic Refried Beans (Black**!**, Traditional**!**, w/Green Chiles**!**), Organic Vegetarian Baked**!**

Arrowhead Mills - Adzuki, Anasazi, Garbanzo Chickpeas, Green Split Peas, Lentils (Green, Red), Pinto, Soybeans

B&M Baked Beans - All Varieties

Birds Eye - All Plain Frozen Vegetables

Bush's Best -

Baked Beans (Bold & Spicy, Boston Recipe, Country Style, Homestyle, Honey, Maple Cured Bacon, Onion, Original, Vegetarian)

Black, Butter (Baby, Large, Speckled)

Cannellini

Chili Beans *(Must Be NEW Recipe)* (Hot, Medium, Mild)

Chili Magic Chili Starter *(Must Be NEW Recipe)* Texas Recipe, Traditional Recipe

Garbanzo

Great Northern

Grillin' Beans (Black Bean Fiesta, Bourbon & Brown Sugar, Smokehouse Tradition, Southern Pit Barbecue, Steakhouse Recipe, Texas Ranchero)

Kidney (Dark Red, Light Red)

Microwaveable Cup Original

Navy

Pinto (Regular, w/Pork)

Red

Refried Beans Traditional

C & W - All Plain Frozen Vegetables

Del Monte - All Canned Vegetables

Eden Organic -

Organic (Aduki, Baked w/Sorghum & Mustard, Black, Black Eyed Peas, Black Soybeans, Butter, Cannellini, Caribbean Black,

B

Garbanzo, Great Northern, Kidney, Navy, Pinto, Small Red),
Organic Dried (Aduki, Black, Black Soybeans, Garbanzo, Green
(Lentils, Split Peas), Kidney, Navy, Pinto, Small Red)
Refried (Black, Blacksoy & Black, Kidney, Pinto, Spicy Black, Spicy
Pinto)
Rice & (Cajun Small Red, Caribbean Black, Garbanzo, Kidney,
Lentils, Pinto)
Fantastic World Foods - Hummus Original, Instant (Black, Refried)
Food Club Brand -
Canned (Baked (Homestyle, Maple Cured, Original, Vegetarian,
w/Onion)
Dried Beans (Blackeyed Pea, Cranberry, Gourmet Soup Blend,
Great Northern, Light Red Kidney, Lima, Navy, Pinto)
French Style Green
French Style Green No Salt Added
Frozen Baby Lima
Frozen Green Cut
Frozen Green Whole
Great Northern (Regular, Southern Style)
Green Beans (Cut Italian, Cut No Salt, French Style, French Style
No Salt, Italian, Wax Cut, Whole)
Green Beans & Potatoes
Green Cut
Kidney (Dark Red, Light Red)
Mixed Southern Style
Navy
October Southern Style
Pinto (Regular, Southern Style, Southern Style w/Onion)
Pork & Beans)
Steamin' Easy (French Cut Green Beans, Green Beans Cut)
Refried Beans (Authentic, Fat Free)
Freshlike - Frozen Plain Vegetables
Full Circle - Canned Organic Baked Beans, Baked Beans Maple &
Onion, Black, Garbanzo, Green Cut, Organic Frozen Cut Beans,

B

Pinto, Red Kidney, Refried (Black, Green Chile & Lime, Vegetarian),
Dried (Kidney, Lentil, Lima, Navy, Pinto)

Giant Brand -
Baked (Brown Sugar & Bacon, Vegetarian)
Black
Canned (Black Eyed Peas, Chick Peas, French Green, Golden Cut
Wax, Lima)
Frozen (Green Beans (& Wax Beans, Cut, French, Whole), Lima
Beans (Baby, Fordhook))
Kidney (Dark Red, Light Red, No Added Salt, Regular)
Organic (Black, Garbanzo, Light Kidney)
Pink
Pinto
Pork & Beans
Red
Romano

Gluty Free - Chickpeas (Salted (Golden ●, White ●), Unsalted
(Golden ●, White ●)), Cranberry ●, Green Bean Chips ●, Organic
Cannellini ●, Salted Edamame ●, Wasabi Beans ●

Grand Selections - Fancy (Cut Green, Whole Green), Frozen
Whole Green

Great Value Brand (Wal-Mart) - Beans & Weiners, Canned Cut
Green, No Salt Added (Cut Green, French Style Green), Whole
Green, Dried (Baby Lima, Black, Garbanzo, Great Northern, Large
Lima, Light Red Kidney, Pinto, Small Red), Dried Peas (Blackeyed,
Chick, Green Split)

Green Giant -
Canned
Cut Green (50% Less Sodium, Regular)
French Style Green
Kitchen Sliced Green
Frozen
Baby Lima
Cut Green

B

Green Beans & Almonds
Select w/No Sauce Whole Green
Simply Steam (Baby Lima, Green Beans & Almonds)
Steamers (Cut Green, Roasted Red Potatoes Green Beans & Rosemary Butter)
Valley Fresh Steamers (Cut Green Beans, Select Whole Green Beans)

Hannaford Brand - All Dried, Baked, Black, Cannellini, Cut Green, Cut Wax, Dark Red Kidney, French Green, Great Northern, Light Red Kidney, No Salt Green (Cut, French), Pinto, Refried (Fat Free, Traditional), Whole Green

HealthMarket - Organic (Black, Cut Green, Dark Red Kidney, French Cut Green, Garbanzo, Pinto)

Heinz - Vegetarian Beans

Hy-Vee -
Black (Refried, Regular)
Blue Lake (Cut Green, French Style Green, Whole Green)
Butter
Chili (Beans, Style, Style in Chili Gravy)
Country Style Baked
Dark Red Kidney
Diced Baby Lima
Dried (Large Lima, Lentils, Mixed Soup, Navy)
Fat Free Refried
Frozen (Cut Green, French Cut Green)
Garbanzo Beans Chick Peas
Great Northern (Dried, Regular)
Home Style Baked
Large Lima
Lentils
Light Red Kidney
Maple Cured Bacon Baked
Navy
Onion Baked

Original Baked
Pinto (Dried, Regular)
Pork & Beans
Red (Dried, Kidney, Regular)
Spicy Refried
Steam In A Bag Frozen Beans
Traditional Refried
Vegetarian Refried

Joan Of Arc - Black, Butter, Dark Red Kidney, Garbanzo, Great Northern, Light Red Kidney, Pinto, Red

Kid's Kitchen - Beans & Wieners

Kirkland Signature - Green Beans

Kroger Brand - All Plain Vegetables (Canned, Frozen), Baked (Country Style, Homestyle, Original), Pork & Beans (Regular, Veggie), Refried (Fat Free, Mexican, Veggie), Unseasoned (Canned, Dry)

Kroger Value - All Plain Vegetables (Canned, Frozen)

Laura Lynn - All Dried Beans, Beans & Franks, Canned (Kidney, Lima), Chili, Cut Green, Fat Free Refried, French Style Green, No Salt Cut Green, Pole, Pork & Beans, Refried

Lowes Foods Brand -
Canned (Baked Brown Sugar & Bacon, Black, Chili, Cut Green No Salt, French, Garbanzo, Great Northern, Green (Cut, French Style, Whole)Lima, Pinto (Regular, w/Pork), Pork & Beans, Red Kidney Beans (Dark, Light), Refried (Fat Free, Regular), Whole Green)
Dry (Baby Lima, Black Eyed Peas, Great Northern, Lentil, Lima, Mixed, Navy, Pinto)
Frozen (Deluxe Whole Green, Green (Cut, French Cut, Regular), Lima (Baby, Deluxe Tiny, Regular), Speckled Butter)

Meijer Brand -
Baked Beans - Organic
Canned Beans (Black (Organic, Regular), Butter, Garbanzo (Organic, Regular), Great Northern, Lima, Mexican Style,

B

Pinto (Organic, Regular), Red Kidney (Dark, Dark Organic, Light, Regular), Refried (Fat Free, Regular, Vegetarian), Refried Organic (Black Bean, Black Bean/Jalapeno, Roasted Chili/Lime, Traditional), Wax Cut)

Canned Green Beans Cut (Blue Lake, French Style (Blue Lake, No Salt, Organic, Veri Green), No Salt, Organic, Veri Green)

Canned Green Beans Whole

Dry Beans (Black, Blackeye, Fordhook)

Frozen (Edamame, Green Beans (Cut, French Cut, Italian Cut), Lima Beans)

Midwest Country Fare - Chili Style, Cut Green, French Style Green, Pork & Beans

Nature's Promise - Organic Cut Green Canned

Nielsen-Massey - Madagascar Bourbon Pure Vanilla Bean Paste ●, Whole Vanilla Beans ●

Nuts Online -

Ceci Fava Mix ●

Chickpeas (Roasted Golden (Salted ●, Unsalted ●), Roasted White (Salted ●, Unsalted ●))

Cranberry Beans ●

Dry Roasted Edamame (Salted ●, Unsalted ●)

Giant Fava Beans ●

Organic Cannellini Beans ●

Organic Dry Roasted Soybeans (Salted Whole ●, Unsalted Whole●)

Simply Green Beans Freeze Dried Vegetables ●

Soy Beans (Dry Roasted Halves ●, Hickory Smoked ●, Spicy BBQ ●)

Wasabi Beans ●

O Organics - Canned (Black, Cut Green, Frozen Whole Green, Garbanzo, Kidney, Pinto)

Old El Paso - Refried Beans (Fat Free, Spicy Fat Free, Traditional, Vegetarian, w/Green Chiles)

Ortega - Black, Refried (Fat Free, Regular, w/Jalapenos)

Pictsweet - All Plain Vegetables (Frozen), Cracked Pepper Seasoned Green, Roasted Garlic Seasoned Baby Whole Green, Seasoned Corn & Black Beans

Private Selections - Frozen Green Beans

Publix -

Canned (Baked (Original, Veggie), Black Beans, Garbanzo,
Green (French Cut, Italian Cut, Lima, Original, Veggi Green),
Kidney (Dark, Light), Pinto, Pork & Beans)

Dry (Baby Lima, Black, Blackeye Peas, Garbanzo, Great Northern,
Green Split Peas, Large Lima, Lentils, Light Red Kidney, Navy,
Pinto, Small Red)

Frozen (Green (Cut, French Cut), Lima (Baby, Fordhook), Speckled
Butter Beans)

Publix GreenWise Market - Organic Canned (Black, Dark Red
Kidney, Garbanzo, Green, Pinto, Soy)

S&W - All Canned Vegetables

Safeway Brand -

Canned (Black (Eyed, Regular), Chick, Dark Kidney, Green (Cut,
Cut No Salt, French Style, Whole), Light Kidney, Lima, Pinto)

Dried (Baby Lima, Black (Eyed, Regular), Great Northern, Green
Split, Large Lima, Lentils, Light Red Kidney, Navy, Pink, Pinto,
Small (Red, White))

Frozen (Baby Lima, Cut, Fordbook Lima, French Style, Whole)

Refried Beans (Fat Free, Traditional, Vegetarian)

Safeway Select - Frozen Whole Green Beans

Spartan Brand -

Canned (Baked (Homestyle, Regular, w/Bacon & Maple Flavor, w/
Onions), Black, Butter, Chili Beans, Dark Red Kidney, Garbanzo,
Great Northern, Green (Cut, French Cut Style, Whole), Light
Red Kidney, Lima, Pinto, Pork & Beans, Red, Wax Cut),

Dried (Black, Black Eyed, Great Northern, Kidney, Lentil, Lima
(Baby, Large), Navy, Pinto)

Frozen (Baby Lima, Fordhook Lima, Green (Cut, French Cut,
Whole))

Stop & Shop Brand - Baby Lima, Black, Brown Sugar & Bacon Baked,
Dark Red Kidney, Fordhook Lima, Garbanzo, Golden Cut Wax,
Green Beans (Cut, French, Italian, No Added Salt, w/Garlic,

B

Whole), Homestyle Baked, Italian, Kidney Light, Lima, Organic Green, Pinto, Red, Romano, Vegetarian Baked

Taco Bell - Refried Beans

Trader Joe's - All Canned Plain **! !**, All Plain Dried Varieties, Frozen Haricot Very Extra Fine Green Beans **! !**, Marinated Bean Salad **! !**

Wegmans Brand -

Baby Lima

Baked Beans (Homestyle, Original, Vegetarian, w/Brown Sugar & Bacon)

Black

Butter

Canned (Black, Dark Red Kidney, Great Northern, Light Red Kidney, Pinto, Pork & Beans In Tomato Sauce, Red, Seasoned Chili)

Cannellini Beans Italian Classics, Cut Green Beans (No Salt, Regular)

Dark Kidney

French Style Green Beans (No Salt, Regular)

Garbanzo Beans Italian Classics

Great Northern

Green (Cut, French Style, Italian Cut, Regular, Whole)

Light Red Kidney

Lima

Pinto

Pork & Beans In Tomato Sauce

Seasoned Chili

Wax Cut

Westbrae - Green Beans (Cut, French Cut), Organic (Black, Chili, Garbanzo, Great Northern, Kidney, Lentils, Pinto, Red, Salad, Soy)

Winn Dixie -

All Dried

Canned Beans (Baby White Lima, Baked, Baked w/Onion, Chili, Dark Red Kidney, Garbanzo, Great Northern, Green & White Lima, Green Cut, Green French Style Sliced, Green Lima,

Green No Salt Added, Green Whole, Light Red Kidney, Navy)
Frozen Green Beans (Butter Speckled, Cut, French Style Sliced, Italian, Organic Cut, Whole)
Frozen Lima Beans (Baby, Fordhook, Petite, Speckled)
Pork & Beans
Refried (Fat Free, Traditional)
Steamable Green Beans Cut
Woodstock Farms - Dried Green Beans, Organic Frozen (Baby French Beans, Cut Green Beans, Lima)

Beef... see also Deli Meat
... *All Fresh Meat Is Gluten-Free (Non-Marinated, Unseasoned)
Always Tender - Flavored Fresh Beef Peppercorn, Non Flavored Fresh Beef
Applegate Farms - Natural (Beef Hot Dogs, Roast Beef), Organic (Frozen Beef Burger, Roast Beef)
Armour - Deli Corned Beef, Pastrami, Roast Beef (Italian Style, Regular)
Boar's Head - All Varieties
Butcher's Cut - Beef Salami, Bulk Wrapped Corned Beef Brisket, Corned Beef Brisket *(Except Seasoning Packet)*, Patties
Carl Buddig - Deli Cuts Roast Beef, Extra Thin Original Regular, Original Regular
Castle Wood Reserve - Deli Meat (Angus Corned Beef, Angus Roast Beef)
Coleman's Natural Foods - All Natural Uncured Hot Dog ●
Columbus Salame - Deli Meat (All Varieties)
Dietz & Watson ▲ -
Corned Beef (Brisket ●, Flat ●)
Dried Beef Classic Top Round ●
Pastrami (Brisket ●, Spiced Beef ●)
Roast Beef (Extra Lean ●, Italian ●, London Broil ●, Oven Roasted All Natural Rare Whole ●, Premium Angus ●, USDA Pepper Choice●)
Seasoned Prime Rib w/Juices ●

B

Eckrich - Deli Meat (Black Angus Roast Beef, Choice Top Roast Beef, Cooked Corned Beef, Italian Roast Beef, Lite Roast Beef, Seasoned Roast Beef)

Five Star Brand - Corned Beef, Jumbo Beef Wieners, Roast Beef, SC Beef Wieners

Garrett County Farms - Beef Franks (4XL Big!, Old Fashioned!, Premium!), Corned Beef Brisket (Half!, Whole!), Sliced (Beef Bologna!, Beef Salami!, Corned Beef!, Roast Beef!), Whole Roasted Beef!

Giant Eagle Brand - Shredded w/BBQ Sauce

Gordon Food Service - Pureed Beef w/Broth, Taco Filling

Great Value Brand (Wal-Mart) - Frozen 100% Pure Beef Patties

Hillshire Farms - Deli Select Roast Beef, Deli Select Thin Sliced Corned Beef, Deli Select Ultra Thin Roast Beef

Hormel - Bread Ready Corned Beef, Corned Beef Hash, Deli Meat Natural Choice Roast Beef, Dried Beef, Fully Cooked Entrees (Beef Roast Au Jus, Italian Style Beef Roast), Natural Choice Deli Counter (Corned Beef, Medium Roast, Rare Roast)

Hy-Vee - Deli Thin Sliced Roast Beef, Thin Sliced (Corned Beef, Regular)

Isaly's - All Deli Meat

John Soules Foods - Fully Cooked Fajitas (Angus Beef, Beef), Ready To Cook Beef For Fajitas

Jones Dairy Farm - Golden Brown All Natural Fully Cooked Beef Sausage Links ●

Kayem - Roast Beef (Classic, Seasoned Garlic, Seasoned Original)

Kirkland Signature - Fresh (Brisket, NY Strip, Ribeye, Ribs, Roast, Steaks, Top Round), Frozen Lean Ground Beef, Ground Beef Patties

Kroger Brand - Beef Franks, Sliced Dried

Lloyd's - Center Cut Beef Ribs w/Original BBQ Sauce, Shredded Beef In Original BBQ Sauce

Meijer Brand - Ground Beef (Chuck Fine, Fine)

Organic Prairie - Fresh Organic Ground Beef 1 lb. (85% Lean, 90%

Lean), Sliced Roast Beef , Frozen Organic (Beef Liver Steak 12 oz., Ground Beef 12 oz., Ground Beef Patties 10.6 oz., New York Strip Steak, Ribeye Steak)

Oscar Mayer - Shaved Deli Fresh (French Dip Roast Beef, Slow Roasted Roast Beef)

Primo Taglio - Cooked Corned Beef, Roast Beef (Caramel Color Added, Coated w/Seasonings)

Private Selections - Frozen Angus Patties (Cheese & Bacon, Chuck, Roasted Onion, Swiss Cheese & Mushrooms), Frozen Charbroiled Burgers (All Natural, w/Cheddar Cheese), Frozen Ground Sirloin Patties

Publix - Premium Certified Beef

Publix GreenWise Market -

Beef (Cubed Steak, For Stew)

Beef Back Ribs

Bottom Round (Regular, Steak)

Brisket Flat

Chuck (Eye Steak, Roast Boneless, Short Rib Boneless, Short Ribs, Steak Boneless)

Eye Round (Regular, Steak)

Flank Steak

Flap Meat

Flat Iron Steak

Ground (Chuck, Chuck For Chili, Chuck Patties, Round, Round Patties)

Porterhouse Steak

Rib Eye (Roast Boneless, Steak Bone In, Steak Boneless)

Rib Roast

Round Cubes

Rump Roast

Shoulder (Roast Boneless, Steak)

Sirloin (Flap Meat, For Kabobs, For Stir Fry, Tip Roast, Tip Side Steak, Tip Steak)

Skirt Steak (Inside, Outside)

B

    Strip Steak Boneless
    T Bone Steak
    Tenderloin (Roast, Steak)
    Top Blade (Roast Boneless, Steak)
    Top Round (For Stir Fry, London Broil, Regular, Steak, Steak Thin Sliced)
    Top Sirloin (Filet Steak, Steak Boneless)
    Tri Tip (Roast, Steak)

Sara Lee - Deli Meat Slices Roast Beef
Spartan Brand - Corned Beef Hash
Sweet Bay - All Fresh Beef, All Fresh Veal
Thumann's - All Varieties ●
Trader Joe's - Fresh All Natural, Fully Cooked & Seasoned Beef Prime Rib, Shepherds Pie Beef
    Wellshire Farms - Roast Beef (Sliced **!!**, Whole **!!**)
    Winn Dixie - Corned Beef Hash

Beef Jerky... see Jerky/Beef Sticks
Beef Sticks... see Jerky/Beef Sticks
Beer
    Alchemist - Celia Saison
    Anheuser-Busch - Redbridge Beer
    Bard's - American Lager
    Bard's Tale Beer - Bard's Gluten Free Beer
    Bi-Aglut (Italy) - Special 76 Lager
    Bosk - Gluten Free Homebrew Kit
    Brauerei Grieskirchen AG (Austria) - Beer Up Glutenfrei Pale Ale
    Carlsberg Brewery (Finland) - Saxon Premium Lager
    Fine Ale Club (England) - Against The Grain
    Glutaner (Belgium) - Glutenfrei Pils
    Green's (England) - Discovery, Endeavor, Herald, Pathfinder, Premium Golden Apple, Premium Pils, Quest
    Hambleton Ales (England) - GFL, Toleration (GFA)
    Lakefront Brewery - New Grist Beer
    Les Bieres de la Nouvelle France (Canada) - Messagere, Messagere

Millet, Messagere Red Ale

New Planet - 3R Raspberry Ale, Tread Lightly Ale

O'Brien (Australia) - Brown Ale, Natural Light, Pale Ale, Premium Lager

Old Hat Brewery - Bees Knees

Ramapo Valley Brewery ▲ - Passover Honey Lager

Schnitzer Brau (Germany) - German Hirse Premium, Hirse Lemon

Sprecher - Mbege, Shakparo

St. Peter's Brewery (England) - G Free

Beets

... *All Fresh Fruits & Vegetables Are Gluten-Free*

Albertsons

Del Monte - All Canned Vegetables

Earthbound Farm - Organic Whole

Food Club Brand - Canned (Pickled, Sliced, Whole)

Giant Brand - Canned (No Salt Added, Regular)

Hannaford Brand - Cut, Sliced, Whole

Hy-Vee - Fancy (Diced, Sliced)

Laura Lynn - Cut, Sliced

Lowes Foods Brand - Canned Cut, Whole

Meijer Brand - Harvard Sweet Sour, Sliced (No Salt, Pickled, Regular), Whole (Medium, Pickled)

Publix - Canned

Pure Market Express ▲ - Mariachi Beet Wrap ●

S&W - All Canned Vegetables, Pickled

Safeway Brand - Canned (Sliced, Whole)

Spartan Brand - Diced, Sliced, Whole

Stop & Shop Brand - Sliced No Salt Added

Trader Joe's - Steamed

Wegmans Brand - Harvard, Sliced (No Salt, Pickled, Regular), Whole (Pickled, Regular)

Berries

... *All Fresh Fruits & Vegetables Are Gluten-Free*

Del Monte - Canned / Jarred Fruit (All Varieties), Fruit Snack Cups (Metal, Plastic)

B

Gluty Free - Dried (Goji Berries ●, Mulberries ●, Organic Goji
   Berries ●)
Kirkland Signature - Frozen Nature's Three
Meijer Brand - Frozen Berry Medley, Frozen Triple Berry Blend
Nuts Online - Dried Fruit (Goji Berries ●, Mulberries ●, Simply
   Boysenberries ●, Simply Elderberries ●)
Publix - Frozen Mixed Berries
Spartan Brand - Frozen Berry Medley
Stop & Shop Brand - Frozen Berry Medley
Wegmans Brand - Berry Medley
Woodstock Farms - Organic Goji, Organic Frozen Mixed Berries
Beverages... see Drinks/Juice
Biscotti
   Orgran ▲ - Amaretti, Classic Chocolate
   Pamela's Products ▲ - Almond Anise, Chocolate Walnut, Lemon
      Almond
   Really Great Food Company ▲ - Anise, Lemon Poppy
   Rose's Bakery ▲ - Almond Biscotti, Chocolate Cherry, Pistachio
      Cranberry
   Silly Yak Bakery - GF Almond Biscotti ●
   Sorella ▲ - Biscottines (Chocolate Almond, Chocolate Chip,
      Cinnamon Swirl, Hazelnut, Vanilla)
   The Grainless Baker ▲ - Almond, Anise
Biscuits
   1-2-3 Gluten Free ▲ - Southern Glory Biscuits ●
   3 Fellers Bakery ▲ - Buttermilk Biscuit Dough, Cheddar Dill Biscuit
      Dough, Cinnamon Raisin Biscuit Dough
   Augason Farms - Gluten Free Buttermilk Biscuit Mix ●
   Better Batter - Pancake & Biscuit Mix
   Bi-Aglut - Biscuit, Granulated Biscuit
   Bob's Red Mill ▲ - Wheat Free Biscuit & Baking Mix
   Cause You're Special ▲ - Hearty Gluten Free Biscuit Mix
   Food-Tek Fast & Fresh ▲ - Quick Bake Biscuit Mix Homestyle
   Gifts Of Nature ▲ - Buttermilk Biscuit & Baking Mix

Grandma Ferdon's ▲ - Baking Powder Biscuit Mix ●, Cinnamon
    Raisin ●
Kneaded Specialties ▲ - Biscuits ●
Mixes From The Heartland ▲ - Biscuit Mix (Country ●, Garlic
    Roasted Pepper ●, Sun Dried Tomato ●)
Namaste Foods ▲ - Biscuits Piecrust & More Mix
Orgran ▲ - Fruit Filled Raspberry
Really Great Food Company ▲ - Biscuit Loaf Mix, Old Time Biscuit
    Mix, Spinach & Cheese Biscuit Mix Sugar Free
Silly Yak Bakery - GF Cheddar Bites ●
Whole Foods Market Gluten Free Bakehouse ▲ - Cheddar Biscuits,
    Cream Biscuits

Blackberries
... *All Fresh Fruits & Vegetables Are Gluten-Free*
Albertsons - All Plain Frozen Fruit
Food Club Brand - Frozen
Giant Brand - Frozen
Gluty Free - Dried ●
Great Value Brand (Wal-Mart) - Frozen
Meijer Brand - Frozen
Nuts Online - Dried Blackberries (Original ●, Simply ●)
Publix - Frozen
Safeway Brand - Frozen
Spartan Brand - Frozen
Stop & Shop Brand - Frozen
Wegmans Brand - Frozen
Winn Dixie - Frozen
Woodstock Farms - Organic Frozen Blackberries

Blueberries
... *All Fresh Fruits & Vegetables Are Gluten-Free*
Albertsons - Frozen
C & W - Frozen
Food Club Brand - Frozen
Full Circle - Organic Blueberries

B

   Giant Brand - Canned w/Syrup, Frozen

   Gluty Free - Dried (Juice Infused ●, Regular ●, Wild Organic ●),
      Freeze Dried ●

   Great Value Brand (Wal-Mart) - Frozen

   Hy-Vee - Frozen

   Kroger Brand - Plain Frozen Fruit

   Meijer Brand - Frozen (Organic, Regular)

   Nuts Online - Dried Blueberries (Natural Dried ●, Natural Dried
      Juice Infused ●, Organic Wild ●, Simply ●)

   Publix - Frozen

   Safeway Brand - Frozen

   Spartan Brand - Frozen

   Trader Joe's - Frozen (Fresh Blueberries, Organic Wild Blueberries,
      Wild Boreal)

   Wegmans Brand - Frozen

   Winn Dixie - Frozen

   Woodstock Farms - Organic Frozen Wild Blueberries

Bok Choy

   *... *All Fresh Fruits & Vegetables Are Gluten-Free*

Bologna

   Applegate Farms - Turkey Bologna

   Armour - Deli (Beef Bologna, Meat Bologna)

   Boar's Head - All Varieties

   Dietz & Watson ▲ - Beef ●, Original ●

   Eckrich - Deli Meat (Beef, Fried, Garlic, Low Sodium, Meat), Lunch
      Meat (Beef, Lite, Regular, Ring)

   Five Star Brand - Beef, Leona, Natural Casing, Pork & Beef

   Honeysuckle White - Turkey

   Hy-Vee - Garlic, German Brand, Regular Bologna, Thick, Thin, Turkey
      Bologna

   Kayem - Beef, German Style, Original

   Kroger Brand - Beef

   Kroger Value - Garlic, Regular, Thick

   Old Wisconsin - Ring Bologna

Publix - Deli Pre Pack Sliced Lunch Meat German Bologna
Wellshire Farms - Sliced Beef Bologna!!

Bouillon/Bouillon Cubes
Better Than Bouillon - Au Jus, Beef, Chicken, Chili, Clam, Fish, Ham, Kosher Passover (Chicken, Vegetable), Lobster, Organic (Beef, Chicken, Mushroom, Turkey, Vegetable), Reduced Sodium Chicken, Turkey, Vegetarian (No Beef, No Chicken)
Caskey's - Beef Flavor Bouillon Cubes
Celifibr ▲ - Bouillon Cubes (Vegetable Medley, Vegetarian Beef, Vegetarian Chicken), Bouillon Soup Base (French Onion, Vegetable Medley, Vegetarian Beef, Vegetarian Chicken)
Edward & Sons - Garden Veggie, Low Sodium Veggie, Not Beef, Not Chick'n
Food Club Brand - Beef Cubes
Giant Brand - Instant (Beef, Chicken), Regular (Beef, Chicken)
Harvest Sun - Organic (Herbal, Low Sodium, Mushroom, Onion, Organic Miso, Vegetable, Yeast Free)
Herb-Ox - Low Sodium (Granulated (Beef, Chicken), Packets (Beef, Chicken)), Packets/Cubes (Regular Beef, Regular Chicken)
Hy-Vee - Bouillon Cubes (Beef, Chicken), Instant Bouillon (Beef, Chicken)
Kroger Brand - Beef (Cubes, Instant)
Kum Chun - Chicken Bouillon Powder
Lee Kum Kee - Chicken Bouillon Powder
Marigold - Organic (Swiss Vegetable (Reduced Salt, Regular), Vegetable (Reduced Salt, Regular, Yeast Free)), Swiss Vegetable (Reduced Salt, Regular)
Massel - Ultracubes (Beef Style, Chicken Style, Vegetable)
Spartan Brand - Soup Bouillon Cube (Beef, Chicken (Cube, Granular))
Stop & Shop Brand - Beef Flavored Bouillon Cubes (Instant, Regular)

Bourbon
... *All Distilled Alcohol Is Gluten-Free*[2]

B Bowls

Amy's - Brown Rice & Vegetable Bowl (Light In Sodium❗, Regular❗), Brown Rice w/Black Eyed Peas & Veggies Bowl❗, Cream Of Rice Hot Cereal Bowl❗, Light & Lean Soft Taco Fiesta❗, Mexican Casserole (Light In Sodium❗, Regular❗), Non Dairy Rice Pasta Baked Ziti Bowl❗, Santa Fe Enchilada❗, Teriyaki❗, Tortilla Casserole & Black Beans❗

Chi-Chi's - Fiesta Plates (Creamy Chipotle Chicken, Salsa Chicken, Savory Garlic Chicken)

Lundberg ▲ - Organic Brown Rice Bowls (Country Wild, Long Grain, Short Grain)

Simply Asia - Rice Noodle Soup Bowl (Garlic Sesame, Sesame Chicken, Spring Vegetable)

Thai Kitchen - Rice Noodle Soup Bowl (Lemongrass & Chili, Roasted Garlic, Spring Onion, Thai Ginger)

Trader Joe's - Frozen Chicken Tandoori Rice Bowl

Bratwurst... see Sausage

Bread... (includes Baguettes, Rolls)

Against The Grain Gourmet - Baguette (Fresh Rosemary, Original), Rolls (Fresh Rosemary, Original)

Aleia's ▲ - Cinnamon Raisin ●, Farmhouse White ●

Andrea's Fine Foods ▲ - Focaccia, Loaf (Dairy Free Multigrain, Dairy Free Sandwich), Rolls (Dinner, Multigrain, Sandwich)

Apple's Bakery ▲ - Loaf (Olive Oil, Seeded Sandwich)

Aunt Gussie's ▲ - Focaccia ●, Kalamata Garlic Bread ●

Barkat - Baguettes, Rolls

Bi-Aglut - Baguette, Breadrolls, Breadsticks, Buckwheat Breadrolls, Mini Baguette, Pizza Sticks, Regular, Rustic Style Bread, Sesame Breadsticks, Toasted Bread

Canyon Bakehouse ▲ - Cinnamon Raisin, Mountain White, Rosemary & Thyme Focaccia, San Juan 7 Grain

Celiac Specialties ▲ - Bread (Apple Cinnamon, Cheddar Herb, Cinnamon Raisin, Flat, Flaxseed, Light White, Multigrain, Navy Bean, White), Breakfast Rolls (Apple, Blueberry), Buns (Hamburger,

Hot Dog, Sub), Garlic Bread, Multigrain Rolls, Multigrain Sandwich, Rolls (Cinnamon, Onion Poppy)

Ceres Kitchen ▲ - Dinner Rolls, Herb, Mock Rye, Multigrain, Sandwich & Hamburger Rolls, White Sandwich

Deerfields Gluten Free Bakery ▲ - Mini Baguette, Rice Bran Dinner Rolls

El Peto ▲ - Cheese, Dinner Rolls (Brown Rice, Cheese, Gourmet, Italian, Multigrain, Raisin), Gourmet, Gourmet Mini Subs, Italian Style, Millet, Potato, Raisin, Supreme Italian Style, Tapioca, White Rice, Whole Grain Brown Rice, Whole Grain (Flax Seed, Multi Grain

Ener-G ▲ -

Sliced Breads (Brown Rice, Corn, Egg Free Raisin, Four Flour, Hi Fiber, Light (Brown Rice, Tapioca, White Rice, White Rice Flax), Papas, Rice Starch, Seattle Brown, Tapioca Loaf (Dinner Rolls, Regular Sliced, Thin Sliced), White (Regular, Rice Flax), Yeast Free (Brown Rice, White Rice))

Specialty Breads (Bread Crumbs, Broken Melba Toast, Communion Wafers, Plain Croutons)

Everybody Eats ▲ - Bagels, Baguette, Banana Bread, Dairy Free Deli Rolls, Deli Rolls, Dinner Rolls, Egg Challah, Multigrain High Fiber Loaf, Pastry Rugelach, White Bread

Food For Life - Almond Rice, Bhutanese Red Rice, Brown Rice, Multi Seed Rice, Raisin Pecan, Rice Pecan, Wheat & Gluten Free Millet Bread, White Rice

French Meadow Bakery - Gluten-Free (Cinnamon Raisin Bread ●, Italian Rolls ●, Sandwich Bread ●)

Gillian's Foods ▲ - Carmalized Onion Rolls, Cinnamon Raisin (Loaf, Rolls), Crostini, English Muffins, Everything Dinner Rolls, French (Bread, Rolls), Garlic Bread, Poppyseed Rolls, Rye No Rye Loaf, Sandwich Loaf, Sesame Seed Rolls

Gluten Free Life ▲ - Country Brown Pure, Multi Grain Pure, Pumpernickle

B

Gluten-Free Creations ▲ - Almond Flax ●, Banana Tea Bread ●, Cheddar Cheese ●, Cinnamon Rolls ●, Herb Baguettes ●, Herb Loaf Bread ●, Herb Rolls ●, Honey Oat ●, Hot Dog Buns ●, Sandwich ●, Seeded Multigrain ●, White ●, Whole Grain ●

Glutino ▲ - English Muffins, Homestyle Wholegrain Brown Rice w/Prebiotics, Premium (Harvest Corn, Brown Rice w/Inulin, Cinnamon & Raisin, Fiber, Flaxseed)

Grandma Ferdon's ▲ - Breadsticks ●, Buttermilk ●, Cinnamon Raisin ●, Cocktail Pumpernickel ●, Dinner Rolls ●, Egg ●, Lefse ●, Pumpernickel ●

Heaven Mills ▲ - Burger Rolls ●, Challa Gluten & Egg Free ●, Gluten & Sugar Free ●, Gluten Egg & Sugar Free ●, Gluten Free ●, Mini Dinner Rolls (Gluten & Egg Free ●, Gluten & Sugar Free ●, Gluten Egg & Sugar Free ●, Gluten Free ●), Frankfurter Buns ●, Mezonos Bread ●, Oat Bread (Gluten & Egg Free ●, Gluten & Sugar Free ●, Gluten Egg & Sugar Free ●, Gluten Free ●), Pita Bread ●, Vunder Bread (Herb ●, Plain ●)

Katz Gluten Free ▲ - Bread (Sliced Challah ●, White ●, Whole Grain ●), Challah (Round ●, Round Oat ●, Round Oat Raisin ●, Round Raisin ●), Chocolate Strip ●, Cinnamon Strip ●, Cookies Chocolate Chip ●, Farfel ●, Honey Loaf ●, Kiska Kugel ●, Rolls (Large Challah Kaiser ●, Oat Challah ●, Sandwich ●, Small Challah Dinner Rolls ●), Wholesome ●

Kinnikinnick ▲ - Brown Sandwich, Candadi Yeast Free Multigrain Rice, Festive, Many Wonder Multigrain Rice, Robins Honey Brown Rice, Sunflower Flax Rice, Tapioca Rice (Cheese, Italian White, Raisin, Regular), White Sandwich, Yeast Free Tapioca

Kneaded Specialties ▲ - Cinnamon Rolls ●, Deluxe Sandwich ●, Dinner Rolls ●, French Bread Loaf ●, French Bread Rolls ●, Orange Danish Rolls ●, Sweet Bread (Banana ●, Cinnamon Raisin ●, Cranberry ●, Pumpkin ●), White Sandwich ●

Lakewood Matzoh - Oat Bread Machine Made, Oat Matzoh Hand Made

bread

B

Laurel's Sweet Treats ▲ - Banzo Bread, Dinner Rolls, Freshly Baked (Cheese Buns, Sandwich Loaves, Sandwich Rolls)

Miller's Gluten Free Foods ▲ - Cinnamon Raisin Bread, Deli Rolls, Sandwich White Bread

Nature's Own - Gluten Free (Extra Fiber White ●, Healthy Multi Grain ●)

Nu-World Foods - Flatbread Amaranth (Buckwheat ●, Garbanzo ●, Sorghum ●)

O'Doughs Bakery ▲ - Buns (Apple Cranberry Breakfast ●, Flax ●, White ●), Loaf (Flax ●, Flax Half ●, White ●, White Half ●)

Orgran ▲ - Crisp Bites (Balsamic Herb, Onion & Chives), Crisp Bread (Rice, Rice & Cracked Pepper, Rice & Garden Herb, Salsa)

PaneRiso ▲ - Brown Rice ●, Flax Seed ●, No Rye Rye ●, Raisin & Cinnamon Bread ●, White Rice ●

Pure Market Express ▲ - Butter Walnut ●, Garlic ●, Onion ●, Tuscan ●

Quejos ▲ - Non Dairy (Banana Bread, Banana Loaf)

Rose's Bakery ▲ - Banana, Dinner Rolls, French Bread (Herbed Rolls, Loaf, Rolls), Millet, Orange Cranberry Tea, Pita, Sandwich Bread, Seeded Sandwich Bread, Teff

Rudi's Gluten-Free Bakery - Cinnamon Raisin ●, Multigrain ●, Original ●

Schar ▲ - Baguette, Bread (Classic White, Hearty Grain, Hearty White, Multigrain), Rolls (Classic White, Sub Sandwich Rolls)

Silly Yak Bakery -

CFGF (Cinnamon Swirl ●, Cranberry Orange Yeast ●, Rice ●, Cinnamon Apple Swirl ●, Cinnamon Raisin ●, Cranberry Orange Sweet ●, Garlic Chive ●, Honey Brown Rice ●, Honey Swirl Brown Rice ●, Multi Seed ●, Onion Dill ●, Raisin Walnut ●, Tomato Basil ●)

GF (Buckwheat ●, Cinnamon Raisin Swirl ●, Cranberry Orange Sweet ●, Amaranth ●, Banana ●, Bavarian ●, Blueberry ●, Blueberry Peach ●, Caraway ●, Cheddar Onion ●, Cherry Almond ●, Cinnamon Apple Swirl ●, Cinnamon Swirl ●, Classic Rice ●, Cottage Dill ●, Cranberry Almond ●, Cranberry Orange

B

Toasting ●, Cranberry Wild Rice ●, Garlic Cheddar ●, Holiday●, Holly's Health ●, Honey Brown Rice ●, Irish Soda ●, Jalapeño Cheddar ●, Lemon Blueberry ●, Lemon Poppy Seed ●, Multi Seed Montina ●, Onion Dill Montina ●, Peach Rice ●, Pumpkin●, Quinoa Poppy Seed ●, Rosemary Red Onion ●Spinach Feta ●, Sunflower Millet ●, Teff & Pumpkin Seed ●, Tomato Basil Feta ●, Tomato Parmesan Spinach ●, Wild Rice & Chives ●)

The Grainless Baker ▲ - Baguette, Cinnamon Raisin, Dinner Rolls, Mock Rye, Sandwich

Trader Joe's - Gluten Free (Bagels, French Rolls), Ryeless "Rye"

Udi's Gluten Free Foods ▲ - Gluten Free (White Sandwich, Whole Grain Loaf)

Whole Foods Market Gluten Free Bakehouse ▲ - Bread (Banana, Cinnamon Raisin, Honey Oat, Prairie, Sandwich, Sundried Tomato & Garlic)

Bread Mix... (includes Baking Mix, Roll Mix)

1-2-3 Gluten Free ▲ - Aaron's Favorite Rolls ●, Meredith's Marvelous Muffin/Quickbread Mix ●

AgVantage Naturals ▲ - Master Blend Baking Mix ●, Multi Grain Bread Mix ●, Sandwich Bread Mix ●

Arnel's Originals - Bread Mix

Arrowhead Mills - All Purpose Baking Mix

Augason Farms - Gluten Free French Bread Mix ●

Authentic Foods ▲ - White Bread Mix, Wholesome Bread Mix

Bob's Red Mill ▲ - Bread Mix (Cinnamon Raisin, Hearty Whole Grain, Homemade Wonderful)

Breads From Anna ▲ - Bread Mix (All Purpose, Banana, Classic Herb, Gluten Free, Original, Pumpkin)

Bready - Gluten Free Hamburger Bun Mix ●, Heavenly White Gluten Free Bread Mix ●, Rye Gluten Free Bread Mix ●, Tuscan Love Affair Gluten Free Bread Mix ●

Cause You're Special ▲ - Bread Mix (Homestyle White, Traditional French)

Chebe ▲ - Bread Mix (All Purpose ●, Cinnamon Rolls ●, Focaccia Italian Flatbread ●, Original ●, Pizza Crust ●), Frozen Dough (Bread Sticks ●, Pizza Crust ●, Rolls ●, Sandwich Buns ●, Tomato Basil Bread Sticks ●), Garlic Onion Breadsticks Mix ●

El Peto ▲ - Breadmaker (Brown, Italian, Potato, White)

Ener-G ▲ - Mix (Corn, Potato, Rice), Potato Mix, Rice Mix

Fearn - Baking Mix (Brown Rice, Rice)

Food-Tek Fast & Fresh ▲ - Bread Mix White

Gifts Of Nature ▲ - Sandwich White Bread & Roll Mix

Gillian's Foods ▲ - All Purpose Baking Mix

Gluten Free Pantry ▲ - Favorite Sandwich Bread Mix, French Bread & Pizza Mix, Yankee Cornbread Mix

Gluten-Free Creations ▲ - Bread Mix (Almond Flax ●, Cinnamon Raisin ●, Honey Oat ●, Sandwich ●, Seeded Multigrain ●)

Gluten-Free Essentials ▲ - All Purpose Baking Mix ●, Holiday Gingerbread ●, Lemon Poppy Seed ●, Multi Grain (Cinnamon Spice ●, Meatloaf Starter ●, Original ●, Zesty Italian ●)

Grandma Ferdon's ▲ - Banana ●, Buttermilk Bread Dough ●

Hodgson Mill ▲ - Gluten Free (Bread Mix, Multi Purpose Baking Mix)

King Arthur Flour ▲ - Gluten Free Bread Mix ●

Kinnikinnick ▲ - All Purpose Mix, Candadi Yeast Free Rice, Cornbread & Muffin Mix, Kinni Kwik Bread & Bun Mix, Kinni Kwik Sunflower Flax, Kinni Kwik Sunflower Flax Bread & Bun Mix, Tapioca Rice

Lakewood Matzoh - Matzoh Meal

Little Bay Baking - Corn Bread Mix ●, Pumpkin Bread Mix ●

Meister's Gluten Free Mixtures ▲ - Bread Mix ●

Mixes From The Heartland ▲ - Sweet Bread Mix (Banana ●, Banana Flax Seed ●, Blueberry ●, Cranberry ●, Hawaiian ●)

Mrs. Crimble's - Bread Mix

Namaste Foods ▲ - Bread Mix

Nuts Online - Gluten Free Bread Mix (Cinnamon Raisin ●, Hearty Whole Grain ●, Homemade ●), Cornbread Mix ●

B

Orgran ▲ - Bread Mix (Alternative Grain Wholemeal, Easy Bake)
Pamela's Products ▲ - Amazing Bread Mix
Really Great Food Company ▲ -
  Bread Mix (Brown Rice, Dark European, French/Country Farm,
    Home Style Cornbread, Irish Soda Bread Mix, Old Fashioned
    Cinnamon, Old Fashioned Cinnamon Bread Mix, Original
    White, Original White, Rye Style)
Schar ▲ - Classic White Bread Mix, Rolls Parbaked Ciabatta
Silly Yak Bakery - GF Classic Rice Bread Mix ●
Simply Organic ▲ - Banana Bread Mix
Sylvan Border Farm - Bread Mix (Classic Dark, Non Dairy, White)
The Cravings Place ▲ - Create Your Own
Timtana Gluten Free - Bread Mix (Gluten Free Timtana Dark ●,
  Gluten Free Timtana Lite Brown ●, Gluten Free Timtana PrOatina
  Brown ●, Gluten Free Timtana PrOatina Lite ●)
Breadcrumbs... see Coating
Breadsticks
  Chebe ▲ - Garlic & Onion Breadsticks Mix ●, Tomato Basil Frozen
    Dough ●
  Glutino ▲ - Pizza Breadsticks, Sesame Breadsticks
  Schar ▲ - Italian Breadsticks
  The Grainless Baker ▲ - Sundried Tomato, TwiStix
Breakfast
  Amy's - Mexican Tofu Scramble !, Tofu Scramble !
  Celiac Specialties ▲ - Breakfast Rolls (Apple, Blueberry), Breakfast
    Sandwiches
  Farmer John - Breakfast Sausage Links & Patties (Hot Habanero, Old
    Fashioned Maple Skinless, Original Roll, Original Skinless,
    Premium PC Lower Fat, Premium Patties Lower Fat)
  Garrett County Farms - Frozen Breakfast Links (Chicken Apple !,
    Original !, Sunrise Maple !, Turkey Maple !)
  Great Value Brand (Wal-Mart) - Sausage (Beef Breakfast, Fully
    Cooked Pork Links, Fully Cooked Turkey Breakfast Patties, Maple
    Pork Patties, Original Pork Patties)

Honeysuckle White - Breakfast Sausage (Links, Patties, Roll)

Ian's - Wheat Free Gluten Free Recipe French Toast Sticks, Wheat Free Gluten Free Wafflewiches (Egg & Maple Cheddar, Maple Sausage & Egg)

Jennie-O Turkey Store - Breakfast Lover's Turkey Sausage, Fresh Breakfast Sausage (Maple Links, Mild Links, Mild Patties), Frozen Fully Cooked Sausage (Links, Patties)

Jimmy Dean -

Breakfast Bowls

Bacon Eggs Potatoes & Cheddar Cheese

D Lights (Turkey Bacon, Turkey Sausage)

Ham Eggs Potatoes & Cheddar Cheese

Sausage Eggs Potatoes & Cheddar Cheese

Breakfast Entrees

Scrambled Egg/Bacon/Cheese/Apples/Hash Brown

Scrambled Egg/Sausage/Cheese/Apples/Hash Brown

Breakfast Skillets (Bacon, Ham, Sausage)

Fully Cooked Hearty Sausage Crumbles (Hot, Original, Turkey)

Fully Cooked Sausage Links (Maple, Original, Turkey)

Fully Cooked Sausage Patties (Hot, Maple, Original, Sandwich Sized, Turkey)

Heat 'N Serve Sausage Links (Hot, Maple, Original)

Heat 'N Serve Sausage Patties

Maple Fresh Sausage (Links, Patties)

Omelets (Ham & Cheese, Sausage & Cheese, Three Cheese Ranch)

Original Fresh Sausage (Links, Patties)

Pork Roll Sausage (All Natural Regular, Hot, Italian, Light, Maple, Mild Country, Regular, Sage)

Johnsonville - Brown Sugar & Honey Links, Original Sausage (Links, Patties), Sausage Roll (Hot, Mild Country, Regular), Vermont Maple Syrup Sausage (Links, Patties), Wisconsin Cheddar Cheese Links

B

Jones Dairy Farm -
    All Natural Sausage (Hearty Pork Links ●, Light Pork & Rice Links ●,
        Little Link Pork ●, Maple Links ●, Original Pork Roll ●, Pork
        Patties●)
    Golden Brown All Natural Fully Cooked
        Beef Sausage Links ●
        Maple Sausage (Links ●, Patties ●)
        Mild Sausage (Links ●, Patties ●)
        Pork & Uncured Bacon Sausage Links ●
        Sausage & Rice Links ●
        Spicy Sausage Links ●
        Turkey Sausage Links ●
Medifast - Scrambled Eggs ●
Only Oats - Breakfast Blend (Apple & Cinnamon ●, Maple &
    Roasted Flax●)
Van's Natural Foods - Wheat & Gluten Free French Toast Sticks !

Broccoli
    *... *All Fresh Fruits & Vegetables Are Gluten-Free*
Albertsons - All Plain Frozen Vegetables
Birds Eye - All Plain Frozen Vegetables
C & W - All Plain Frozen Vegetables
Dr. Praeger's - Broccoli Littles !
Earthbound Farm - Organic Whole
Food Club Brand - Cut, Frozen Chopped, Spears, Steamin' Easy
    Broccoli Cuts
Freshlike - Frozen Plain Vegetables
Giant Brand - Frozen (Broccoli Cauliflower & Pepper Mix, Broccoli
    Corn & Red Peppers Mix, Chopped, Cuts, Florets)
Green Giant -
    Frozen Broccoli & Carrots w/Garlic & Herbs Seasoned
    Broccoli & Cheese Sauce
    Broccoli Spears & Butter Sauce
    Chopped
    Immunity Boost

Steamers (Broccoli & Cheese Sauce, Broccoli Cauliflower Carrots & Cheese Sauce, Cheesy Rice & Broccoli)

Valley Fresh Steamers (Broccoli Cuts, Chopped Broccoli, Select Broccoli Florets)

Hy-Vee - Frozen (Chopped, Cuts, Florets)

Kroger Brand - All Plain Vegetables (Canned, Frozen)

Kroger Value - All Plain Vegetables Frozen

Lowes Foods Brand - Frozen (Chopped, Cuts, Deluxe Baby Florets, Deluxe Florets, Spears)

Meijer Brand - Frozen (Chopped, Cuts, Spears)

Mezzetta - Broccoli Flowerettes

Midwest Country Fare - Frozen (Chopped, Cuts)

Nuts Online - Simply Broccoli Freeze Dried Vegetables ●

Pictsweet - All Plain Frozen Vegetables

Private Selections - All Plain Frozen Vegetables

Publix - Frozen (Chopped, Cuts, Spears)

Safeway Brand - Frozen (Cuts, Florets, Steam In Bag)

Spartan Brand - Cuts, Florets, Spears

Stop & Shop Brand - Broccoli (Chopped, Cuts, Spears), Broccoli & Cauliflower

Trader Joe's - Frozen Broccoli Florets, Frozen Organic Broccoli Florets

Wegmans Brand - Broccoli (Chopped, Cuts), Broccoli Cuts & Cauliflower Florets, Spears

Winn Dixie - Frozen (Chopped, Cuts, Florets, Spears), Steamable Broccoli Cut

Woodstock Farms - Organic Frozen Broccoli Florets

Broth

Baxters - Chicken

Bowman & Landes - Chicken, Turkey

Caskey's - Beef, Chicken

College Inn Broth - Garden Vegetable, Tender Beef Bold, White Wine & Herb Culinary Chicken

Food Club Brand - Beef, Chicken *(Box Only)* (Reduced Sodium, Regular)

B

Full Circle - Chicken**!**, Vegetable**!**
Giant Brand - Beef, Chicken
Hannaford Brand - Chicken *(Only In Resealable Box)*
Health Valley - 40% Less Sodium Chicken, No Salt Added (Beef, Chicken)
Hy-Vee - Chicken
Imagine - Low Sodium (Beef, Free Range Chicken, Vegetable), No Chicken, Regular (Beef, Free Range Chicken, Vegetable)
Kroger Brand - Canned (Beef, Chicken, Fat Free (Beef, Chicken, Vegetable)), Culinary Stock (Beef, Chicken)
Lowes Foods Brand - Beef, Chicken (Low Sodium, Regular)
Meijer Brand - Chicken
Member's Mark - All Natural Chicken Broth
Midwest Country Fare - Chicken
Nature's Basket - Chicken (Low Sodium, Regular, Vegetable)
Nature's Promise - All Natural Beef, Organic (Chicken, Vegetable)
O Organics - Chicken, Low Sodium Chicken, Vegetable
Pacific Natural Foods -
    Natural (Beef, Free Range Chicken)
    Organic (Beef, Free Range Chicken, Mushroom, Vegetable)
    Organic Low Sodium (Free Range Chicken, Vegetable)
Progresso - Beef Flavored, Chicken (Reduced Sodium, Regular)
Publix - Beef, Chicken
Safeway Brand - Beef, Chicken (Box, Canned, Fat Free Reduced Sodium)
Shelton's - Chicken (Fat Free Low Sodium, Regular), Organic (Chicken, Chicken Fat Free Low Sodium)
Spartan Brand - Beef, Chicken
Stop & Shop Brand - Beef, Chicken, Ready To Serve Chicken Broth
Swanson - Chicken Broth (Canned, Carton), Natural Goodness Chicken Broth (Canned, Carton), Vegetable Broth Canned
Trader Joe's - Organic (Free Range Chicken**!!**, Hearty Vegetable**!!**, Low Sodium Chicken**!!**), Savory Broth Concentrate Reduced Sodium

Winn Dixie - Canned (Clear Beef, Clear Chicken)

Brown Sugar... see Sugar

Brownies/Brownie Mix

1-2-3 Gluten Free ▲ - Devilishly Decadent Brownies ●, Divinely
  Decadent Brownies ●

Andrea's Fine Foods ▲ - Truffle Brownies

Arrowhead Mills - Gluten Free Brownie Mix

Augason Farms - Gluten Free Chocolate Chip Brownie Mix ●

Aunt Gussie's ▲ - Brownie ●

Authentic Foods ▲ - Double Chocolate Brownie Mix

Better Batter - Fudge Brownie Mix

Betty Crocker ▲ - Gluten Free Chocolate Brownie Mix

Bob's Red Mill ▲ - Gluten Free Brownie Mix

Breakaway Bakery ▲ - Brownie Batter ●

Cause You're Special ▲ - Chocolate Fudge

Celiac Specialties ▲ - Brownie Mix, Brownies (Plain, Round, Tray)

Ceres Kitchen ▲ - Chocolate Brownie Loaf Cake

Cherrybrook Kitchen - Gluten Free Fudge Brownie Mix *(Box Must
  Say Gluten-Free)*

Choices Rice Bakery ▲ - Brownie Mix

Cookies For Me - Bites, Brownies

Crave Bakery ▲ - Brownies (Dark Chocolate, Toasted Pecan)

Deb's Farmhouse Kitchen - Dark Chocolate Walnut Fudge ●

Deerfields Gluten Free Bakery ▲ - Triple Chocolate Brownie, Triple
  Chocolate Brownie Cookie

Dowd & Rogers ▲ - Brownie Mix Dark Chocolate

El Peto ▲ - Brownie Mix

Ener-G ▲ - Brownies

Everybody Eats ▲ - Brownies Dairy Free Fudge

Foods By George ▲ - Brownies

Food-Tek Fast & Fresh ▲ - Minute Gooey Brownie Decadence

Frankly Natural Bakers - Cherry Berry, Java Jive, Misty Mint,
  Wacky Walnut

B

French Meadow Bakery - Gluten Free (Frozen Fudge Brownies ●, Fudge Brownie Bites ●, Fudge Brownies ●)

Gifts Of Nature ▲ - Chocolate Fudge Brownie Mix

Gillian's Foods ▲ - Brownie Mix

Gluten Free & Fabulous ▲ - Brownie Bites ●

Gluten Free Life ▲ - Brownies, The Ultimate Gluten Free Cake Muffin & Brownie Mix

Gluten Free Pantry ▲ - Chocolate Truffle Brownie Mix

Gluten-Free Creations ▲ - Rich Brownie Mix ●

Gluten-Free Essentials ▲ - Brownie Mix (Chocolate Mint Fudge ●, Decadent Chocolate Fudge ●, Speedy Bake Fudge ●)

Gopal's - Brownie (Cherry, Original)

Grandma Ferdon's ▲ - Brownies ●

Hodgson Mill ▲ - Gluten Free Brownie Mix

King Arthur Flour ▲ - Gluten Free Brownie Mix ●

Kinnikinnick ▲ - JB Brownie Squares

Kneaded Specialties ▲ - Ooey Gooey Fudge ●

Laurel's Sweet Treats ▲ - Chocolate Dream Brownie Mix

Medifast - Brownie ●

Mixes From The Heartland ▲ - Brownie Mix (Microwave ●, Pumpkin ●, Sweet Potato ●)

Mrs. Crimble's - Double Chocolate Brownies

Namaste Foods ▲ - Blondies Mix, Brownie Mix

Pamela's Products ▲ - Chocolate Brownie Mix

Pure Market Express ▲ - Brownie Bites w/Vanilla Frosting ●

Quejos ▲ - Non Dairy (Chocolate, Dark Chocolate)

Really Great Food Company ▲ - Aunt Tootsie's Brownie Mix

Rose's Bakery ▲ - Brownies

Silly Yak Bakery - GF Brownies ●

Simply Organic ▲ - Cocoa Brownie Mix

The Cravings Place ▲ - Ooey Gooey Chocolatey Chewy Brownie Mix

The Grainless Baker ▲ - Brownies

The Naked Cookie - Gluten Free Chocolate Brownie Batter (Dark, Milk, Standard, White)

Trader Joe's - Gluten Free Brownie Mix
WOW Baking Company ▲ - Chocolate Brownie ●

Bruschetta
Classico - All Varieties
Member's Mark
Santa Barbara
Tassos - Mediterranean, Olivara
Trader Joe's - Bruschetta Sauce Fresh!!, Grilled Vegetable, Mixed
    Olive, Regular!!, Sun Dried Tomato

Brussel Sprouts
*... *All Fresh Fruits & Vegetables Are Gluten-Free*
Birds Eye - All Plain Frozen Vegetables
C & W - All Plain Frozen Vegetables
Food Club Brand - Frozen (Petite, Regular)
Green Giant - Frozen Baby Brussels Sprouts & Butter Sauce
Hy-Vee - Frozen
Lowes Foods Brand - Brussel Sprouts, Deluxe Baby
Meijer Brand - Frozen
Mezzetta - Dilled Brussels Sprouts
Midwest Country Fare - Frozen
Pictsweet - Frozen
Publix - Frozen
Safeway Select - Petite
Spartan Brand - Frozen
Stop & Shop Brand
Trader Joe's - All Plain Frozen
Wegmans Brand - Frozen (In Butter Sauce, Regular)
Winn Dixie - Frozen

Buckwheat
Arrowhead Mills
Arzu - Chai ●, Original ●, Southwest ●
Bob's Red Mill ▲ - Organic Buckwheat (Groats, Kasha)
Gluty Free - Raw Organic White ●
Pocono - Buckwheat Flour Light, Whole

B Buckwheat Groats
Arrowhead Mills
Wolff's - Whole
Buffalo Meat
Trader Joe's - Classic Buffalo Burger, Flame Grilled Buffalo Patties
Buffalo Wing Sauce... see Wing Sauce
Buffalo Wings... see Wings
Buns
Canyon Bakehouse ▲ - Hamburger
Celiac Specialties ▲ - Buns (Hamburger, Hot Dog, Sub)
Chebe ▲ - Sandwich Buns Frozen Dough ●
Cybro's - Gluten Free Rice Rolls
El Peto ▲ - Hamburger Buns (Brown Rice, Italian, Multigrain, Potato),
    Hot Dog Buns (Italian, Potato)
Ener-G ▲ - Hamburger Buns (Brown Rice, Seattle Brown, Tapioca,
    White Rice), Hot Dog Buns (Seattle Brown, Tapioca)
Food-Tek Fast & Fresh ▲ - Minute Hamburger Bun Mix
Gluten-Free Creations ▲ - Hamburger Buns (Regular ●, White ●),
    Hot Dog Buns ●
Grandma Ferdon's ▲ - Hamburger ●, Hot Dog ●
Heaven Mills ▲ - Burger Rolls ●, Frankfurter Buns ●
Kinnikinnick ▲ - Tapioca Rice Buns (Cinnamon, Hamburger Buns,
    Hot Cross, Hot Dog, Tray)
Kneaded Specialties ▲ - Hamburger Buns w/Sesame Seeds ●,
    Hamburger ●, Hot Dog ●
Quejos ▲ - Cheese (Black Olives, Extra Cheese, Flaxseed & Almond,
    Fresh Garlic, Fresh Jalapeno, Fresh Spinach & Onion, Sundried
    Tomato & Basil), Non Dairy (Flaxseed & Almond, Fresh Spinach
    & Onion, Tropical Treat), Soya (Fresh Jalapeno, Plain, Sundried
    Tomato & Basil)
Rose's Bakery ▲ - Hamburger, Hot Dog
Schar ▲ - Classic White Rolls
Silly Yak Bakery -
    CFGF (Garlic Chive ●, Multi Seed ●, Onion Dill ●, Raisin Walnut●,
    Rice Millet ●, Tomato Basil Buns ●)

GF (Amaranth ●, Bavarian●, Buckwheat ●, Caraway ●, Cheddar Onion ●, Classic Rice ●, Cottage Dill ●, Cranberry Orange Toasting ●, Cranberry Wild Rice ●, Cranberry Wild Rice ●, Dill Montina ●, Holiday ●, Holly's Health ●, Honey Brown Rice ●, Jalapeño Cheddar ●, Multi Seed Montina ●, Quinoa Poppy Seed ●, Raisin Walnut Montina ●, Rosemary Red Onion ●, Sesame Sunflower Millet ●, Spinach Feta ●, Teff and Pumpkin Seed ●, Tomato Basil Feta ●, Tomato Parmesan Spinach ●, Wild Rice and Chives ●)

The Grainless Baker ▲ - Hamburger, Hoagie, Hot Dog

Whole Foods Market Gluten Free Bakehouse ▲ - Hamburger Buns

Burgers

... *All Fresh Ground Meat Is Gluten-Free (Non-Marinated, Unseasoned)

Amy's - Bistro Burger **!**

Applegate Farms - Organic (Beef, Turkey)

Asherah's Gourmet - Vegan Burgers (Chipotle ●, Original ●)

Butcher's Cut - Beef Burgers

Butterball - Turkey Burgers Frozen (All Natural, Seasoned)

Dr. Praeger's - California Veggie Burger **!**

Gordon Food Service - Cooked Turkey Burgers

Great Value Brand (Wal-Mart) - 100% Frozen Beef Patties

Henry & Lisa's - Salmon Burgers Wild Alaskan (Regular, Teriyaki)

Honeysuckle White - Fresh Ground Turkey Patties, Frozen Turkey Burgers

Jennie-O Turkey Store - Fresh Lean Turkey Patties, Frozen Turkey Burgers

Kirkland Signature - Frozen (Ground Beef Patties, Frozen Ground Sirloin Patties, Frozen Turkey Burgers)

Nature's Promise - Veggie Burgers (Garlic & Cheese, Soy Vegetable, Vegan Soy Vegetable)

Organic Prairie - Frozen Organic Ground Beef Patties 10.6 oz.

Perdue - Ground Burgers (Chicken, Turkey)

Shelton's - Turkey

Sol Cuisine - Organic Falafel, Original, Spicy Bean, Vegetable

B

Sunshine Burgers - Organic (Barbecue, Breakfast, Falafel, Garden Herb, Original, South West)

Trader Joe's - Chili Lime Chicken, Classic Buffalo, Flame Grilled Buffalo Patties, Premium Salmon Patties **!!**, Salmon, Tofu Veggie **!**

Wellshire Farms - All Natural Frozen (Beef Hamburgers **!!**, Turkey **!!**)

Wild Wood Organics - Tofu Veggie Burgers (Original, Shiitake, Southwest)

Winn Dixie - Frozen Angus Beef Patties (Original, w/Grill Seasoning, w/Sweet Onion)

Burrito Seasoning Mix... see also Seasonings

Old El Paso

Burritos

Amy's - Gluten Free Burritos (Cheddar Cheese **!**, Dairy Free **!**)

GlutenFreeda ▲ - Beef & Potato, Chicken & Cheese, Vegetarian (& Dairy Free, Bean & Cheese)

Butter... see also Spread

Breakstone - Salted, Salted Whipped, Unsalted, Unsalted Whipped

Cabot - 83 - Salted, Unsalted

Coburn Farms - Butter Spread

Country Crock - All Spreadable Butters

Earth Balance ▲ - Natural Buttery Spread (Olive Oil, Original, Soy Free, Soy Garden), Natural Shortening, Organic Buttery Spread Original Whipped, Vegan Buttery Sticks

Eden Organic - Apple, Apple Cherry, Montmorency Tart Cherry

Food Club Brand - Margarine (Patties, Spread)

Full Circle - Organic Salted Butter

Fungus Among Us - Black Truffle

Garelick Farms - Salted Sweet Cream Butter

Giant Brand - 48% Margarine Spread, Quarters (Salted, Unsalted)

Gluty Free - Organic Cacao Butter ●

Gordon Food Service - Margarine (Reddies, Whipped)

Great Value Brand (Wal-Mart) - Buttery Spread, Cardio Choice (Light, Regular), Margarine, Sweet Cream Butter (Salted, Unsalted), Vegetable Oil Spread

Hannaford Brand - Salted, Tastes Like Butter (Light 40% Vegetable Oil, Regular 58% Vegetable Oil), Unsalted

Horizon Organic - All Varieties

Hy-Vee - Best Thing Since Butter, Sweet Cream Butter (Quarters & Solid, Unsalted, Whipped), Unsalted Sweet Quarters

I Can't Believe It's Not Butter - All Varieties

Ian's - Soy Butter 4 Me

Kirkland Signature - Salted (Organic, Regular), Unsalted

Kroger Brand - Butter, Margarine

Land-O-Lakes - Butter w/Olive Oil, Fresh Buttery Taste, Garlic Butter, Honey Butter, Margarine, Salted Butter, Spreadable Butter w/Canola Oil, Unsalted Butter, Whipped Salted Butter, Whipped Unsalted Butter

Laura Lynn - Butter, Margarine Spread (Quarters, Squeezeable, Taste Like Butter)

Lowes Foods Brand - Margarine (Patties, Quarters, Soft 1 Lb, Squeeze), Sweet Cream (Salted, Unsalted)

Lucerne - Butter (Salted, Unsalted), Whipped

Manischewitz - Apple Butter

Meijer Brand - Butter AA CTN Quarters

Nature's Promise - Organic

Nuts Online - Organic Cacao Butter ●, Prune Butter ●

Odell's - Clarified Butter, Original Popcorn Butter, Seafood Butter

Organic Valley - Cultured Unsalted, European Style Cultured, Pasture Cultured, Salted, Whipped Salted

Phildesco - Coconut

Prairie Farms - Salted, Unsalted

Publix - Salted, Sweet Cream, Unsalted, Whipped (Salted, Unsalted)

Purity Farms - Organic Ghee Clarified Butter

Smart Balance -
Extra Virgin Olive Oil (Light, Original)
Heart Right (Light, Original)
Omega 3 (Light, Original)
Original (Light, Organic, Regular, w/Flax, w/Flax Light)

B

C

Sticks 50/50 (Butter Blend, Omega 3 Butter Blend, w/Extra Virgin Olive Oil)

w/Calcium

Whipped Low Sodium Lightly Salted

Spartan Brand - 48% Spread, 70% Quarters Spread, Butter, Is It Butter 70% Spread, Soft Tub Margarine, Unsalted

Spectrum - Spread

Stop & Shop Brand - Butter Quarters (Salted, Unsalted)

Tillamook - All Varieties !

Trader Joe's - All Varieties

Wegmans Brand - Club Pack Sweet Cream Butter Sticks, Finishing Butter (Bearnaise, Chipotle Lime, Garlic Cheese, Lemon Dill), Solid Butter, Sweet Cream Butter Sticks (Salted, Unsalted), Whipped Tub (Salted, Unsalted)

Winn Dixie - Salted, Unsalted, Whipped

Woodstock Farms - Organic Butter (Salted, Unsalted)

Buttermilk... see Milk

C

Cabbage

*... *All Fresh Fruits & Vegetables Are Gluten-Free*

Cake/Cake Mix

1-2-3 Gluten Free ▲ - Delightfully Gratifying Bundt Poundcake ●, Devil Food Cake Mix ●, Peri's Perfect Chocolate Bundt Poundcake ●, Yummy Yellow Cake Mix ●

AgVantage Naturals ▲ - Angel Food Cake Mix ●, Dark Chocolate Cake Mix ●, Vanilla Supreme Cake Mix ●

Amy's - Gluten Free Organic Chocolate Cake !

Andrea's Fine Foods ▲ -

Carrot Spice

Chocolate Cake w/(Chocolate Icing, White Icing)

Chocolate Chunk White Icing

Gooey Butter

Yellow Cake w/(Chocolate Icing, White Icing)

C

Apple's Bakery ▲ - White Layer Cake Kit

Arrowhead Mills - Bake With Me Gluten Free Cupcake Mix (Chocolate, Vanilla), Gluten Free Vanilla Cake Mix

Augason Farms - Gluten Free Cake Mix (Angel Food ●, Chocolate ●, Yellow ●)

Authentic Foods ▲ - Cake Mix (Chocolate, Devil's Food Chocolate Lemon, Vanilla)

Betty Crocker ▲ - Gluten Free Cake Mix (Devil's Food, Yellow)

Bi-Aglut - Plum Cake

Bob's Red Mill ▲ - Cake Mix (Chocolate, Vanilla)

Breakaway Bakery ▲ - Cupcake Batter (Chocolate ●, Chocolate Chip ●, Golden Cinnamon Lemon ●)

Cause You're Special ▲ - Golden Pound, Moist (Lemon, Yellow), Rich Chocolate

Celiac Specialties ▲ - Angel Food Cake, Angel Wings, Coffee Cake, Mini Boston Creme Pie, Pumpkin Cake

Ceres Kitchen ▲ - Carrot Loaf, Cheesecake (Chocolate Chip, New York Style (10", 7"), Swirl (Lemon, Raspberry)), Chocolate (Brownie Loaf Cake, w/Chocolate Frosting, w/White Frosting), Lemon w/Lemon Frosting, White (w/Chocolate Frosting, w/White Frosting)

Cherrybrook Kitchen - Gluten Free Chocolate Cake Mix *(Box Must Say Gluten Free)*, Gluten Free Yellow Cake Mix *(Box Must Say Gluten Free)*

Crave Bakery ▲ - 6" Decorated Chocolate, 8" Sugar Free Cheesecake, Chocolate Cupcake, Mama Z's Chocolate Cake

Deerfields Gluten Free Bakery ▲ - Cheesecake, Coffeecakes (Blueberry Cream Cheese, Pecan Sour Cream), Mini Chocolate Cupcakes

Dowd & Rogers ▲ - Cake Mix (Dark Vanilla, Dutch Chocolate, Golden Lemon)

EasyGlut - Cake Mix (Devil's Food, Yellow)

El Peto ▲ - Cake Mix (Chocolate, Lemon, White)

El Torito - Sweet Corn Cake Mix

C

Ener-G ▲ - Poundcake

Fabe's Bakery - 6" Gluten Free Cake (Chocolate Banana ●, Chocolate Fudge ●, Homestyle Carrot ●)

Foods By George ▲ - Cake (Crumb, Poundcake)

Food-Tek Fast & Fresh ▲ - Cake Mix Dairy Free Minute (Chocolate, Cinnamon Coffee, White, Yellow), Double Chocolate

Full Circle - Gluten Free Spice Cake Mix

Gifts Of Nature ▲ - Yellow Cake Mix

Gluten Free Life ▲ - The Ultimate Gluten Free Cake Muffin & Brownie Mix

Gluten Free Pantry ▲ - Chocolate Chip Cookie & Cake Mix, Decadent Chocolate Cake Mix, Old Fashioned Cake & Cookie Mix

Gluten-Free Creations ▲ - Angel Food Cake ●, Carrot Picnic Cake ●, Cinnamon Coffee Cake ●, Winkies ●

Gluten-Free Essentials ▲ - Mix (Extreme Chocolate Cake ●, Holiday Gingerbread ●, Yellow Velvet Cake ●), Speedy Bake Mix (Chocolate Mud ●, Spice Is Nice ●, Yella Vanilla ●)

Grandma Ferdon's ▲ - Angel Food Cake Mix ●, Carrot Cake ●, Coffee Cake ●

Heaven Mills ▲ - Cake (Brownie ●, Carrot ●, Marble Strip Chocolate●), Sprinkled Cupcakes ●, Strip Cake Chocolate ●

Hodgson Mill ▲ - Gluten Free (Chocolate Cake Mix, Yellow Cake Mix)

Jennies ▲ - Pound Cake Minis (Classic ●, Marble ●, Raisin ●)

Katz Gluten Free ▲ - Cupcake (Chocolate ●, Vanilla ●), Marble Cake ●

King Arthur Flour ▲ - Gluten Free Chocolate Cake Mix ●

Kinnikinnick ▲ - Cake Mix (Angel Food, Chocolate, Sponge, White)

Kneaded Specialties ▲ - Coffee Cake ●, Cupcakes (Chocolate ●, Vegan Chocolate Creme ●, Vegan Vanilla Creme ●, White ●), Luscious Lemonade Cake ●

Laurel's Sweet Treats ▲ - Cake Mix (Cinnamon Spice, Mom's Chocolate, Vanilla)

Little Bay Baking - Sponge Cake Mix ●, Yellow Cake Mix ●

Mixes From The Heartland ▲ - Cake Mix (Cheesecake ●, Chocolate Angel Food ●, Chocolate Poundcake ●, Cinnamon Orange ●, Lime Angel Food ●, Lime Poundcake ●, Orange Angel Food ●, Pineapple Poundcake ●, Raspberry Poundcake ●, Strawberry Angel Food ●, Strawberry Poundcake ●, Vanilla Angel Food ●, Vanilla Poundcake ●)

Mrs. Crimble's - Bakewell Cake Slices

Namaste Foods ▲ - Cake Mix (Chocolate, Spice, Vanilla)

New Harvest Naturals - Cake (Classic GF Poundcake, Raisin Poundcake)

O'Doughs Bakery ▲ - Cake (Banana ●, Carrot ●, Chocolate ●)

Orgran ▲ - Cake Mix (Chocolate, Vanilla)

Pamela's Products ▲ - Cake (Chocolate Fudge Cake w/Chocolate Frosting, Pamela's Coffee Cake w/Nut Topping), Cake Mix (Chocolate, Classic Vanilla), Cheesecake (Agave Sweetened New York, Hazelnut, New York, White Chocolate Raspberry, Zesty Lemon)

Pure Market Express ▲ - Cheesecake (Chocolate ●, Key Lime ●)

Really Great Food Company ▲ - Cake Mix (Angel Food, Banana Bread, Chocolate, Chocolate Cupcake, Colonial Spice, Devil's Food, Gingerbread, Golden, Grandma's Poundcake, Lemon Poppy, Orange, Pineapple, Pumpkin Bread, Pumpkin Spice, White, Yellow), Coffee Crumb Cake

Ruby Range - Gluten Free Baking Mix (Chocolate Truffle Cake & Cupcakes ●, Spice Cake & Cupcakes ●)

Silly Yak Bakery -
  CFGF (Classic Rice Cake ●, Frosted Chocolate Cupcake ●, Frosted Vanilla Cupcake ●)
  GF (Chocolate Rice Cake ●, Classic Rice Cake ●, Frosted Chocolate (Cupcake ●, Rice Cake ●), Frosted Vanilla (Cupcake●, Rice Cake ●), Majestic Valley Cake (Almond Sour Cream Coffee●, Apple Walnut Sour Cream Coffee ●, Blueberry Sour Cream Coffee●, Pumpkin Pecan Sour Cream Coffee ●, Raspberry Sour Cream Coffee ●, Sour Cream Coffee ●), Marble Rice Cake ●)

C

Simply Organic ▲ - Carrot Cake Mix, Cocoa Cayenne Cupcake Mix

Skye Foods - Heart Cake ●, Spice Cake ●

Sof'ella - Gluten Free Chocolate Cake Mix & Frosting Mix ●

Sylvan Border Farm - Cake Mix (Chocolate, Lemon)

The Cravings Place ▲ - Cake & Cookie Mix, Cinnamon Crumble
    Coffeecake Mix, Create Your Own, Dutch Chocolate Cake Mix

The Grainless Baker ▲ - Mini Cake (Carrot, Coffee)

The Lite-Ful Cheesecake ▲ - Cheesecake (Amaretto Almond ●,
    Blueberry ●, Chocolate Bliss ●, Chocolate Swirl ●, Cinnamon ●,
    Grand ●, Kahlua ●, Lemon ●, Mandarin ●, Mocha ●, Peanut
    Butter ●, Plain Vanilla ●, Pumpkin ●, Strawberry ●)

Three Senses Gourmet - Souffle (Caramel Chocolate, Chocolate)

Trader Joe's - Flourless Chocolate Cake **! !**

Whole Foods Market Gluten Free Bakehouse ▲ - Carrot Cake,
    Chocolate, Cupcakes (Chocolate, Vanilla)

New Harvest Naturals - Marble Pound Cake

Candy/Candy Bars

Amanda's Own - All Varieties

Andes - Crème De Menthe Sugar Free, Thins (Cherry Jubilee,
    Crème De Menthe, Mint Parfait, Toffee Crunch)

Benecol - Smart Chews

Bequet - Handmade Caramels

Candy Tree - Licorice (Cherry (Bites, Laces, Vines), Raspberry (Bites,
    Laces, Vines), Strawberry (Bites, Laces, Vines))

Caramel Apple Pops

Carb Safe - Sugar Free Chocolate Bars Dark

Caring Candies - Sugar Free Lollipops

Cella's - Chocolate Covered Cherries (Dark, Milk)

Charleston Chew - Chocolate, Mini Vanilla, Strawberry, Vanilla

Charms - Blow Pops (Bubblegum, Minis, Regular), Flat Pops, Fluffy
    Stuff (Regular, Tear Jerkers), Sweet Pops

ChocAlive - Truffles (Almond, Chocolate Chip Mint, Coconut, Dark
    Chocolate, Dark Chocolate Crunch, Pistachio)

Coffee Rio's - All Flavors

Creme Savers - Strawberry & Creme

Cry Baby - Extra Sour (Bubble Gum, Candy), Gumballs, Tears, Twist Gum

Dots - Crows, Fruit Flavor, Tropical Flavor, Yoghurt Flavor

Enjoy Life ▲ - Boom Choco Boom (Dairy Free Rice Milk Bar ●, Dairy Free Rice Milk w/Crispy Rice Bar ●, Dark Chocolate Bar ●),

Food Club Brand - Butterscotch Discs, Candy Corn, Cinnamon Buttons, Circus Peanuts, Gummi (Bears, Worms), Orange Slices, Party Mix, Smarties, Sour Worms, Spice Drops, Starlight Mints (Regular, Spearmint)

Frooties - Fruit Flavored Chewy Candy

Giant Brand - Assorted (Fruit Filled, Kiddie Mix, Star Drops, Starlights), Butter Toffee, Butterscotch Disks, Candy Corn, Candy Necklaces, Circus Peanuts, Gummy Blue Sharks, Gum Drops, Gummi Bears, Neon Sour Crawlers, Orange Slices, Peach Rings, Red Ju Ju (Coins, Fish), Sour Gummi Worms, Spice Drops, Jelly Beans, Lemon Drops, Mints Canada Wintergreen, Cinnamon Starlights, Pastel, Silver, Soft Peppermints, Spearmint (Leaves, Starlights), Starlights, Pina Colada Coated Cashews, Root Beer Barrels, Royal Mix, Smarties, Sour Balls, Strawberry Buds, Watermelon Hard Candy

Gimbal's Fine Candies - All Varieties

Glutino ▲ - Candy Bars (Chocolate Peanut Butter, Dark Chocolate, Milk Chocolate)

Goelitz - Candy Corn

Great Value Brand (Wal-Mart) - Candy Corn, Cinnamon Discs, Fruit Slices, Gummy Bears, Orange Slices, Root Beer Barrels, Spearmint Starlight Mints, Spice Drops, Starlight Mints

Hannaford Brand - Butterscotch, Canada (Mints, Wintergreen), Chocolate (Covered Raisins!, Non Pareils!), Circus Peanuts, Double Dipped Peanuts!, Gummi (Bears, Sour Neon Worms, Worms), Hostess Mix, Jelly Beans, Jelly Rings, Jumbo Gum Drops, Licorice Bears, Orange Slices, Spice Drops, Sugar Free (Cinnamon Buttons, Peppermint Starlights, Rootbeer Barrels)

Haribo - Alphabet Letters, Build A Burger, Centipedes, Clown Fish, Colossal Crocs, Fizzy Cola, Frogs, Fruit Blasts, Fruit Salad, Fruity

C

Frutti, Gold Bears, Grapefruit, Gummi Apples, Happy Cola, Mini Rainbow Frogs, Peaches, Pink Grapefruit, Raspberries, Rattle Snakes, Root Beer Barrels, Roulettes (Mega, Regular), Sour Cherries, Stock Cars, Strawberries, Strawberries & Cream, Super Cola, Techno Bears, Tropi Frutti, Twin Cherries

Hershey's -

Heath Bar

Jolly Ranchers (Gummies, Hard Candy)

Kisses (Milk Chocolate, Milk Chocolate Meltaways, Milk Chocolate w/Almonds, Milk Chocolate w/Caramel, Milk Chocolate w/Cherry Cordial Crème, Rich Dark Chocolate, Special Dark Chocolate)

Milk Chocolate Bar (Original, w/Almonds)

Mr. Goodbar

PayDay

Reese's Peanut Butter Cups (Original)

Skor

York Peppermint Patty

Hy-Vee -

Assorted Gum Balls

Butterscotch Buttons

Chocolate (Caramel Clusters, Covered Raisins, Peanut Clusters, Stars)

Cinnamon Imperials

Circus Peanuts

Double Dipped Chocolate Covered Peanuts

Dubble Bubble Gum

Dum Dum Suckers

Gum Drops

Gummi (Bears, Peach Rings, Sour Worms, Worms)

Lemon Drops

Milk Chocolate Carmel Cups

Milk Chocolate Peanut Butter Cups

Orange Slices

Smarties
Spice Drops
Starlight Mints
Tootsie Flavored Rolls
Tootsie Pops
Wax Bottles
Indie Candy -
All Natural Sugar Free Bon Bons
Chocolate (Angel, Dancing Santa)
Christmas (Lights Lollipops, Tree Gummies)
Dark Chocolate (Covered Glacee' Oranges, Drizzled Fresh
   Marshmallows, Lollipop Shapes)
Halloween (Chocolate Lollipops, Crystal Lollipop Assortment,
   Gummies Allergen Free)
Lollipop (Birthday Bouquet, Flowers)
Make Your Own Gummies Kit
Swirly Lollipops
Zoo Animals (Gummis, Lollipops)
Jelly Belly - Jelly Beans (All Varieties)
Junior Mints - Deluxe, Inside Outs, Junior (Caramels, Mints), Minis
Kroger Brand -
Candy Corn
Dinner Mints
Gummi (Assorted Orange Slices, Bears, Fruit Slices, Sour Bears,
   Sour Slices, Sour Worms, Worms)
Hard Candy (Butterscotch, Mix, Peppermint, Spearmint)
Jelly Beans
Juju Fish
Salt Water Taffy
Soft Mints
Sugar Free Drops (Apple, Butterscotch, Lemon, Mixed Fruit)
Let's Do...Organic - Gummy Bears (All Varieties)
Lifesavers - All Varieties

C

Lowes Foods Brand - Candy Corn, Chocolate (Peanuts, Raisins), Cinnamon Imperials, Dubble Bubble Gum, Gummi (Bears, Worms, Worms Sour), Kiddie Mix, Laffy Taffy, Orange Slices, Rainbow Dinner Mints, Starlight Mints, Sweet Twists

M & M's - All Varieties *(Except M & M's Pretzel)*

Manischewitz - Chocolate Frolic Bears, Fruit Slices, Hazelnut Truffles, Mallo Cups, Max's Magic Lollycones, Mini Sour Fruit Slices, Patties (Peppermint, Tender Coconut), Raspberry Gel Bars, Swiss Chocolate Mints

Maple Grove Farms Of Vermont - Blended Maple, Pure Maple

Mars - Dove Chocolates (All Varieties), M & M's *(All Varieties Except M & M's Pretzel)*, Milky Way Products *(All Varieties Except The Milky Way Bar)*, Munch Bar, Snickers, Snickers Dark Bar

Munch Bar

Necco - Banana Split Chews, Canada Mint & Wintergreen Lozenges, Candy Eggs Easter, Candy Stix, Clark Bar, Haviland Chocolate Thin Mints, Mary Janes (Peanut Butter Kisses, Regular), Mint Julep Chews, Skybar, Squirrel Nut (Caramels, Zippers), Sweethearts Conversation Hearts *(Valentines Only)*, Talking Pumpkins Halloween, Wafers

Nestle - Baby Ruth, Bit O Honey, Butterfinger *(Except Crisp & Stixx)*, Goobers, Milk Chocolate, Nips (Regular, Sugar Free), Oh Henry, Raisinets, Sno Caps, Spree

Newman's Own Organics - All Chocolate Bars *(Except Crisp Rice)*, All Chocolate Cups

Nik-L-Nip - Wax Bottles

Nuts Online - Turkish Delight (Almond ●, Mixed Nut ●, Pistachio ●)

Organic Nectars - Raw Cacao (54%, 70%, 85%, Golden White, Nut Milk, Raspberry)

Orgran▲ - Molasses Licorice

Private Selections - Gourmet Jelly Beans

Publix - Double Dipped Chocolate Peanuts!!, Gummi (Sour Worms!!, Worms!!), Party Time Mix!!, Smarties Candy!!, Spearmint Starlight Mints!!, Starlight Mints Candy!!

Pure Market Express▲ - Bliss Balls ●

Razzles - Gum (Regular, Sour, Tropical)

Safeway Brand - Gummi Bears, Gummi Worms Regular, Jelly Beans, Star Light Mints

Seitenbacher - Cherry Dolphins, Roses For You, Smooch Lions, Strawberry Alligators, Sunhats (Black Currant, Cherry, Passion Fruit, Strawberry), Vampires Lunch

Sharkies▲ - Kids Sports Chews Berry Blasters, Kids Sports Chews Tropical Splash, Organic Energy Sports Chews (Berry Blast, Citrus Squeeze, Fruit Splash, Watermelon Scream)

Simply Enjoy - Yoghurt Coated Cranberries

Sipahh - Milk Flavoring Straws

Skittles - All Varieties

Smarties - Smarties

Snickers - Dark, Snickers Original

Sour Patch Kids - All Varieties

Spangler▲ - Candy Canes, Cane Classics, Dum Dum (Canes, Chewy Pops, Pops), Marshmallow Circus Peanuts, Saf T Pops, Swirl Saf T Pops

St. Claire's Organics - All Candy, Mints, Sweets (Licorice, Organic Ginger), Tarts (Lemon, Lime, Peach, Raspberry)

Starburst - All Varieties

Stop & Shop Brand - Assorted (Fruit Filled Candy, Star Drops, Starlights), Blue Gummi Sharks, Butter Toffee, Butterscotch Disks, Canada Wintergreen, Candy Corn, Candy Necklaces, Cinnamon Starlights, Fish, Gum (Balls, Bears, Drops), Jelly Beans, Kiddie Mix, Lemon Drops, Neon Sour Crawlers, Orange Slices, Pastel Mints, Peach Rings, Pina Colada Coated Cashews, Red Jug Coins, Root Beer Barrels, Royal Mix, Silver Mints, Smarties, Soft Peppermints, Sour Balls, Sour Gummi Worms, Spearmint (Leaves, Starlights), Spice Drops, Starlight Mints, Strawberry Buds, Watermelon Hard Candy

Sugar Babies - Sugar Babies (Caramel Apple, Chocolate Covered, Original)

C

Sugar Daddy - Caramel Pops

Sugar Mama - Caramels

Surf Sweets - Gummi (Bears, Swirls, Worms), Jelly Beans, Sour Berry Gummi Bears

Swedish Fish - Aqualife, Assorted, Red

Taffy Tree ▲ - All Varieties

The Ginger People - Crystallized Ginger Candy!, Gin Gins!, Gin Gins Boost!, Ginger Chews (Hot Coffee!, Original!, Peanut!, Spicy Apple!)

The Naked Cookie - Nut Brittle (Almond, Cashew, Macadamia, Peanut, Pecan, Pistachio)

Tootsie Roll - Child's Play Assortment Of Favorites, Tootsie Fruit Rolls, Tootsie Pops (Bunch Pops, Miniatures, Original, Pop Drops), Tootsie Roll (Mini Chews, Regular, Sugar Free)

Trader Joe's - Almond Clusters, Brown Rice Marshmallow Treats, English Toffee, Green Tea Mints, Lumpy Bumpy Bar, Organic Pops, Pecans Praline, Yogurt Raisins

Wack-O-Wax - Wax Fangs, Wax Lips

Wonka - Bottlecaps!, Gobstoppers (Chewy!, Original!), Laffy Taffy, Laffy Taffy Rope, Lik M Aid Fun Dip, Mix-Ups!, Nerds (Chewy!, Regular!), Pixy Stix, Runts (Chewy!, Original!), Spree, Sweet Tarts!

Woodstock Farms - Vegetarian (Gummy Cubs, Jelly Pebbles)

Yummy Earth - Lollipops

Zip-A-Dee - Mini Pops

Canned Chicken

Giant Brand - Premium Chunk Breast In Water

Great Value Brand (Wal-Mart) - Chunk Chicken Breast

Hormel - Chicken, Chunk Meats Breast Of Chicken

Meijer Brand - Chicken Chunk White

Member's Mark - Premium Chunk Chicken (Breast In Water, Breast In Water)

Spartan Brand - Chunk Chicken Breast

Sweet Sue - Chunk White

Canned Ham
   Great Value Brand (Wal-Mart) - Luncheon Meat
   Hormel - Chunk Meats Ham
   Malone's - Ham Spread, Potted Meat
   SPAM - Classic, Hickory Smoke Flavored, Less Sodium, Lite
   Underwood - Deviled Ham Spread
Canned Salmon... see Fish
Canned Tuna... see Tuna
Canned Turkey
   Hormel - Chunk Meats Turkey
   Member's Mark - Premium Chunk Turkey Breast In Water
   SPAM - Oven Roasted Turkey
Canola Oil... see Oil
Cantaloupe
   *... *All Fresh Fruits & Vegetables Are Gluten-Free*
   Gluty Free - Dried Chunks ●, Dried ●
   Nuts Online - Dried Fruit (Chunks ●, Dried ●)
Capers
   B&G - Capote, Nonpareil
   Mezzetta - Capote Capers, Nonpareil (Capers, Capers In
     Balsamic Vinegar)
   Safeway Select - Nonpareil
   Star - Imported Nonpareil Capers
   Trader Joe's - Nonpareil
   Wegmans Brand - Italian Classics (Capote, Nonpareil)
Cappuccino... see Coffee
Caramel... see Candy/Candy Bars and/or Dip/Dip Mix
Carbonated Beverages... see Soda Pop/Carbonated Beverages
Carrots
   *... *All Fresh Fruits & Vegetables Are Gluten-Free*
   Albertsons - All Plain Vegetables Canned & Frozen
   Birds Eye - All Plain Frozen Vegetables
   C & W - All Plain Frozen Vegetables
   Del Monte - All Canned Vegetables
   Earthbound Farm - Bunched & Cello, Carrot Dippers, Mini Peeled

C

Food Club Brand - Canned (Peas & Sliced Carrots, Sliced, Sliced No Salt), Frozen (Crinkle Cut, Whole Baby)

Freshlike - Frozen Plain Vegetables

Giant Brand - Canned w/Syrup, Frozen Peas & Diced Carrots

Grand Selections - Frozen Whole Carrots

Great Value Brand (Wal-Mart) - Canned Sliced Carrots, Microwavable Plastic Cup Frozen

Hannaford Brand - All Frozen, Sliced, Whole Baby

Hy-Vee - California, Classic Cut & Peeled Baby, Frozen Crinkle Cut, Sliced

Kroger Brand - All Plain Vegetables (Canned, Frozen)

Laura Lynn - Sliced Carrots, Whole Baby Carrots

Lowes Foods Brand - Deluxe Whole Baby, Peas & Carrots, Sliced

Meijer Brand - Canned Sliced (No Salt, Regular), Frozen Carrots (Crinkle Cut, Whole Baby)

Mezzetta - Gourmet Baby

Midwest Country Fare - Sliced Carrots

Nuts Online - Simply Carrots Freeze Dried Vegetables ●

Pictsweet - All Plain Frozen Vegetables

Publix - Canned Carrots, Frozen (Crinkle Cut, Whole Baby)

Publix GreenWise Market - Organic (Baby, Carrots, Chips, Juicing, Shredds, Snack)

S&W - All Canned Vegetables

Safeway Brand - Carrots Sliced

Spartan Brand - Canned (Peas & Sliced Carrots, Sliced), Frozen (Crinkle Cut, Peas & Carrots, Whole Baby)

Stop & Shop Brand - Carrots

Wegmans Brand - Baby Cut, Carrots/Potatoes/Celery & Onions, Crinkle Cut, Organic (Baby Cut, Regular), Sliced Carrots (No Salt Added, Regular), Whole Style

Winn Dixie - Frozen (Crinkle Cut, Whole Baby)

Cashews... see Nuts

Cauliflower

... *All Fresh Fruits & Vegetables Are Gluten-Free*

Albertsons - All Plain Vegetables Frozen

Birds Eye - All Plain Frozen Vegetables
C & W - All Plain Frozen Vegetables
Earthbound Farm - Organic Whole
Food Club Brand - Frozen Florets
Freshlike - Frozen Plain Vegetables
Giant Brand - Frozen
Green Giant - Frozen (Cauliflower & Cheese Sauce, Steamers Broccoli Carrots Cauliflower & Cheese Sauce)
Hy-Vee - Frozen Cauliflower Florets
Kroger Brand - All Plain Vegetables (Canned, Frozen)
Lowes Foods Brand - Frozen Cauliflower
Meijer Brand - Frozen Cauliflower Florets
Mezzetta - Dilled, Hot
Midwest Country Fare - Frozen Cauliflower
Pictsweet - All Plain Vegetables (Frozen)
Publix - Frozen
Safeway Brand - Frozen
Spartan Brand - Frozen Florets
Trader Joe's - All Plain Frozen
Wegmans Brand - Florets
Winn Dixie - Frozen

Caviar
Romanoff - Black (Lumpfish, Whitefish), Red (Lumpfish, Salmon)

Celery
... *All Fresh Fruits & Vegetables Are Gluten-Free*

Cereal
Amy's - Cream Of Rice Hot Cereal Bowl!
Ancient Harvest Quinoa - Quinoa Flakes
Arrowhead Mills - Hot (Rice & Shine, Yellow Corn Grits), Maple Buckwheat Flakes, Rice Flakes Sweetened
Bakery On Main - Granola (Apple Raisin Walnut ●, Cranberry Orange Cashew ●, Extreme Fruit & Nut ●, Nutty Cranberry Maple●, Rainforest ●)
Barbara's Bakery - Honey Rice Puffins, Multigrain Puffins, Organic Brown Rice Crisps

C

Better Balance - Apple Cinnamon, French Vanilla, Honey Almond

Bob's Red Mill▲ - Creamy Rice Hot Cereal (Organic, Regular), Flaxseed Meal, Gluten Free Mighty Tasty Hot, Organic Creamy Buckwheat

Cerealvit - Benevit Multigrain, Choco Stars, Coffee Flakes, Corn Flakes

Chex▲ - Chocolate, Cinnamon, Corn, Honey Nut, Rice

Earth's Best Organic Baby Food - Whole Grain Rice Cereal (Apples, Plain)

Eco-Planet▲ - 7 Whole Grains Hot Cereal (Apples & Cinnamon ●, Maple & Brown Sugar ●, Original ●)

El Peto▲ - Balls (Coco, Corn), Corn Flakes (Naturally Sweetened, No Refined Sugar, Whole Grain), Cream Of Rice (w/Apple & Cinnamon, White, Whole Grain Brown)

Ener-G▲ - Rice Bran

Enjoy Life▲ - Crunchy Flax ●, Crunchy Rice ●, Granola (Cinnamon Crunch ●, Cranapple Crunch ●, Very Berry Crunch ●)

Erewhon - Aztec Crunchy Corn & Amaranth, Brown Rice Cream, Corn Flakes, Crispy Brown Rice (Cocoa, Gluten Free Regular, w/ Mixed Berries), Rice Twice, Strawberry Crisp

General Mills▲ - Chex (Chocolate, Cinnamon, Corn, Honey Nut, Rice)

Gerber - Boxed Cereal Rice w/(Apples, Mixed Fruit), Rice Cereal DHA Brain & Eye Development, Rice Single Grain Cereal

Glutano▲ - Cornflakes

Gluten Free Sensations▲ - Cream Of Brown Rice, Granola (Apple Crisp, Cherry Vanilla Almond, Cranberry Pecan, French Vanilla Almond)

Glutino▲ - Apple & Cinnamon, Honey Nut, Sensible Beginnings (Berry, Frosted, Original)

Gluty Free - Super Food (Acai Blueberry ●, Cacao Crunch ●, Chia Ginger ●, Hemp & Greens ●)

Health Valley - Corn Crunch Ems!!!

Hodgson Mill▲ - Gluten Free Creamy Buckwheat w/Milled Flax

Kinnikinnick▲ - KinniKrisp Rice Cereal

Lundberg▲ - Hot 'N Creamy Purely Organic Rice

Meijer Brand - Grits (Buttered Flavored Instant, Quick)

Montana Monster Munchies - Whole Grain Oat Bran ●

Nabisco - Cream Of Rice Hot Cereal

Nature's Path - Corn Puffs**!**, Country Maple Sunrise**!**, Country Vanilla Sunrise**!**, Envirokidz Organic (Amazon Frosted Flakes, Gorilla Munch, Koala Crisp, Leapin Lemurs, Peanut Butter Panda Puffs), Millet Puffs**!**, Nature's Path Organic (Corn Flakes, Crispy Rice, Honey'd Corn Flakes, Mesa Sunrise, Whole O's), Rice Puffs**!**

New Morning - Cocoa Crispy Rice

Nuts Online - Organic Hot Cereal (Amaranth ●, Buckwheat Toasted●, Raw White Buckwheat ●), Superfood Cereal (Acai Blueberry ●, Cacao Crunch ●, Chia Ginger ●, Hemp & Greens ●), Teff Whole Grain Hot Cereal ●

Nu-World Foods - Amaranth Berry Delicious ●, Amaranth Cinnamon Delight ●, Amaranth O's (Original ●, Peach ●), Cereal Snaps (Cinnamon ●, Cocoa ●, Original ●), Puffed Amaranth Cereal ●

Only Oats - Oat Bran ●

Orgran▲ - Itsy Bitsy Cocoa O's, Multigrain O w/Quinoa, Puffed Amaranth Breakfast Cereal, Rice O's Wild Berry

Pocono - Cream Of Buckwheat

Pure Market Express▲ - Count Rawcula ●, Honey Wheaties ●, Strawberry Crunch ●

Ruth's Hemp Power - Chia Goodness (Apple Almond Cinnamon, Cranberry Ginger, Original)

Seitenbacher - Musli #7, Whole Grain Cornflakes

Shiloh Farms - Organic Soybean Flakes**!!**

Trader Joe's - Gluten Free Granola, Golden Roasted (Flaxseed w/ Blueberries, Whole Flaxseed)

Wegmans Brand - Fruity Rice Crisps

Chamomile Tea... see Tea

Champagne

 ... *All Champagne made in USA is Gluten-Free*[2]

C Cheese

Albertsons - All (Blocks, Shredded, Singles, String), Ricotta Cheese (Part Skim, Whole)

Andrew & Everett - All Varieties

Applegate Farms -
   Natural (American, Cheddar, Emmentaler Swiss, Havarti, Monterey Jack w/Jalapeno Peppers, Muenster, New York Sharp Aged Cheddar, Provolone)
   Organic (American, Cheddar, Monterey Jack, Muenster Kase, Provolone)
   Probiotic Yogurt Cheese

Athenos -
   Blue Crumbled
   Feta (Basil & Tomato, Black Peppercorn, Garlic & Herb, Lemon Garlic & Oregano, Mild, Reduced Fat Tomato & Basil, Reduced Fat Traditional, Roasted Red Pepper & Garlic, Traditional)
   Gorgonzola Crumbled

Bakers & Chefs - Cheddar Cheese Sauce

Belgioioso - American Grana, Asiago, Auribella, Burrata, Crescenza Stracchino, Fontina, Fresh Mozzarella, Gorgonzola, Italico, Kasseri, Mascarpone, Parmesan, Pepato, Peperoncino, Provolone, Ricotta Con Latte, Romano, Unwrap & Roll, Vegetarian Parmesan

Boar's Head - All Varieties

Borden - All Varieties *(Except Applewood Bacon Cheddar)*

Breakstone - Ricotta

Cabot -
   Aged Cheddars (Extra Sharp, Mild, New York Extra Sharp, Private Stock, Seriously Sharp, Sharp)
   Flavored Cheddars (Chili Lime, Chipotle, Garlic & Herb, Habanero, Horseradish, Sun Dried Tomato Basil, Tuscan)
   Other Cheeses (All Natural Swiss Slices, American Slices, Colby Jack, Monterey Jack, Muenster, Pepper Jack)
   Reduced Fat Cheddars (50%, 50% Jalapeno, 50% Pepper Jack, 75%)
   Shredded Cheeses (Fancy Blend, Mozzarella, Swiss)

Specialty Cheddars (Classic Vermont, Clothbound Wheel, Old
School, Private Stock, Vintage Choice)

Cheez Wiz - Cheese Dip Original

Coburn Farms - Deli Sliced Cheese *(Except Deluxe American)*,
Moo Sticks Mozzarella String Cheese, Ricotta Whole Milk,
Shredded Cheese

Cracker Barrel - Cheddar (2% Extra Sharp, Extra Sharp White, Sharp
White, Vermont Sharp White), Colby White, Fontina, Havarti, Swiss
(Baby, Emmentaler)

Dietz & Watson▲ -

Aalsbruk (Aged Gouda ●, Edam ●, Gouda ●, Smoked Gouda ●)

Aged Provolone ●

American (White ●, Yellow ●)

Baby Swiss ●

Champagne ●

Cheddar (Champagne ●, Peppadew ●, Pepperoni ●, Sharp ●,
w/Buffalo Wing Hot Sauce ●, w/Horseradish & Smokey Bacon ●,
w/Roasted Garlic ●, w/Toasted Onion ●)

Colby ●

Colby Jack ●

Danish (Blue ●, Fontina ●, Havarti ●)

Double Cream Cheddar ●

Feta ●

Gorgonzola ●

Havarti w/Dill ●

Jalapeno Jack ●

Jarlsberg ●

Lacy Swiss ●

Monterey Jack ●

Muenster ●

New York State (Aged Cheddar (w/Habanero & Jalapeno
Peppers●, w/Horseradish ●, w/Jalapeno & Cayenne Peppers ●,
Xtra Sharp ●, XXXtra Sharp ●)

Pepper Jack ●

C

Port Wine Cheddar ●

Sharp Italian Table Cheese w/Tomato & Basil ●

Smoked Cheddar ●

Swiss Gruyere ●

Swiss ●

Triple Cream Bergenost ●

Whole Milk Mozzarella ●

Dorothy Lane Market - Mozzarella (All Varieties)

Eat In The Raw - Parma Vegan Parmesan (Chipotle Cayenne, Original)

Finlandia -

Club Store Products (Deli Slices (Monterey Jack/Colby Jack, Muenster), Imported Deli Slices (Light Swiss, Swiss, Thin Sliced Swiss))

Deli Slices Imported (Double Gloucester, Gouda, Havarti, Light Swiss, Muenster, Swiss, Thin Sliced Swiss)

Deli Sticks Imported (Gouda, Havarti, Light Swiss, Muenster, Swiss) Sliced To Order (Imported Light Swiss, Imported Muenster, Imported Swiss, Lappi)

Specialty Cheeses (Oltermanni Baby Muenster, Swiss, Viola)

Follow Your Heart - Vegan Gourmet (Cheddar, Monterey Jack, Mozzarella, Nacho)

Food Club Brand -

Cheddar Cheese Sauce, Cheese Bar Cheddar (All Varieties)

Chunk Cheddar (Medium, Mild, Sharp)

Colby Jack

Cottage Cheese (Low Fat, Non Fat)

Monterey Jack

Mozzarella

Pepper Jack

Shredded (Cheddar, Colby Jack, Italian Blend, Mexican Blend, Mild Cheddar, Mozzarella, Parmesan, Pizza Blend, Sharp Cheddar, Swiss)

Sliced (American, Sharp Cheddar, Swiss)

Spray Aerosol (American, Cheddar, Sharp Cheddar)

Swiss

C

Friendship - All Varieties
Galaxy Nutritional Foods - All Varieties (Veggy, Rice, Rice Vegan,
    Vegan, Veggie, Wholesome Valley Organic)
Giant Eagle Brand -
    4 Cheese Italian Shredded
    Cheddar Shredded (Mild, Sharp)
    Chunk Cheddar (Extra Sharp, Mild, New York Extra Sharp, New
        York Sharp, New York White, Sharp)
    Colby Jack Chunk
    Easy Melt
    Fancy Shredded Cheddar (Mild, Sharp)
    Four Cheese Mexican Shredded
    Individually Wrapped Singles (2%, 2% Sharp, Pepper Jack, Regular,
        Sharp)
    Mexican Blend Shredded
    Monterey Jack Chunk
    Mozzarella (Ball, Regular, Whole Milk)
    Parmesan Shredded
    Pepper Jack Chunk
    Taco Blend Shredded
    Sliced (Colby Jack, Deluxe American, Muenster, Pepper Jack,
        Provolone, Sharp Cheddar, Swiss)
    Swiss Chunk
Gopal's - Rawmesan, Rawmesan Herbs N Spice
Gordon Food Service -
    Chunk (2% Mozzarella, Colby, Colby Jack, Mild Cheddar, Monterey
        Jack Hot Pepper, Monterey Jack Mild)
    Cottage (Large Curd, Small Curd)
    Mozzarella Loaf (2%, 3%)
    Sliced (3% Mozzarella, Colby Jack, Mild Cheddar, Monterey Jack,
        Monterey Jack Pepper, Natural Provolone, Swiss)
    Shredded Cheddar String
Great Value Brand (Wal-Mart) - All Deli Style Slices, All Shredded,
    American Slices (Deluxe, Fat Free Evaporated Milk), American

C

Slices Reduced Fat, Chunk Cheese (All Flavors), Easy Melt, Parmesan, Reduced Fat Parmesan Style Grated Topping

Hannaford Brand - All (Blocks, Shredded, Sliced), Cheese Spread, Parmesan Grated, Parmesan Romano, Ricotta

Horizon Organic - All Varieties

Hy-Vee -

American (Cheese Food, Fat Free Singles, Singles, Singles 2% Milk)

Cheddar (Extra Sharp, Fancy Shredded Jack, Fancy Shredded Mild 2%, Finely Shredded Mild, Lil' Hunk Mild, Medium, Medium Longhorn, Mild, Mild Cubes, Mild Hunk, Mild Shredded, Mild Slices, Sharp, Sharp Hunk, Sharp Longhorn, Sharp Shredded)

Colby (1 Lb, Half Moon Longhorn, Hunk, Longhorn, Slice Singles) Colby Jack (1 Lb, Cubes, Fancy Shredded, Finely Shredded, Half Moon Longhorn, Hunk, Lil' Hunk, Shredded, Slices)

Hot Pepper

Monterey Jack (1 Lb, Hunk)

Mozzarella (1 Lb, Fancy Shredded, Fancy Shredded 2% Milk, Hunk, Shredded, Sliced Low Moisture Part Skim)

Muenster (1 Lb, Slices)

Nacho Cheese

Parmesan (Grated, Shredded)

Pepper Jack Cheese (1 Lb, Cubes, Hunk, Singles, Slices)

Provolone Cheese (1 Lb, Slices)

Ricotta Cheese (Low Fat, Part Skim)

Shredded Blends (Fancy 4 Italian, Mexican Blend, Pizza, Taco)

Swiss (1 Lb, Fat Free Slices, Singles, Slices)

Isaly's - All Original Cheeses

Kirkland Signature -

American Slices, Block (Colby Jack, Sharp Cheddar)

Seasoned Rotisserie

Shredded (Cheddar Jack, Mexican Style Blend, Mild Cheddar, Mozzarella, Parmigiano Reggiano)

Kraft -

Block (Cheddar & Monterey Jack, Colby & Monterey Jack, Extra

C

Sharp Cheddar, Medium Cheddar, Mild Cheddar, Monterey Jack)
Crumbles (Blue Cheese, Colby & Monterey Jack, Feta, Sharp Cheddar, Three Cheese)
Deli Fresh Slices (2% Swiss, Colby Jack, Mild Cheddar, Mozzarella, Pepper Jack Spicy, Provolone, Sharp Cheddar, Swiss)
Easy Cheese (American, Cheddar, Sharp Cheddar)
Natural Shredded
  2% Milk (Colby & Monterey, Mild Cheddar, Sharp Cheddar)
  Cheddar (Cheddar Jack, Mild, Mild Cheddar & Monterey Jack, Mild Finely Shredded, Organic, Sharp Finely Shredded)
  Colby & Monterey Jack (Finely Shredded, Regular)
  Italian Style Five Cheese
  Mexican Cheddar Jack Regular
  Mexican Four Cheese
  Monterey Jack
  Mozzarella (Fat Free, Low Moisture Part Skim)
  Pizzeria
  Swiss
Shredded (Parmesan, Parmesan & Romano, Parmesan Romano & Asiago, Reduced Fat Parmesan Style Grated)
Singles (2% Milk (American, Pepperjack, Sharp Cheddar, Swiss), Deli Deluxe (American, Sharp Cheddar), Fat Free (American, Sharp Cheddar, Swiss), Regular (American, Sharp Cheddar), Select American)
Snackables (String Cheese, Twists 2% Milk)
Velveeta (2% Milk, Mexican Mild, Pepper Jack)
Kroger Brand - Cheese (Bars, Cubes, Shredded, Sliced)
Land-O-Lakes -
Cheddar (Extra Sharp, Medium, Mild, Sharp)
  Cheddarella
Chunk (American (White, Yellow), Colby, Monterey Jack, Mozzarella)
Deli Slices (American, Co Jack, Muenster, Pepper Jack, Provolone, Swiss)

C

Singles Processed American

Snack 'N Cheese To Go (Chedarella, Co Jack (Reduced Fat, Regular), Medium Cheddar, Mild Cheddar (Reduced Fat, Regular))

Laughing Cow - Mini Babybel (All Varieties), Wedges (All Varieties)

Laura Lynn - Cheese Chunks, Parmesan, Parmesan & Romano, Ricotta

Lifetime - All Varieties

Lifeway▲ - All Varieties

Lisanatti -

Almond Cheese (Cheddar, Garlic & Herb, Jalapeño Jack, Mozzarella)

Muncheeze Snack Sticks (American, Mozzarella)

Rice Cheese (Cheddar, Mozzarella, Pepper Jack)

Senora Lupe (Chipotle, Manchego, Mild Jalapeno, Quesadilla)

Shreds (3 Cheese Blend, Cheddar, Mozzarella, Parmesan, Pepper Cheddar)

Slices (Cheddar, Pepper Jack, Swiss)

SoySation (Chunk (Cheddar, Mozzarella, Pepper Jack))

Litehouse - Bleu Cheese Crumbles, Classic Feta, Heart Of Bleu Cheese, Monarch Mountain Gorgonzola Crumbles

Lowes Foods Brand -

American Processed Slices

Cheddar (Extra Sharp Bar, Fancy Shredded Mild, Fancy Shredded Sharp, Medium Bar, Medium Chunk, Mild Bar, Mild Chunk, Mild Shredded, NY Sharp Chunk, Sharp Bar, Sharp Chunk, Sharp Slices, Shredded, Shredded Sharp)

Cheddar Jack Shredded

Colby Chunk

Colby Jack (Bar, Chunk, Shredded)

Hot Pepper Jack Chunk

Monterey Jack Chunk

Mozzarella (Bar, Chunk, Fancy Shredded, Shredded, Sliced)

Muenster Chunk

Parmesan Shredded

Pepper Jack (Bar, Slices)

Provolone Sliced

Ricotta (Low Fat, Whole Milk)

Shredded Blends (Fancy Italian, Fancy Mexican, Fancy Pizza
 w/Mozzarella & Cheddar, Taco Blend)

Swiss (Chunk, Sliced)

Lucerne - Cheese (All Varieties)

Meijer Brand -

Aerosol Cheese (American, Cheddar, Sharp Cheddar)

American Processed Slices

Cheddar (Fancy Mild Shredded, Fancy Sharp Shredded, Fancy
 Shredded, Medium Bar, Midget Horn, Mild Bar, Mild Chunk,
 Sharp Bar, Sharp Chunk, Sharp Shredded Zipper Pouch,
 Shredded Zipper Pouch, Sliced Longhorn Half Moon, X Sharp Bar)

Cheddar Marble C&W Cheddar

Cheddar/Monterey Jack (Bar, Fancy Shred Zip Pouch)

Cheese Food Individually Wrapped (2% American, 2% Sharp, Fat
 Free Sharp, Sliced Pepper, Swiss)

Cheezy Does It (Jalapeño, Spread Loaf)

Colby (Bar, Chunk, Fancy Shredded)

Colby Jack (Bar, Fancy Shredded, Longhorn Half Moon, Sliced Single)

Colby Longhorn (Full Moon, Half Moon, Half Moon Sliced)

Colby Midget Horn

Hot Pepper Jack Chunk

Italian Blend Fancy Shredded

Mexican Blend (Fancy Shredded, Shredded)

Monterey Jack Chunk

Mozzarella (Fancy Shredded, Shredded, Sliced Single)

Mozzarella Low Moisture Part Skim (Bar, Chunk, Shredded, Sliced
 Chunk, Square, String Cheese)

Muenster Sliced Single

Parmesan (1/3 Less Fat, Grated)

Parmesan & Romano Grated

C

Pepperjack (Bar, Sliced Stack Pack)

Pizza Blend Shredded

Provolone Stacked Slice

String Cheese

Swiss (Chunk, Sliced Sandwich Cut, Sliced Single), Taco/Nacho Fancy Shredded

Melissa's - Soy Shreds (Cheddar, Mozzarella), Soy Slices (American, Cheddar, Jalapeno)

Midwest Country Fare - American Sandwich Slices, Shredded Cheese (Cheddar, Mozzarella)

Organic Valley -

Baby Swiss

Cheddar (Mild (Regular, Shredded), Raw (Mild, Sharp), Reduced Fat & Sodium, Sharp, Vermont (Extra Sharp, Medium, Sharp))

Colby

Feta

Mexican Blend Shredded

Monterey Jack (Reduced Fat, Regular)

Mozzarella

Muenster

Pepper Jack

Provolone

Ricotta

Stringles (Cheddar, Colby Jack, Mozzarella)

Wisconsin Raw Milk Jack Style

Ortega - Nacho Cheese Sauce Pouch

Primo Taglio - Cheddar (American, Imported Aged White, Medium, Mild), Danish Havarti (Regular, w/Dill), Jack Hot Pepper, Lacy Swiss, Muenster, Provolone, Smoked Fontina, Swiss

Publix -

Natural (Cheddar (Extra Sharp, Medium, Mild, Sharp), Colby, Colby Jack, Monterey Jack (& Cheddar Shredded, Regular, w/Jalapeno Peppers), Mozzarella, Muenster, Provolone, Ricotta, Shredded (Italian 6-Cheese Blend, Mexican 4 Cheese Blend), Swiss)

Processed (American Cheese Food Pasteurized Processed Singles (Regular, Thick Slice), Cheese Spread**!!**, Deluxe American Slices, Imitation Mozzarella Shredded, Swiss Cheese Pasteurized Processed Singles)

Specialty (Asiago Wedge, Blue Crumbled, Creative Classic Queso (Blanco, De Freir), Crumbled Goat, Feta (Chunk, Crumbled, Crumbled Reduced Fat, Reduced Fat Chunk), Garden Jack Stick, Garlic & Herb Cheese Spread, Gorgonzola Crumbled, Horseradish Jack Stick, Hot Pepper Cheese Spread, Parmesan (Grated, Shredded, Wedge), Pepper Jack Reduced Fat, Salsa Jack Stick)

Pure Market Express▲ - Artisanal (Cheddar Spread ●, Cilantro Jalapeno Cheese ●, Creamy Herb Cheese ●, Good As Gouda●, Mexi Cheese ●, Pepper Jack Cheese ●, Simply Basil ●, Spicy Peppercorn ●, Sundried Tomato Basil Cheese ●, Wasabi Chive ●)

Ragu - Cheesy Double Cheddar Sauce

Rice Shreds (Galaxy Nutritional Foods) - All Varieties (Rice, Rice Vegan, Vegan, Veggie, Veggy, Wholesome Valley Organic)

Riega - Sauce Mix (Alfredo, Pepper Jack, White Cheddar, Yellow)

Road's End Organics - Organic (GF Alfredo Chreese Mix, GF Cheddar Chreese Mix)

Safeway Brand - Grated Parmesan

Safeway Select - Parmesan Shredded

Sara Lee - Slices (Mild Cheddar, Mozzarella), Slices (Aged Swiss, American, Baby Swiss, Hot Pepper Monterey Jack, Longhorn Colby, Longhorn Colby Jack, Muenster, Smoked Provolone)

Sargento -

Artisan Blends (Authentic Mexican, Double Cheddar, Mozzarella & Provolone, Parmesan, Parmesan Romano, Swiss, Whole Milk Mozzarella, Wisconsin Sharp White Cheddar)

Bistro Blends (Chipotle Cheddar, Italian Pasta Cheese, Mozzarella & Asiago w/Roasted Garlic, Mozzarella w/Sun Dried Tomatoes & Basil, Nacho & Taco, Sharp Wisconsin & Vermont Cheddar w/Real Bacon, Taco)

C

Classic Blends (4 Cheese Mexican, 6 Cheese Italian, Pizza Double)

Classic Chef Style (Mild Cheddar, Mozzarella, Sharp Cheddar)

Classic Fancy (Cheddar Jack, Colby Jack, Mild Cheddar, Monterey Jack, Mozzarella, Sharp Cheddar)

Deli Style (Aged Swiss, Baby Swiss, Chipotle Cheddar, Colby, Colby Jack, Duo Pack (Medium Cheddar & Colby Jack, Provolone & Mild Cheddar, Swiss & Baby Swiss), Gouda, Havarti, Jarlsberg, Limited Editon (Aged Provolone, Pasture Grazed Cheddar), Medium Cheddar, Mild Cheddar, Monterey Jack, Mozzarella, Muenster, Pepper Jack, Provolone, Reduced Fat (Provolone, Swiss), Sharp Cheddar, Sharp Provolone, Swiss, Vermont Sharp White Cheddar)

Fine Cheeses (Grated Parmesan, Grated Parmesan & Romano, Fat Free Ricotta, Hard Grating Parmesan, Light Ricotta, Part Skim Ricotta, Whole Milk Ricotta)

Limited Edition (Italian Blend Aged Provolone, Pasture Grazed Cheddar)

Natural (Chipotle Cheddar Sticks, Colby Jack (Cubes, Sticks), Light String Cheese, Mild Cheddar (Cubes, Sticks), Stars & Moons,
String, Twirls)

Reduced Fat (Deli Style (Colby Jack, Medium Cheddar, Pepper Jack), Shredded (4 Cheese Italian, 4 Cheese Mexican, Colby Jack, Mild Cheddar, Mozzarella, Sharp Cheddar))

Reduced Sodium (Deli Style (Colby Jack, Pepper Jack, Provolone), Mild Cheddar, Mozzarella))

Snacks (Limited Editon (Aged Provolone, Pasture Grazed Cheddar), Mild Cheddar Bars, Pepper Jack Sticks, Reduced Fat (Colby Jack Sticks, Sharp Cheddar Sticks), Sharp Cheddar Sticks, String, SunBursts, Twirls, Vermont Sharp White Cheddar Sticks))

Spartan Brand -

American 2% Milk Singles (Fat Free, Regular)

Cheddar Chunk Cheese (Medium, Milk, Sharp, Xtra Sharp)

Colby Cheese (Chunks, Shredded, Sliced)

Colby Jack Cheese (Chunks, Shredded, Sliced)

Fancy Shredded Cheese (Colby Jack, Italian Blend, Mexican Blend, Mild Cheddar, Mozzarella, Parmesan, Sharp Cheddar, Taco)

Mild Cheddar Cheese (Shredded, Sliced)

Monterey Jack Cheese (Chunks, Shredded)

Mozzarella Cheese (Chunks, Round, Shredded, Sliced)

NY Sharp Cheddar Cheese Chunks

Parmesan Italian Shredded

Parmesan Shredded (Regular, Romano)

Pizza Blend Shredded

Processed American (Deluxe Sliced, Sliced)

Sharp Cheddar Shredded

String Cheese

Swiss Cheese (Chunks, Sliced)

Taco Spice Shredded

Tasty Bite - Paneer Makhani **!**

The Vegetarian Express - Parma Zaan Sprinkles **!**

Tillamook - All Varieties **!**

Trader Joe's - All Blocks *(Except Dubliner Irish Stout Cheese)*, Parmesan & Romano Cheese Blend, Shredded, Soy Cheese Slices, Wedges *(Except Dubliner Irish Stout Cheese)*

Velveeta - 2% Milk, Mexican Mild, Pepper Jack

Wayfare - We Can't Say It's Cheese (Cheddar Sauce ●, Cheddar Spread ●, Hickory Cheddar ●, Mexi Cheddar ●)

Wegmans Brand -

American Cheese White Slices

Cheese Spread (Artichoke Asiago, Bacon Chive, Buffalo Wing Cheddar, Garlic & Herb)

Colby Jack (2%, Block, Shredded, Thin Sliced)

Extra Sharp Cheddar (White, Yellow)

Fancy Shredded (Mexican, Mild Cheddar, Pizza, Taco)

Fat Free American Slices (Reduced Fat, Regular)

Longhorn Style Colby

C

Mild Cheddar (Shredded, White, White Shredded, Yellow)

Monterey Jack

Mozzarella Cheese (2% Shredded, Low Moisture Part Skim Shredded, Low Moisture Part Skim String, Low Moisture Part Skim Thin Sliced, Whole Milk Shredded)

Muenster (Block, Light Block, Thin Sliced)

Parmesan Cheese (Fancy Shredded w/Romano, Finely Shredded, Grated, Grated w/Romano)

Pepper Jack (2% Slices, Block, Hot)

Provolone (2% Thin Sliced, All Natural Thin Sliced, Mild Block, Mild Slices)

Reduced Fat 2% Yellow Slices

Romano Grated

Sharp Cheddar (Extra Sharp White, Extra Sharp Yellow, Fat Free Slices, Reduced Fat Slices, Shredded, Thin Sliced, Vermont White), Swiss (Block, Light Block, Light Sliced, Thin Sliced, Thin Sliced 2%)

Winn Dixie -

American Pasteurized Process Cheese (American, Deluxe, Reduced Fat)

Blue Cheese

Cheddar (Extra Sharp, Jack, Medium, Mild, NY Extra Sharp, NY Sharp)

Colby (Jack, Regular)

Feta

Gorgonzola

Italian Blend Shredded

Mexican Blend

Monterey Jack (Regular, w/Jalapeno Peppers)

Mozzarella

Muenster

Parmesan (& Romano, Grated)

Pasteurized Process Swiss Cheese Product

Pimento Cheese (Chunky, Regular, w/Jalapenos)

Provolone

Ricotta (All Types)

String Cheese

Swiss

White Cheddar

Cheese Puffs... see Snacks

Cheese Spread... see Cheese and/or Spread

Cheesecake... see Cake/Cake Mix

Cherries

... *All Fresh Fruits & Vegetables Are Gluten-Free

Cella's - Chocolate Covered Cherries (Dark, Milk)

Food Club Brand - Frozen Dark Sweet Cherries, Maraschino (Green, Red, Red w/Stems), Pitted Red Tart

Fruit Advantage - Premium Dried Cherries

Giant Brand - Canned Red Tart Pitted In Water, Frozen Dark Sweet, Sweet In Heavy Syrup (Dark, Light),

Gluty Free - Dried (Bing ●, Rainier ●, Sour ●)

Great Value Brand (Wal-Mart) - Maraschino

Hy-Vee - Frozen Cherry Berry Blend, Red Maraschino Cherries (Regular, w/Stems)

Kroger Brand - Maraschino

Lowes Foods Brand - Maraschino (Red, Red w/Stems)

Lucky Leaf - Red Tart Pitted Cherries, Cherries Jubille

Meijer Brand - Frozen (Dark Sweet, Tart), Maraschino Cherry (Red, Red w/Stems)

Mezzetta - Maraschino Cherries (w/Stems, w/o Stems)

Midwest Country Fare - Maraschino Cherries

Musselman's - Red Tart Pitted Cherries

Nuts Online - Dried Fruit (Bing ●, Organic Bing ●, Rainier ●, Simply ●, Sour Tart ●)

Publix - Frozen (Cherries, Dark Sweet Cherries), Maraschino

S&W - All Canned/Jarred Fruits

Safeway Brand - Frozen Dark Sweet, Maraschino Cherries

Santa Barbara Olive Co. - Maraschino (Green, Red)

C

Spartan Brand - Frozen Dark Sweet Cherries, Maraschino Cherries Red (Regular, Salad, w/Stems)

Stop & Shop Brand - Frozen Dark Sweet Cherries

Trader Joe's - Dark Chocolate Covered Cherries, Frozen Very Cherry Berry Blend

Wegmans Brand - Dark Sweet, Maraschino (Jumbo w/o Stems, w/o Stems, w/Stems), Triple Cherry Fruit Mix In Light Syrup

Winn Dixie - Dark Sweet Cherries, Maraschino Cherries

Woodstock Farms - Dark Chocolate Cherries, Dried Cherries Unsulphured, Organic Frozen Dark Sweet Cherries, Yogurt Cherries

Chewing Gum

5 - All Varieties

B Fresh

Between - Dental Gum

Big League Chew - All Varieties

Big Red

Bubblicious - All Varieties

Charms - Blow Pops (Minis, Regular, Super)

Dentyne Ice - All Varieties

Doublemint

Dubble Bubble

Eclipse - All Varieties

Extra - All Varieties

Freedent - All Varieties

Giant Brand - Gum Balls

Glee Gum - All Varieties

Hubba Bubba - All Varieties *(Except Tape)*

Indie Candy - Make Your Own Chewing Gum Kit

Juicy Fruit - All Varieties

Lowes Foods Brand - Double Bubble Gum

Meijer Brand - Nicotine Gum (Mint, Regular)

Nicorette

Orbit

Orbit White

Spearmint

Stride - All Varieties

Trident - All Varieties

Winterfresh

Chick Peas... see Beans

Chicken... see also Deli Meat

... *All Fresh Chicken Is Gluten-Free (Non-Marinated, Unseasoned)*

Al Fresco -

Breakfast Sausages (Apple Maple, Country Style, Wild Blueberry)

Dinner Sausage Fully Cooked (Buffalo Style, Roasted Garlic, Roasted Pepper & Asiago, Spicy Jalapeno, Spinach & Feta, Sundried Tomato, Sweet Apple, Sweet Italian Style)

Fresh Dinner Sausages (Buffalo Style, Sweet Apple, Sweet Italian Style)

Tomato & Basil Chicken Meatballs

Always Tender - Fresh Flavored Chicken (Italian, Lemon Pepper, Roast)

Applegate Farms - Gluten Free Chicken Nuggets ●, Organic (Roasted Chicken Breast, Smoked Chicken Breast)

Bell & Evans - Gluten Free Breaded Chicken Breast (Garlic Parmesan, Regular), Gluten Free Breaded Chicken Patties (Italian Style, Regular), Gluten Free Chicken Breast Tenders, Gluten Free Chicken Nuggets

Boar's Head - All Varieties

Bumble Bee - Prime Fillet Chicken Breast (Lightly Seasoned w/ Garlic & Herbs, w/Barbeque Sauce, w/Southwest Seasonings)

Butcher's Cut - Boneless Skinless Chicken Breast, Young Chicken Thighs

Butterball - Chicken Breast Strips (Grilled, Oven Roasted, Southwestern Style), Deli Meat Thin Sliced Oven Roasted Chicken Breast

Carl Buddig - Deli Cut Rotisserie Chicken, Extra Thin Original Regular, Fix Quix Regular, Original Regular

C

Castle Wood Reserve - Deli Meat Oven Roasted Chicken
Chi-Chi's - Fiesta Plates (Creamy Chipotle, Salsa, Savory Garlic)
Coleman's Natural Foods -
    Bone In Skin On Thigh ●
    Boneless Skinless (Breast ●, Fresh For The Freezer Breasts ●, Thigh●)
    Buffalo Style Wings ●
    Chicken Sausage (Mild Italian ●, Spicy Andouille ●, Spicy Chipotle●, Spicy Chorizo ●, Spicy Italian ●, Spinach & Feta Cheese ●, Sun Dried Tomato & Basil ●, Sweet Apple w/Maple Syrup ●)
    Drummettes ●
    Drumsticks ●
    Fresh for the Freezer Breasts ●
    Gluten Free Nuggets ●
    Gourmet Meatballs (Buffalo Style ●, Chipotle Cheddar ●, Italian Parmesan ●, Pesto Parmesan ●, Spinach Fontina Cheese & Roasted Garlic ●, Sun Dried Tomato Basil Provolone ●)
    Organic (Bone In Skin On Thigh ●, Split Breast ●, Whole Chicken ●, Wings ●)
    Split Breast ●
    Sweet Apple ●
    Tomato & Basil ●
    Uncured Hickory Smoked ●
    Whole Chicken ●
    Wings ●
Columbus Salame - Deli Meat (All Varieties)
Dietz & Watson▲ - Breast Of Chicken (Honey Barbecue ●, Rotisserie ●, Southern Fried ●), Buffalo ●, Gourmet Breast ●
Dinty Moore - Microwave Meal Rice w/Chicken
Eckrich - Deli Meat Fried Chicken Breast
Empire Kosher - Chicken Bologna Slices, Chicken Franks, Fresh Chill Pack, Fresh Rotisserie, Frozen, Fully Cooked Barbecue Chicken (Fresh, Frozen), Individually Quick Frozen Chicken Parts, Rendered Chicken Fat

Farmer John - California Natural Chicken Sausage (Chicken Brat Smoked, Lemon Cracked Pepper Chicken Smoked, Mango & Habanero Smoked)

Food Club Brand - Chunk White Chicken, Fresh (Breast, Tenders, Wings)

Garrett County Farms - Chicken Franks**!**, Dino Shaped Chicken Bites**!**, Frozen Chicken Apple Breakfast Links**!**

GF Naturals - 1oz. Boneless Wing ●, 2oz. Tender ●, 4oz. All Natural Filet ●, 4oz. Whole Muscle Filet ●

Giant Eagle Brand - Shredded w/BBQ Sauce, Wrapped Breasts

Gordon Food Service - Pureed Chicken w/Broth

Great Value Brand (Wal-Mart) - Canned Chunk Chicken Breast, Frozen (Boneless Skinless Breast, Drumsticks, Thighs), Frozen Wing Sections

Hannaford Brand - Chicken Breast Chunk In Water

Hans All Natural - Breakfast Links (Organic ●, Skinless ●), Chicken Sausage (Spinach & Feta ●, Spinach Fontina & Garlic ●, Sun Dried Tomato Provolone ●), Gourmet Meatballs (Buffalo Style ●, Sweet Basil Parmesan ●)

Hillshire Farms - Deli Select Oven Roasted Chicken Breast

Honeysuckle White - Chicken Breast Deli Meat (BBQ, Buffalo Style, Oil Browned), Wings (Barbecue Glazed, Buffalo Style, Oven Roasted)

Hormel - Carved Chicken Breast (Grilled, Oven Roasted), Chunk Meats (Breast Of Chicken, Chicken), Natural Choice Chicken Strips (Grilled, Oven Roasted)

Hy-Vee - 100% Natural Fresh (Boneless Skinless, Boneless Skinless Breasts, Breast Tenderloins, Drumsticks, For Roasting w/Neck & Giblets, Gizzards, Leg Quarters, Split Breasts, Split Breasts w/Ribs, Thighs, Whole Cut Up w/Neck & Giblets, Wing Drummettes, Wings, Young w/Neck & Giblets), Canned 98% Fat Free Breast Of Chicken, Thin Sliced Chicken

Ian's - Wheat Free Gluten Free Recipe (Chicken Finger Kids Meal, Chicken Nuggets, Chicken Patties)

C

Jennie-O Turkey Store - Deli Chicken Breast (Buffalo Style, Mesquite Smoked, Oven Roasted)

John Soules Foods -
   Fully Cooked Chicken Breast Fillets (Italian Style, Rotisserie)
   Fully Cooked Chicken Breast Strips (Grilled, Italian Style, Rotisserie)
   Fully Cooked Chicken Fajitas
   Ready To Cook (Chicken Breast For Fajitas, Chicken Thigh For Fajitas)

Kayem - Chicken Breast Rotisserie Style

Kirkland Signature - Chunk Chicken Breast, Fresh Breasts, Frozen (Breasts, Tenderloin, Thighs, Wings), Grilled Breast Strips

Kroger Brand - Canned (Premium, Regular), Fresh & Frozen Plain (Breast, Thighs, Wings), Pouch

Laura Lynn - Boneless Skinless Chicken Breast

Lloyd's - Shredded Chicken In (Honey Hickory BBQ Sauce, Original BBQ Sauce)

Manor House - All Varieties In 4lb. Resealable Bags

Meijer Brand - Canned Chicken Chunk White, Sliced Chipped Meat

Member's Mark -
   Canned Premium Chunk Chicken Breast In Water
   Chicken Sausage (Gourmet Chicken & Apple, Mozzarella & Roasted Garlic, Spinach Asiago, Sundried Tomato w/Provolone Cheese)
   Premium Chunk Chicken Breast In Water

Nature's Basket - Frozen Chicken Breasts

O Organics - Fresh Chicken Breast (Regular, Tenders)

Organic Prairie - Fresh Organic (Chicken Hot Dogs 12 oz., Sliced Roast Chicken Breast), Frozen Organic (Boneless Skinless Chicken Breasts, Chicken Hot Dogs 10.5 oz., Chicken Italian Sausage, Ground Chicken 12 oz., Whole Young Chicken), Roast Chicken Breast Slices

Oscar Mayer -
   Chicken Breast Cuts (Honey Roasted, Oven Roasted),
   Deli Fresh (Oven Roasted Chicken Breast 98% Fat Free, Thin Sliced Oven Roasted Chicken Breast)

Shaved Deli Fresh (Cajun Seasoned Chicken Breast, Rotisserie Style Chicken Breast)

Perdue -
Buffalo Chicken Wings Hot 'N Spicy
Ground Chicken (Breast Of Chicken, Burgers)
Individually Frozen Chicken (Breasts, Tenderloins, Wings)
Oven Roasted Carving Chicken Breast
Perfect Portions Boneless Skinless Chicken Breast (Italian Style, Regular, Tomato Basil)
Rotisserie Chicken (Barbeque, Italian, Lemon Pepper, Oven Roasted, Toasted Garlic, Tuscany Herb Roasted)
Rotisserie Oven Stuffer Roaster (Breast, Regular)
Short Cuts Carved Chicken Breast (Grilled Italian, Grilled Southwestern, Honey Roasted, Original Roasted)

Publix - All Natural Fresh, Deli Rotisserie Chicken Apple Wood Smoked!!, Barbecue Flavored w/Barbecue Seasoning (& Sauce!!, Regular!!), Lemon Pepper Flavored w/Lemon & Herb Seasoning!!, Original Roasted!!, Frozen Boneless Skinless Chicken (Breasts, Cutlets), Chicken Breast Tenderloins, Chicken Wingettes

Publix GreenWise Market - Boneless Breast, Boneless Thighs, Cutlet, Drummettes, Drumsticks, Fillet, Ground Chicken, Skinless Drumstick, Skinless Thighs, Split Breast, Tenderloin, Thighs, Whole, Wings

Rocky Jr. - Bone In Skin On Thigh ●, Boneless Skinless (Breast ●, Thigh ●), Breast Tenders ●, Drummettes ●, Drumsticks ●, Rocky Dogs Uncured Hot Dog ●, Split Breast ●, The Range Chicken ●, Whole Chicken ●, Wings ●

Rosie - Organic Bone In Skin On Thigh ●, Boneless Skinless (Breast, Thigh ●), Breast Tenders ●, Drummettes ●, Drumsticks ●, Split Breast ●, Whole Chicken ●, Wings ●

Safeway Brand - Canned Chunk White Breast

Sara Lee - Deli Meat Slices Oven Roasted Chicken Breast

Saz's - Barbecue Chicken Meat Tub

C

S'Better Farms▲ - Chicken (Ballontine, Fingers, Party Wings, Siciliano, Szechwan)

Shaner's - Frozen (Breast Tenders, Breasts w/Rib Meat, Drumsticks, Split Breasts w/Ribs)

Shelton's - Capon, Free Range (Breasts, Thighs, Whole), Organic (Boneless/Skinless Breast, Breast, Cut Up, Whole Chicken, Whole Legs)

Signature Cafe - Roasted Chicken Homestyle

Smart Chicken - All Varieties

Smart Ones - Frozen Entrees (Creamy Tuscan Chicken, Fiesta Chicken, Grilled Chicken In Garlic Herb Sauce, Home Style Chicken, Honey Dijon Chicken, Lemon Herb Chicken Piccata)

SPAM - Hickory Smoke Flavored

Spartan Brand - Canned Chicken Breast Chunk, Frozen Boneless Skinless (Breasts, Tenders)

Stop & Shop Brand - Premium Chunk Chicken Breast In Water, Simply Enjoy (Butter Chicken, Pad Thai w/Chicken)

Sweet Bay - All Fresh Chicken

Thumann's - All Varieties ●

Trader Joe's -

Artichoke Patties, BBQ Pulled Chicken Breast In Smoky BBQ Sauce

Chicken Salad (Gourmet w/Currants, Wine Country w/Cranberries)

Fresh All Natural

Frozen Chicken (Chile Verde, Gorgonzola, Pomodoro)

Frozen Chicken Wings

Fully Cooked & Seasoned Roasted Chicken ! !

Grilled Breast Strips (Balsamic & Rosemary ! !, Chili Lime ! !, Lemon Pepper ! !, Plain ! !)

Grilled Chicken Breast Strips (Balsamic & Rosemary ! !, Chili Lime ! !, Lemon Pepper ! !, Plain ! !)

Grilled Chicken Salad w/Orange Vinaigrette

Handcrafted Chicken & Cheese Tamales

Just Chicken Plain

Tropical Traditions - Whole Chicken, Whole Chicken Cut Into Parts
Tyson - All Natural Fresh (All Varieties)
Valley Fresh - All Varieties
Wellshire Farms - Chicken Franks**! !**, Oven Roasted Chicken Breast**! !**
Wellshire Kids▲ - Dino Shaped Chicken Bites Refrigerated ●
Winn Dixie - Canned Breast, Frozen (Breasts, Tenderloins)

Chicken Broth... see Broth
Chicken Noodle Soup... see Soup
Chicken Nuggets... see Chicken
Chicken Wings... see Wings

Chiles
Chi-Chi's - Green Chiles
La Victoria - Green Chiles Fire Roasted (Diced, Whole)
Meijer Brand - Diced Mild Mexican Style
Old El Paso - Green Chiles (Chopped, Whole)
Ortega - Diced Hot, Green (Diced, Whole)
Safeway Brand - Diced Green
Spartan Brand - Green Chiles

Chili
Albertsons - Hot w/Beans, w/Beans
Amy's - Medium Black Bean**!**, Organic Chili (Medium**!**, Medium
    Light In Sodium**!**, Medium w/Vegetables**!**, Southwestern Black
    Bean**!**, Spicy**!**, Spicy Light In Sodium**!**)
Food Club Brand - Chili w/Beans, Diced Mild
Frontera - Chipotle & Black Bean
Hormel - Chili Master (Chipotle Chicken No Bean, Chipotle
    Chicken w/Beans, White Chicken Chili w/Beans), Chili w/Beans
    (Chunky, Hot, Regular)
Hy-Vee - Hot Chili w/Beans, Mild w/Beans
Kettle Cuisine - Angus Beef Steak Chili w/Beans ●, Chicken Chili
    w/White Beans ●, Three Bean ●
Meijer Brand - Chili (No Beans Regular, w/Beans Regular), Hot Dog
    Chili Sauce
Mimi's Gourmet - Black Bean & Corn, Chipotle Black Bean Chili
    w/Rice, Spicy White Bean & Jalapeno, Three Bean w/Rice

C

  Shelton's - Mild Chicken, Mild Turkey, Spicy Chicken, Spicy Turkey

  Spartan Brand - w/Beans

  Stagg - Chunkero, Classic, Dynamite Hot, Ranch House Chicken, Silverado Beef, Steak House, Vegetable Garden, White Chicken

  Texas Pete - Chili No Beans

  Trader Joe's - Beef Chili w/Beans, Chicken Chili w/Beans, Organic Vegetarian **!!**, Vegetarian 3 Bean Chili

  Wegmans Brand - Spicy Red Lentil Chili

  Winn Dixie - w/Beans

Chili Powder

  Chugwater Chili

  Durkee - Dark

  Hy-Vee

  Marcum Spices

  McCormick - Hot Mexican Style, Regular

  Meijer Brand

  Midwest Country Fare

  Spartan Brand

  Spice Islands

  Tones

Chili Sauce

  A Taste Of Thai - Garlic Chili Pepper Sauce, Sweet Red Chili Sauce

  Food Club Brand

  Frank's RedHot - Chile 'N Lime

  Giant Brand - Regular

  Great Value Brand (Wal-Mart) - Regular

  Hannaford Brand

  Heinz

  Hy-Vee

  Kroger Brand

  La Victoria - Red

  Las Palmas - Red Chile

  Laura Lynn

Lee Kum Kee - Sriracha Chili
Meijer Brand - Hot Dog Chili
Safeway Brand
Spartan Brand
Thai Kitchen - Roasted Red Chili Paste, Spicy Thai, Sweet Red
Trader Joe's - Chili Pepper **!!**, Sweet **!!**
Wegmans Brand

Chips

   Arico - Casava Chips (Barbeque Bliss, Ginger On Fire, Original, Sea Salt Mist)

   Baked Lay's - Original **!!**, Parmesan & Tuscan Herb **!!**, Sour Cream & Onion **!!**, Southwestern Ranch **!!**

   Baked Ruffles - Cheddar & Sour Cream **!!**, Original **!!**

   Baked Tostitos - Scoops Tortilla Chips **!!**

   Beanitos - Black Bean **!**, Cheddar Cheese **!**, Chipotle BBQ **!**, Pinto Bean and Flax **!**

   Better Made Snack Foods - Baked Potato (All Varieties), Potato Sticks (All Varieties), Regular Potato (All Varieties), Tortilla (All Varieties)

   Boulder Canyon Natural Foods -

      Canyon Cut Potato Chips (Honey Barbeque, Salt & Cracked Pepper, Sour Cream & Chives, Totally Natural)

      Kettle Cooked Potato Chips (50% Reduced Salt, 60% Reduced Sodium, Balsamic Vinegar & Rosemary, Chipotle Ranch, Hickory Barbeque, Jalapeno Cheddar, Limon, No Salt Added, Olive Oil, Parmesan & Garlic, Red Wine Vinegar, Sea Salt & Cracked Pepper, Spinach & Artichoke, Sweet Lemon & Cracked Pepper, Tomato & Basil, Totally Natural)

      Rice & Adzuki Bean Snack Chips (Chipotle Cheese, Lemon & Cracked Black Pepper, Natural Salt, Sundried Tomato w/Basil)

      Tortilla Strips w/Hummus (Lightly Salted, Sesame)

   Brothers All Natural ▲ - Potato Crisps (Black Pepper & Sea Salt, Fresh Onion & Garlic, Original w/Sea Salt, Szechuan Pepper & Fresh Chives)

C

Cape Cod -
> Potato
>> 40% Reduced Fat
>> Buttermilk Ranch
>> Cheddar Jack & Sour Cream
>> Classic
>> Five Cheese
>> Jalapeno & Aged Cheddar
>> Parmesan & Roasted Garlic
>> Robust Russet
>> Sea Salt & (Cracked Pepper, Vinegar, Vinegar 40% Less Fat)
>> Sour Cream & Green Onion
>> Sweet & Spicy Jalapeno
>> Sweet Mesquite Barbeque (40% Less Fat, Regular)
>> Sweet & Salty

Chi-Chi's - All Varieties

Covered Bridge Potato Chips▲ - Old Fashioned Kettle Style (Creamy Dill ●, Sea Salt ●, Sea Salt & Cracked Pepper ●, Sea Salt & Vinegar ●, Smokin' Sweet BBQ ●, Sweet Potato w/Cinnamon & Brown Sugar ●)

Deep River Snacks - Asian Sweet & Spicy, Cracked Pepper & Sea Salt, Lightly Salted, Mesquite BBQ, Original Salted, Rosemary & Olive Oil, Salt & Vinegar, Sweet Maui Onion, Zesty Jalapeno

Doritos -
> 1st Degree Burn Blazin' Jalapeno!!
> 2nd Degree Burn Fiery Buffalo!!
> 3rd Degree Burn Habanero!!
> Baked Nacho Cheese!!
> Blazin' Buffalo & Ranch!!
> Collisions (Cheesy Enchilada & Sour Cream!!, Pizza Cravers & Ranch!!)
> Cool Ranch!!
> Late Night (All Nighter Cheeseburger!!, Last Call Jalapeno Popper!!, Tacos At Midnight!!)

Reduced Fat (Cool Ranch**!!**, Nacho Cheese**!!**)
Salsa Verde**!!**
Spicy Nacho**!!**
Toasted Corn**!!**

Dorothy Lane Market - Kettle Cooked Potato Chips, Organic Tortilla Chips

Eat Smart - Garden Veggie (Crisps ●, Stix), MultiGrain Tortilla ●, Naturals Crispy Waffle

Eden Organic - Brown Rice

Flamous Brands - Falafel Chips (Original ●, Spicy ●)

Food Club Brand - Corn Chips (Big Dipper, Regular), Potato Chips (BBQ, Kettle Cooked, Original, Salt & Pepper, Sour Cream & Cheddar, Sour Cream & Onion, Wavy Original), Tortilla Chips Bite Size White Mini Rounds, White Corn (Restaurant Style, Rounds)

Food Should Taste Good - Tortilla Chips (Blue Corn ●, Cheddar ●, Chocolate ●, Jalapeno ●, Lime ●, Multigrain ●, Olive ●, Sweet Potato●, The Works ●, White Cheddar ●, Yellow Corn ●)

Fritos - Corn Chips (Lightly Salted**!!**, Original**!!**, Scoops**!!**), Honey BBQ Flavor Twists**!!**

Frontera - Tortilla Chips (Blue Corn, Lime w/Sea Salt, Thick & Crunchy, Thin & Crispy)

Full Circle - All Natural (BBQ, Natural Potato, Ripple), Kettle Cooked (Lightly Salted, Salt & Vinegar), Organic Tortilla Chips (Blue Corn, White Corn, Yellow Corn), Popcorn (Salted, White Cheddar)

Garden Of Eatin' - Mini Tortilla Rounds (White, Yellow), Baked Yellow Chips, Black Bean, Blue Chips (No Salt Added, Regular), Key Lime Jalapeno, Little Soy Blues, Popped Blues, Red Chips, Sesame Blues, Sunny Blues, Three Pepper, Tortilla Baked Blue Chips, White Chips, White Strips, Yellow Chips, Veggie Chips (Beet & Garlic, Vegetable Medley)

Giant Brand - Nacho Tortilla, Plain Potato, Salt & Vinegar, Sour Cream & Onion, Wavy Cut Potato, White Restaurant Tortilla (Regular, Rounds)

Glenny's - Spud Delites Natural Potato Crisps (Sea Salt**!** ●, Sour Cream & Onion**!** ●, Texas BBQ**!** ●)

C

Gluty Free - Banana ●, Fruit ●, Green Bean ●, Organic Banana ●, Veggie (No Added Salt ●, Regular ●)

Good Health Natural Foods▲ - Potato Chips (Avocado Oil (Barcelona Barbeque, Chilean Lime, Regular), Glories Sweet, Olive Oil (Cracked Pepper & Sea Salt, Rosemary, Sea Salt))

Goraw▲ - Super Chips (Pumpkin ●, Spirulina ●)

Gordon Food Service -
Potato (Regular, Rippled (Regular, Sour Cream & Onion, Sweet Barbecue)
Tortilla (Round Yellow, Salted Triangles, White (Round, Triangle)

Grandma Ferdon's▲ - Taco Seasoned Tortilla Chips ●, Tortilla Chips●

Green Mountain Gringo▲ - Tortilla Strips (Blue Corn ●, Original ●, White Corn ●)

Hannaford Brand - Cheese Curls (Baked, Crunchy), Potato (Original, Ripple, Sour Cream & Onion, Wave), Tortilla (Bite Size, Restaurant Style, Yellow)

HealthMarket - Organic Tortilla Corn (Blue, White, Yellow)

Herr's -
Corn Chips (BBQ Flavor, Regular)
Potato Chips (Cheddar & Sour Cream, Crisp 'N Tasty, Heinz Ketchup, Honey BBQ, Jalapeno Kettle, Lightly Salted, No Salt, Old (Bay, Fashioned), Original Kettle, Red Hot, Ripple, Russet Kettle, Salt & (Pepper, Vinegar))
Tortilla Chips (Bite Size Dippers, Nachitas, Restaurant Style)

J. Higgs - Barbeque, Cheezies Puffs, Cheezies Spicy Hot, Classic Potato, Cornies, Ripple Potato

Kettle Brand -
Baked Potato Chips (Aged White Cheddar, Hickory Honey Barbeque, Salt & Fresh Ground Pepper, Sea Salt, Sea Salt & Vinegar)
Krinkle Cut Potato Chips (Classic Barbeque, Salt & Fresh Ground Pepper, Sea Salt)
Organic Potato Chips (Chipotle Chili Barbeque, Lightly Salted, Salt & Fresh Ground Pepper, Sea Salt)

Potato Chips (Backyard Barbeque, Buffalo Bleu, Death Valley Chipotle, Honey Dijon, Jalapeno, New York Cheddar, Sea Salt & Vinegar, Sour Cream Onion & Chive, Spicy Thai, Sweet Onion, Tuscan Three Cheese, Unsalted, Yogurt & Green Onion)

Kroger Brand - Cornito, Max Flavor Tortilla (Nacho Cheese, Ranch, Spicy Salsa), Pork Rinds Original, Potato (Classic, Sour Cream & Onion, Wavy), Tortilla (Bite Size, Chipotle, Lime, Regular, Sea Salt)

Late July - Dude Ranch ●, Mild Green Mojo ●, Sea Salt By The Seashore ●

Laura Lynn - Corn Chips, Mini Corn Tortilla, Nacho Tortilla, Potato Chips, Ranch Tortilla, Ripple Potato, Sour Cream & Onion Potato

Laurel Hill▲ - Tortilla Chips (Multigrain ●, Olive Caper ●, Pepita & Spice ●, Sea Salt & Lime ●)

Lay's -

Potato Chips

Balsamic Sweet Onion!!

Cajun Herb & Spice!!

Cheddar & Sour Cream!!

Chile Limon!!

Classic!!

Dill Pickle!!

Garden Tomato & Basil!!

Hot & Spicy Barbecue!!

Kettle Cooked (Crinkle Cut BBQ!!, Crinkle Cut Original!!, Jalapeno!!, Maui Onion!!, Original!!, Reduced Fat Original!!, Sea Salt & Cracked Pepper!!, Sea Salt & Vinegar!!, Sharp Cheddar!!)

Light Original!!

Lightly Salted!!

Limon!!

Natural Sea Salt Thick Cut!!

Pepper Relish!!

Salt & Vinegar!!

Sour Cream & Onion!!

Southwest Cheese & Chiles**!!**
Tangy Carolina BBQ**!!**
Wavy (Au Gratin**!!**, Hickory BBQ**!!**, Ranch**!!**, Regular**!!**)
Lay's Stax - Potato Crisps (Cheddar, Mesquite Barbecue, Original, Ranch, Salt & Vinegar, Sour Cream & Onion)
Lowes Foods Brand -
Corn Chips
Potato Chips (BBQ, Original, Ripple, Sour Cream & Onion)
Tortilla Chips (Restaurant Style, White Round)
Lundberg▲ - Rice Chips (Fiesta Lime, Honey Dijon, Nacho Cheese, Pico De Gallo, Santa Fe Barbecue, Sea Salt, Sesame & Seaweed, Wasabi)
Manischewitz - Potato Chips (All Varieties)
Maui Style - Potato Chips (Onion**!!**, Regular**!!**)
Michael Season's - Baked Thin Potato Crisps (Cheddar & Sour Cream, Original, Sweet Barbecue), Thin & Crispy (Honey Barbecue, Lightly Salted, Mediterranean, Ripple Lightly Salted, Salt & Pepper, Unsalted)
Miguel's - Organic Tortilla Dippers (Everything ●, Three Pepper ●, Vegetable & Seed ●), Plantain Strips (Honey, Salted), Tortilla Chips (Blue Corn, White Corn)
Miss Vickie's - Kettle Cooked Potato Chips (Hand Picked Jalapeno**!!**, Sea Salt & Cracked Pepper**!!**, Sea Salt & Vinegar**!!**, Simply Sea Salt**!!**, Smokehouse BBQ**!!**)
Mr. Krispers - Baked Nut Chips Toasted Almond ●, Baked Rice Krisps (Barbecue ●, Nacho ●, Sea Salt & Pepper ●, Sour Cream & Onion ●, Sun Dried Tomato & Basil ●, White Cheddar & Herbs ●), Multi Seed Chips Original ●, Tasty Snack Crackers Original Sesame ●
New Hampshire Wildcats - White & Blue Corn Tortilla Chips
Nuts Online - Carrot Chips ●, Fruit Chips ●, Green Bean Chips ●, Sweet Potato Chips ●, Taro Chips ●, Veggie Chips (No Salt Added●, Regular ●)
Old Dutch - Corn Chips Original, Potato Chips Baked (Barbeque, Cheddar & Sour Cream, Original), Bar B Q, Dill Pickle, Onion &

Garlic, Original, RipL, RipL Cheddar & Sour Cream, Sour Cream & Onion, Tortilla Chips (Bite Size Original, Dip Strips, Fiesta, White Corn, Yellow Corn)

On The Border - Tortilla Chips (Blue Corn, Cafe Style, Cantina Thins, Premium Rounds, Southwest Thins)

Ortega - Round Tortilla Chips

Pan De Oro - Tortilla Chips (Blue ●, Red White & Blue ●, Regular ●)

Pinnacle Gold - Natural Baked Potato Chips Original, Natural Baked Veggie Chips

Popchips - Potato (Barbecue**!!**, Cheddar**!!**, Original**!!**, Parmesan Garlic**!!**, Salt & Pepper**!!**, Sea Salt & Vinegar**!!**, Sour Cream & Onion**!!**)

Potato Flyers - Homestyle Barbeque, Original, Sea Salt & Vinegar, Sour Cream & Onion

Pringles - Fat Free (Original, Sour Cream & Onion)

Publix - Potato Chips (Dip Style, Original Thins, Salt & Vinegar, Wavy Style), Tortilla Chips (White Corn, White Corn Restaurant Style, Yellow Corn Round Style)

Publix GreenWise Market - Tortilla Chips Blue, Yellow

Pure Market Express▲ - BBQ Thins ●, Chili Lime Chips ●, Corn Chips ●, Mexi Chips ●, Pizza Chips ●

Que Pasa▲ - Hand Cut Organic Corn, Organic Corn Tortilla Chips (Blue, Red, White, Yellow)

RW Garcia - Flax ●, Mixed Bag Tortilla Chips (Yellow & Blue Corn ●, Yellow & Red Corn ●, Yellow & White Corn ●), Spice ●, Thai ●, Tortilla Chips Classic (Blue Corn ●, Extra Thin ●, Yellow Corn ●), Organic Blue ●, Stone Ground ●, Veggie Tortilla Chips ●

Riceworks - Gourmet Brown Rice Crisps (Baked Cinnamon, Parmesan, Salsa Fresca, Sea Salt, Sweet Chili, Tangy BBQ)

Ruffles - Baked (Cheddar & Sour Cream Potato Crisps**!!**, Original Potato Crisps**!!**), Potato Chips Authentic Barbecue**!!**, Cheddar & Sour Cream**!!**, Natural Reduced Fat Sea Salted**!!**, Original (Light**!!**, Reduced Fat**!!**, Regular**!!**), Sour Cream & Onion**!!**

Santitas - Tortilla Chips (White Corn Triangles**!!**, Yellow Corn (Corn Strips**!!**, Corn Triangles**!!**, Rounds**!!**))

C

Skeete & Ike's - Organic Sea Salt‼

Snyder's Of Hanover - Corn Tortilla Chips (Restaurant Style, White, Yellow), Multigrain Tortilla Chips ●, Potato Chips (Barbeque, Hot Buffalo Wing, Jalapeno, Kosher Dill, Original, Ripple Potato, Salt & Vinegar, Sour Cream & Onion)

Solea - Olive Oil Chips (Cracked Pepper & Salt, Rosemary, Sea Salt), Polenta Chips (Mediterranean Lime‼, Sea Salt‼, Tuscan Barbeque‼)

Spartan Brand - Corn, Kettle Cooked (Jalapeno, Mesquite BBQ, Original, Reduced Fat), Potato (Regular, Ripple), Sour Cream & Onion

Stop & Shop Brand - Potato (Kettle Cooked, Plain, Rippled, Salt & Vinegar, Sour Cream & Onion, Wavy Cut), Tortilla (Nacho, White Restaurant, White Round, Yellow Round)

Terra Chips -
    Classic Potato Chips Au Naturel Unsalted
    Exotic Potato Chips Blues
    Exotic Vegetable Chips (Harvest Sea Salt, Original Chips)
    Krinkle Cut Kettles (Sea Salt, Sea Salt & Vinegar)
    Lemon Pepper Unsalted
    Red Bliss (Fine Herbs, w/Olive Oil)
    Sweet Potato Chips (Crinkles Sea Salt, Plain, Sweets & Beets, Sweets & Carrots)
    Yukon Gold Original

The Mediterranean Snack Food Co. - Baked Lentil (Cucumber Dill, Sea Salt, Sea Salt & Cracked Pepper), Veggie Medley

Tostitos -
    Dipping Strips‼
    Restaurant Style (All Natural Blue Corn‼, Blue Corn‼)
    Tortilla Chips
        Bite Size Rounds‼
        Crispy Rounds‼
        Dipping Strips‼
        Restaurant Style (Hint Of Lime‼, Natural Yellow Corn‼, Original‼)
        Scoops (Baked‼, Hint Of Jalapeno‼, Original‼)

Trader Joe's -

Organic Chips

Baked Tortilla (Blue Corn, Nacho)

Corn Dippers!!

Corn Tortilla (Blue!!, White!!, Yellow!!)

Restaurant Style White Corn Tortilla Chips

Tortilla Longboard

Regular Chips (BBQ Potato, Blue Corn Tortilla, Corn Tortilla Strips White, Hickory BBQ Potato!!, Red Bliss Potato, Round Popped Potato (Barbecue!!, Salted!!), Salsa Tortilla, Salt N' Vinegar Potato!!, Salted Potato!!, Sea Salt & Pepper Rice Crisps, Soy & Flaxseed Tortilla (Regular, Spicy), Sweet Potato!!, Vegetable Root!!, Veggie (& Flaxseed Tortilla, Regular!!), Yellow Corn Tortilla Chips),

Ridge Cut Potato Chips (Lightly Salted!!, Salt N Pepper!!)

Roasted Plantain

Tortilla Chips Reduced Guilt Tortilla Strips!!

UTZ -

All Natural Kettle Cooked (Dark Russet, Gourmet Medley, Lightly Salted, Sea Salt & Vinegar)

Corn Chips (Barbeque, Plain)

Home Style Kettle Cooked Plain

Kettle Classics (Dark Russet, Jalapeno, Plain, Smokin' Sweet Potato, Spicy Smokin' Sweet Potato, Sweet Potato)

Kettle Cooked (Barbeque, Grandma, Plain)

Mystic Kettle Cooked Chips (Dark Russet, Plain, Reduced Fat)

Regular Chips (Barbeque, Carolina BBQ, Cheddar & Sour Cream, Crab, Honey BBQ, No Salt (BBQ, Regular), Plain (Ripple, Wavy Cut), Red Hot, Reduced Fat, Salt & Pepper, Salt & Vinegar, Sour Cream & Onion), Tortilla Chips (Baked, Cheesier Nacho, Restaurant Style, White Corn)

Wegmans Brand -

Corn (Original, Tortilla 100% White Corn (Bite Size Round, Blue Corn, Crisp Round, Lime Flavored, Restaurant Style), Yellow Corn Tortilla)

C

    Kettle (Memphis BBQ, Original, Sea Salt & Cracked Pepper)

    Potato (Original, Salt & Vinegar, Sour Cream & Onion, Wavy)

Winn Dixie - Cheddar & Sour Cream, Cheese Curls, Cheese Puffs, Classic, Nacho Cheese, Natural (Jalapeno, Original, Reduced Fat), Pork Rinds, Sour Cream & Onion, Tortilla, Wavy, Wavy Ranch

Wise -

    Dipsy Doodles (Wavy Corn Chips (BBQ, Original), Nacho Twisters)

    Jalapeno Cheddar

    Potato Chips (All Natural, Lightly Salted, New York Deli Kettle Cooked (All Natural, Buffalo Wing, Jalapeno, Salt & Pepper, Salt & Vinegar), Onion & Garlic, Ridgies (All Natural, Cheddar & Sour Cream, Sour Cream & Onion), Salt & Vinegar, Unsalted, Wise Wavy)

    Tortilla Chips Bravos (Crispy Rounds, Nacho Cheese, Restaurant Style)

Chocolate

Andes - Crème De Menthe, Thins (Cherry Jubilee, Crème De Menthe, Mint Parfait, Sugar Free, Toffee Crunch)

Baker's - Bittersweet, German's Sweet, Select (Bittersweet, Semi Sweet), Semi Sweet, White

Carb Safe - Sugar Free Chocolate Bars Dark

Cella's - Chocolate Covered Cherries (Dark, Milk)

Chocolate Dream - Creamy Sweet, Dark (Almond, Pure, Raspberry, Rice Crunch)

Cote d'Or -

    Lait (Intense, Petits)

    Noir (70% Cacao, 86% Cacao, De Noir Petits, Orange)

Dagoba - All Chocolate, Chocodrops, Chocolate Covered Espresso Beans, Organic Cacao Nibs

Dove - Dove Chocolates (All Varieties)

Earth Source Organics▲ - Organic Raw Chocolate Bar (Acai ●, Caramel ●, Goji ●, Maca ●)

Endangered Species▲ -

All Natural Chocolate Bars (Dark Chocolate (Extreme ●, Supreme ●), Dark Chocolate w/(Blueberries●, Cacao Nibs ●, Cranberries & Almonds ●, Espresso Beans ●, Hazelnut Toffee ●, Mint●, Raspberries●), Milk Chocolate w/(Almonds ●, Cherries●), Milk Chocolate ●)

All Natural Chocolate Squares (Dark w/Cranberries & Almonds ●, Dark w/Mint ●, Extreme Dark ●, Smooth Milk ●, Supreme Dark●)

Chimp Mints ●

Dark Chocolate Halloween Treats ●

In Jute Favors (Dark ●, Milk ●)

Organic Bites Bug Bites (Dark ●, Milk ●)

Organic Chocolate Bars (Dark ●, Dark Chocolate (& Cherry ●, & Orange ●), Dark Chocolate w/(Goji Berry Pecans & Maca ●, Cacao Nibs Yacon & Acai ●, Golden Berry & Lucuma ●), Milk Chocolate (& Peanut Butter ●, Regular ●, Smooth ●))

Enjoy Life▲ - Boom Choco Boom (Dairy Free Rice Milk Bar ●, Dairy Free Rice Milk w/Crispy Rice Bar ●, Dark Chocolate Bar ●), Semi Sweet Chocolate Chips ●

Gerbs Pumpkin Seeds - Dark Chocolate Pumpkin Seed Clusters ●

Ghirardelli -

Baking Bars (60% Bittersweet, 70% Cacao Extra Bittersweet, 100% Cocoa Unsweetened, Milk, Semi Sweet, White)

Filled Chocolate (60% Cacao Dark w/Caramel‼, Dark w/ Mint‼, Dark w/Raspberry‼, Milk w/Caramel‼, Milk w/Peanut Butter‼)

Intense Dark (Espresso Escape‼, Evening Dream 60% Cacao‼, Midnight Reverie 86% Cacao‼, Sea Salt Soiree‼, Toffee Interlude‼, Twilight Delight 72% Cacao‼)

Luxe Milk (Almond‼, Hazelnut‼, Milk‼, Toffee‼)

Solid Chocolate (60% Cacao Dark‼, White w/Vanilla‼)

Glutino▲ - Candy Bars (Chocolate Peanut Butter, Dark Chocolate, Milk Chocolate)

Gluty Free - Organic (Dark Chocolate Almonds ●, Dark Chocolate Raisins ●, Milk Chocolate Raisins ●, Raw Cacao Nibs ●)

C

Hershey's -
Heath Bar
Kisses (Milk Chocolate, Milk Chocolate Meltaways, Milk
 Chocolate w/Almonds, Milk Chocolate w/Caramel, Milk
 Chocolate w/Cherry Cordial Crème, Rich Dark Chocolate,
 Special Dark Chocolate)
Milk Chocolate Bar (Original, w/Almonds)
Mr. Goodbar
PayDay
Reese's Peanut Butter Cups Original
Skor
York Peppermint Patty

Indie Candy - Chocolate Angel, Chocolate Dancing Santa, Dark
 Chocolate Covered "Oreos", Dark Chocolate Lollipop Shapes,
 Halloween Chocolate Lollipops, Make Your Own Chocolate Kit

Manischewitz - Chocolate Frolic Bears, Chocolate Morsels, Hazelnut
 Truffles, Mallo Cups, Patties (Peppermint, Tender Coconut), Swiss
 Chocolate Mints

Mars - Dove Chocolates (All Varieties), M & M's *(All Varieties Except
 M & M's Pretzel)*, Milky Way Products *(All Varieties Except The
 Milky Way Bar)*, Munch Bar, Snickers, Snickers Dark Bar

Milky Way - All Varieties *(Except The Original Milky Way Bar)*

Necco - Candy Eggs Easter, Clark Bar, Haviland Thin Mints, Skybar,
 Squirrel Nut (Caramels, Zippers), Talking Pumpkins Halloween

Nestle - Baby Ruth, Bit O Honey, Butterfinger *(Except Crisp & Stixx)*,
 Goobers, Milk Chocolate, Nips (Regular, Sugar Free), Oh Henry,
 Raisinets, Sno Caps

Newman's Own Organics - All Chocolate Bars *(Except Crisp Rice)*,
 All Chocolate Cups

Nuts Online - Chocolate Covered (Pumpkin Seeds ●, Sunflower
 Seeds ●, Toasted Corn ●), Organic Cacao Paste ●, Organic
 Chocolate Covered Cacao Nibs ●, Organic Sugar Cacao Nibs●,
 Raisins Organic (Dark Chocolate Covered ●, Milk Chocolate
 Covered ●), Raw Cacao Almonds & Raisins ●, Raw Cacao Brazil

Nuts & Mulberries ●, Raw Organic Cacao Nib ●, White Chocolate
Chip Almonds Cashews & Cacao Nibs ●

Organic Nectars - Raw Cacao 54%

Oskri Organics - Honey Mint Patties

Safeway Select - Creamy Milk Chocolate, Extra Dark, Milk
Chocolate w/Hazelnuts

Simply Enjoy -

Dark Chocolate Coated (Amaretto Cranberries, Cappuccino
Crunch Bits, Caramel Squares, Cherries, Coffee Beans,
Cranberries, Kona Almond Coffee Beans, Raspberry Sticks,
Strawberries)

Milk Chocolate Coated (Butter Toffee Squares, Cashews, Cherries,
Cocoa Almonds, Peanuts, Pecan Caramel Patties, Raisins)

White Chocolate Coated Coffee Nuggets

Whole Chocolate Covered Raspberries

Sjaak's -

Bite Sized Organic Chocolates (Almond Butter Bites, Chocolate
Caramel, Chocolate Covered Almonds, Chocolate Covered
Hazelnuts, Dark Chocolate Covered Almonds, Dark Chocolate
Covered Hazelnuts, Dark Chocolate Hearts, Extra Dark Bites,
Ginger Bites, Hazelnut Butter Bites, Hearts Of Cherry, Milk
Chocolate Hearts, Mint Bites, Mint Mills, Orange Bites, Peanut
Butter Bites, Raspberry Bites, Winter Wonderfuls)

Organic Chocolate

Dark Chocolate Bars (Almond, Regular, w/Creamy Caramel,
w/Espresso, w/Green Tea, w/Mint, w/Raspberry)

Extra Dark 70%

Milk Chocolate (Regular, w/Almond Butter, w/Almonds, w/
Creamy Caramel, w/Peanut Butter)

Raspberry Truffle

Stop & Shop Brand -

Simply Enjoy Dark Chocolate (Amaretto Coated Cranberries,
Cappuccino Crunch Bits, Caramel Squares, Covered (Cherries,
Coffee Beans, Cranberries, Kona Almond Coffee Beans,
Strawberries)

C

Raspberry Sticks

Simply Enjoy Milk Chocolate (Butter Toffee Squares, Coated Cashews, Cocoa Almonds, Covered (Cashews, Cherries, Peanuts, Raisins), Pecan Caramel Patties, White Chocolate Coated Coffee Nuggets, Whole Chocolate Covered Raspberries)

Suncups - Dark Chocolate, Milk Chocolate

thinkThin - Brownie Crunch, Chocolate (Fudge, Mudslide), Dark Chocolate, Peanut Butter (Chunky, Creamy), thinkThin Bites (Chocolate Toffee Nut, Cookies & Cream, White Chocolate Raspberry), White Chocolate Chip

Toblerone - Dark, Fruit & Nut, Milk Chocolate, Minis Milk Chocolate, Minis White Chocolate, White

Trader Joe's -

70% Belgian Dark Chocolate Sea Shells

Chocolate (Almond Clusters, Dark Clouds, Espresso Beans, Milk Clouds, Sunflower Seed Drops)

Chocolate Covered (Blueberries, Orange & Raspberry Sticks)

Confection Perfection Dark Chocolate Cubes

Covered Raisins

Dark Chocolate (Almonds Sea Salt & Sugar, Clouds, Mint Creams, Mint UFO's)

Dark Chocolate Covered (Almonds, Caramels, Cherries, Espresso Beans, Ginger, Power Berries, Raisins, Toffee)

Milk & Dark Chocolate Covered Almonds

Milk Chocolate Clouds

Peanut Butter Cups (Mini, Regular)

Unsweetened Belgian Baking Chocolate

Tropical Source - Dark Chocolate Bars (Mint Crunch, Raspberry, Rice Crisp, Rich, Toasted Almond)

Woodstock Farms -

Dark w/Evaporated Cane Juice (Almonds, Ginger)

Organic Dark w/Evaporated Cane Juice (Almonds, Chocolate Chips, Raisins)

Organic Milk w/Evaporated Cane Juice (Almonds, Raisins)

C

Chocolate Bars... see Candy/Candy Bars and/or Chocolate

Chocolate Chips... see Baking Chips

Chocolate Dip
> **Food Club Brand** - Microwaveable Coating (Chocolate, Vanilla)
> **Marzetti** - Chocolate Fruit Dip
> **Walden Farms** - Chocolate Fruit Dip

Chocolate Milk... see Milk

Chocolate Sauce
> **Emmy's Organics▲** - Peppermint, Regular
> **Wegmans Brand** - Chocolate (Milk, Raspberry, Triple Chocolate)

Chocolate Syrup... see Syrup

Chutney
> **Baxters** - Albert's Victorian, Cranberry & Caramelized Red Onion, Crushed Pineapple & Sweet Pepper, Spiced Fruit, Sweet Caramelized Onion Carrot & Orange, Tomato
> **Garner's** - Organic Apple & Onion Sweet
> **Native Forest** - Chutney (All Varieties)
> **Sharwood's** - Green Label (Mango, Mango Chili, Mango Smooth)
> **Trader Joe's** - Mango Ginger **!!**
> **Wild Thymes** - Apricot Cranberry Walnut, Caribbean Peach Lime, Mango Papaya, Plum Currant Ginger

Cider/Cider Mix
> **Crispin** - Artisanla Reserves (Honey Crisp, Lansdowne, The Saint), Natural Hard Apple Cider (Brut, Light, Original)
> **Doc's Draft** - Apple, Pear, Raspberry *(Alcoholic)*
> **Kroger Brand** - Instant Spiced (Regular, Sugar Free)
> **Lucky Leaf** - Apple Cider, Sparkling Apple Cider
> **Magners** - Cider *(Alcoholic)*
> **Musselman's** - Cider, Fresh Pressed, Sparkling Cider
> **Pure Market Express▲** - Mulled Apple Cider ●
> **Safeway Brand** - Apple Cider
> **Sonoma Sparkler** - Natural (Peach, Pear, Raspberry), Organic (Apple, Lemonade)
> **Strongbow** - *(Alcoholic)*

C

Woodchuck Hard Cider▲ - Hard Cider (All Varieties) *(Alcoholic)*
Woodpecker▲ - Premium Cider *(Alcoholic)*
Wyder's▲ - Hard Cider (All Varieties) *(Alcoholic)*

Cinnamon... see also Seasonings
Albertsons
Durkee - Ground
McCormick - Ground, Sticks
Spice Islands
Tones
Watkins - Purest Ground

Cinnamon Rolls
Celiac Specialties▲ - Cinnamon Rolls
Chebe▲ - Cinnamon Roll Mix ●
Everybody Eats▲ - Cinnamon Sticky Buns
Grandma Ferdon's▲ - Regular ●
Heaven Mills▲ - Chocolate Buns ●, Cinnamon Buns ●
Pure Market Express▲ - Cinnamon Rolls ●
Silly Yak Bakery▲ - CFGF Cinnamon Roll ●, GF Cinnamon Roll ●
The Grainless Baker▲ - Cinnamon Buns
Udi's Gluten Free Foods▲ - Gluten Free Cinnamon Rolls

Clams
*... *All Fresh Seafood Is Gluten-Free (Non-Marinated, Unseasoned)*
Bumble Bee - Chopped, Fancy Smoked, Fancy Whole Baby, Minced
Chicken Of The Sea - Minced, Premium Whole Baby Clams,
    Whole Baby Clams
Crown Prince - Baby Boiled, Baby Clams Smoked In Oil, Natural
    (Baby Clams Boiled in Water, Clam Juice, Smoked Baby Clams In
    Olive Oil)
Ocean Prince - Chopped

Club Soda... see Soda Pop/Carbonated Beverages

Coating
A Taste Of Thai - Spicy Peanut Bake
Aleia's▲ - Plain ●, Savory ●
Bi-Aglut - Bread Crumb Coating

Celiac Specialties▲ - Seasoned Bread Crumbs

Choice Batter - Original Recipe w/Spices ●, Unspiced ●

Dakota Lakes - Gourmet Coating ●

El Peto▲ - Bread Crumbs

Ener-G▲ - Breadcrumbs

Gillian's Foods▲ - Breadcrumbs (Cajun Style, Italian Style, Plain)

Gluten-Free Essentials▲ - Breading & Batter Mix (Seasoned ●, Unseasoned ●)

Glutino▲ - Bread Crumbs

Grandma Ferdon's▲ - Bread Crumbs ●, Fish Batter Mix ●

Hol Grain▲ - Batter Mix (Onion Ring ●, Tempura ●), Brown Rice Bread Crumbs ●, Crispy Chicken Coating Mix ●

Kinnikinnick▲ - Bread Cubes, Chocolate Cookie Crumbs, Graham Style Crumbs, Panko Style Bread Crumbs

Laurel's Sweet Treats▲ - All Purpose Batter Mix

Miller's Gluten Free Foods▲ - Seasoned Bread Crumbs

Nu-World Foods - Amaranth Bread Crumbs ●

Orgran▲ - All Purpose Rice Crumbs, Corn Crispy Crumbs

Schar▲ - Bread Crumbs

Southern Homestyle▲ - Corn Flake Crumbs, Tortilla Crumbs

The Grainless Baker▲ - Seasoned Bread Crumbs, Unseasoned Bread Crumbs

Cocktail Mix

Big Bucket - Margarita, Mojito, Strawberry Margarita/Daiquiri

Margaritaville - Margarita Mix (Mango, Regular)

Mr. & Mrs. T's -

Bloody Mary

Bold & Spicy *(Except Premium Blend)*

Original *(Except Premium Blend)*

Mai Tai

Manhattan

Margarita

Old Fashioned

Pina Colada

C

Strawberry Daiquiri/Margarita
Sweet & Sour
Tom Collins
Whiskey Sour
On The Border -
Buckets (Cran Appletini, Frozen Margarita, Mango Passion, Mojito,
Pina Colada, Pomegranate, Sangria, Strawberry Frozen Daiquiri,
Strawberry Mango)
Straight Ups (Cosmopolitan, Cran Appletini, Mango Passion,
Margarita, Margarita Lite, Mojito, Pina Colada, Pomegranate,
Sangria, Strawberry Mango, Strawberry Margarita)
Rose's - Grenadine, Infusions (Blue Raspberry, Cosmopolitan,
Pomegranate Twist, Sour Apple), Infusions Light Mix
(Cosmopolitan, Tropical Fruit Twist), Mango, Passion Fruit,
Sweetened Lime Juice, Traditional
Simply Enjoy - Mixer (Cosmopolitan, Lemon Drop Martini,
Margarita, Mojito, Watermelon Martini)
Stop & Shop Brand - Simply Enjoy Mixer (Cosmopolitan, Lemon
Drop Martini, Margarita Cocktail, Mojito Cocktail, Watermelon
Martini)
Cocktail Sauce... see also Seafood Sauce
Captain's Choice
Food Club Brand
Frontera - Cocktail & Ceviche Sauce (Cilantro Lime, Tomato
Chipotle)
Giant Brand - Seafood Cocktail Sauce
Hannaford Brand
Heinz - Cocktail Sauce, Zesty
Hy-Vee - Cocktail Sauce For Seafood
Ken's Steak House - Blue Label, Green Label
Kroger Brand
Lee Kum Kee - Shrimp Sauce
Legal - Seafood Cocktail
Lou's Famous - Cocktail Sauce

McCormick - Extra Hot, Golden Dipt, Lemon Butter Dill (Fat Free, Regular), Lemon Herb, Mediterranean, Original Cocktail Sauce, Santa Fe Style, Scampi, Seafood Sauce Cajun Style

Old Bay

Private Selections - Zesty

Royal Food Products - Garden Fresh, Royal Deluxe

Safeway Brand

Spartan Brand

Steels Gourmet - Agave

Stop & Shop Brand - Seafood Cocktail Sauce

Trader Joe's - Seafood Cocktail Sauce**!!**

Cocoa Mix/Powder

Albertsons - Cocoa Mix

Caribou - Guittard Drinking Chocolate (Dark, Milk, White)

Coburn Farms - Chocolate Milk Mix, Hot Cocoa Mix, Milk Chocolate, No Sugar Added Mix

Dagoba - Drinking Chocolate (Authentic, Chai, Unsweetened, Xocolatl Hot Chocolate), Professional Cocoa Powder

Food Club Brand - Baking Cocoa, Cocoa Mix Marshmallow Supreme, Cocoa Mix No Sugar Added, Hot Cocoa (Mini Marshmallows, Regualr)

Ghirardelli -
Baking Cocoa (Premium Unsweetened Cocoa, Sweet Ground Chocolate & Cocoa)
Chocolate Hazelnut
Chocolate Mocha
Double Chocolate
White Mocha

Giant Brand - Hot Cocoa (Mini Marshmallows, Regular)

Ginger Evans - Baking Cocoa, Cocoa

Gloria Jean's - All Hot Chocolate Varieties

Gordon Food Service - Hot Cocoa Mix (Bulk, No Sugar Added, Packet)

Hannaford Brand - Regular, w/Marshmallows

C

Hershey's - Chocolate Syrup (Lite, Regular, Special Dark), Cocoa (Special Dark, Unsweetened Regular)

Hy-Vee - Instant Chocolate Flavored Drink Mix, Instant Hot Cocoa (No Sugar Added, Regular)

Kroger Brand - All Varieties

Kroger Value - Cocoa

Lowes Foods Brand - Hot Cocoa Mix (Regular, w/Marshmallows)

Medifast - Hot Cocoa ●

Meijer Brand - Instant Marshmallow, No Sugar Added, Organic Regular, Regular, Sugar Free, w/Marshmallows

Midwest Country Fare - Hot Cocoa Mix, Instant Chocolate Flavored Drink Mix, No Sugar, Regular, Rich Chocolate, w/Marshmallows

Nuts Online - Organic Cacao Powder ●, Raw Organic Cacao Powder ●

Private Selections - Cocoa Supreme (All Flavors)

Safeway Brand - Hot Cocoa Mix (Fat Free, w/Marshmallows), Instant Chocolate Drink Mix

Safeway Select - European Café Style (Regular, White Chocolate)

Shiloh Farms - Organic Cocoa Powder **! !**

Spartan Brand - Cocoa Canned, Hot Cocoa Mix (Lite, Regular, w/Marshmallows)

St. Claire's Organics - Hot Cocoa (Cherry, Mandarin)

Stop & Shop Brand - Hot Cocoa (Fat Free No Sugar Added, Light, Mini Marshmallows, Regular)

Trader Joe's - Conacado Organic Cocoa, Organic Cocoa Powder, Sipping Chocolate

Watkins - Baking Cocoa

Winn Dixie - Classic, Marshmallow, No Sugar Added Cocoa Mix Type

Coconut

Albertsons - Fancy Flake Sweetened

Baker's - Angel Flake Sweetened In Bag, Angel Flake Sweetened In Cans

Food Club Brand - Flake

Ginger Evans - Sweetened

Gluty Free - Diced Dried ●, Shredded Organic ●, Unsweetened (Chips ●, Organic Chips ●)

Great Value Brand (Wal-Mart) - Sweetened Flaked Coconut

Hannaford Brand - Fancy Sweetened

Hy-Vee - Coconut, Sweetened Flake Coconut

Kroger Brand - Regular, Sweetened

Laura Lynn

Let's Do...Organic - Creamed, Flakes Organic Unsweetened, Organic (Flakes, Unsweetened), Shredded (Reduced Fat, Regular, Unsweetened)

Lowes Foods Brand - Flakes

Nuts Online - Diced ●, Organic Unsweetened Chips ●, Shredded Organic ●, Unsweetened Chips ●

Peter Paul - Flour, Toasted Coconut Chips

Phildesco - Desiccated, Sweetened, Toasted

Publix - Coconut Flakes

Safeway Brand - Coconut Sweetened

Spartan Brand - Coconut Flakes

Tropical Traditions - Chips, Flakes, Shredded

Wegmans Brand - Sweetened Flaked

Winn Dixie

Woodstock Farms - Organic Medium Shred

Coconut Milk

A Taste Of Thai - Lite, Regular

Ka-Me - Lite**!**, Regular**!**

Native Forest - Organic (Classic, Light)

Peter Paul - Coconut Cream, Regular

Phildesco - Regular

So Delicious - Original ●, Unsweetened ●, Vanilla ●

Thai Kitchen - Lite, Organic (Lite, Regular), Regular

Trader Joe's - Light

Cod... see Fish

... *All Fresh Fish Is Gluten-Free (Non-Marinated, Unseasoned)*

C Coffee

Adina - Barista Brews (Double XXPresso, Mocha Madness), Organic Coffees (Ethiopian Espresso, Indian Chai Latte, Mayan Mocha, Sumatran Vanilla Latte)

Albertsons - All Varieties

Biggby - All Coffee Drinks *(Except Chocolate Chip Freeze)*

Brown Gold - All Varieties

Caribou - All Coffee Beans, All Ground Coffee, All Iced Coffee

Folger's - All Instant & Roasts

Food Club Brand - Ground Coffee (Classic Roast, Columbian, Decaf, French Roast, Lite, Master Blend, Original Blend Roast, Special Roast), Instant Coffee (Decaf, Regular)

Full Circle - Organic (Ground (Decaffeinated, Ecothentic Espresso, Ethiopia, Guatemala, Morning Blend, Sumatra), Whole Bean (Blue Coast Blend, Bolivia))

Gloria Jean's - All Brewed Coffee

Great Value Brand (Wal-Mart) - 100% Colombian Classic Ground Coffee (Naturally Decaf, Regular), Dark Roast 100% Arabica Premium Ground Coffee, Instant Coffee Naturally Decaf Premium, Instant Coffee Regular

Green Mountain Coffee - All Varieties

Hannaford Brand - All Varieties

Higgins & Burke - All Varieties

Hy-Vee - 100% Colombian, Breakfast Blend, Classic Blend, Classic Decaf, Coffee (Instant, Regular), Decaf (Instant, Regular), French Roast

Kirkland Signature - 100% Columbian, Cafe Cappuccino, Dark Roast Decaf, Decaf, Pouches, Regular

Kroger Brand - All Varieties

Kroger Value - All Varieties

Lowes Foods Brand - Bag 100% Colombian (Decaf, Regular), French Roast, Signature Blend, Brick (100% Colombian, Decaf, French Roast, Lite, Regular), Instant (Decaf, Regular), Singles Microwaveable

Maxwell House -
   Coffee Bags (Decaf, Master Blend, Regular)
   Filter Packs & Singles (Decaf, Original)
   French Vanilla (Regular, Sugar Free, Sugar Free & Decaffeinated)
   General Foods International (Cafe Fancais, Cafe Vienna)
   Ground (All Varieties)
   Hazelnut
   Instant (Decaf, Original, Reduced Caffeine/Lite)
   International Cafe (Cappuccino (Original, Toasted Hazelnut))
   Latte (Chai, Mocha, Vanilla Bean, Vanilla Caramel)
   Suisse Mocha (Regular, Sugar Free, Sugar Free & Decaffeinated)

McDaniel's - Ground, Instant (Decaffeinated, Regular)

Medifast - Cappuccino ●

Meijer Brand - Decaf, French Roast, Ground (Colombian, French Roast, Lite 50% Decaf), Regular

Member's Mark - Cappuccino (French Vanilla, Mocha)

Midwest Country Fare - Classic Blend

Mother Parkers - All Varieties

Mountain Blend - Instant

Nescafe - Classic Instant, Taster's Choice Instant Flavored, Non Flavored, Singles (All Varieties)

O Organics - All Coffee Beans

Pacific Natural Foods - Organic Simply Coffee (Latte, Mocha, Vanilla Latte)

Private Selections - All Varieties

Publix - All Varieties

Pura Vida - All Varieties *(Except French Vanilla)*

Safeway Brand - Decaf Classic Roast, Espresso Coffee Beans

Safeway Select - Whole Bean Flavored

Sanka - Decaf Coffee

Spartan Brand - French Roast, Ground (Colombian, Decaf Roast, Half Caff, Regular Roast), Instant (Decaf, Regular), Regular

Taster's Choice - All Varieties

Trader Joe's - All Coffee

C

Tully's - All Varieties

Wegmans Brand -

Ground (100% Colombian, 100% Colombian Medium Roast, Breakfast Blend Light Roast, Breakfast Blend Light Roast Decaf, Decaf, Espresso Dark Roast, French Roast, Lite Caffeine, Lite Caffeine Medium Roast, Traditional)

Instant

Pure Origin Coffee (Day Break Roast, Ground Jamaican Mid Day, Kona Evening, Smooth Morning, Sumatra Night)

The Ultimate Coffee Adventure (All Varieties)

Traditional Coffee Singles

Whole Bean Coffee (100% Colombian Medium Roast, Breakfast Blend Light Roast, Espresso Dark Roast, Espresso Dark Roast Decaf)

Winn Dixie - All Varieties

Yuban - Ground (100% Arabica, 100% Columbian, Breakfast Blend, Dark Roast, Decaf, Hazelnut, Original), Instant Regular, Organic (Latin American, Medium Roast)

Coffee Creamer... see Creamer

Cold Cuts... see Deli Meat

Cole Slaw Dressing... see Salad Dressing

Collards... see Greens

Communion Wafers

Ener-G▲ - Communion Wafers

Concentrate... see Drinks/Juice

Cones

Barkat - Ice Cream Cones, Waffle Cones

Cerrone Cone - Waffle Cones

Goldbaum's▲ - Gluten Free Ice Cream Cones (Regular, Sugar)

Let's Do...Organic - Gluten Free Ice Cream Cones

PaneRiso▲ - Ice Cream Cups ●

Cookie Mix... see also Cookies/Cookie Dough

1-2-3 Gluten Free▲ - Chewy Chipless Scrumdelicious Cookies Mix ●, Lindsay's Lipsmackin' Roll Out & Cut Sugar Cookies Mix ●, Sweet Goodness Pan Bars ●

3 Fellers Bakery▲ - Cookie Dough (Chocolate Chip, Chocolate Chip w/Pecans, Oatmeal Raisin, Sugar)

Arrowhead Mills - Gluten Free Chocolate Chip Mix

Augason Farms - Gluten Free (Basic ●, Chocolate Chip ●)

Authentic Foods▲ - Gourmet Dark Chocolate Chunk Cookie Mix

Betty Crocker▲ - Gluten Free Chocolate Chip Cookie Mix

Bob's Red Mill▲ - Chocolate Chip

Cause You're Special▲ - Chocolate Chip, Classic Sugar, Classic Sugar

Ceres Kitchen - Best Ever Sugar Cookie Mix

Cherrybrook Kitchen - Gluten Free Chocolate Chip Cookie Mix *(Box Must Say Gluten Free)*, Sugar Cookie Mix *(Box Must Say Gluten Free)*

Doodles Cookies - Double Chocolate Chip Habanero, Organic Gluten Free Nut Butter, Organic Gluten Free Sugar

Earthly Treats▲ - Sugar Cookie Mix ●

Food-Tek Fast & Fresh▲ - Cookie Mix (Chocolate Chip, Double Chocolate Chip, Sugar)

Full Circle - Gluten Free Cookie Mix

Gifts Of Nature▲ - Fancy Cookie Mix, Triple Treat Cookie Mix

Gluten Free Life▲ - The Ultimate Gluten Free Cookie Mix

Gluten Free Pantry▲ - Cookie & Cake Mix (Chocolate Chip, Old Fashioned)

Gluten Free Sensations▲ - Chocolate Chip Cookie Mix, Sugar Cookie Cutout Mix

Gluten-Free Essentials▲ - Chocolate Chip Cookie Mix ●, Cocoa Mudslide ●, Mini Mint Marvels ●, Speedy Bake Mix (Chocolate Chip ●, Make Mine Chocolate ●)

Hodgson Mill▲ - Gluten Free Cookie Mix

Hol Grain▲ - Chocolate Chip ●

InclusiLife▲ - Cookie Dough (Chocolate Chip ●, Fudge Brownie ●, Sugar ●)

Jules Gluten Free▲ - Cookie Mix ●, Graham Cracker/Gingersnap Mix●

King Arthur Flour▲ - Gluten Free Cookie Mix ●

C

    Kinnikinnick▲ - Cookie Mix

    Laurel's Sweet Treats▲ - Chocolate Chip, Gourmet Chocolate Cookie w/White Milk Chocolate Chips, Roll 'Em Out Sugar

    Little Bay Baking - Cookie Bar Mix ●, Gingerbread Cookie Mix ●

    Marion's Smart Delights▲ - Cookie & Muffin Mix ●, Lemon Bar Baking Mix ●

    Namaste Foods▲ - Cookie Mix

    Only Oats - Grandma's Oatmeal Cookie Mix ●

    Pamela's Products▲ - Chocolate Chunk Cookie Mix

    Pure Living - Cookie Mix (European Chocolate Truffle w/Tart Cherry Slivers ●, Julienne Cranberries Zante Currants & Essence Of Raspberry Orange Bloosom ●, Saigon Cinnamon Oat Zante Currants & Essence Of Chai Tea ●)

    Really Great Food Company▲ - Butter, Chocolate Crinkle, Versatile

    Ruby Range - Old Fashioned Cookies Gluten Free Baking Mix ●

    Silly Yak Bakery - GF (Holiday Cut Out Cookie Dough Mix ●, Snickerdoodle Cookie Mix)

    The Cravings Place▲ - Chocolate Chunk (Double, Regular), Create Your Own, Peanut Butter, Raisin Spice

    WOW Baking Company▲ - Cookie Dough (Chocolate Chip ●, Ginger Molasses ●, Peanut Butter ●, Sugar ●)

  Cookies/Cookie Dough

    AgVantage Naturals▲ - Basic Cookie Mix ●

    Aleia's▲ - Almond Horn ●, Chocolate Chip ●, Chocolate Coconut Macaroon ●, Coconut Macaroon ●, Ginger Snap ●, Peanut Butter ●, Pignoli Nut ●, Snickerdoodle ●

    Andean Dream - Cookies (Chocolate Chip, Cocoa Orange, Coconut, Orange Essence, Raisins & Spice)

    Andrea's Fine Foods▲ - Chocolate Chip, Gooey Truffle, Oatmeal, Sugar

    Apple's Bakery▲ - Gluten Free Cookies (Butterscotch Walnut, Chocolate Cherry Ranch Fudge, Chocolate Chip No Nut, Coconut Meltaway, Dried Cranberry White Chocolate, Dusty Miller Molasses, Lemon Drop, Spice Gem, White Chocolate Macadamia Nut)

C

Aunt Gussie's▲ -
  Big Chocolate Chip Cookie ●
  Big Sugar Cookie ●
  Gluten Free Cookies (Chocolate Chip ●, Chocolate Spritz ●, Sugar
    Free Chocolate Chip ●, Sugar Free Vanilla Spritz ●)
  Mini Chocolate Chip Cookies ●
  Vanilla Swirl Cookies ●

Bi-Aglut - Chocolate Wafers, Cioco Frollino, Cocoa Cream Filled
  Wafers, Snack w/Hazelnut Filling, Snack w/Milk Filling, Sugar Free
  Frollino

Biscottea - Gluten Free Tea Shortbreads (Blueberry, Chai, Earl Grey)

Breakaway Bakery▲ - Chocolate Chip Cookie Dough ●

Cherrybrook Kitchen - Mini Cookies (Gluten Free Chocolate Chip
  (Box Must Say Gluten Free), Gluten Free Vanilla Graham *(Box
  Must Say Gluten Free)*

Choices Rice Bakery▲ - Bird's Nest, Brownie White Chocolate Chip,
  Chocolate Chip, Cranberry Almond Biscotti, Ginger,
  Mediterranean Macaroons, Raisin Sunflower

Cookie Momsters▲ - Chocolate Chip, Double Chocolate Chip,
  Soy Free (Chocolate Chip, Double Chocolate), Sugar

Cookies For Me - Chocolate Chip, Decorated Sugar Cookies,
  Ginger Spice, Lemon Iced Sugar, Mini, Snicker Doodle

Crave Bakery▲ - Monster Cookie

Deerfields Gluten Free Bakery▲ - Chips 'N Wally, Chocolate
  Dreams, Day Dreams, Lemon Buttons, Lotsa Chips, Sugar Buttons,
  Triple Chips, Triple Chocolate Brownie Cookie

Di Manufacturing - Gluten Free Chocolate Chip Cookie Dough ●,
  Gluten Free Cookies (M & M ●, Macadamia Nut ●)

El Peto▲ - Almond Shortbread, Carob Chip, Chocolate (Chip,
  Coconut Macaroons, Hazelnut), Cinnamon/Hazelnut, Coconut
  Macaroons, Gingerbread, Hazelnut/Raspberry, Old Fashion Sugar

Emmy's Organics▲ - Macaroons (Chai Spice, Chocolate Orange,
  Coconut Vanilla, Dark Cacao, Lemon Ginger, Mint Chip)

C

Ener-G▲ - Chocolate (Chip Biscotti, Chip Potato, Regular), Cinnamon, Ginger, Sunflower Cookies, Vanilla, White Chocolate Chip

Enjoy Life▲ - Chewy Chocolate Chip ●, Double Chocolate Brownie●, Gingerbread Spice ●, Happy Apple ●, Lively Lemon ●, No Oats "Oatmeal" ●, Snickerdoodle ●

Everybody Eats▲ - Chocolate Chip, Sugar

Fabe's Bakery - Organic Mini Macaroons ●

Foods By George▲ - Pecan Tarts

French Meadow Bakery - Gluten Free (Chocolate Chip Cookie Dough ●, Chocolate Chip Cookies ●, Coconutty Macaroons ●)

Gillian's Foods▲ - Chocolate Chip, Cookie Dough, M&M, Sugar

Glenny's - Gluten Free (Chocolate Chip ●, Oatmeal Raisin ●)

Glow Gluten Free▲ - Chocolate Chip ●, Double Chocolate Chip ●, Gingersnap ●, Snickerdoodle ●

Glutano▲ - Cookies (Butterkeks, Choco Chip, Chocolate O's, Cocoa Wafers, Custard Creams, Hoops, Lemon Wafers, Luxury)

Gluten Free & Fabulous▲ - Bites (Brownie ●, Butterscotch ●, Chocolate Chip Cookies ●, Savory ●, Shortbread ●)

Gluten Free Life▲ - Deluxe (Chocolate Chip, Flax Shortbread, Snicker Doodle, Sugar)

Gluten-Free Creations▲ - Chocolate Chip ●, Frozen Cookie Dough Chocolate Chip Cookies ●, Frozen Cookie Dough Sugar Cookies●, Oatmeal Raisin ●, Pecan Wedding ●, Snickerdoodle ●

Gluten-Free Essentials▲ - Vanilla Sugar Cookies ●

GlutenFreeda▲ - Real Cookies (Chip Chip Hooray, Chocolate Minty Python, Peanut Envy, Peanut Paul & Mary, Sugar Kookies)

Glutino▲ - Chocolate Chip Cookies, Chocolate Vanilla Creme, Vanilla Creme, Wafers (Chocolate, Lemon, Vanilla)

Gopal's - Nature's Gift Cookies (Almond Raisin, Goldenberry Brazil, Hazelnut Cherry, Macadamia Goji, Pineapple Flax)

Goraw▲ - Super Cookies (Chocolate ●, Original ●)

Grandma Ferdon's▲ -
   Cookie Dough (Chocolate ●, Cut Out ●, Gingersnap ●, Peanut Butter ●)

Cookies (Chocolate Grande ●, Ginger Snap ●, Peanut Butter ●)
Lemon Bars ●, Pumpkin Bar Mix ●, Pumpkin Bars ●

Heaven Mills▲ -
Cookies (Chocolate Chip ●, Honey ●, Hamantaschen (Apricot ●, Raspberry ●), Rugelach (Chocolate ●, Cinnamon ●, Vanilla ●)
Sugar Free (Chocolate Chip ●, Vanilla Chocolate Chip ●),
Vanilla (Chocolate Chip ●, Regular ●, Sprinkle ●))

Homefree - Gluten Free Cookies (Mini Oatmeal Chocolate Chip ●, Oatmeal ●)

Ian's - Wheat Free Gluten Free Cookie Buttons (Chocolate Chip, Crunchy Cinnamon)

Indie Candy - Dark Chocolate Covered "Oreos"

Jennies▲ - Zero Carb Macaroons (Carob, Chocolate, Coconut)

Jo-Sef▲ -
Animal Cookies (Chocolate ●, Vanilla ●)
Sandwich Cookies (Chocolate O's ●, Cinnamon O's ●, Vanilla O's●)
Square Cookies (Chocolate ●, Cinnamon ●, Vanilla ●)

Katy Sweet▲ -
Chewy Pralines (Coconut Pecan ●, Maple Walnut ●, Peanut Pie ●, Pecan ●)
Cookie Cutters (Bayou Bites ●, Enchantments ●, Fleur De Lis ●, Hearts ●, Lone Stars ●, Longhorns ●, Razorbacks ●, Sooners ●)
Creamy Pralines (Fudge Pecan ●, Maple Walnut ●, Original Pecan ●, Original Walnut ●)
No Sugar Added Chewy Pralines (Almond ●, Mixed ●, Pecan ●, Walnut ●)
Organic Chewy Pralines (Maple Walnut ●, Original Pecan ●)
Organic Creamy Pralines (Fudge Pecan ●, Maple Walnut ●, Original Pecan ●, Original Walnut ●)

Katz Gluten Free▲ - Apricot Tart ●, Chocolate Dipped ●, Colored Sprinkle ●, Raspberry Tart ●, Rugelech (Chocolate ●, Cinnamon ●), Vanilla ●

C

Kay's Naturals - Cookie Bites (Cinnamon Almond, Honey Almond)

Kinnikinnick▲ - Chocolate Cookie Crumbs, Ginger Snap, KinniKritters Animal Cookies (Chocolate, Graham Style, Regular), KinniToos Sandwich Cookies (Chocolate Vanilla, Fudge Creme, Vanilla Creme), Montana's Chocolate Chip

Kneaded Specialties▲ - Chocolate Cherries Jubilie ●, Chocolate Chip ●, Double Chocolate Chip ●, Holiday Sugar ●, Lemon Sugar ●, Snickerdoodle ●, Vegan Chocolate Cookie Dreams ●

Kookie Karma - All Varieties ●

Lucy's▲ - Cookie (Chocolate Chip ●, Cinnamon Thin ●, Oatmeal Cookie ●, Sugar ●)

Manischewitz - Caramel Cashew Patties, Chocolate Frolic Bears

Mary's Gone Crackers▲ - Cookies (Chocolate Chip ●, Ginger Snaps ●, N'Oatmeal Raisin ●)

Mi-Del - Arrowroot Animal !, Chocolate Chip !, Cinnamon Snaps !, Ginger Snaps !, Pecan !, Sandwich Cookies (Chocolate !, Royal Vanilla *(Package Must Say Gluten Free)* !)

Mim's Kitchen - Ready to Bake Cookies (Chocolate Chip ●, Chocolate Chocolate Chip ●, Peanut Butter Chocolate Chip ●, Sugar ●, White Chocolate Macadamia Nut ●)

Montana Monster Munchies - Legacy Valley Original Cookie ●

Mrs. Crimble's - Macaroons (Chocolate, Coconut, Jam Coconut Rings), Peanut Cookies

Namaste Foods▲ - Blondies Mix, Cookie Mix

Nana's - Cookie Bars (Berry Vanilla ●, Chocolate Munch ●, Nana Banana ●), Cookie Bites (Fudge ●, Ginger Spice ●, Lemon Dreams ●), No Gluten Cookie (Chocolate ●, Chocolate Crunch ●, Ginger ●, Lemon ●)

Nature's Path - Envirokidz Organic Animal Cookies Vanilla

Orgran▲ -
  Amaretti Biscotti
  Classic Chocolate Biscotti
  Classic Chocolate Cookie
  Itsy Bitsy Bears

Mini Outback Animals (Chocolate, Vanilla)

Outback Animals (Chocolate, Vanilla)

Wild Raspberry Fruit Flavored Biscuits

Pamela's Products▲ -

Butter Shortbread

Chocolate Chip (Mini, Walnut)

Chunky Chocolate Chip

Extreme Chocolate Mini Cookies

Ginger (Mini Snapz, w/Sliced Almonds)

Lemon Shortbread

Organic (Chocolate Chunk Pecan Shortbread, Dark Chocolate/ Chocolate Chunk, Espresso Chocolate Chunk, Old Fashion Raisin Walnut, Peanut Butter Chocolate Chip, Spicy Ginger w/ Crystallized Ginger)

Peanut Butter

Pecan Shortbread

Shortbread Swirl

PaneRiso▲ - Chocolate Chip ●, Cinnamon ●, Coconut ●, Double Chocolate Delite ●, Ginger Snap ●, Maple ●, Orange ●, Soft Chocolate Chip ●

Pure Market Express▲ - Caramel Macaroons ●, Chocolate Chip Cookies ●, Chocolate Chocolate Chip Cookies ●, Chocolate Macaroons ●, Macaroon Trio ●, No Bake Cookies ●, Vanilla Macaroons ●

Quejos▲ - Butter Shortbread, Non Dairy (Chocolate Chip, Dark Chocolate Chip, Hemp Heart, Hemp Heart Raisin)

Rose's Bakery▲ -

Cookies Chocolate Chip

Gingersnap

Macaroons

Mudslide

Oatmeal (Cranberry Chocolate Chip, Original)

Snickerdoodle

Sugar Free (Double Chocolate, Lemon Ginger, Oatmeal Raisin Cookie)

C

Schar▲ -
Chocolate Dipped Cookies
Chocolate Hazelnut Bars,
Cookies (Chocolate O's, Chocolate Sandwich Cremes,
Shortbread, Vanilla Sandwich Cremes)
Ladyfingers
Wafers (Cocoa, Hazelnut, Vanilla)

Silly Yak Bakery -
CFGF Cookies (Cranberry Almond ●, Gingerbread ●,
Snickerdoodle ●)
GF Cookies (Chocolate Chip ●, Cranberry Almond ●, Cranberry
Oatmeal Walnut ●, Gluten-Free Chocolate Pecan ●, M&M●,
Oatmeal ●, Oatmeal Chocolate Chip ●, Oatmeal Raisin ●,
Peanut Butter ●, Peanut Butter Chocolate Chip ●, Raisin Pecan●,
Snickerdoodle ●, Sugar ●)

Skye Foods - Chocolate Chip ●, White Chocolate Macadamia Nut ●

Squirrel's Bakery - Gluten Free Cinnamon Chocolate !, Gluten Free
Coconut Chocolate Chip !

Sunstart - Crunch Chocolate Chip, Golden (Chocolate Wrapped,
Ginger, Raspberry, Supreme), Dessert Bars (Caramel & Chocolate
Delights, Rocky Road)

The Grainless Baker▲ - Biscotti (Almond, Anise), Butterfly (Apricot,
Raspberry), Oatmeal, Pastry Cream Sandwich

The Naked Cookie - Gluten Free (Cafe Con Leche, Chocolate,
Chocolate Mint, Death By Chocolate Macaroons, Fiesta Sugar,
Macaroon, Naked, Peanut Butter, Sugar)

Trader Joe's - Flourless Chocolate Walnut Cookies, Gluten Free
Ginger Snaps, Meringues (All Varieties) ! !

Whole Foods Market Gluten Free Bakehouse▲ - Cookies
(Chocolate Chip, Molasses Ginger, Nutmeal Raisin, Peanut Butter)

WOW Baking Company▲ -
Cookie
Chocolate Chip ●
Chocolate Ginger Molasses ●

  Oregon Oatmeal ●
  Peanut Butter ●
  Snickerdoodle ●
  Sugar ●
 ZeroGrano - Chocolate Wafers, Frollini
Cooking Spray
 Albertsons - Buttery, Canola Oil, Vegetable
 Crisco - Butter, Olive Oil, Original
 Emeril's - Creamery Butter Flavor, Original Canola Oil
 Food Club Brand - Butter, Canola Oil, Olive Oil
 Hannaford Brand - Butter Flavored, Canola, Olive Oil
 Hy-Vee - Butter, Canola, Olive Oil, Vegetable Oil
 Kirkland Signature - Canola
 Lowes Foods Brand - Butter, Regular
 Manischewitz - All Varieties
 Mazola - No Stick (Butter, Original), Pure (Butter, Extra Virgin
  Olive Oil, Original)
 Meijer Brand - Butter, Olive Oil Extra Virgin, Vegetable Oil
 Midwest Country Fare - Vegetable Oil
 O Organics - Canola Oil, Olive Oil
 Publix - Butter Flavored, Grill, Olive Oil, Original Canola
 Safeway Brand - Butter Flavored, Canola Oil, Grill, Olive Oil,
  Vegetable Oil
 Smart Balance - Non Stick, w/Organic Soy
 Spartan Brand - Butter Flavored, Extra Virgin Olive Oil, Regular
 Stop & Shop Brand - Butter Flavored, Canola Oil, Garlic Flavored,
  Grill Spray, Olive Oil, Vegetable
 Trader Joe's - All Canola Oil Sprays
 Wegmans Brand - Canola Oil, Corn Oil, Natural Butter Flavor
  Canola Oil, Olive Oil
 Winn Dixie - Butter, Canola Oil, Corn Oil, Grill, Olive Oil
Cooking Wine
 Eden Organic - Mirin Rice
 Holland House - All Varieties

C

Publix
Regina - All Varieties

Corn
... *All Fresh Fruits & Vegetables Are Gluten-Free*

Albertsons - Canned (Creamed Style, Regular), Frozen

Birds Eye - All Plain Frozen Vegetables

C & W - All Plain Frozen Vegetables

Del Monte - All Canned Vegetables

Food Club Brand -
Canned (Cream Style, Crisp & Sweet, Gold & White, Golden, White, Whole Kernel (No Salt, Regular))
Frozen (Chuck Wagon, Corn On Cob, Steamin' Easy Whole Kernel Corn, Super Sweet Cob Mini Ear, White Super Sweet, Whole Kernel)

Freshlike - Frozen Plain Vegetables

Full Circle - Organic Frozen Whole Kernel Corn, Organic Gold Corn

Giant Brand -
Canned (Cream Style, Mexican, No Salt Added, Whole Kernel)
Frozen (Cut, On The Cob (Regular, Supersweet))

Gluty Free - Organic Purple Corn Kernels ●, Sweet Corn Freeze Dried ●

Grand Selections - Crisp & Sweet Whole Kernel, Frozen (Super Sweet Cut, White Shoepeg)

Great Value Brand (Wal-Mart) -
Canned (Cream Style Corn, Golden Sweet Whole Kernel Corn, No Salt Added Golden Sweet Whole Kernel Corn)
Microwaveable Plastic Cups Golden Kernel Corn

Green Giant -
Canned
Cream Style Sweet Corn
Mexicorn
Niblets (Extra Sweet, No Salt Added, Whole Kernel Extra Sweet Corn, Whole Kernel Sweet Corn)

Southwestern Style
Super Sweet Yellow & White Corn
White Shoepeg Corn

Frozen
Cream Style Corn
Nibblers (12 Count, 24 Count)
Shoepeg White Corn & Butter Sauce
Steamers Niblets Corn
Valley Fresh Steamers (Extra Sweet Niblets, Niblets Corn, Select White Shoepeg Corn)

Hannaford Brand - Cream Style, Crisp & Sweet, Whole Kernel

HealthMarket - Organic Whole Kernel

Hy-Vee - Corn On The Cob, Cream Style Golden Corn, Frozen Cut Golden Corn, Steam In A Bag Frozen Corn, Whole Kernel (Corn, Gold Corn, White Sweet Corn)

Kirkland Signature - Sweet

Kroger Brand - All Plain Vegetables (Canned, Frozen)

Kroger Value - All Plain Vegetables (Canned, Frozen)

Laura Lynn - Corn (No Salt Whole Kernel, Whole Kernel)

Lowes Foods Brand - Canned White, Frozen (Corn Cob Full Ear, Corn Cob Mini Ear, Cut)

Meijer Brand -
Canned (Cream Style, Golden Sweet Organic, Whole Kernel (Crisp & Sweet, Golden, Golden No Salt, White))
Frozen (Corn Cob Mini Ear, Corn On The Cob, Whole Kernel, Whole Kernel Golden)

Mezzetta - Gourmet Baby

Midwest Country Fare - Cream Style, Frozen Cut, Whole Kernel

Native Forest - Organic Cut Baby Corn

Nature's Promise - Organic Canned

Nuts Online - Simply Sweet Corn Freeze Dried Vegetables ●

O Organics - Canned Whole Kernel, Frozen Golden Cut

Pictsweet - All Plain Vegetables (Frozen), Seasoned Corn & Black Beans

C

Private Selections - All Plain Vegetables (Frozen White Corn, Organic Yellow)

Publix - Canned (Cream Style Golden, Golden Sweet, Whole Kernel), Frozen (Corn On The Cob, Cut)

Publix GreenWise Market - Organic Canned Whole Kernel

S&W - All Canned Vegetables

Safeway Brand - Cream Style, Frozen Corn On The Cob, No Salt Whole Kernel, Steam In Bag (Petite, White)

Spartan Brand - Canned Golden (Crisp & Sweet, Sweet Corn Cream Style, Whole Kernel), Frozen (Baby Corn Blend, Corn On The Cob, Mini Ear Corn On The Cob, Plain, White Super Sweet)

Stop & Shop Brand - Corn (& Butter, & Peas, Cut, Mexican Style, On The Cob, Super Sweet Corn On The Cob), Whole Kernel Corn

Trader Joe's - Frozen (Cut White Corn, Organic Super Sweet Cut Corn, Roasted Corn), Frozen Pacific Northwest Cut White Corn

Wegmans Brand -
Canned (Bread & Butter, Cream Style Golden Sweet, Crisp 'N Sweet Whole Kernel, Whole Kernel, Whole Kernel No Salt)
Frozen (Baby Corn Cleaned & Cut, Bread & Butter Sweet Whole Kernel, Super Sweet Steamable, Whole Kernel In Butter Sauce)

Westbrae - Whole Kernel (Golden, White)

Winn Dixie -
Canned (Creamed Style, White Whole Kernel, Yellow Whole Kernel, Yellow Whole Kernel No Salt)
Frozen Corn (Organic Yellow Cut, Steamable Yellow Cut, White Cut, Yellow Cut)
Frozen Corn On The Cob (Mini, Regular)

Woodstock Farms - Organic Frozen Cut Corn Regular, Supersweet (Regular, White), Toasted Corn

Corn Dogs

Ian's - Wheat Free Gluten Free Recipe Popcorn Turkey Corn Dogs

S'Better Farms▲ - Beef Corn Dogs

Corn Syrup... see Syrup

Cornbread/Cornbread Mix

1-2-3 Gluten Free▲ - Micah's Mouthwatering Corn Bread Mix●

Bob's Red Mill▲ - Gluten Free Cornbread Mix

Celiac Specialties▲ - Corn Bread Mix

Chi-Chi's - Fiesta Sweet Corn Cake Mix

El Torito - Sweet Corn Cake Mix

Food-Tek Fast & Fresh▲ - Dairy Free Minute Cornbread Mix

Gifts Of Nature▲ - Buttermilk Cornbread Mix

Gluten Free Pantry▲ - Yankee Cornbread

Grandma Ferdon's▲ - Cornbread Mix●

Kinnikinnick▲ - Cornbread & Muffin Mix

Laurel's Sweet Treats▲ - Good Ol' Corn Bread

Little Bay Baking - Corn Bread Mix●

Mixes From The Heartland▲ - Corn Bread Mix●

Orgran▲ - Cornbread & Muffin Mix

Really Great Food Company▲ - Home Style Cornbread Mix

The Cravings Place▲ - Grandma's Unsweetened

The Grainless Baker▲ - Corn Muffins

Whole Foods Market Gluten Free Bakehouse▲ - Cornbread

Corned Beef... see also Beef

Albertsons - Hash

Armour - Corned Beef Hash

Carl Buddig - Extra Thin Original Regular, Original Regular

Castle Wood Reserve - Deli Meat Angus Corned Beef

Dietz & Watson▲ - Brisket●, Flat●

Food Club Brand - Hash

Great Value Brand (Wal-Mart) - Corned Beef Hash

Hargis House - Hash

Hormel - Corned Beef Hash, Deli Bread Ready, Natural Choice
    Deli Counter Regular

Kayem - Extra Lean

Meijer Brand - Hash, Sliced Chipped Corned Beef Meat

Spartan Brand - Hash

Wellshire Farms - Corned Beef Brisket (Half !!, Whole !!),
    Round Corned Beef !!, Sliced Round Corned Beef !!

C Cornflake Crumbs... see Coating

Cornish Hens
  Shelton's - Game Hens

Cornmeal
  Arrowhead Mills - Organic Blue, Organic Yellow
  Bob's Red Mill▲ - Cornmeal
  Cause You're Special▲ - Cornmeal
  Gifts Of Nature▲ - Yellow Cornmeal
  Hodgson Mill - Organic Yellow, Plain White, Plain Yellow
  Kinnikinnick▲
  Publix - Plain Yellow
  Really Great Food Company▲ - Cornmeal
  Safeway Brand - Yellow Corn Meal
  Shiloh Farms - Polenta (Coarse Corn Meal)**! !**

Cottage Cheese
  Albertsons - 4%, Low Fat 1%
  Breakstone - Cottage Doubles (Apple Cinnamon, Blueberry,
      LiveActive (Peach, Pineapple, Strawberry), Peach, Pineapple,
      Raspberry, Strawberry), Large Curd (2%, 4%), LiveActive (Mixed
      Berry, Plain), Small Curd (2%, 2% w/Pineapple, 4%, Fat Free)
  Cabot - All Varieties
  Coburn Farms - 2%, 4%
  Daisy Brand - Low Fat, Regular
  Food Club Brand - Large Curd, Low Fat, Non Fat, Small Curd,
      w/Pineapple
  Friendship - All Varieties
  Hannaford Brand - All Varieties
  Hood - All Varieties
  Horizon Organic - All Varieties
  Hy-Vee - 1% Low Fat Small Curd, 4% Large Curd, 4% Small Curd
  Kemps - All Varieties
  Kroger Brand - All Varieties
  Lactaid - All Varieties
  Lowes Foods Brand - 4%, Non Fat, Small Curd

Lucerne - Cottage Cheese *(Except Fruit Added)*
Michigan Brand - All Varieties
Midwest Country Fare - 1% Small Curd, 4% Small Curd
Nancy's - All Cultured Dairy & Soy Products
Prairie Farms - Fat Free, Large Curd, Low Fat, Small Curd
Publix - Fat Free, Large Curd 4%, Low Fat, Low Fat
w/Pineapple, Small Curd 4%
Shamrock Farms - Fat Free, Low Fat, Traditional
Spartan Brand - Large Curd 4%, Low Fat 1%, Small Curd
(Non Fat, Regular)
Stop & Shop Brand - Cottage Cheese (Calcium Added, Low Fat,
Non Fat w/Pineapple)
Wegmans Brand - 1% Large Curd, Fat Free Pineapple, Small Curd
(1%, 4%)
Winn Dixie - 4% Large Curd, 4% Small Curd, Fat Free, Low Fat

Couscous
Lundberg▲ - Brown Rice (Mediterranean Curry, Plain Original,
Roasted Garlic & Olive Oil, Savory Herb)

Crabmeat
... *All Fresh Seafood Is Gluten-Free (Non-Marinated)
Bumble Bee - Lump, Pink Crabmeat, White
Chicken Of The Sea - All Crab Products
Crown Prince - Fancy Pink, Fancy White, Lump White, Natural
Fancy White Lump
Great Value Brand (Wal-Mart) - Smoked Crab Meat
Ocean Prince - Pink
Port Side - Imitation Crabmeat
Private Selections - Canned

Crackers
Andre's - Crackerbread (Cheddar Cheese, Country Onion, Old
World Rye, Original, Roasted Garlic, Sweet Cinnamon, Tangy
Parmesan, Toasted Sesame, Zesty Italian)
Back To Nature - Rice Thins (Sesame Ginger, Tomato Herb,
White Cheddar)

C

Bi-Aglut - Crackertoasts, Fette Tostate (Mediterranean, Original), Original, Regular

Blue Diamond - Nut Thins (Almond ●, BBQ ●, Cheddar Cheese ●, Country Ranch ●, Hazelnut ●, Hint Of Sea Salt ●, Pecan ●, Smokehouse ●)

Crunchmaster - Multi Grain (Five Seed, Original ●), Multi Seed (Original ●, Roasted Garlic ●, Rosemary & Olive Oil ●, Toasted Onion ●), Rice Crackers (Artisan Four Cheese ●, Toasted Sesame ●)

Eden Organic - Brown Rice, Nori Maki Rice

Edward & Sons -

Brown Rice Snaps (Black Sesame, Cheddar, Onion Garlic, Salsa, Tamari (Seaweed, Sesame), Toasted Onion, Unsalted Plain, Unsalted Sesame, Vegetable)

Exotic Rice Toast (Jasmine Rice & Spring Onion, Purple Rice & Black Sesame, Thai Red Rice & Flaxseeds)

Ener-G▲ - Cinnamon, Gourmet, Seattle

Flackers - Dill, Rosemary, Savory

Foods Alive - Flax Crackers (BBQ, Hemp, Italian Zest, Maple & Cinnamon, Mexican Harvest, Mustard, Onion Garlic, Original)

Glutino▲ - Gluten Free Crackers (Cheddar, Multigrain, Original, Vegetable, Table)

Hol Grain▲ - Brown Rice (Lightly Salted ●, No Salt ●, Onion & Garlic ●, Organic ●, w/Sesame Seeds Lightly Salted ●)

Ka-Me▲ - Rice Crackers (Cheese, Plain, Seaweed, Sesame, Wasabi *(Package Must Say Gluten Free)*)

Kookie Karma - All Varieties ●

Mary's Gone Crackers▲ - Black Pepper ●, Caraway ●, Gone Crackers Just The Crumbs (Caraway ●, Original ●, Savory ●), Herb ●, Onion ●, Original ●

Mr. Krispers - Tasty Snack Crackers Original Sesame ●

Mrs. Crimble's - Mini Cheese Crackers, Original Cheese, Rosemary & Onion, Sun Dried Tomato & Pesto

Organ▲ - Crackers Premium Deli, Crispibites (Balsamic Herb, Corn, Onion & Chive)

Pure Market Express▲ - Carrotini Crackers ●, Italian Flax Crackers ●, Thai Flax Crackers ●

Real Foods▲ -
  Corn Thins (BBQ, Cracked Pepper & Lemon, Feta & Sundried
    Tomato, Multigrain, Original, Sesame, Sour Cream & Chives,
    Soy & Linseed, Tasty Cheese)
  Rice Thins Regular
Roland - Rice Crackers Feng Shui (Original, Seaweed Wrapped,
  Wasabi)
RW Garcia - 5 Seed (Onion & Chive ●, Rosemary & Garlic ●,
  Tellicherry Cracked Pepper ●)
Sakata - Traditional Rice (Cheddar Cheese, Original, Seaweed)
San-J - Rice Crackers (Black Sesame ●, Sesame ●, Tamari ●)
Schar▲ - Cheese Bites, Snack, Table Crackers
Sharwood's - Spiced Thai Crackers
Simplyrice - Organic Brown Rice Crisps (Sea Salt, Spicy Chili, Tangy
  Tamari)
The Grainless Baker▲ - Cheese Snackers
The Kitchen Table Bakers - Gourmet Wafer Crisps (Aged
  Parmesan ●, Everything ●, Flax Seed ●, Garlic ●, Italian Herb ●,
  Jalapeno ●, Rosemary ●, Sesame ●)
Trader Joe's - Savory Thins (Edamame, Minis, Original)
Wellaby▲ - Cheese Ups (Classic, Parmesan, Smoked), Mini (Grated
  Parmesan, Original Cheese, Red Cheddar), Regular (Classic
  Cheese, Feta Oregano & Olive Oil, Parmesan & Sun Dried Tomato,
  Rosemary & Onion)
ZeroGrano - Crackers

Cranberries
  *... *All Fresh Fruits & Vegetables Are Gluten-Free*
  Gluty Free - Dried ●, Organic Dried ●
  Nuts Online - Dried Fruit (Natural Juice Infused ●, Organic ●,
    Simply ●, Sliced ●, Whole ●)
  Publix - Frozen
  Stop & Shop Brand - Yogurt Coated Cranberries
  Trader Joe's - Frozen Sliced Sweetened Cranberries
  Woodstock Farms - Dried Yogurt Covered, Organic Sweetened,
    Sweetened

C Cranberry Sauce
 Albertsons
 Baxters
 Food Club Brand
 Great Value Brand (Wal-Mart) - Jellied, Whole Berry
 Hannaford Brand
 Hy-Vee - Jellied, Whole Berry
 Lowes Foods Brand
 Marzetti - Homestyle
 Ocean Spray - Jellied, Whole Berry
 Publix - Whole
 S&W - All Canned/Jarred Fruits
 Safeway Brand - Jellied, Whole
 Spartan Brand - Jellied, Whole
 Wegmans Brand - Jellied, Whole Berry
 Wild Thymes - Apple Walnut, Fig, Raspberry, Original
 Winn Dixie - Jellied
Cream... see Milk and/or Creamer
Cream Cheese
 Albertsons - Neufchatel, Regular, Spread Light, Whipped
 Breakstone - TempTee Whipped Cream Cheese
 Coburn Farms - Neufchatel, Regular, Spread
 Follow Your Heart - Cream Cheese Alternative
 Great Value Brand (Wal-Mart) - Chive & Onion, Fat Free, Light,
  Regular, Strawberry, Whipped
 Hannaford Brand - 1/3 Less Fat, Fat Free, Neufatchel, Regular
 Horizon Organic - All Varieties
 Hy-Vee - 1/3 Less Fat, Blueberry, Fat Free (Regular, Soft, Strawberry),
  Garden Vegetable, Onion & Chives, Regular, Soft (Light, Regular),
  Strawberry, Whipped
 Kroger Brand - All Varieties
 Lowes Foods Brand - Bar, Neufchatel Bar Less Fat, Soft
  (Light, Regular)
 Lucerne - Soft (Neufchatel, Onion & Chive, Strawberry, Whipped
  Spread), Soft Bars (Fat Free, Garden Vegetable, Light)

C

Nancy's - All Cultured Dairy & Soy Products
Organic Valley - Neufchatel, Regular
Philadelphia Cream Cheese -
    Block (Fat Free, Light, Neufchatel 1/3 Less Fat, Original)
    Cream Swirls (Blueberry, Peaches 'N Cream, Strawberry, Triple
        Berries 'N Cream)
    Tubs
        1/3 Less Fat
        Blueberry
        Chive & Onion (1/3 Less Fat, Regular)
        Fat Free
        Garden Vegetable (1/3 Less Fat, Regular)
        Honey Nut
        Jalapeno Light
        Light
        Pineapple
        Raspberry
        Regular
        Roasted Garlic Light
        Salmon
        Spinach & Artichoke
        Strawberry (1/3 Less Fat, Fat Free, Regular)
        Sundried Tomato & Basil
    Whipped (Cinnamon 'N Brown Sugar, Garlic 'N Herb, Mixed Berry,
        Ranch, Regular, w/Chives)
Publix - Fat Free (All Flavors), Light (All Flavors), Neufchatel, Regular
    (All Flavors), Soft (All Flavors)
Spartan Brand - Bar, Tubs (Lite, Neufchatel, Regular, Strawberry,
    Whipped)
Stop & Shop Brand - Fat Free, Lite (Chive & Onion, Garden
    Vegetable, Honey Walnut, Plain, Strawberry), Neufchatel Cheese
Trader Joe's - All Varieties
Wegmans Brand - Chive & Onion, Fat Free, Honey Nut, Light,
    Neufchatel 1/3 Less Fat, Original, Pineapple, Strawberry, Whipped

C **Cream Puffs**

The Grainless Baker▲ - Cream Puffs

Creamer

Albertsons - Coffee Creamers (All Flavors), Liquid & Powder, Non Dairy Creamer

Coffee-Mate - All Varieties (Liquid, Powder)

Cremora - Non Dairy Creamer (Lite & Creamy, Original)

Food Club Brand -

Non Dairy Coffee Creamer (Fat Free French Vanilla, Fat Free Hazelnut, French Vanilla, Hazelnut, Original)

Powdered (Amaretto, Chocolate, Dulce De Leche, Fat Free, French Vanilla, Hazelnut, Irish Cream, Lite, Regular, Sugar Free (French Vanilla, Hazelnut))

Garelick Farms - Fresh (Half & Half, Light Cream), Ultra Pasteurized (Fat Free Half & Half, Half & Half, Heavy Cream, Light Cream)

Giant Brand - Coffee Cream, Half & Half (Fat Free, Regular), Non Dairy

Giant Eagle Brand - Coffee Cream Light, Half & Half (Fat Free, Regular), Non Dairy Creamer

Gordon Food Service - Half & Half (Aseptic, Regular), Non Dairy Liquid

Great Value Brand (Wal-Mart) - Powdered (Extra Rich, Fat Free, French Vanilla, Hazelnut, Regular), Refrigerated Liquid Ultra Pasteurized

Hannaford Brand - Non Dairy Creamer, Refrigerated

Hood - Country Creamer (Fat Free, Regular)

Horizon Organic - All Varieties

Hy-Vee - Shelf Stable Coffee Creamer (Creamy Chocolate, Fat Free, French Vanilla, Hazelnut, Original, Vanilla Caramel), Refrigerated (French Vanilla, Hazelnut), Refrigerated Fat Free (French Vanilla, Hazelnut)

International Delight - All Varieties

Kroger Brand - Refrigerated

Laura Lynn - Half & Half

Lowes Foods Brand - Non Dairy (Fat Free French Vanilla, French Vanilla, Hazelnut, Lite, Original)

Lucerne - Coffee Creamer French Vanilla (Fat Free, Regular), Original, Powdered, Half & Half, Liquid Creamer (Creme Brule, Hazelnut), Vanilla Caramel

McDaniel's - Enhanced Non Dairy (French Vanilla, Original)

Meijer Brand - Ultra Pasteurized Non Dairy Creamer

Member's Mark - Non Dairy

MimicCreme - Sugar Free Sweetened, Sweetened, Unsweetened

Nestle - Coffee Mate All Varieties (Liquid, Powder)

Prairie Farms - Half & Half (Fat Free, Heavy Whipping, Regular, Ultra Pasteurized, Ultra Pasteurized Heavy Whipping Cream, Whipped Cream Aerosol)

Publix - Liquid Coffee Creamer, Fat Free Non Dairy Creamer, Half & Half (Fat Free, Regular), Powder Non Dairy Creamer (French Vanilla, Lite, Regular)

Shamrock Farms - Fat Free Half & Half (French Vanilla, Regular), Half & Half, Heavy Cream

Silk Soymilk - French Vanilla, Hazelnut, Original

Simply Smart - Half & Half Fat Free

So Delicious - Coconut Milk (French Vanilla ●, Hazelnut ●, Original ●)

Spartan Brand - Coffee Creamer Powdered Non Dairy (French Vanilla, Hazelnut, Lite, Regular, Vanilla Caramel)

Stop & Shop Brand - Fat Free Non Dairy Creamer

Winn Dixie - Half & Half (Fat Free, Regular), Non Dairy Coffee Creamer (Fat Free, Original), Whipping (Heavy, Regular)

Crepes

Pure Market Express▲ - Banana Crepes ●, Maple Apple Crepes ●

Crispbread

Orgran▲ - Crispbread (Corn, Essential Fibre, Rice & Cracked Pepper, Rice & Garden Herb, Salsa Corn, Toasted Buckwheat, Toasted Multigrain)

Riega - Crispbreads (Rice Corn, Tomato Basil)

Schar▲ - Cheese Bites, Crispbread

C Crisps

Baked Lay's - Potato Crisps (Original **!!**, Parmesan And Tuscan Herb **!!**, Sour Cream & Onion **!!**, Southwestern Ranch **!!**)

Baked Ruffles - Potato Crisps (Cheddar & Sour Cream **!!**, Original **!!**)

Brothers All Natural▲ -
Fruit Crisps (Asian Pear, Banana, Fuji Apple, Pineapple, Strawberry, Strawberry Banana, White & Yellow Peach)
Potato Crisps (Black Pepper & Sea Salt, Fresh Onion & Garlic, Original w/Sea Salt, Szechuan Pepper & Fresh Chives)

Full Circle - Barbecue, Ranch, Sea Salt

Glenny's - Soy Crisps (Apple Cinnamon ●, Barbeque ●, Caramel ●, Cheddar ●, Cool Ranch ●, Lightly Salted ●, No Salt Added ●, Olive Oil ●, Onion & Garlic ●, Organic (Barbeque ●, Creamy Ranch ●, Sea Salt ●, White Cheddar ●), Salt & Pepper ●, White Cheddar ●)

Grace Island Specialty Foods▲ - All Varieties

Lay's Stax - Potato Crisps (Cheddar, Mesquite Barbecue, Original, Ranch, Salt & Vinegar, Sour Cream & Onion)

Michael Season's - Baked Potato Crisps (Cheddar & Sour Cream, Original, Sweet Barbecue)

Mr. Krispers - Baked Nut Chips Toasted Almond ●, Baked Rice Krisps (Barbecue ●, Nacho ●, Sea Salt & Pepper ●, Sour Cream & Onion ●, Sun Dried Tomato & Basil ●, White Cheddar & Herbs ●), Multi Seed Chips Original ●, Tasty Snack Crackers Original Sesame ●

Munchos - Regular Potato Crisps **!!**

Orgran▲ - Crispibites (Balsamic Herb, Onion & Chive, Original Corn)

Riceworks - Gourmet Brown Rice Crisps (Baked Cinnamon, Parmesan, Salsa Fresca, Sea Salt, Sweet Chili, Tangy BBQ)

Simplyrice - Organic Brown Rice Crisps (Sea Salt, Spicy Chili, Tangy Tamari)

The Kitchen Table Bakers - All Parmesan Gourmet Wafer Crisps ●

Trader Joe's - Sea Salt & Pepper Rice Crisps

Croutons
Aleia's▲ - Classic ●, Parmesan ●

Gillian's Foods▲ - Garlic Croutons
Miller's Gluten Free Foods▲ - Seasoned
Rose's Bakery▲ - Seasoned
Whole Foods Market Gluten Free Bakehouse▲ - Croutons

Cucumbers
   ... *All Fresh Fruits & Vegetables Are Gluten-Free*

Cupcakes... see also Cake/Cake Mix
Andrea's Fine Foods▲ -
   Chocolate Chunk
   Chocolate Cupcakes (Chocolate Icing, White Icing)
   Mini Cupcakes (Chocolate (Chocolate Icing, White Icing),
      Chocolate Chunk White Icing, Yellow (Casein Free, Casein Free
      White Icing, White Icing))
   Yellow Cupcakes (Casein Free, Chocolate Icing, White Icing)
Crave Bakery▲ - Chocolate, Confetti, Vanilla
Heaven Mills▲ - Sprinkled ●

Curry Paste
A Taste Of Thai - Curry Paste (Green, Panang, Red, Yellow)
Sharwood's - Green Curry Paste, Red Curry Sauce, Thai Yellow
   Curry Sauce
Thai Kitchen - Curry Paste (Green, Red, Roasted Red Chili)

Curry Powder... see also Seasonings
Durkee
McCormick
Tones

D

Dates
Gluty Free - Coconut Dates ●, Dried Medjool ●, Organic (Dried
   Medjool ●, Dried Pitted ●), Pitted ●
Nuts Online - Dried Fruit (Jumbo Medjool ●, Organic Medjool ●,
   Organic Pitted ●, Pitted ●)

D Deli Meat

Applegate Farms -

Natural (Black Forest Ham, Coppa, Genoa Salami, Herb Turkey, Honey & Maple Turkey Breast, Honey Ham, Hot Genoa Salami, Hot Soppressata, Pancetta, Pepperoni, Roast Beef, Roasted Turkey, Slow Cooked Ham, Smoked Turkey Breast, Soppressata, Turkey Bologna, Turkey Salami)

Organic (Genoa Salami, Herb Turkey Breast, Roast Beef, Roasted Chicken, Smoked Chicken, Smoked Turkey Breast, Uncured Ham)

Armour -

Beef (Corned Beef, Italian Style Roast Beef, Pastrami, Roast Beef)

Bologna (Beef, Meat)

Ham (Cooked, Cooked Ham & Water Product, Honey Cured, Lite, Spiced Luncheon Meat, Virginia Brand)

Sandwich Style Pepperoni

Turkey (Oven Roasted, Oven Roasted w/Broth, Smoked)

Boar's Head - All Varieties

Busseto - Bresaola, Coppa (Dry, Hot), Dry Salami (Black Pepper, Italian, Rosette De Lyon), Herbs De Providence, Pancetta, Pepper Coated Salami, Premium Genoa Salami, Prosciutto

Butcher's Cut - Beef Bologna, Deli Sliced Smoked Ham, Deli Style Roast Beef, Value Red Meat Bologna

Butterball -

Extra Thin Sliced Deep Fried Turkey Breast (Buttery Herb, Cajun Style, Original, Thanksgiving Style)

Extra Thin Turkey Breast (Honey Roasted, Oven Roasted, Rotisserie Seasoned, Smoked)

Lean Family Size (Honey Roasted Turkey Breast, Oven Roasted Turkey Breast, Smoked Turkey Breast, Turkey Bologna, Turkey Ham)

Thick Sliced Deep Fried Turkey Breast (Cajun Style, Original, Thanksgiving Style)

Thin Sliced Oven Roasted Chicken Breast

Thin Sliced Turkey Breast (Honey Roasted, Oven Roasted, Rotisserie Seasoned, Smoked)

Carl Buddig -
Deli Cuts (Baked Honey Ham, Brown Sugar Baked Ham, Honey Roasted Turkey, Oven Roasted Turkey, Pastrami, Roast Beef, Rotisserie Chicken, Smoked Ham, Smoked Turkey)
Extra Thin Original (Beef, Brown Sugar Ham, Chicken, Corned Beef, Ham, Honey Ham, Honey Roasted Turkey, Mesquite Turkey, Oven Roasted Turkey, Pastrami, Turkey)
Original (Beef, Brown Sugar Ham, Chicken, Corned Beef, Ham, Honey Ham, Honey Roasted Turkey, Mesquite Turkey, Oven Roasted Turkey, Pastrami, Turkey)

Castle Wood Reserve - Angus Corned Beef, Angus Roast Beef, Black Forest Ham, Genoa Salami, Hard Salami, Herb Roasted Turkey, Hickory Smoked Turkey, Honey Ham, Oven Roasted Chicken, Oven Roasted Turkey, Smoked Ham, Turkey Pastrami, Virginia Brand Smoked Ham

Columbus Salame - All Varieties

Dietz & Watson ▲ -
Beef (London Broil Roast Beef ●, Premium Homestyle Roast Beef ●, Spiced Pastrami ●)
Black Forest Smoked Turkey ●
Bologna (Beef ●, Regular ●)
Capocollo (Hot ●, Sweet ●)
Chicken (Buffalo Style ●, Southern Fried ●)
Ham (Black Forest Smoked ●, Capacolla ●, Cooked ●, Gourmet Lite Cooked ●, Smoked Maple ●, Tavern ●, Virginia Brand ●)
Liverwurst ●
Mortadella ●
P&P Loaf ●
Pancetta ●
Prosciutto ●
Salami (Cooked ●, Genoa ●)
Sopressata ●

D   Eckrich -
    Deli Counter
      Bologna (Beef, Fried, Garlic, Low Sodium, Meat)
      Chicken Fried Chicken Breast
      Corned Beef Cooked
      Ham (Black Forest Brand Nugget, Brown Sugar Nugget,
         Canadian Maple, Chopped, Ham Steak, Honey Cured,
         Honey Maple, Imported, Lite, Off The Bone, Smoked Pitt,
         Spiced Luncheon Meat, Spiral Sliced Holiday, Virginia Baked)
      Loaf (Braunschweiger, Head Cheese, Honey, Jalapeno, Minced
         Luncheon, Old Fashioned, Olive, Peppered, Pickle & Pimento,
         Souse)
      Pastrami Regular
      Pepperoni Regular
      Regular Summer Sausage
      Roast Beef (Black Angus, Choice Top, Italian, Lite, Seasoned)
      Salami (Cotto, Genoa, Hard, Reduced Fat Hard)
      Turkey (Fried Skinless, Mesquite Smoked, Oven Roasted,
         Smoked Pitt)
    Lunch Meat
      Bologna (Beef, Lite, Meat, Ring Bologna)
      Ham (Chopped, Cooked, Virginia Brand Thin Sliced)
      Loaf (Ham & Cheese, Honey, Old Fashioned, Olive, Pickle)
      Pepperoni Regular
      Salami (Cotto Salami, Hard Salami)
  Fairgrounds - Honey Ham, Premium Ham (Chopped, Cooked)
  Farmer John - Lunch Meats (Brown Sugar & Honey Ham, Lower
    Sodium Sliced Ham, Premium Oven Roasted Turkey Breast, Sliced
    Ham, Sliced Turkey)
  Giant Brand - 97% Fat Free Cooked Ham, Turkey (97% Fat Free
    Honey, 97% Fat Free Oven Roasted, Smoked)
  Gordon Food Service - Sliced Turkey Breast (Regular, Smoked)
  Great Value Brand (Wal-Mart) -
    97% Fat Free (Baked Ham Water Added, Cooked Ham, Honey
    Ham Water Added)

Fat Free (Smoked Turkey Breast, Turkey Breast)
Thinly Sliced (Honey Turkey, Mesquite Smoked Turkey Breast,
    Oven Roasted Turkey, Smoked Ham, Smoked Honey Ham)
Hannaford Brand - Sliced (Cooked Ham, Danish Brand Ham,
    Honey Ham, Oven Roasted Turkey), Thin Sliced (Black Forest
    Turkey Breast, Honey Cured Turkey Breast, Honey Ham, Oven
    Roasted Turkey, Roast Beef)

Hillshire Farms -
    Deli Select
        Baked Ham
        Brown Sugar Baked Ham
        Corned Beef
        Honey (Ham, Roasted Turkey Breast)
        Mesquite Smoked Turkey Breast
        Oven Roasted (Chicken Breast, Turkey Breast)
        Roast Beef
        Smoked (Chicken Breast, Ham, Turkey Breast)
    Deli Select Premium Hearty Slices
        Honey (Ham, Roasted Turkey)
        Oven Roasted Turkey Breast
        Virginia Brand Baked Ham
    Deli Select Ultra Thin
        Brown Sugar Baked Ham
        Hard Salami
        Honey (Ham, Roasted Turkey Breast)
        Mesquite Smoked Turkey
        Oven Roasted Turkey Breast
        Pastrami
        Roast Beef
        Smoked Ham

Honeysuckle White -
    Chicken Breast (BBQ, Buffalo Style, Oil Browned)
    Lunch Meats Deli Sliced
        Hickory Smoked Turkey Breast (Honey, Regular)

Oven Roasted Turkey Breast
Turkey Pastrami
Turkey Bologna
Turkey Breast Deli Meats
  Cajun Style Hickory Smoked
  Golden Roasted
  Hickory Smoked (Original, Pastrami, Peppered)
  Honey Mesquite Smoked
  Oil Browned
  Original Rotisserie
  Oven Prepared
Turkey Breast Estate Recipe
  Buffalo Style
  Canadian Brand Maple
  Dry Roasted
  Hickory Smoked (Honey Pepper, Original, Sun Dried Tomato)
  Honey Smoked
  Mesquite Smoked
  Turkey Ham
Hormel -
  Bread Ready
    Cooked Pastrami
    Corned Beef
    Ham
    Hard Salami
    Honey Ham
    Oven Roasted Turkey Breast
    Prosciutto Ham
    Roast Beef
    Smoked Ham
    Smoked Turkey Breast
  Natural Choice
    Cooked Deli Ham
    Deli Counter (Cherrywood Ham, Cooked Ham, Corned

Beef, Honey Mesquite Turkey Breast, Medium Roast Beef,
Oil Browned Turkey Breast, Oven Roasted Turkey Breast,
Pastrami, Rare Roast Beef, Smoked Ham)
Hard Salami
Honey Deli (Ham, Turkey)
Pepperoni
Roast Beef
Smoked Deli (Ham, Turkey)
Hy-Vee - Loaf (Pickle, Spiced Luncheon), Luncheon Meat
Jennie-O Turkey Store -
Deli Chicken Breast (Buffalo Style, Mesquite Smoked, Oven
Roasted)
Grand Champion Turkey Breast (Hickory Smoked, Homestyle Pan
Roasted, Honey Cured, Mesquite Smoked, Oven Roasted,
Tender Browned)
Hickory Smoked Turkey Breast (Cracked Pepper, Garlic Pesto,
Honey Cured, Sun Dried Tomato)
Natural Choice Turkey Breast (Oven Roasted, Peppered, Tender
Browned)
Northwestern Turkey (Hickory Smoked, Oven Roasted)
Smoked Turkey Breast (Hickory, Honey Cured, Mesquite)
Turkey Breast (Apple Cinnamon, Garlic Peppered, Honey (Maple,
Mesquite), Hot Red Peppered, Italian Style, Maple Spiced,
Mesquite Smoked, Oven Roasted, Peppered, Smoked
(Peppered, Regular), Tender Browned, Tomato Basil)
Turkey Store Oven Roasted Turkey Breast
Kayem -
Bologna (Beef, German Style, Large, Original)
Extra Lean Corned Beef
Ham (Amber Honey Cured, Black Forest, Carving, Honeycrust,
Olde English Tavern, Peppercrust)
Old World Liverwurst
Olive Loaf
Pastrami (Extra Lean Black, New England Red, New York Style
Black)

D

Peppercrust Loaf

Pickle & Pepper Loaf

Roast Beef (Classic, Seasoned Garlic Oven Roasted, Seasoned Original Oven Roasted)

Turkey (Buffalo Style Breast, Homestyle Breast, Homestyle Breast w/Skin On)

Kirkland Signature - Ham (Extra Lean, Smoked Honey), Oven Roasted Turkey Breast

Kroger Brand -

Deli Style (Chicken, Honey Smoked Turkey, Smoked Ham, Smoked Turkey)

Fat Free (Honey Ham, Oven Roasted White Turkey, Smoked Ham)

Honey Turkey Breast Fat Free

Lean Sliced (Pastrami, Turkey)

Luncheon Canned

Oven Roasted White Turkey

Thin Sliced (Honey Ham, Honey Turkey, Mesquite Smoked Turkey, Oven Roasted Turkey, Roast Beef, Smoked Ham)

Kroger Value - Deli Shaved (Ham, Turkey), Ham (Chopped, Cooked, Honey, Turkey), Turkey (Ham, White)

Nature's Promise - All Varieties

Norwestern Deli Turkey - Hickory Smoked, Oven Roasted

Oscar Mayer -

Baked Cooked Ham

Boiled Ham

Bologna (All Varieties)

Chopped Ham

Deli Fresh Meats

Cooked Ham, Honey Ham, Oven Roasted (98% Fat Free Turkey, Chicken Breast, Turkey Breast), Smoked Turkey Breast, Smoked Ham)

Honey Ham

Lean White Honey Smoked Turkey

Oven Roasted White Turkey
Shaved Deli Fresh Meats
  Black Forest Ham
  Brown Sugar Ham
  Cajun Seasoned Chicken Breast
  Cracked Black Peppered Turkey Breast
  French Dip Roast Beef
  Honey Ham
  Honey Smoked Turkey Breast
  Mesquite Turkey Breast
  Oven Roasted Turkey Breast
  Rotisserie Style Chicken Breast
  Slow Roasted Roast Beef
  Smoked Ham
  Smoked Turkey Breast
  Virginia Brand Ham
Smoked Ham
Smoked White Turkey
Thin Sliced Deli Fresh
  Brown Sugar Ham
  Honey Smoked Turkey Breast
  Mesquite Turkey Breast
  Oven Roasted Chicken Breast
  Oven Roasted Turkey Breast
  Smoked Ham
  Smoked Turkey Breast

Perdue -
Deli Dark Turkey Pastrami Hickory Smoked, Deli Pick Ups
  Sliced Turkey (Golden Browned, Honey Smoked, Mesquite
  Smoked, Oven Roasted, Smoked)
Deli Pick Ups Sliced Turkey Ham Honey Smoked
Deli Turkey (Bologna, Breast Oil Browned, Ham Hickory Smoked,
  Salami)
Sliced Chicken Breast Oil Fried

D

Primo Naturale - Sliced (Dried Pepperoni, Original Salami, Premium Genoa Salami, Salami w/Black Pepper, Salami w/Herbs, Sopressata)

Primo Taglio -
Black Forest Ham w/Natural Juices Coated w/Caramel Color
Cervelat Salami
Chicken Breast Oven Roasted Browned In Hot Cottons
Cooked Corned Beef
Genoa Salami
Maple Ham Old Fashioned w/Natural Juices
Mortadella Black Pepper Added
Pancetta
Pastrami Coated w/Spices Caramel Color Added
Prosciutto Dry Cured Ham
Roast Beef Coated w/Seasonings Caramel Color Added
Salami Coated w/Gelatin & Black Pepper
Sopressata
Turkey Breast w/Natural Smoke Flavoring

Publix -
Deli Pre Pack Sliced Lunch Meat (Beef Bottom Round Roast, Cooked Ham, Extra Thin Sliced (Honey Ham, Oven Roasted Turkey Breast, Smoked Turkey Breast), German Bologna, Hard Salami (Genoa, Reduced Fat), Hickory Smoked Maple Ham, Low Salt Ham, Smoked Turkey, Sweet Ham, Tavern Ham, Turkey Breast)

Sara Lee -
Deli Slices
Brown Sugar Ham
Cooked Ham
Cracked Pepper Turkey Breast
Hardwood Smoked Turkey Breast
Hickory Smoked Ham
Honey Ham
Honey Roasted Turkey Breast

>>> Oven Roasted Chicken Breast
Oven Roasted Turkey Breast
Roast Beef
Virginia Brand Baked Ham

Smithfield - Ham (Black Forest, Brown Sugar, Chopped, Cooked, Turkey, Virginia Brand), Turkey Breast (Mesquite, Oven Roasted, Smoked)

Thumann's - All Varieties ●

Trader Joe's - Oven Roasted Turkey Breast, Sliced Prosciutto, Smoked Turkey Breast

Wegmans Brand - Chicken Breast Cutlets (Honey Mustard, Italian, Rosemary Balsamic Tangy), Corned Beef w/Juices, Pork Tenderloin Honey Mustard, Turkey Breast No Salt, Turkey Oven Browned

Winn Dixie - All Varieties *(Except Ham & Cheese Loaf)*, Thin Sliced All Varieties *(Except Chicken & Corned Beef)*

Dill Pickles... see Pickles
Dinner Meals... see Meals
Dip/Dip Mix

Andrea's Fine Foods▲ - Spinach Artichoke

Cabot - Bacon Horseradish, French Onion, Garden Veggie, Ranch, Salsa Grande

Cedarlane - 5 Layer Mexican Dip

Cheez Wiz - Cheese Dip Original

Coburn Farms - French Onion Dip

Cool Whip - Dips (Chocolate, Strawberry Creme)

Country Crossings - Microwavable Cheese Dip

Eat Smart - Naturals (Salsa Con Queso, Tres Bean Dip)

Emeril's - Classic Onion, Kicked Up Guacamole, Veggie Ranch

Fantastic World Foods - Original Hummus

Food Club Brand - French Onion Dip (Regular, w/Bacon), Original Bean Dip, Ranch Dip, Salsa Con Queso

Fritos - Bean Dip**!!**, Chili Cheese Dip**!!**, Hot Bean Dip**!!**, Jalapeno & Cheddar Cheese Dip**!!**, Mild Cheddar Cheese Dip**!!**

D

Frontera - Guacamole Mix

Giant Brand - Dip (French Onion, Ranch, Refrigerated Veggie, Spinach Artichoke & Cheese)

Gordon Food Service - Honey Mustard Dip Cup

Great Value Brand (Wal-Mart) - French Onion, Jalapeno Mexican Style Queso Dip, Ranch Chip, White Salsa Con Queso

Hannaford Brand - French Onion Dip, Italian Dressing Mix, Ranch Dip, Ranch Dip Mix

Herr's - Bean, Jalapeno Cheddar, Mild Cheddar

Hy-Vee - Bacon & Cheddar, Dill Vegetable, French Onion, Fruit Dip, Ranch & Dill, Salsa, Toasted Onion, Vegetable Party

Kemps - French Onion, Ranch Style

Kroger Brand - Bean Dip (Black Bean, Chipotle), Green Onion, Party Dip Ranch, Ranch, Salad Magic (Ranch, Zesty Italian), Spinach, Viva Con Queso (Monterey Jack & Salsa, Salsa & Cheese)

Lay's - French Onion Dip**!!**, Smooth Ranch Dip**!!**

Litehouse - Avocado, Chocolate (Caramel, Yogurt Fruit), Cinnamon Caramel, Cream Cheese Alternative, Dilly Dip (Lite, Regular), French Onion, Garden Veggie Ranch, Lite Ranch, Low Fat Caramel, Original Caramel, Ranch, Ranch Veggie Dippers, Southwest Ranch, Strawberry Yogurt Fruit, Vanilla Yogurt Fruit

Lowes Foods Brand - French Onion, Ranch

Marzetti -

Blue Cheese

Caramel Apple (Cinnamon Caramel, Fat Free, Light, Old Fashioned, Peanut Butter)

Chocolate Fruit

Cream Cheese Fruit (Regular, Strawberry)

Dill (Fat Free, Light, Regular)

French Onion (Light, Regular)

French Vanilla Yogurt Fruit Light

Guacamole

Horseradish

Ranch (Celery & Carrot Dip, Fat Free, Light, Organic, Regular)

Spinach

D

McCormick - Dip Mix Ranch

Mixes From The Heartland▲ - Dessert Dip Mix (Black Raspberry●, Cantaloupe ●, Key Lime ●, Lemon ●, Orange ●, Pumpkin Pie●, Raspberry ●, Strawberry ●), Snack Dip Mix (Cucumber ●, Cucumber Dill ●, Dilly ●, Fiesta ●, Garlic Roasted Pepper ●, Garlic Sun Dried Tomato ●, Green Chili Veggie ●, Italian Veggie ●, Spinach & Chives ●, Veggie ●)

On The Border - Bean, Golden Cheddar Queso, Monterey Jack Queso, Monterey White Salsa Con Queso, Salsa Con Queso

Ortega - Salsa Con Queso

Pace - Salsa Dip (Medium, Mild)

Prairie Farms - Bacon Cheddar, French Onion, Jalapeño Fiesta Dip, Ranch

Publix - French Onion, Green Onion, Guacamole

Road's End Organics - Non Dairy Nacho Chreese Dip (Mild, Spicy)

Salpica - Dip (Chipotle Black Bean, Cowboy Red Bean, Cowboy White Bean, Salsa Con Queso)

Santa Barbara - Five Layer Dip

Scarpetta - Spreads (Artichoke & Olive, Asparagus, Olive & Almond, Red Pepper & Eggplant, Spicy Red Pepper)

Sharwood's - Green Label Mango Chutney & Chilli

Spartan Brand - Dip (French Onion, Ranch)

Stop & Shop Brand - Refrigerated (Artichoke & Cheese, French Onion, Ranch, Spinach, Veggie)

Taco Bell - Black Bean Con Queso, Chili Con Queso w/Beef, Salsa Con Queso (Medium, Mild)

Tostitos - Creamy Southwestern Ranch Dip**!!**, Creamy Spinach Dip**!!**, Monterey Jack Queso**!!**, Salsa Con Queso Dip**!!**, Smooth & Cheesy Dip**!!**, Zesty Bean & Cheese Dip**!!**

Trader Joe's - Blue Cheese w/Roasted Pecan, Cilantro & Chive Yogurt, Fat Free Spicy Black Bean, Guacamole (Avocado's Number, w/Spicy Pico de Gallo**!!**), Queso Cheese Dip**!**, Spinach

UTZ - Cheddar & Jalapeno, Mild Cheddar Cheese, Mt. Misery Mike's Salsa Dip, Sweet Salsa Dip

D

Walden Farms - Fruit Dip (Caramel, Chocolate, Marshmallow), Veggie & Chip Dip (Bacon, Blue Cheese, French Onion, Ranch)

Wegmans Brand - Dill, French Onion, French Onion Light, Ranch, Salsa Con Queso Cheddar Cheese Dip, Veggies & Dip

Wise - French Onion *(Jar Only)*, Ranch, Salsa Con Queso

Donuts/Doughnuts

Celiac Specialties▲ -

Donuts (Chocolate, Coconut)

Donut Holes (Cinnamon Sugar, Glazed, Plain, Powder Sugar)

Donuts (Cinnamon Sugar, Glazed, Plain, Powder Sugar)

Mini Donuts (Cinnamon Sugar, Plain, Powder Sugar)

Ener-G▲ - Chocolate Iced Doughnuts, Plain Doughnut (Holes, Regular)

Gluten-Free Creations▲ - Chocolate Marble ●, Chocolate ●, Cinnamon & Sugar ●, Insane Chocolate ●, Plain Jane ●, Superb Sprinkles ●

Glutino▲ - Glazed (Chocolate, Original)

Grandma Ferdon's▲ - Donut Holes ●, Plain ●

Kinnikinnick▲ - Chocolate Dipped, Cinnamon Sugar, Maple Dipped, Pumpkin Spice, Vanilla Glazed

Pure Market Express▲ - Donut Holes ●

Dressing... see Salad Dressing and/or Stuffing

Dried Fruit

Bare Fruit - Bananas, Bananas & Cherries, Cherries, Cinnamon Apple, Fuji Apple, Granny Smith Apple, Mangos, Pears, Pineapple & Mangos, Pineapples

Brothers All Natural▲ - Fruit Crisps (Asian Pear, Banana, Fuji Apple, Pineapple, Strawberry, Strawberry Banana, White & Yellow Peach)

Dole - All Dried Fruit *(Except Real Fruit Bites)*

Earthbound Farm - Cranberries, Dates, Mangos, Plums, Premium Jumbo Raisins, Thompson Seedless Raisin Mini Packs, Thompson Seedless Raisins

Eden Organic - Cranberries, Montmorency Dried Tart Cherries, Wild Blueberries

Fairfield Farms - Prunes, Raisins

Food Club Brand - Prunes Pitted

Fruit Advantage - Blueberries, Organic Blueberries, Premium Dried Cherries, Red Raspberries, Strawberries

Gluty Free - Apples ●, Bing Cherries ●, Blackberries ●, Blueberries ●, California Apricots ●, California Figs ●, Cantaloupe ●, Cantaloupe Chunks ●, Cinnamon Apples ●, Cranberries ●, Currants ●, Diced (Apricots ●, Mango ●, Papaya ●, Pineapple ●), Dried Nectarines●, Freeze Dried (Bananas ●, Blueberries ●, Fruit Cocktail ●, Strawberries ●), Goji Berries ●, Guava ●, Juice Infused Blueberries●, Kiwi ●, Mango ●, Medjool Dates ●, Mission Figs ●, Mulberries●, Natural Papaya ●, Natural Pineapple ●, Organic (Apples ●, California Figs ●, Cranberries ●, Goji Berries ●, Mango ●, Medjool Dates ●, Mission Figs ●, Persimmons ●, Pineapple ●, Pitted Dates●, Pitted Prunes ●, Strawberries ●, Turkish Apricots ●, Turkish Figs ●, Wild Blueberries ●), Papaya Chunks ●, Papaya ●, Peaches ●, Pears●, Persimmons ●, Pineapple ●, Pluots ●, Rainier Cherries ●, Red Raspberries ●, Sour Cherries ●, Star Fruit ●, Strawberries ●, Sun Dried Tomatoes ●, Turkish Apricots ●, Turkish Figs ●, Unsulphured Mango ●, White Peaches ●

Great Value Brand (Wal-Mart) - 100% Natural California Sun Dried Raisins, Pitted Prunes

Hy-Vee - Apples, Apricots, Banana Chips, Blueberries, Cherries, Cranberries, Mixed (Berries, Fruit), Pineapple

Member's Mark - Mediterranean Dried Apricots

Mrs. May's Naturals - All Varieties ●

NoNuttin' Foods▲ - Cherry Fruit Snacks ●, Sulfite Free Dried Apples●

Nuts Online -
  Apple (Cinnamon Wedges ●, Infused Dried Wedges ●, Organic Chips ●)
  Apples (Diced Fuji ●, Dried ●, Organic Dried ●, Simply Organic ●)
  Apricots (California ●, Diced ●, Dried ●, Organic California ●, Organic Turkish ●)

D

Banana (Chips ●, Organic Chips ●), Bananas (Organic Simply ●, Simply ●)

Blackberries ●

Blueberries (Dried ●, Natural Dried ●, Natural Dried Juice Infused●, Organic Wild ●, Simply ●)

Cantaloupe (Dried ●, Dried Chunks ●)

Cherries (Bing ●, Organic Bing ●, Rainier ●, Simply ●, Sour Tart ●)

Cranberries (Natural Juice Infused ●, Organic ●, Simply ●, Sliced ●, Whole Dried ●)

Currants ●

Dates (Jumbo Medjool ●, Organic Medjool ●, Organic Pitted ●, Pitted ●)

Diced Fruit Medley ●

Figs (California ●, Diced ●, Mission ●, Organic California ●, Organic Calimyrna ●, Organic Mission ●, Organic Turkish ●, Turkish ●)

Fruit Chips ●

Ginger (Crystallized ●, Organic Crystallized ●)

Goji Berries ●

Guava ●

Kiwi ●

Lemons ●

Mango Dried (Diced ●, Less Sugar Added ●, Organic ●, Regular ●)

Mulberries ●

Nectarines (Dried ●, Natural ●, Organic ●, White ●)

Organic Dried Oranges ●

Organic Goji Berries ●

Organic Lucuma Slices ●

Papaya Dried Diced ●

Peaches (Diced ●, Dried ●, Natural ●, Organic ●, Simply ●, White ●)

Pears (Diced ●, Dried ●, Natural ●, Organic ●, Simply ●)

Persimmons (Dried ●, Organic ●)

Pineapple Dried (Chunks ●, Diced ●, Regular ●)

Plums Angelino ●

Pluots ●

Raisins (Crimson ●, Dark ●, Jumbo (Flame ●, Golden ●, Golden Flame ●, Thompson Seedless ●), Midget ●, Organic (Dark Chocolate Covered ●, Milk Chocolate Covered ●), Organic ●)
Raspberries (Dried Red ●, Organic Red ●, Simply ●)
Simply Black Currants ●, Blackberries ●, Boysenberries ●, Elderberries ●, Fruit Cocktail ●, Grapes ●, Pomegranates ●)
Strawberries (Dried ●, Natural Dried Juice Infused ●, Organic ●, Organic Simply ●, Simply ●, Simply Whole ●)
Strawberry Rhubarb ●
Tomatoes (Julienne ●, Sun Dried (Organic ●, Regular ●, w/Olive Oil●))
Oskri Organics - *3.5 oz Bags Only* (Apricots, Blueberries, Cherries, Cranberries, Dates, Figs, Golden Raisins, Prunes, Strawberries)
Publix - Dried Plums
Safeway Brand - Berries & Cherries, Cranberries, Island Inspirations, Raisins
Sensible Foods - Apple Harvest, Cherry Berry, Orchard Blend, Tropical Blend
Shiloh Farms - Cranberries!!, Pitted Prunes!!, Turkish Apricots!!, Wild Blueberries!!
Spartan Brand - Cranberries, Pitted Prunes, Raisins
Sun-Maid - Raisins (Baking, Golden, Natural California, Regular), Zante Currants
thinkFruit - Dried Fruit Snacks (Blueberries, Cherry, Cinnamon Apple, Cranberries, Peaches, Pineapple Tidbits)
Trader Joe's - Roasted Plantain Chips
Wegmans Brand - Dried (Apricots, Cherries, Cranberries, Philippine Mango, Pitted Prunes, Tropical Pineapple, Wild Blueberries), Seedless Raisins
Wild Garden - Apricots, Mango, Pineapple
Woodstock Farms -
   Apple Rings (Organic, Unsulphured)
   Apricots Turkish
   Banana Chips (Organic, Sweetened)

D

Blueberries
Calmyrna Figs
Cherries Unsulphured
Cranberries (Sweetened, Yogurt Covered)
Dates Deglet w/Pit
Ginger (Organic Crystalized w/Raw Sugar, Slices Unsulphured)
Goji Berries
Mango Diced
   Slices (Regular, Unsulphured)
Organic Black Mission Figs
Organic California Medjool Dates w/Pit
Organic Kiwi Slices
Organic Pitted Prunes
Organic Raisins (Flame!, Jumbo Thompson, Select Thompson, Thompson)
Papaya Spears Lo Sugar Unsulphered
Pineapple Slices Unsulphered
Thompson Raisins

Drink Mix

Cera - CeraLyte (50 ●, 70 ●, 90 ●), CeraSport (All Varieties) ●, CeraSport EXI (All Varieties) ●

Country Time - All Flavors

Crystal Light -

Decaf Iced Tea (Lemon, Regular)
Enhanced (Energy Wild Strawberry, Fiber Raspberry Peach, Focus Citrus Splash, Hunger Satisfaction Strawberry Banana, Immunity Natural Cherry Pomegranate, Metabolism Green Tea Peach Mango)
Iced Tea (Green Tea Honey Lemon, Green Tea Peach Mango, Green Tea Raspberry, Peach, Raspberry, Regular)
Pure Fitness (Grape, Lemon Lime, Strawberry Kiwi)
Refreshment (Cranberry Apple, Fruit Punch, Lemonade, Pink Lemonade, Raspberry Ice, Raspberry Lemonade, Strawberry Kiwi, Strawberry Orange Banana, White Grape)

Skin Essentials (Pomegranate, White Peach Tea)
Sunrise (Classic Orange, Ruby Red Grapefruit, Tangerine
Strawberry)

Flavor Aid - Powdered Soft Drinks

Food Club Brand - Drink Mixes (Cherry, Grape, Lemonade,
Orange, Tropical Punch), Drink Stix (Iced Tea, Lemonade, Peach
Tea, Raspberry Ice), Iced Tea Mix

Giant Brand - Powdered Drink Mix (Cherry, Grape, Iced Tea,
Lemonade (Pink, Regular), Orange, Strawberry, Sugar Free (Fruit
Punch, Iced Tea, Lemon Lime, Lemonade), Tropical Punch)

Hannaford Brand - Regular (Cherry, Fruit Punch, Lemonade,
Orange, Strawberry), Sugar Free (Fruit Punch, Iced Tea, Lemon
Lime, Lemonade, Raspberry Lemonade)

Hawaiian Punch - All Varieties

Hy-Vee - Splash Drink Mix (Cherry, Grape, Lemonade, Orange,
Raspberry, Strawberry, Tropical, Tropical Fruit Punch), Sugar
Free Splash Drink Mix (Fruit Punch, Iced Tea, Lemonade, Pink
Lemonade, Raspberry)

Kool-Aid - Fun Fizz (All Varieties), Soft Drink Mix Sugar Free (All
Varieties), Soft Drink Mix Sugar Sweetened (All Varieties), Soft
Drink Mix Unsweetened (All Varieties)

Meijer Brand - Breakfast Orange, Cherry, Chocolate Flavor, Grape,
Ice Tea Lemon Sugar Free, Lemonade, Lemonade Stix, Orange
(Free & Lite, Regular), Pink Lemonade (Regular, Sugar Free), Punch,
Raspberry Stix, Raspberry Sugar Free, Strawberry (Flavor, Regular),
Strawberry/Orange/Banana

Nestea - Instant Iced Tea Mix (Sweetened Lemonade Flavored,
Sweetened w/Lemon, Unsweetened Decaf, Unsweetened
Regular)

Safeway Brand - Cherry (Light, Regular), Instant Chocolate, Peach
(Light, Regular), Pink (Light, Regular), Spiced Apple Cider,
Strawberry (Light, Regular), Sugar Free Raspberry & Lemonade

Spartan Brand - Cherry, Fruit Punch, Lemonade, Pink Lemonade,
Raspberry

D

Splash Out - Fruit Punch, Lemonade

Wegmans Brand - Powdered Drink Mix (Lemonade Flavor,
Pink Lemonade)

Winn Dixie - Regular (Cherry, Fruit Punch, Grape, Lemonade,
Orange, Pink Lemonade, Raspberry, Strawberry Kiwi), Sugar Free
(Fruit Punch, Lemon Iced Tea, Lemonade, Peach Iced Tea, Pink
Lemonade)

Wyler's - Powdered Soft Drinks (Light, Regular, Sugar Free)

Drinks/Juice (Non-Carbonated)

... (Carbonated Drinks... see Soda Pop/Carbonated Beverages)

Adina - Barista Brews (Double XXPresso, Mocha Madness), Holistics
(Blackberry Hibiscus w/Rooibos ●, Coconut Guava w/Lychee●,
Cranberry Grapefruit w/Goji ●, Jade Green Tea w/Tulsi ●,
Mango Orange w/Chamomile ●, Passion Peach w/Amalaki ●,
Pomegranate Acai w/Yumberry ●), Organic Coffees (Ethiopian
Espresso, Indian Chai Latte, Mayan Mocha, Sumatran Vanilla Latte)

Albertsons - All 100% Juices

Apple & Eve - All Products

Bionaturae - Organic (Apple, Apricot, Bilberry, Carrot Apple, Peach,
Pear, Plum, Sicilian Lemon, Sour Cherry, Strawberry, Wildberry)

Bragg - Organic Apple Cider Vinegar Drink (Apple Cinnamon,
Concord Grape Acai, Ginger Spice, Vinegar & Honey)

Calistoga - Sparkling Juice Beverages (All Flavors)

Campbell's - Tomato Juice (Healthy Request, Low Sodium,
Organic, Original)

Capri Sun - All Flavors

Ceres - All Varieties

Cott - All Varieties

Country Time - Lemonade

Crystal Geyser - All Juice Squeeze Flavors, All Tejava Flavors

Dei Fratelli - Juice Tomato (Regular, Tasty Tom Spicy), Vegetable

Diane's Garden - Tomato Juice, Vegetable

Dole - All Fruit Juice

Earthbound Farm - Carrot

Eden Organic - Apple Juice, Cherry Concentrate, Concord Grape, Montmorency Tart Cherry Juice

Enviga - Sparkling Green Tea (Berry, Regular)

Food Club Brand -

Canned Juice

Unsweetened (Grapefruit, Orange, Pink Grapefruit)

Frozen Juice

Concentrate 100% Grape

Apple,

Fruit Punch

Grapefruit

Lemonade

Orange Juice (High Pulp, Original, Pulp Free, w/Calcium)

Pink Lemonade

Juice

Apple

Cranberry (Apple, Blend, Cocktail, Light, Raspberry, White Cocktail, White Peach, White Strawberry)

Cranberry Grape (Light, Regular)

Fruit Punch

Grape

Grapefruit

Grapefruit & Tangerine

Kiwi Strawberry

Lemon

Lime

Pineapple

Pomegranate (Blueberry, Original)

Prune

Ruby Red Grapefruit

Tomato (Clam, Regular)

Vegetable

White Grape

D

Juice A Lot (Berry, Cherry, Punch)

Lemonade

Refrigerated

Orange Juice (From Concentrate, Groves Best, Premium, Pulp Added, w/Calcium)

Premium Grapefruit Juice

Tea

Thirst Quenchers (Berry Rain Type, Fruit Punch, Glacial Chill, Lemon Lime, Orange)

Fruit Advantage - Juice Concentrates (All Varieties)

Fruit2O - All Varieties

Full Circle - Organic (Apple, Blueberry Juice, Cranberry Cocktail, Cranberry Red Raspberry, Grape, Tomato Juice, Vegetable Juice)

Fuze -

Empower (Goji Wild Berry, Pomegranate Acai Berry)

Refresh (Banana Colada, Peach Mango, Strawberry Banana, Strawberry Guava)

Slenderize (Blueberry Raspberry, Cranberry Raspberry, Dragonfruit Lime, Strawberry Melon, Tangerine Grapefruit, Tropical Punch)

Tea (Black & Green Tea, Diet Green Tea w/Orange Ginger, Diet White Tea w/Pomegranate, Green Tea w/Honey, White Tea Agave Gogi Berry)

Vitalize (Blackberry Grape, Fruit Punch, Orange Mango)

Garelick Farms - Chug (Apple Juice, Fruit Punch, Lemonade, Orange Juice from Concentrate, Orange Juice Not from Concentrate), Orange Juice Big Chug (Calcium Rich, From Concentrate)

Giant Brand -

Bottled (Apple Juice (100% Natural Sparkling, Cocktail From Concentrate), Coolers (Berry Berry, Big Apple, Cosmic Orange, Fruit Punch, Goofy Grape), Fruit Punch Juice, Kids Happy Drinks, Prune Juice w/Pulp, Strawberry Kiwi Juice, Tomato Juice, Tropical Juice Drink, Wild Cherry Juice Drink)

Frozen Juice Concentrate (100% Grape, Cocktail (Cranberry, Grape, White Grape), Fruit Punch (Green, Red), Lemonade (Pink, Regular), Limeade, Orange, Wildberry Punch)

Refrigerated Juice (Grapefruit (Premium Ruby Red Not From Concentrate, Regular), Orange (Not From Concentrate, Strawberry, Cranberry, From Concentrate, w/Added Calcium, w/Pulp))

Gold Peak - Iced Tea Lemon

Gordon Food Service - Concentrate (Apple, Cranberry Cocktail, Fruit Punch, Orange, Pineapple, Prune)

Great Value Brand (Wal-Mart) -

From Concentrate (100% Juice Unsweetened Apple Juice, Cranberry, Cranberry Apple, Cranberry Black Cherry, Cranberry Grape, Cranberry Juice Blend, Grape, Grape Cranberry, Natural Strength Lemon Juice, Pineapple, Ruby Red Grapefruit, Unsweetened White Grapefruit Juice, Vegetable Juice, White Grape, White Grape Peach)

Frozen Juice Concentrate (100% Grape, Apple, Country Style Orange Juice Pure Unsweetened, Florida Grapefruit Juice Pure Unsweetened, Fruit Punch, Grape Juice Drink, Lemonade, Limeade, Orange Juice w/Calcium, Pink Lemonade), Prune Juice

Refrigerated Orange Juice (Country Style, High Pulp, Pulp Free Regular, Pulp Free w/Calcium, Regular w/Calcium)

Vegetable Juice Blends (Acai Mixed Berry, Light Pomegranate Blueberry, Light Strawberry Banana)

Hannaford Brand - All (Frozen, Refrigerated, Shelf Stable)

Hansen's - All Varieties

Hawaiian Punch - All Varieties

Hollywood - Organic Carrot Juice

Honest -

Ade (Orange Mango w/Mangosteen, Pomegranate Blue, Super Fruit Punch)

D

Kids (Apply Ever After, Berry Berry Good Lemonade, Goodness Greatness, Super Fruit Punch, Tropical Tango Punch)

Mate (Agave, Maqui Berry, Sublime, Tropical Tango Punch)

Hood - All Juices

Hy-Vee -

100% Juice Blend (Blueberry Pomegranate, Cherry Pomegranate, Cranberry, Cranberry Apple, Cranberry Raspberry)

Apple

Apple Cranberry Splash

Chocolate Nutritional Supplement (Plus, Regular)

Concord Grape Juice

Frozen Concentrate (Apple Light Regular, Fruit Punch, Grape Juice Cocktail, Grapefruit Juice, Lemonade, Limeade, Orange (Regular, w/Calcium), Pineapple, Pink Lemonade)

Juice Cocktail From Concentrate (Cranberry, Cranberry Apple, Cranberry Grape, Cranberry Raspberry, Grapefruit, Lemon, Light (Apple, Apple Cherry, Apple Kiwi Strawberry, Apple Raspberry, Grape), Light Cranberry Raspberry, Ruby Red Grapefruit)

Juice From Concentrate (100% Apple, 100% Grapefruit w/ Calcium, 100% Unsweetened Prune, 100% Unsweetened Prune, 100% Unsweetened Prune w/Pulp, 100% White Grape, Apple, Apple Calcium Fortified, Apple Kiwi, Country Style Orange, Cranberry Strawberry, Lemon, Lemonade, Light (Apple Raspberry, Grape Cranberry), Orange Juice, Orange Juice w/Calcium, Pineapple, Pomegranate, Prune Juice, Tomato, Unsweetened Apple Cider, Vegetable)

Just (Apple, Berry, Cherry, Fruit Punch, Grape, Orange Tangerine)

Lite (Blue Fruit Punch, Cranberry, Cranberry Grape, Cranberry Raspberry, Fruit Punch, Grape Punch, Orange Punch)

No Concentrate (Country Style Orange, Orange, Orange w/ Calcium, Ruby Red Grapefruit)

Splash (Fruit Punch, Orange Pineapple)

Strawberry Kiwi Punch

Strawberry Nutritional Supplement (Plus, Regular)

Vanilla Nutritional Supplement (Plus, Regular)

Izze - All Varieties

Kirkland Signature - Frozen Orange Juice Concentrate, Juice (Apple, Apple Peach & Passionfruit, Cranberry, Cranberry Raspberry), Organic Carrot Juice

Knudsen - All Varieties *(Except For Sensible Sippers)*

Kool-Aid - Bursts (Berry Blue, Cherry, Grape, Lime, Tropical Punch), Juice Jammers (All Varieties)

Kroger Brand - Active Lifestyle Drink Sticks, Frozen (All Varieties), Fruit Juices, In An Instant Drink Powders, Shelf Stable Juices, Vegetable Juice

Lakewood - All 100% Pure Fruit & Vegetable

Langers Juices - All Flavors

Laura Lynn - Juice (Apple, Cocktail, Cranberry (Blend, Regular), Grape, Grapefruit, Lemon, Light (Cranberry Blends, Fruit Punch), Peach, Prune, Sports Drink, Vegetable, White (Cranberry, Cranberry Blend, Grape))

Lincoln - Apple Juice

Litehouse - Apple Cider (All Varieties)

Lowes Foods Brand - Cranberry Grape Light, Juice (Apple (Natural ●, Regular ●), Cranberry Apple, Cranberry Cocktail (Light, Regular), Cranberry Grape Regular, Cranberry Raspberry, Grape, Grape Cocktail Light, Grove Select Orange, Lemon (Regular, Squeeze), Lemonade, Orange (Original, Premium), Orange Plus Calcium, Original w/Calcium, Premium Cranberry Blend 100% Juice, Prune, Vegetable Juice, White Grape)

Lucky Leaf - Apple (Cider, Juice, Premium Juice, Sparkling Cider)

Manischewitz - Grape Juice

Medifast - Fortified Drinks (Cranberry Mango ●, Tropical Punch ●)

Meijer Brand -

100% Juice (Berry, Cherry, Cranberry/Raspberry, Grape, Punch)

Cranberry Juice Drink (Grape, Raspberry, Strawberry, White)

Drink Thirst Quencher (Fruit Punch, Lemon Lime, Orange)

D

Frozen Concentrate Juice (Apple, Fruit Punch, Grape, Grapefruit, Lemonade, Limeade, Orange, Pink Lemonade, White Grape)

Frozen Concentrate Orange Juice (High Pulp, Pulp Free, w/ Calcium)

Fruit Punch (Genuine, Light, Regular)

Juice (Apple, Apple Natural, Cherry, Fruit Mix, Grape, Grapefruit, Lemon, Lime, Pineapple, Pink Grapefruit, Prune, Ruby Red Grapefruit, Tangerine & Ruby Red, White Grape, White Grapefruit)

Juice Blend (Acai & Blueberry, Acai & Grape, Pomegranate & Blueberry, Pomegranate & Cranberry, White Cranberry, White Grape & Peach, White Grape & Raspberry)

Juice Cocktail (Cranapple, Cranberry (Light, Regular), Cranberry Grape (Light, Regular), Cranberry Raspberry (Light, Regular), Cranberry Strawberry, Cranberry White Peach, Light Grape Splenda, Ruby Red Grapefruit (Light, Light 22%, Regular), White Cranberry, White Cranberry Peach, White Cranberry Strawberry, White Grape, White Grapefruit)

Juice Refrigerated Orange (Original, Reconstituted)

Juice Refrigerated Orange Premium (Calcium Carafe, Carafe, Hi Pulp Carafe, Original, Pulp, w/Calcium)

Lemon Juice Squeeze Bottle

Orange Reconstituted (Original, Pulp, w/Calcium)

Organic Juice (Apple, Concord Grape, Cranberry, Lemonade)

Splash (Berry Blend, Strawberry/Kiwi, Tropical Blend)

Midwest Country Fare - 100% Unsweetened From Concentrate (Apple Cider, Apple Juice), 100% Concentrated Orange Juice, Juice Cocktail (Cranberry, Cranberry Apple, Cranberry Raspberry), Juice From Concentrate Grape

Minute Maid - Lemonade (Light, Original), Multi Vitamin Orange Juice, Pomegranate Blueberry, Pomegranate Flavored Tea, Pomegranate Lemonade

Mondo - Fruit Squeezers (Chillin' Cherry, Global Grape, Kiwi Strawberry Splash, Legendary Berry, Outstanding Orange, Primo Punch)

Mott's - All Varieties

Mountain Sun - Bottled (Blueberry Green Tea, Grape & Acai, Pomegranate & Black Cherry, Pomegranate Rooibos Tea, Pure Cranberry)

Musselman's - Apple (Cider, Fresh Pressed Apple Cider, Juice, Premium Juice, Sparkling Cider)

Nantucket Nectars - All Varieties

Nature Factor - Organic Young Coconut Water

Nature's Promise - Organic Cranberry Juice From Concentrate, Pomegranate Juice (Blueberry Blend, Cranberry Blend, Regular Bottled)

Nestea - Green Tea Citrus Diet, Green Tea Citrus Regular, Lemon (Diet, Sweetened), Red Tea

Nestle - Juicy Juice (All Flavors), Sparkling Juicy Juice Fruit Juice (All Flavors)

Newman's Own -

Gorilla Grape,

Green Tea w/Honey

Lemonade (Lightly Sweetened, Old Fashioned Roadside Virgin, Organic, Pink Virgin, Pomegranate, Reduced Sugar Pink)

Orange Mango Tango

Raspberry Kiwi Juice Cocktail

Virgin Lemon Aided Iced Tea

Virgin Limeade

O Organics - Bottle Juices (Apple, Berry Blend, Blueberry Blend, Cranberry Cocktail, Grape, Lemonade, Unfiltered Apple), Refrigerated Orange

Ocean Spray - All Varieties

Organic Valley - Orange Juice (Calcium Added, w/Pulp, w/o Pulp)

Phildesco - Coconut Water

Powerade - Ion 4 (Fruit Punch, Grape, Lemon Lime, Mountain Berry Blast, Sour Lemon, Strawberry Lemonade, White Cherry, Zero)

D

Prairie Farms - Flavored Drinks (Blue Raspberry, Fruit Punch, Grape, Lemon, Lemon Lime, Lemonade, Orange, Pink Lemonade), Orange Juice (Light Pulp Premium, No Pulp, Plus Calcium, Regular)

Publix -

From Concentrate

Orange Juice (Regular, w/Calcium)

Ruby Red Grapefruit Juice

Frozen Concentrated Orange

Refrigerated (Premium Orange Juice (Calcium Plus, Grove Pure, Old Fashioned, Original), Premium Ruby Red Grapefruit Juice)

Shelf Stable (Apple, Cranberry (Apple Juice Cocktail, Juice Cocktail, Reduced Calorie Cocktail), Grape, Grape Cranberry Juice Cocktail, Lemonade Deli Old Fashion, Pineapple, Raspberry Cranberry Juice Cocktail, Ruby Red Grapefruit Regular, Tomato, White Grape)

Publix GreenWise Market - Organic (100% Apple, Cranberry, Grape, Lemonade, Tomato)

Pure Market Express ▲ - Cacao Bean ●, Classic Q ●, Drop Of Sunshine Juice ●, Green Sweet Tart Juice ●

ReaLemon - 100% Lemon Juice

ReaLime - 100% Lime Juice

Safeway Brand -

Frozen (Apple, Berry Punch, Cranberry, Grape, Lemonade, Limeade, Orange, Orange Country Style, Orange w/Calcium, Pink Lemonade, Raspberry Lemonade)

Juice (Apple (Cider, Regular), Cranberry (Apple, Cocktail, Light Cocktail, Light Raspberry, Raspberry), Grape (Light, Regular), Grapefruit (Cocktail, Pink, Regular, Ruby Red Cocktail, White), Lemon, Orange, Prune, Tomato, Vegetable, White Grape)

Santa Cruz - 100% Citrus (All Varieties), Bottled Juice (All Varieties), Champagne Style Sparkling Juice (All Varieties), Juice Boxes (All Varieties), Organic Sparkling Beverages (All Varieties), Super Fruits (All Varieties)

D

Simply - Apple, Grapefruit, Lemonade (Original, w/Raspberry), Limeade, Orange (w/Calcium & Vitamin D Pulp Free, Grove Made High Pulp, Original Pulp Free, w/Mango Pulp Free, w/Pineapple Pulp Free)

Snapple - 100% Juices (All Varieties), Apple Juice, Cranberry Raspberry, Diet Cranberry Raspberry, Fruit Punch, Grape Berry Punch, Grapeade, Kiwi Strawberry, Lemonade, Mango Madness, Noni Berry, Orangeade, Peach Mangosteen, Pink Lemonade, Raspberry Peach, Very Cherry Punch

SoBe -
   Adrenaline Rush (Original, Sugar Free)
   Black & Blue Berry Brew
   Energize (Citrus Energy, Green Tea, Mango Melon, Power Fruit Punch)
   Energy
   Green Tea
   Lean Diet (Cranberry Grapefruit, Fuji Apple Cranberry, Honey Green Tea, Raspberry Lemonade)
   Smooth (Black & Blue Berry Brew, Orange Cream, Pina Colada, Strawberry Banana, Strawberry Daiquiri)
   Vita Boom (Cranberry Grapefruit, Orange Carrot)

Sonoma Sparkler - Natural (Peach, Pear, Raspberry), Organic (Apple, Lemonade)

Spartan Brand -
   Apple Cider
   Apple Juice (Apple Cherry, Regular)
   Apricot
   Cranberry Juice Cocktail (Lite, Low Calorie, Regular)
   Cranberry Juice Drink (Apple, Pomegranate, Raspberry)
   Frozen Concentrate Fruit Punch
   Grape Juice (Regular, White)
   Grape Juice Cocktail
   Grapefruit Juice Lemonade
   Lemon Juice

D

Orange Juice (Country Style, Pulp Free, Regular, w/Calcium)
Pineapple
Pink Lemonade
Pomegranate
Premium Orange Juice (Country Style Pulp, Regular, w/Calcium),
Reconstituted Orange Juice (Country Style Pulp, Regular, w/Calcium)
Tomato Juice
Vegetable Juice Cocktail

Sunny D - All Varieties

Sweet Leaf - Bottled Original Lemonade

Tampico - All Beverages

The Ginger People - Ginger Beer**!**, Ginger EnerGizer**!**, Ginger Juice**!**, Ginger Soother**!**, Lemon Ginger Beer**!**

Tipton Grove - Apple Juice 100% Juice

Trader Joe's -
Concentrate (Lemon, Orange)
French Market Sparkling Beverages (All Flavors)
Juices (All Varieties)
Organic Mango Lemonade
Organic Sparkling Beverages (All Flavors)

Tropicana - All 100% Juices

V8 -
Diet Splash (Berry Blend, Tropical Blend)
Splash (Berry Blend, Fruit Medley, Mango Peach, Strawberry Kiwi Blend, Tropical Blend)
Splash Smoothies (Strawberry Banana, Tropical Colada),
V Fusion (Acai Mixed Berry, Cranberry Blackberry, Goji Raspberry, Passionfruit Tangerine, Peach Mango, Pomegranate Blueberry, Pomegranate w/Green Tea, Raspberry Green Tea, Strawberry Banana, Tropical Orange)
V Fusion Light (Acai Mixed Berry, Cranberry Blackberry, Peach Mango, Pomegranate Blueberry, Strawberry Banana)
Vegetable Juice (100% Vegetable Juice, Calcium Enriched,

Essential Antioxidants, High Fiber, Low Sodium, Low Sodium
Spicy Hot, Organic, Spicy Hot)

Vitaminwater (Glaceau) - All Varieties

Vruit - Apple Carrot, Berry Veggie, Orange Veggie, Tropical

Walnut Acres - Apple Juice

Wegmans Brand -

100% Juice (Cranberry (Blend, Raspberry), Ruby
Red Grapefruit Blend)

Frozen Juice Concentrate (Apple, Fruit Punch, Lemonade,
Limeade, Orange, Pink Lemonade)

Juice (Apple (Natural Style, Regular), Cranberry (Peach, Raspberry,
Regular), Grape (Juice Cocktail, Regular, White), Grapefruit,
Juice Blends (Berry, Cherry, Cranberry Apple, Cranberry
Concord Grape, Orange Peach Mango, Ruby Red Grapefruit,
Sparkling Cranberry, White Grape Cranberry, White Grape
Peach), Lemon Juice, Orange (Regular, Unsweetened), Prune,
White Grape (Peach Blend, Raspberry Blend, Regular))

Juice From Concentrate (100% Juice (Orange, Tomato, Vegetable
No Salt Added, Vegetable Regular), Blueberry Flavor Juice
Blend, Lemon, Lemonade, Limeade, Orange Juice (Regular, w/
Calcium), Pineapple Orange, Pomegranate Flavor Juice Blend,
Prune)

Organic Juice From Concentrate (Apple, Apricot Nectar,
Cranberry, Mango Nectar, Orange)

Premium 100% Juice Orange (Extra Pulp, No Pulp, Some Pulp, w/
Calcium, w/Calcium & Vitamins)

Ruby Red Grapefruit

Premium Orange Juice (No Pulp, Some Pulp)

Punch (Berry, Fruit)

Welch's - All Varieties

Winn & Lovett - Juice (Black Cherry, Cranberry, Pomegranate)

Winn Dixie -

Frozen Juice (All Varieties)

Juice (Cranberry, Cranberry Apple, Cranberry Raspberry, Light
Cranberry, Light Cranberry Grape, Light Grape, Pomegranate

D
E

Blend, Pomegranate Blueberry Blend, Pomegranate Cranberry Blend, Premium Apple, Reconstituted Lemon, Ruby Red Grapefruit, Ruby Red Grapefruit Cocktail, Vegetable)

Juice From Concentrate (Apple, Apple Cider, Grape, Grapefruit, Prune, Prune w/Pulp, White Grape)

Nectar Drinks (Guava, Mango, Mango Pineapple Guava, Peach, Pear)

Orange Juice (From Concentrate, From Concentrate w/Calcium, Premium Not From Concentrate)

Organic Juice (Apple, Cranberry, Grape, Lemonade, Mango Acai Berry Blend, Orange Mango Blend, Tomato)

Woodstock Farms - Non Organic Juices (All Varieties), Organic Juices (All Varieties)

Yo-J - All Varieties

Yoo-Hoo - All Varieties

Zola - Acai (Original, w/Blueberry, w/Pineapple)

Duck
... *All Fresh Poultry Is Gluten-Free (Non-Marinated, Unseasoned)*
Shelton's - Duckling

Duck Sauce
Ah So - Duck Sauce

Dumplings
Grandma Ferdon's▲ - Frozen Parsley ●
Mixes From The Heartland▲ - Country Dumpling Mix ●
Mrs. Crimble's - Dumpling Mix
Philadelphia Gluten Free Ravioli Pasta Company - Potato & Spinach Gnocci ●, Traditional Potato Gnocci ●
Skye Foods - Hungarian Egg Dumplings ●
Star Ravioli - Gluten Free (Gnocchi, Spinach Gnocchi)

E

Edamame
C & W - All Plain Frozen Vegetables

Imperial Gourmet - All Natural Edamame
Meijer Brand - Edamame Soybeans
Melissa's - In Shell
Nuts Online - Dry Roasted Edamame (Salted ●, Unsalted ●), Organic
 Dry Roasted Soybeans (Salted Whole ●, Unsalted Whole ●), Soy
 Beans (Dry Roasted Halves ●, Hickory Smoked ●, Spicy BBQ ●),
 Wasabi Beans ●
O Organics - Frozen
Private Selections - All Plain Vegetables Frozen
Safeway Brand - Frozen
Safeway Select - Shelled Boiled
Stop & Shop Brand - In Pod
Sunrich Naturals - Fiesta Blend, In The Shell, Organic, Shelled
Trader Joe's - Frozen (Fully Cooked, Shelled Soybeans, Soybeans
 in Pod, Soycutash)
Woodstock Farms - Organic Frozen Edamame (Shelled, Whole Pods)

Egg Replacer/Substitute
 All Whites - All Varieties
 Better'n Eggs - All Varieties
 Coburn Farms - Eggzactly (100% Egg Whites, Regular)
 Ener-G▲ - Egg Replacer
 Food Club Brand - Great Egg Spectations
 Giant Brand - 100% Egg Whites, Eggs Made Simple
 Great Value Brand (Wal-Mart) - Liquid Egg Whites, Liquid Eggs
 Hannaford Brand - Egg Mates, Egg Whites
 Horizon Organic - All Varieties
 Lucerne - Liquid Eggs All Whites
 Meijer Brand - Refrigerated Egg Substitute
 NuLaid - Egg Substitute
 Orgran▲ - No Egg Egg Replacer
 Publix - Egg Stirs
 Spartan Brand - Eggmates
 Wegmans Brand - Egg Busters, Liquid Egg Whites

E Eggnog

> Hannaford Brand
> Hood - Cinnamon, Gingerbread, Golden, Light, Pumpkin, Sugar Cookie, Vanilla
> Horizon Organic
> Lactaid
> Prairie Farms - Regular
> Shamrock Farms - Low Fat, Regular
> Stop & Shop Brand - Light, Regular
> Trader Joe's
> Vitasoy - Holly Nog

Eggplant

> ... *All Fresh Fruits & Vegetables Are Gluten-Free*
> Tasty Bite - Punjab Eggplant!
> Trader Joe's - Caponata Appetizer, Frozen Misto Alla Grigio!!, Garlic Spread

Eggs

> ... *All Fresh Eggs Are Gluten-Free*

Emulsifier

> Augason Farms - Gluten Free (Lecithin Granules ●, Lecithin Powder ●)

Enchilada Sauce

> Food Club Brand
> Frontera - Classic Red Chile
> Hy-Vee - Mild
> Kroger Brand - Chipotle, Fire Roasted Red, Verde
> La Victoria - Green Mild, Red (Hot, Mild), Red Chili
> Las Palmas - Red
> McCormick - Enchilada Sauce Mix
> Safeway Brand
> Spartan Brand

Enchiladas

> Amy's -
>> Black Bean Vegetable Light In Sodium!

Cheese Regular **!**

Light & Lean Black Bean & Cheese Enchilada **!**

Santa Fe Enchilada Bowl **!**

Whole Meals (Cheese Enchilada **!**, Enchilada w/Spanish Rice & Beans **!**, Verde Spinach & Cheese Enchilada **!**)

Cedarlane - Gluten Free Enchilada Meal, Gluten Free Enchiladas, Three Layer Enchilada Pie

Trader Joe's - Frozen Chicken Enchiladas In Salsa Verde, Organic Black Bean & Corn

Energy Bars... see Bars

Energy Drinks

AMP - Elevate, Lightning, Overdrive, ReLaunch, Sugar Free, Traction

Blue Sky - Blue (Natural, Shot, Zero Calorie), Cafe (Mountain Mocha, Vanilla Sky), Juiced Energy

CalNaturale Svelte▲ - Sustained Energy Protein Drink (Cappuccino ●, Chocolate ●, French Vanilla ●, Spiced Chai ●)

Emerge - All Varieties

Full Throttle - Blue Agave, Citrus, Coffee (Caramel, Mocha), Red Berry

Hansen's - All Varieties

Inko's - White Tea Energy

Monster - Absolutely Zero, Assault, DUB Edition, Energy + Juice (Khaos, Lo Carb, M 80, MIXXD), Hammer X Presso, Heavy Metal, Import, Import Light, Java Monster (Chai Hai, Irish Blend, Lo Ball, Loco Moca, Mean Bean, Nut Up, Originale, Russian), Nitrous (Anti Gravity, Killer B, Super Dry), Regular

No Fear - Motherload, Sugar Free, Super Energy

NOS - All Varieties

Red Bull - Cola, Energy Shots, Regular, Sugar Free

Red Rain - Diet, Regular

SoBe - Adrenaline Rush (Original, Sugar Free)

Vio - Vibrancy Drinks (Citrus Burst, Peach Mango, Tropical Colada, Very Berry)

E English Muffins

    Aunt Gussie's - English Muffins (Cinnamon Raisin●, Plain●)

    Celiac Specialties▲ - English Muffins

    El Peto▲ - Regular

    Ener-G▲ - Brown Rice English Muffins Flax, English Muffins

    Food For Life - Wheat & Gluten Free Brown Rice

    Foods By George▲ - English Muffins (Cinnamon Currant, No Rye Rye, Plain), Muffins (Blueberry, Corn)

    Gluten-Free Creations▲ - English Muffins ●

    Glutino▲ - Premium English Muffins

    Grandma Ferdon's▲ - Regular ●

Espresso... see Coffee

Extract

    Albertsons - Imitation Vanilla, Pure Vanilla

    Baker's - Imitation Vanilla

    Durkee - Vanilla (Imitation, Pure)

    Flavorganics - Almond, Anise, Caramel, Chocolate, Coconut, Hazelnut, Lemon, Orange, Peppermint, Rum, Vanilla

    Food Club Brand - Imitation Flavoring (Coconut, Orange, Peppermint, Rum, Vanilla), Pure Extract (Almond, Lemon)

    Gordon Food Service - Imitation Almond, Pure Lemon

    Great Value Brand (Wal-Mart) - Imitation Vanilla

    Hannaford Brand - Imitation (Almond, Vanilla), Pure (Lemon, Vanilla)

    Hy-Vee - Vanilla (Imitation, Pure)

    Kroger Brand - All Extracts

    Marcum - Imitation Vanilla, Pure Vanilla Extract

    McCormick -

        100% Organic Pure Madagascar Vanilla

        Cinnamon

        French Vanilla Blend

        Gourmet Collection

        Imitation (Almond, Banana, Cherry, Clear Vanilla, Coconut, Maple, Rum, Strawberry, Vanilla Butter & Nut)

Premium Vanilla
Pure (Almond, Anise, Lemon, Mint, Peppermint, Vanilla)
Raspberry
Root Beer
Meijer Brand - Imitation Vanilla, Vanilla
Midwest Country Fare - Imitation Vanilla Flavor
Nielsen-Massey -
Orange Blossom Water ●
Pure (Almond ●, Chocolate ●, Coffee ●, Lemon ●, Madagascar
    Bourbon Vanilla ●, Mexican Vanilla ●, Orange ●, Organic Vanilla ●,
    Peppermint ●, Tahitian Vanilla ●, Vanilla Extract Blend ●)
Rose Water ●
Publix - Almond, Lemon, Vanilla
Safeway Brand - All Varieties
Spartan Brand - Imitation Vanilla, Pure Vanilla
Spice Islands - Vanilla (Imitation, Pure)
Tones - Vanilla (Imitation, Pure)
Trader Joe's - Vanilla
Watkins - Pure Almond, Pure Lemon, Pure Orange, Pure
    Peppermint, Pure Vanilla
Wegmans Brand - Vanilla Extract

F

Fajita Seasoning Mix... see also Seasonings
McCormick - Fajita Seasoning Packet
Old El Paso - Seasoning Mix
Safeway Brand
Falafel Mix
Authentic Foods▲
Gluty Free ●
Heaven Mills▲ ●
Orgran▲

F Feta Cheese... see Cheese
Fettuccini... see Pasta

Figs
> **Gluty Free** - Dried California ●, Mission ●, Organic (California ●, Mission ●, Turkish ●), Turkish ●
> **Nuts Online** - Dried Fruit California ●, Diced ●, Mission ●, Organic (California ●, Calimyrna ●, Mission ●, Turkish ●), Turkish ●

Fish
> *... *All Fresh Fish Is Gluten-Free (Non-Marinated, Unseasoned)*
> **Captain's Choice** - Cod Fillets
> **Crown Prince** - Kipper Snacks, Natural Kipper Snacks
> **Dr. Praeger's** - All Natural Potato Crusted (Fish Fillets!, Fish Sticks!, Fishies!)
> **Giant Brand** - Filet Of Mackerel
> **Great Value Brand (Wal-Mart)** - Canned Alaskan Pink Salmon
> **Henry & Lisa's** - Fish Nuggets Wild Alaskan
> **Hy-Vee** - Canned Alaskan Pink Salmon, Frozen (Salmon, Tilapia)
> **Ian's** - Wheat Free Gluten Free Recipe (Fish Sticks, Lightly Battered Fish)
> **Kirkland Signature** - Fresh (Catfish, Steelhead, Tilapia), Frozen (Pacific Cod Fillets, Steelhead Trout, Tilapia Fillets)
> **Kroger Brand** - Canned Jack Mackerel
> **Meijer Brand** - Canned Salmon (Pink, Sock Eye Red)
> **Member's Mark** - Canned Atlantic Salmon In Water
> **Morey's** - Marinated Tilapia (Lemon Pepper, Seasoned Grill, Sweet Mango), Smoked (Goldies, Lake Trout, Whitefish)
> **Ocean Prince** - Imitation Abalone
> **Port Side** - Canned (Jack Mackerel, Pink Salmon), Frozen (Ocean Perch, Pollock, Salmon Filets, Tilapia, Whiting)
> **Publix** - Fillets (Bass, Cod, Flounder, Haddock, Halibut, Mahi Mahi, Orange Roughy, Snapper, Swordfish Fillets, Whiting)
> **Pure Market Express▲** - Julie's Sushi ●
> **Starfish** - Crispy Battered Wild Caught Fish (Cod ●, Haddock ●, Halibut ●)

Sweet Bay - All Frozen Fillets
Trader Joe's -
  Marinated Ahi Tuna Steaks
  Pink Salmon Skinless Boneless
  Premium Salmon Patties**!!**
  Salmon Burger
  Seasoned Mahi Mahi Fillets
  Skinless Boneless Sardines In Olive Oil
  Smoked Salmon
Wegmans Brand -
  Alaskan Halibut
  Atlantic Salmon Fillets Farm Raised
  Chilean Sea Bass
  Lobster Tail
  Orange Roughy
  Pacific Cod
  Smoked Salmon (Nova, Scottish Style)
  Sockeye Salmon
  Swordfish
  Tilapia Fillets
  Yellowfin Tuna Sashimi Grade
Whole Catch - Frozen Fillet (Cod, Mahi Mahi, Sockeye Salmon, Swordfish)
Winn Dixie - Frozen (Cod, Grouper, Tilapia, Whiting)

Fish Sauce
  A Taste Of Thai - Regular
  Thai Kitchen - Premium Fish Sauce

Fish Steaks
  Crown Prince - In Lousiana Hot Sauce, In Mustard, w/Green Chilies
  Ocean Prince - In Lousiana Hot Sauce, In Oil, w/Green Chilies

Fish Sticks
  Dr. Praeger's - All Natural Potato Crusted (Fish Sticks**!**, Fishies**!**)
  Ian's - Wheat Free Gluten Free Recipe Fish Sticks

F Flan
    Kozy Shack - All Varieties
    Royal - All Varieties

Flax Seed
    Arrowhead Mills - Flax Seed Meal, Flax Seeds (Golden, Regular)
    Bob's Red Mill▲ - Flaxseed Meal (Golden, Original), Organic Flaxseed (Golden, Original)
    Gluty Free - Organic Flax Seed Meal ●, Organic Golden ●
    Hodgson Mill▲ - Brown Milled, Organic Golden Milled, Travel Flax All Natural Milled, Travel Flax Organic Golden Milled, Whole Grain Brown
    Nature's Path - Organic FlaxPlus Flaxseeds, Organic FlaxPlus Meal !
    Shiloh Farms - Brown Flax Meal ! !, Golden Flax Seeds ! !
    Spectrum - Organic (Ground, Ground w/Mixed Berries, Roasted Tomato, Whole)
    Trader Joe's - Golden Roasted (Flax Seed w/Blueberries, Whole)

Flax Seed Oil... see Oil

Flour
    AgVantage Naturals▲ - Master Blend ●, Millet Flour ●, Premium Fine Milled Sorghum Flour ●, Quinoa Flour ●, Rice Flour ●, Sorghum Flour ●
    Amazing Grains - Montina (All Purpose Flour Blend, Brown Rice Flour Blend, Pure Baking Flour Supplement)
    Andrea's Fine Foods▲ - Gluten Free Flour Blend, Super Fine Grind Rice (Brown, Sweet)
    Arrowhead Mills - All Purpose Baking Mix, Brown Rice, Organic (Buckwheat, Millet, Soy, White Rice)
    Augason Farms - Gluten Free (Bette's Original ●, Brown Rice ●, Featherlite ●, Tapioca Flour/Starch ●)
    Authentic Foods▲ -
        Almond Meal
        Arrowroot
        Bette's Flour Blend (Featherlight Rice, Four)
        Brown Rice Flour Superfine

Garbanzo
Garfava
Gluten Free Classical Blend
Multi Blend Gluten Free
Potato (Flour, Starch)
Sorghum
Sweet Rice Flour Superfine
Tapioca
White (Corn, Rice Flour Superfine)

Bay State Milling - Gluten Free All Purpose Flour ●

Better Batter - Gluten Free All Purpose Flour

Bisquick▲ - Gluten Free Pancake & Baking Mix

Bob's Red Mill▲ - Almond Meal/Flour, Black Bean, Brown Rice, Fava Bean, Garbanzo & Fava, Garbanzo Bean, Gluten Free (All Purpose Baking, Sorghum), Green Pea, Hazelnut Meal/Flour, Millet, Organic (Amaranth, Brown Rice, Coconut, Quinoa, White Rice), Potato, Sweet White Rice, Tapioca, Teff, White (Bean, Rice)

Cause You're Special▲ - All Purpose, White Rice

Celiac Specialties▲ - Celiac Specialties Flour Blend

Chateau Cream Hill Estates - Lara's Whole Grain Oat Flour ●

ConAgra Mills - All Purpose Blend ●, Amaranth ●, Millet ●, Multigrain ●, Quinoa ●, Sorghum ●, Teff ●

Deerfields Gluten Free Bakery▲ - Quick Mix For Sugar Buttons

Domata - Gluten Free All Purpose Flour ●, Seasoned ●

Dowd & Rogers▲ - California Almond, Italian Chestnut

Eagle Mills - All Purpose Multigrain Flour Blend

EasyGlut - Rice

El Peto▲ - All Purpose Flour Mix, Arrowroot, Bean, Brown Rice, Corn, Flax Seed, Millet, Organic Amaranth, Potato, Quinoa, Sorghum, Soya, Sweet Rice, Tapioca Starch, White Rice

Ener-G▲ - Brown Rice, Gluten Free Gourmet Blend, Potato (Flour, Starch), Sweet Rice, Tapioca, White Rice

Expandex▲ - Modified Tapioca Starch ●

Flour Nut - Almond Flour

F

Gifts Of Nature▲ - All Purpose Blend, Baby Lima Bean, Brown Rice, Chick Pea, Montina All Purpose Flour Blend, Sweet Rice, Tapioca, White Rice

Gillian's Foods▲ - Potato Starch, Brown Rice, Chick Pea, Imported Tapioca, Rice

Glutano▲ - Flour Mix It

Gluten Free Mama▲ - Gluten Free Coconut Nut Blend Flour ●, Mama's Almond Blend ●

Gluten Free Pantry▲ - All Purpose Gluten Free Baking Flour

Gluten-Free Creations▲ - Baking Flours (Basic ●, Enriched ●, Sweet ●)

Gluty Free - All Purpose Baking ●, Almond ●, Arrowroot Powder ●, Chestnut ●, Chia Seed ●, Chickpea ●, Hazelnut ●, Natural Almond●, Organic Brown Rice ●, Organic Coconut ●, Pistachio ●, Potato ●, Tapioca ●, White Chia Seed ●

Grandma Ferdon's▲ - Grandma Ferdon's Flour Mix ●, Potato ●, Rice (Sweet ●, White ●)

Heaven Mills - Oat Flour

Hodgson Mill▲ - Gluten Free All Purpose Baking Flour, Soy Flour (Organic, Regular)

Jules Gluten Free▲ - All Purpose Flour ●

King Arthur Flour▲ - Gluten Free Multi Purpose Flour ●

Kinnikinnick▲ - All Purpose Celiac, Brown Rice, Corn, Soya, Sweet Rice, White Rice

Laurel's Sweet Treats▲ - Baking Flour Mix

Let's Do...Organic - Coconut Flour

Lundberg▲ - Brown Rice Flour (California Nutra Farmed, Organic California)

Meister's Gluten Free Mixtures▲ - All Purpose Gluten Free Flour ●

Mixes From The Heartland▲ - All Purpose ●, Mix (Brown Rice ●, Tapioca Flour Starch ●, White Rice ●), Potato ●

Montana Monster Munchies - Whole Grain Oat Flour ●

Montina▲ - All Purpose Baking Flour Blend ●, Brown Rice Flour ●, Pure Baking Supplement ●

Namaste Foods▲ - Perfect Flour Blend
Nuchia - 100% Chia Seed ●, Original Chia Seed ●
Nuts Online -
   Arrowroot Powder ●
   Flour
      Almond ●
      Cashew ●
      Chestnut ●
      Chia ●
      Chickpea ●
      Gluten Free (All Purpose Baking ●, Black Bean ●, Corn ●, Fava Bean ●, Garbanzo Fava ●, Green Pea ●, Masa Harina Corn●, Organic Coconut ●, Sweet White Rice ●, Sweet White Sorghum●, White Bean ●)
      Hazelnut ●
      Millet ●
      Natural Almond ●
      Organic (Almond ●, Amaranth ●, Brown Rice ●, Quinoa ●, White Rice ●)
      Peanut ●
      Pistachio ●
      Potato ●
      Sprouted Super ●
      Tapioca ●
      Teff●
      White Chia ●
Nu-World Foods - Amaranth (Flour ●, Pre Gel Powder ●, Toasted Bran Flour ●)
Only Oats - Oat Flour ●
Organ▲ - All Purpose Pastry Mix, Gluten Substitute, Plain All Purpose, Self Raising
Peter Paul - Coconut Flour
Phildesco - Coconut Flour
Pocono - Buckwheat Flour

F

PrOatina Gluten Free - Gluten Free Oat Flour ●
Really Great Food Company▲ - All Purpose Rice, Brown Rice,
  Sweet Rice, Tapioca, White Rice
Ruby Range - Mesquite ●, Ruby Range Mix (Basic ●, Flour ●,
  Spice ●), Teff ●
Shiloh Farms - Almond ‼, Brown Rice ‼, Corn ‼,
  Mesquite ‼, Potato ‼, Quinoa ‼, Tapioca ‼, Teff ‼
Sylvan Border Farm - General Purpose Flour
Timtana Gluten Free - Timtana Gluten Free All Purpose Flour ●
Tom Sawyer▲ - All Purpose Gluten Free
Tropical Traditions - Organic Coconut Flour
Twin Valley Mills▲ - Sorghum Flour

Food Coloring
  Durkee - All Varieties
  Food Club Brand - Set
  Hy-Vee - Assorted
  Kroger Brand - Food Colors
  McCormick - All Varieties
  Safeway Brand - Assorted
  Spice Islands
  Tones

Frankfurters... see Sausage

French Fries
  Alexia Foods -
    Crispy Potatoes w/Seasoned Salt Waffle Fries !
    Julienne Fries (Spicy Sweet Potato !, Sweet Potato !, w/Sea Salt
      Yukon Gold !)
    Olive Oil & Sea Salt Oven Fries !
    Olive Oil Parmesan & Roasted Garlic Oven Reds !
    Olive Oil Rosemary & Garlic Oven Fries !
    Organic (Classic Oven Crinkles !, Oven Crinkles Onion & Garlic !,
      Oven Crinkles Salt & Pepper !, Yukon Gold Julienne Fries w/Sea
      Salt !)
    Yukon Gold Potatoes w/Seasoned Salt Potato Nuggets !
  Chester's - Flamin' Hot Flavored Fries ‼

Giant Brand - Frozen (Crinkle Cut, Crispy, Extra Crispy Crinkle Cut, Shoestring, Steak Fries, Straight Cut)

Gordon Food Service -
½" Oven
Extra Long (1/2", Coated (1/4", 3/8", 5/16"), 5/16" w/Skin, Steak)
Long (1/2", 3/8", 5/16", Steak)
Wedge Cut w/Skin

Hannaford Brand - Frozen (Crinkle Cut, Shoestring, Steak Style, Straight Cut)

Ian's - Alphatots

Lowes Foods Brand - Crinkle Cut, Shoestring, Steak Cut

Meijer Brand - Crinkle Cut, Original, Shoestring, Steak Cut

Ore-Ida -
Cottage Fries
Country Style Steak Fries
Crispers
Easy Fries Golden Crinkles
Extra Crispy (Fast Food Fries, Golden Crinkles, Seasoned Crinkles)
Golden (Crinkles, Fries)
Golden Twirls
Pixie Crinkles
Shoestrings
Steak Fries
Sweet Potato Fries
Waffle Fries
Zesties
Zesty Twirls

Publix - Frozen (Crinkle Cut, Fast Food Style, Golden, Southern Style Hash Browns, Steak Fries, Tater Bites)

Spartan Brand - Frozen (Crinkle Cut, Extra Crispy Fast, French Fried, Steak)

Winn Dixie - Frozen (Crinkle Cut, French, Matchstick, Shoestring, Steak Cut)

Woodstock Farms - Organic Frozen (Crinkle Cut Oven Fries, Shredded Hash Browns, Tastee Taters)

F

French Toast
  Ian's - Wheat Free Gluten Free Recipe French Toast Sticks
  Van's Natural Foods - Wheat & Gluten Free French Toast Sticks **!**
Frosting... see Baking Decorations & Frostings
Frozen Desserts... see Ice Cream
Frozen Dinners... see Meals
Frozen Vegetables... see Mixed Vegetables
Frozen Yogurt... see Ice Cream
Fruit Bars... see Bars and/or Ice Cream
Fruit Cocktail
  Albertsons - Heavy Syrup, Light
  Del Monte - Canned/Jarred Fruit (All Varieties), Fruit Snack Cups
    (Metal, Plastic)
  Food Club Brand - In Heavy Syrup, In Juice
  Giant Brand - Canned (In Heavy Syrup, In Pear Juice, Very Cherry In
    Light Syrup, w/Splenda), Fruit Mix In Heavy Syrup
  Gluty Free - Freeze Dried ●
  Great Value Brand (Wal-Mart) - In Heavy Syrup
  Hannaford Brand - All Fruit Cups
  Hy-Vee - Lite, Regular
  Laura Lynn - Canned
  Lowes Foods Brand - In Heavy Syrup, In Juice
  Meijer Brand - Heavy Syrup, In Juice, In Pear Juice Lite
  Midwest Country Fare
  Publix - Canned (In Heavy Syrup, Lite In Pear Syrup)
  Safeway Brand - Canned (Lite, Regular)
  Spartan Brand - Heavy Syrup, Light Juice
  Stop & Shop Brand - Heavy Syrup, Pear Juice, Splenda
  Wegmans Brand - In Heavy Syrup, In Pear Juice, Regular
  Winn Dixie - Fruit Cocktail (Heavy Syrup, Light Syrup)
Fruit Drinks... see Drinks/Juice
Fruit Leather ...see also Fruit Snacks
  Kaia Foods▲ - Goji Orange ●, Lime Ginger ●, Spiced Apple ●,
    Vanilla Pear ●

Matt's Munchies - Fruit Leathers (Apple Licious ●, Apple Pie ●, Banana ●, Chili Chocolate ●, Choco Nana ●, Ginger Spice ●, Island Mango ●, Mango ●, Raspberry Delight ●)

Stretch Island Fruit Co. - All Varieties

Trader Joe's - All Varieties

Fruit Salad

Meijer Brand - Tropical

Native Forest - Organic Tropical

Safeway Brand - Tropical Fruit

Fruit Snacks ... see also Snacks

Albertsons - Fruit Snacks

Annie's - Organic Bunny Fruit Snacks (Berry Patch!!, Summer Strawberry!!, Sunny Citrus!!, Tropical Treat!!)

Brothers All Natural▲ - Fruit Crisps (Asian Pear, Banana, Fuji Apple, Organic Strawberry, Pineapple, Strawberry, Strawberry Banana, White & Yellow Peach)

Food Club Brand - Fruit Snacks (Curious George, Dinosaurs, Sharks, Variety Pack)

Fruit By The Foot - Berry Blast, Berry Tie Dye, Boo Berry, Color By The Foot, Minis (Berry Wave, Trick Or Treat Berry, Wicked Webs Halloween), Razzle Blue Blitz, Strawberry, Tropical Twist, Variety Pack (Berry Tie Dye, Color By The Foot, Strawberry), Watermelon

Fruit Gushers -

Blue Raspberry

Flavor Shock

Halloween Tropical Mix

Mouth Mixers Punch Berry

Strawberry

Strawberry/Tropical

Triple Berry Shock

Tropical

Tropical Spooky Fruit

Variety Pack Strawberry/Watermelon

Watermelon Blast

F

Fruit Roll-Ups -
   Around The World
   Blastin' Berry Hot Colors
   Boo Berry Razzle Boo Blitz
   Flavor Wave
   Franken Berry Strawberry Scream
   Minis (Screamin' Strawberry, Strawberry Craze, Wildberry Punch)
   Scoops Fruity Ice Cream Flavors
   Stickerz (Berry Cool Punch, Mixed Berry, Tropical Berry)
   Strawberry
   Strawberry Sensation
   Tropical Tie Dye
   Variety Pack (Simply Fruit Wildberry/Strawberry, Stickerz, Stickerz
      Mixed Berry/Tropical Berry, Strawberry/Berry Cool Punch)
Fruit Shapes -
   Care Bears
   Comics
   Create A Bug
   Dora The Explorer
   Easter
   Halloween
   My Little Pony
   Nickelodeon
   Scooby Doo
   Shark Bites
   Spiderman
   Sponge Bob
   Sunkist Mixed Fruit
   Transformers
   Valentine Hearts
   Value Pack (Nickelodeon Tropical, Sunkist)
   Variety Pack Scooby Doo/Looney Tunes
Giant Brand - Build A Bear, Curious George, Dinosaur, Justice
   League, Peanuts, Sharks, Underwater World, Veggie Tales

Great Value Brand (Wal-Mart) - Fruit Smiles

Kroger Brand

NoNuttin' Foods▲ - Cherry Fruit Snacks ●

Publix - Dinosaurs, Rescue Heroes, Sharks, Snoopy, Veggie Tales

Safeway Brand - Creatures, Curious George, Fruity Shapes, Fruity
   Sprockets

Spartan Brand - Build A Bear, Curious George, Dinosaurs, Star Wars,
   Variety Pack

Stretch Island Fruit Co. - FruitaBu (Smoooshed Apple, Smoooshed
   Grape, Smoooshed Strawberry)

thinkFruit - Dried (Blueberries, Cherry, Cinnamon Apple,
   Cranberries, Peaches, Pineapple Tidbits)

Welch's - All Varieties

Fruit Spread... see Jam/Jelly... see Spread

Fudge

Katy Sweet▲ - Fudge (Pecan ●, Plain ●, Walnut ●), Organic Fudge
   (Pecan ●, Plain ●, Walnut ●)

G

Gai Lan

   ... *All Fresh Fruits & Vegetables Are Gluten-Free*

Garbanzo Beans... see Beans

Garlic

   ... *All Fresh Garlic Is Gluten-Free*

Earthbound Farm - Organic Garlic

Lee Kum Kee - Minced

Mezzetta - Crushed Garlic, Spicy Pickled Garlic

Trader Joe's - Crushed Regular, Frozen Crushed Garlic

Garlic Powder... see Seasonings

Garlic Salt... see Seasonings

Gelatin

Food Club Brand - All Regular, All Sugar Free

G

Giant Brand - Mix (Cherry, Orange, Raspberry), Refrigerated Fun Pack, Rainbow Fruit, Rainbow Parfait, Sugar Free (Black Cherry, Cherry, Fun Pack, Strawberry)

Gifts Of Nature▲ - Unflavored Beef Gelatin

Ginger Evans - Cherry, Orange, Strawberry, Sugar Free (Cherry, Orange, Strawberry)

Gordon Food Service - Gelatin Mix (Assorted (Citrus, Red), Cherry, Lemon, Lime, Orange, Peach, Raspberry, Strawberry)

Great Value Brand (Wal-Mart) - Regular (Lemon, Lime, Orange, Peach, Strawberry), Sugar Free (Cherry, Lime, Orange, Raspberry, Strawberry, Strawberry Banana)

Hannaford Brand - Sugar Free (Cherry, Lime, Orange, Raspberry)

Hy-Vee - Gelatin (Berry Blue, Cherry, Cranberry, Lemon, Lime, Orange, Raspberry, Strawberry, Strawberry Banana), Sugar Free (Cherry, Cranberry, Lime, Orange, Raspberry, Strawberry)

Jell-O -

Regular Instant
Apricot
Berry Blue
Black Cherry
Blackberry Fusion
Cherry
Cranberry
Grape
Island Pineapple
Lemon
Lime
Margarita
Melon Fusion
Orange
Peach
Pina Colada
Raspberry
Strawberry (Banana, Daquiri, Kiwi, Regular)

Tropical Fusion
Watermelon
Wild Strawberry
Snack Cups (Strawberry, Strawberry/Orange, Strawberry/
Raspberry)
Sugar Free Low Calorie
Black Cherry
Cherry
Lemon
Lime
Mixed Fruit
Orange
Peach
Raspberry
Strawberry (Banana, Kiwi, Regular)
Sugar Free Snack Cups (Cherry/Black Cherry, Lime/Orange,
Peach/Watermelon, Raspberry/Orange, Strawberry, Strawberry
Kiwi/Tropical Berry)
Jelly Belly - All Varieties
Kool-Aid - Gels (All Varieties)
Kroger Brand - Flavored, Plain, Snack Cups
Meijer Brand -
Gelatin Dessert (Berry Blue, Cherry, Cranberry, Grape, Lime,
Orange, Raspberry, Strawberry, Unflavored, Wild Strawberry)
Sugar Free Gelatin Dessert (Cherry, Cranberry, Lime, Orange,
Raspberry, Strawberry)
Royal - All Varieties
Spartan Brand - Berry Blue, Cherry (Regular, Sugar Free), Lemon,
Lime (Regular, Sugar Free), Orange (Regular, Sugar Free),
Raspberry (Regular, Sugar Free), Strawberry (Regular, Sugar Free)
Stop & Shop Brand - Gelatin (Cherry, Cranberry, Orange,
Raspberry), Refrigerated (Gelatin Fun Pack, Rainbow Fruit
Gelatin), Refrigerated Sugar Free Gelatin Fun Pack Regular
Wegmans Brand - Sugar Free (Cherry & Black Cherry, Grape & Fruit
Punch, Lemon Lime & Orange, Orange & Raspberry, Strawberry)

G Gin

... *All Distilled Alcohol Is Gluten-Free[2]

Ginger

    Gluty Free - Crystallized ●, Organic Crystallized ●

    Lee Kum Kee - Minced

    Nuts Online - Dried Fruit (Crystallized ●, Organic Crystallized ●)

    The Ginger People - Grated!, Organic Minced!, Organic
        Natural Pickled Sushi!, Syrup!

    Wel-Pac - Pickled Ginger (Benzi, Kizami), Sushi Ginger

Ginger Ale... see Soda Pop/Carbonated Beverages

Glaze

    Ah So - Ham Glaze

    Boar's Head - All Varieties

    Daddy Sam's - Salmon Glaze

    Litehouse - Dessert Glaze (Peach, Strawberry, Sugar Free Strawberry)

    Marzetti - Glaze For (Blueberries, Peaches, Strawberries,
        Sugar Free Strawberries)

Graham Crackers

    Celiac Specialties▲ - Graham Cracker Crumbs

    Jules Gluten Free▲ - Graham Cracker/Gingersnap Mix ●

    Kinnikinnick▲ - Graham Style Cracker Crumbs, S'moreables
        Graham Style Crackers

    Laurel's Sweet Treats▲ - Honey Grahamless Crackers

    The Grainless Baker▲ - Crumbs, Regular, Snackers

Grains

    Arrowhead Mills - Amaranth, Hulled Millet, Quinoa

    Bob's Red Mill▲ - Organic Amaranth, Quinoa Organic, Teff Whole

    Eden Organic - Brown Rice Flakes, Buckwheat, Millet, Quinoa, Red
        Quinoa, Wild Ric

    Nuts Online -

        Gluten Free (Brown Rice Farina ●, Corn Grits Polenta●, Corn
          Meal●, Millet Grits ●, Organic Brown Rice Farina ●, Rice Bran ●,
          Sweet White Sorghum Grain ●)

        Organic (Amaranth ●, Buckwheat Toasted ●, Millet ●, Purple Corn
          Kernels ●, Quinoa ●, Raw White Buckwheat ●)

Simply Sweet Corn ●
Teff Whole Grain ●
Yellow Corn Meal ●
Shiloh Farms - Hulled Millet**!!**, Whole Sorghum**!!**

Granola

Bakery On Main - Apple Raisin Walnut ●, Cranberry Orange
Cashew ●, Extreme Fruit & Nut ●, Fiber Power (Cinnamon Raisin ●,
Triple Berry), Nutty Cranberry Maple ●, Rainforest ●

Deb's Farmhouse Kitchen - Cherry Almond ●, Oatmeal Cookieola ●

Deerfields Gluten Free Bakery▲ - Almond Cherry, Chocolate
Chip, Vanilla Maple

Emmy's Organics▲ - Raw Almond

Enjoy Life▲ - Granola Crunch (Cinnamon ●, Cranapple ●, Very
Berry ●)

Flax4Life▲ - Apple Cinnamon ●, Banana Coconut ●, Chocolate
Chip ●, Cranberry Orange ●, Hawaiian Pineapple Coconut &
Mango ●

Gluten Free Sensations▲ - Apple Crisp, Cherry Vanilla Almond,
Cranberry Pecan, French Vanilla Almond

GlutenFreeda▲ - Apple Almond Honey, Cranberry Cashew Honey,
Raisin Almond Honey

Goraw▲ - Granola (Apple Cinnamon ●, Live ●, Live Chocolate ●,
Simple ●)

Jessica's Natural Foods - Almond Cherry, Chocolate Chip, Vanilla
Maple

Kaia Foods▲ - Buckwheat Granola (Cocoa Bliss ●, Dates & Spices ●,
Raisin Cinnamon ●)

Kookie Karma - All Varieties ●

Love Grown Foods▲ - Apple Walnut Delight ●, Cocoa Goodness ●,
Raisin Almond Crunch ●, Simply Oats ●, Sweet Cranberry Pecan ●

Montana Monster Munchies - Bridger Blueberry ●, Chinook
Chocolate ●, Cut Bank Cranberry ●, Mariah's Gold Peanut ●, Red
Lodge Raisin ●

Mrs. Crimble's - Crumble Mix

G   NoNuttin' Foods▲ - Granola Clusters Vanilla (Caramel ●, Cinnamon●)
    Pure Market Express▲ - Tennessee Grawnola ●
    Rose's Bakery▲
    Silly Yak Bakery - GF Granola w/Fruit ●
    Trader Joe's - Gluten Free Granola
    Udi's Gluten Free Foods▲ - Gluten Free (Au Naturel, Cranberry, Original, Vanilla)
    Whole Foods Market Gluten Free Bakehouse▲ - Fruit & Nut Granola

Grape Leaves
    Krinos - Imported
    Mezzetta - California Grape Leaves
    Peloponnese - Dolmas, Grape Leaves

Grapefruit
    ... *All Fresh Fruits & Vegetables Are Gluten-Free*
    Del Monte - Canned/Jarred Fruit (All Varieties), Fruit Snack Cups (Metal Regular, Plastic Regular)
    Kirkland Signature - Red Grapefruit Cups
    Meijer Brand - Sections (In Juice, In Syrup)
    Winn Dixie - Canned Regular

Grapes
    ... *All Fresh Fruits & Vegetables Are Gluten-Free*

Gravy/Gravy Mix
    Barkat - Vegetable Gravy
    Cuisine Sante▲ - Au Jus Clear Gravy ●
    Full Flavor Foods - Gravy (Beef●, Chicken ●, Pork ●, Turkey ●)
    Imagine - Organic (Roasted Turkey Flavored, Savory Beef Flavored)
    Lawry's - Turkey Gravy **! !**
    Massel - Chicken Style Gravy Powder, Supreme Gravy Mix
    Maxwell's Kitchen - Gravy Mix (Brown Beef, Chicken, Pork, Turkey)
    Mayacamas - Brown, Chicken, Savory Herb, Turkey
    Orgran▲ - Gravy Mix
    Road's End Organics - Organic Gravy Mix (Delicious Golden, Savory Herb, Shitake Mushroom)
    Trader Joe's - All Natural Turkey Gravy

Green Beans... see Beans

Green Olives... see Olives

Green Peppers

   ... *All Fresh Fruits & Vegetables Are Gluten-Free*

Green Tea... see Tea

Greens

   ... *All Fresh Fruits & Vegetables Are Gluten-Free*

   Albertsons - Canned & Frozen Mustard Greens, Canned & Frozen Turnip Greens

   Birds Eye - All Plain Frozen Vegetables

   Bush's Best - Chopped (Collard, Kale, Mixed, Mustard, Turnip, Turnip w/Diced Turnips)

   C & W - All Plain Frozen Vegetables

   Food Club Brand - Canned (Mustard Greens, Turnip Greens), Frozen (Chopped Collards, Mustard Greens Chopped, Turnip Chopped)

   Giant Brand -

      Frozen

         Collard

         Kale (Chopped, Leaf)

         Mustard (Chopped, Leaf)

         Spinach (Chopped, Leaf, Whole Leaf)

         Turnip

   Lowes Foods Brand - Frozen (Chopped Collard, Turnip Greens)

   Meijer Brand - Canned Chopped (Kale, Mustard, Turnip), Chopped (Collards, Kale, Mustard, Turnip)

   Pictsweet - All Plain Vegetables (Frozen)

   Publix - Frozen (Collard Chopped, Turnip Chopped, Turnip w/Diced Turnips)

   Publix GreenWise Market - Mixed Baby Blend

   Spartan Brand - Chopped (Collard, Mustard, Turnip)

   Stop & Shop Brand - Collard Greens, Mustard Greens

   Winn Dixie -

      Canned (Collard No Salt, Mustard, Turnip)

      Frozen (Collard Greens Chopped, Mustard Greens, Steamable Mixed Vegetables)

G Grits

Bob's Red Mill▲ - Gluten Free Corn Grits/Polenta, Soy Grits
Food Club Brand - Instant Grits (Butter Pecan, Regular), Quick Grits
Meijer Brand - Butter Flavored Instant, Quick
San Gennaro Foods - Southern Style

Groats

Arrowhead Mills - Buckwheat
Chateau Cream Hill Estates - Lara's Oat Groats ●
Montana Monster Munchies - Raw & Sproutable Oat Groats ●
Pocono - Kasha Whole Buckwheat

Ground Beef

... *All Fresh Meat Is Gluten-Free (Non-Marinated, Unseasoned)*

Ground Turkey

... *All Fresh Meat Is Gluten-Free (Non-Marinated, Unseasoned)*

Guacamole ... see also Dip/Dip Mix

Calavo - Mild Spice, Pico De Gallo Recipe Medium Spice
Emeril's - Kicked Up Guacamole Dip
Fischer & Wieser - Guacamole Starter
Marzetti - Regular
Ortega - Guacamole Mix
Publix - Regular
Santa Barbara - Regular
Trader Joe's - Avocado's Number, w/Spicy Pico De Gallo ! !

Guar Gum

AgVantage Naturals▲ ●
Authentic Foods▲
Bob's Red Mill▲
Gillian's Foods▲
Gluten-Free Essentials▲ ●
Grandma Ferdon's▲ ●
Kinnikinnick▲
Nuts Online ●

Gum... see Chewing Gum

H

Half & Half... see Milk

Halibut... see Fish

Ham... see also Deli Meat

 Applegate Farms - Natural (Black Forest, Honey, Slow Cooked), Organic Uncured Ham

 Armour - 1877 (Canadian Maple, Honey Cured, Virginia Baked), Deli (Cooked, Cooked Ham & Water Product, Honey Cured, Lite, Spiced Luncheon Meat, Virginia Brand)

 Bar S - Classic Chopped, Deli Shaved (Black Forest, Honey, Smoked), Deli Style (Honey, Smoked), Deli Thin Cut (Honey, Smoked), Extra Lean Cooked, Premium Deli (Honey, Smoked), Steaks (Honey, Smoked)

 Boar's Head - All Varieties

 Butcher's Cut - Shank Cut Ham, Spiral Sliced *(Glaze Packet Is Not Gluten Free)*, Whole Smoked Ham

 Carl Buddig -
  Deli Cuts (Baked Honey Ham, Brown Sugar Baked Ham, Smoked Ham)
  Extra Thin Original (Brown Sugar Ham, Honey Ham, Regular)
  Fix Quix Smoked Ham
  Original (Brown Sugar Ham, Honey Ham, Regular)

 Castle Wood Reserve - Deli Meat (Black Forest Ham, Honey Ham, Smoked Ham, Virginia Brand Smoked Ham)

 Celebrity - Boneless Cooked

 Columbus Salame - Deli Meat (All Varieties)

 Cure 81 - Regular

 Dietz & Watson▲ -
  Black Forest (Cooked ●, Cured Honey ●, Deep Smoked ●, Smoked●)
  Branded Cooked ●
  Breakfast Ham Fillets w/Water Added ●
  Brown Sugar & Molasses ●

H

Cajun ●
Chef Carved (Hickory Smoked ●, Regular ●)
Chopped ●
Classic Trimmed & Tied w/Natural Juices ●
Cooked Round ●
Cubes ●
Gourmet Lite (Cooked ●, Virginia Decorated ●, Virginia Low Salt ●)
Honey (Cured Dinner ●, Cured Tavern ●)
Imported Cooked ●
Maple Glazed ●
Pepper ●
Prosciutto (Classico Trimmed ●, Regular ●)
Rosemary ●
Semi Boneless Smoked ●
Square Red Pepper ●
Steak (Brown Sugar & Molasses ●, Honey ●, Maple Cured ●,
    Traditional ●)
Tavern ●
Tiffany ●
Tomato & Basil ●
Virginia Baked ●

Eckrich -
Deli Meat (Black Forest Brand Nugget, Brown Sugar
    Nugget, Canadian Maple, Chopped, Ham Steak, Honey Cured,
    Honey Maple, Imported, Lite, Off The Bone, Smoked Pitt,
    Spiced Luncheon Meat, Spiral Sliced Holiday, Virginia Baked)
Lunch Meat (Chopped, Cooked, Virginia Brand Thin Sliced)

Fairgrounds - Lunch Meat Honey Ham, Premium Ham
(Chopped, Cooked)

Farmer John - Bone In Ham Premium Sliced Ham Steaks, Ham
Steaks (Clove, Maple, Original, Pineapple & Mango), Lunch Meats
Ham (Brown Sugar & Honey, Sliced Cooked)

Five Star Brand - Bavarian, Cottage Ham, Golden Hickory, Honey
Cured, Lower Sodium Virginia, Spiced Cello

Garrett County Farms -
  Black Forest Boneless Nugget**!**
  Deli (Black Forest**!**, Virginia**!**)
  Sliced (Black Forest**!**, Breakfast Virginia Brand Boneless Ham
    Steak**!**, Turkey Ham (Ham Steak**!**, Original**!**), Virginia Brand
    Deli Ham**!**)
Giant Brand - 97% Fat Free Cooked Ham
Giant Eagle Brand - Boneless (Half, Quarter, Whole), Ground,
  Semi Boneless (Half, Whole)
Great Value Brand (Wal-Mart) - 97% Fat Free (Baked Ham Water
  Added, Cooked Ham, Honey Ham Water Added), Thinly Sliced
  Smoked (Ham, Honey Ham)
Habbersett - Dainty Ham, Ham Slices, Ham Steak
Hillshire Farms -
  Deli Select (Brown Sugar Baked Ham, Smoked Ham)
  Deli Select Ultra Thin (Brown Sugar Baked Ham, Honey Ham)
  Whole/Half (All Flavors)
Hormel -
  Black Label (Canned, Chopped)
  Bread Ready Deli Counter Prosciutto
  Chunk Meats Ham
  Diced
  Ham Patties
  Natural Choice Deli Counter (Cherrywood Smoked, Cooked,
    Smoked)
  Natural Choice Ham (Cooked Deli, Honey, Smoked Deli)
Hy-Vee - 96% Fat Free (Cubed Cooked, Diced Cooked), Cooked
  Ham, Deli Thin Slices (Brown Sugar, Honey, Smoked), Thin Sliced
  (Ham w/Natural Juices, Honey Ham w/Natural Juices)
Isaly's - All Deli Meat
Jennie-O Turkey Store - Refrigerated Turkey Ham Honey Cured
Jones Dairy Farm -
  Boneless Fully Cooked (Dainty Hickory Smoked ●, Half Family ●,
    Whole Family ●)

H

Deli Style Ham Slices (Honey & Brown Sugar ●, Old Fashioned Cured ●)

Slices Naturally Hickory Smoked ●

Steak Hickory Smoked ●

Whole Boneless Country Club ●

Whole Hickory Smoked (Fully Cooked, Short Shanked ●, Old Fashioned Cure ●)

Kayem - Deli Ham (Amber Honey Cured, Black Forest, Carving, Honeycrust, Olde English Tavern, Peppercrust)

Kirkland Signature - Deli Meat (Extra Lean, Smoked Honey), Smoked (Applewood Half, Spiral Sliced Hickory)

Kroger Brand - Cooked, Cubed, Diced, Steaks

Meijer Brand - 97% Fat Free (Honey Ham, Sliced Cooked Ham), Double Smoked, Honey Roasted, Sliced Chipped

Oscar Mayer -

Deli Fresh Meats (Cooked Ham, Honey Ham, Smoked Ham)

Deli Meat (Baked Cooked, Boiled, Chopped, Honey, Smoked)

Shaved Deli Fresh Meats (Black Forest, Brown Sugar Ham, Honey Ham, Smoked Ham, Virginia Brand Ham)

Thin Sliced Deli Fresh (Brown Sugar Ham, Smoked Ham)

Primo Taglio - Black Forest Ham w/Natural Juices, Maple Ham Old Fashioned, Prosciutto Dry Cured Ham

Publix - Deli Pre Pack Lunch Meat (Cooked Ham, Extra Thin Sliced Honey Ham, Low Salt Ham, Sweet Ham, Tavern Ham), Deli Salad Ham, Hickory Smoked Ham Semi Boneless, Fully Cooked, Honey Cured Ham w/Brown Sugar Glaze (Bone In Ham, Boneless Ham)

Russer - Reduced Sodium Cooked, Smoked Virginia

Safeway Brand - Boneless Honey

Safeway Select - 2 lbs Half Boneless

Sara Lee - Deli Meat Slices (Brown Sugar Ham, Cooked Ham, Hickory Smoked Ham, Honey Ham, Virginia Brand Baked Ham)

Smithfield - All Spiral & Glazed Hams (Except HEB Private Label, Boneless Ham, Ham Steak, Quarter Ham

SPAM - Classic, Hickory Smoke Flavored, Less Sodium, Lite

Spartan Brand - Frozen Ham Loaf, Whole Boneless

Stop & Shop Brand - Cooked Ham (97% Fat Free, w/Natural Juices 98% Fat Free), Danish Brand Ham w/Natural Juices 97% Fat Free

Underwood - Deviled Ham Spread

Wegmans Brand - 97% Fat Free, Boneless Brown Sugar Cured, Ham Slices Boneless, Maple Cured, Old Fashioned Off The Bone (Brown Sugar Cured Ham, Double Smoked Ham), Organic Uncured Ham, Thin Shaved (Ham, Honey Maple Flavored Ham, Smoked Ham, Smoked Honey Ham), Virginia Baked

Wellshire Farms -

Black Forest (Boneless Half **!!**, Boneless Nugget **!!**, Deli **!!**, Quarter **!!**, Sliced **!!**)

Glazed Boneless Half **!!**

Old Fashioned Boneless (Half **!!**, Whole **!!**)

Semi Boneless (Half **!!**, Whole **!!**)

Sliced (Breakfast **!!**, Tavern **!!**)

Smoked Ham (Hocks **!!**, Shanks **!!**)

Turkey Half Ham **!!**

Virginia Brand (Boneless Steak **!!**, Buffet **!!**, Deli **!!**, Nugget Honey **!!**, Quarter **!!**, Sliced **!!**)

Virginia Buffet Half **!!**

Hamburger Buns... see Buns

Hamburgers... see Burgers

*... *All Fresh Meat Is Gluten-Free (Non-Marinated, Unseasoned)*

Hash Browns... see Potatoes

Hearts Of Palm

*... *All Fresh Fruits & Vegetables Are Gluten-Free*

Del Monte - All Canned Vegetables

Native Forest - Organic Hearts Of Palm

Trader Joe's - All Varieties

Herbal Tea... see Tea

Herbs

*... *All Fresh Herbs Are Gluten-Free*

Hoisin Sauce

Premier Japan - Wheat Free

Wok Mei - All Natural Hoisin

H

Hollandaise Sauce
  Mayacamas - Gourmet Sauce
Hominy
  Bush's Best - Golden, White
  Food Club Brand - Canned (Golden, White)
  Great Value Brand (Wal-Mart) - Canned (White, Yellow)
  Hy-Vee - Golden, White
  Lowes Foods Brand - White
  Meijer Brand - White
  Safeway Brand - Golden, White
  Spartan Brand - Golden, White
  Winn Dixie - Golden, White
Honey
  Albertsons - Honey
  Bakers & Chefs - Pure Honey
  Bramley's - Golden, Golden Honey
  Food Club Brand - Honey
  Full Circle - Organic 100% Pure Honey
  Gordon Food Service - Honey Packets
  Great Value Brand (Wal-Mart) - Clover Honey
  Hannaford Brand - All Varieties
  Hy-Vee - Honey, Honey Squeeze Bear
  Kroger Brand
  Kroger Value
  Lowes Foods Brand - Squeeze Bear
  Meijer Brand - Honey, Honey Squeeze Bear
  Publix - Clover, Orange Blossom, Wildflower
  Publix GreenWise Market - Organic Honey
  Safeway Brand - Pure
  Safeway Select - Regular
  Spartan Brand - Regular
  Trader Joe's - All
  Tropical Traditions - Canadian Raw Honey
  Virginia Brand - 100% All Natural

Wegmans Brand - Clover, Orange Blossom, Squeezeable Bear
Winn Dixie
Honey Mustard Sauce... see Mustard
Horseradish Sauce
  Baxters - Regular
  Boar's Head - All Varieties
  Di Lusso - Regular
  Dietz & Watson▲ - Cranberry ●, Hot & Chunky ●, Red ●, Smokey ●
  Heinz - Horseradish Sauce
  Hy-Vee - Prepared Horseradish
  Kroger Brand
  Lou's Famous - Horseradish Organic
  Manischewitz - All Varieties
  Marzetti - Horseradish Veggie Dip
  Melissa's - Cream Style
  Mezzetta - Cream Style Horseradish
  Royal Food Products - Royal Deluxe (w/Real Horseradish, Zesty)
  Simply Delicious - Organic Creamed Horseradish
  Wegmans Brand - Horseradish Cream, Prepared Horseradish
  Woeber's - Sandwich Pal Horseradish Sauce
Hot Chocolate Mix... see Cocoa Mix/Powder
Hot Dog Buns... see Buns
Hot Dogs... see Sausage
Hot Sauce
  Albertsons
  Bone Suckin' Sauce - Habanero Sauce
  Dave's Gourmet -
    Adjustable Heat
    Cool Cayenne
    Crazy Caribbean
    Ginger Peach
    Hot Sauce & Garden Spray
    Hurtin' Habanero
    Hurtin' Jalapeño

H

    Insanity Sauce

    Jammin' Jerk

    Jump Up & Kiss Me (Chipotle, Original, Passionfruit)

    Roasted (Garlic, Red Pepper & Chipotle)

    Scotch Bonnet

    Temporary Insanity

    Total Insanity

    Ultimate Insanity

Food Club Brand - Louisiana

Frank's RedHot - Chile 'N Lime, Original, Xtra Hot

Frontera - Hot Sauce (Chipotle, Habanero, Jalapeno, Red Pepper)

Giant Brand - Regular

Gifts Of Nature ▲ - Sriracha Hot Sauce

Hannaford Brand

La Victoria - Chunky Jalapeno, Salsa Brava

Mezzetta - California Habanero Hot Sauce Twist & Shout, California Hot Sauce

Mr. Spice Organic - Tangy Bang Hot

Texas Pete - Garlic, Hotter Hot, Original

The Wizard's - Hot Stuff

Trader Joe's - Jalapeno

Trappey's - Bull Brand Louisiana Hot Sauce, Chef Magic Jalapeno Sauce, Indi Pep Pepper Sauce, Louisiana Hot Sauce, Mexi Pep Hot Sauce, Pepper Sauce, Red Devil Cayenne Pepper Sauce

Winn Dixie - Louisiana Hot

Hummus

Athenos -

    Hummus (Artichoke & Garlic, Black Olive, Cucumber Dill, Greek Style, Original, Pesto, Roasted (Eggplant, Garlic, Red Pepper), Scallion, Spicy Three Pepper)

    NeoClassic Hummus (Original, Original w/Sesame Seeds & Parsley, Roasted Garlic w/Garlic & Parsley, Roasted Red Pepper w/Red Peppers & Parsley)

Casbah Natural Foods - Hummus

Fantastic World Foods - Original Hummus

H

I

Marzetti - Black Bean, Garden, Original, Roasted Garlic, Roasted Red Pepper, Southwest Chipotle

Melissa's - Edamame, Roasted Red Pepper, Traditional

Pure Market Express▲ - Hummus & Onion ●, Hummus w/Carrotini Crackers ●, Tuscan Hummus ●

Salpica - Chipotle Hummus Dip

Trader Joe's - Chipolte Pepper **!!**, Edamame, Garlic **!!**, Kalamata Olive **!!**, Mediterranean **!!**, Organic **!!**, Original **!!**, Roasted Garlic **!!**, Smooth & Creamy (Cilantro & Jalapeno, Classic Rice Bread Mix, Roasted Red Pepper, Spicy), Three Layer **!!**, Tomato & Basil **!!**, w/Freshly Ground Horseradish **!!**

Tribe - All Varieties (Classic, Organic, Origins)

Wegmans Brand - Regular, Traditional Flavor w/A Hint Of Lemon

Wild Garden - Black Olive, Fire Roasted Red Pepper, Jalapeno, Red Hot Chili Pepper, Roasted Garlic, Sundried Tomato, Sweet Pepper, Traditional

Wild Wood - Classic, Indian Spice, Low Fat Classic, Raspberry Chipotle, Roasted Red Pepper, Spicy Cayenne

I

Ice Cream... (includes Frozen Desserts, Frozen Yogurt, Sherbet, Sorbet)

Albertsons - Chocolate, Chocolate Chip, Fudge Bars, Junior Pops, Neopolitan, Sherbet (Orange, Rainbow), Sundae Cups, Vanilla, Vanilla & Chocolate

Breyer's -

All Natural

Butter Almond

Butter Pecan

Caramel Praline Crunch

Chocolate (Black Raspberry, Crackle, Extra Creamy, Regular, Triple)

Chocolate Chip

Coffee

Dulche De Leche

Lactose Free Vanilla
Mint Chocolate Chip
Peach
Rocky Road
Strawberry
Vanilla (Caramel, Cherry, Chocolate, Chocolate Strawberry,
    Extra Creamy, French, Fudge Twirl, Homemade, Regular)
Carb Smart Bar (Chocolate, Fudge, Vanilla, Vanilla & Almond)
No Sugar Added (Butter Pecan, French Vanilla, Vanilla, Vanilla
    Chocolate Strawberry),
Pure Fruit Bars (Berry Swirls, Pomegranate Blends, Strawberry
    Orange Raspberry),
Smooth & Dreamy Fat Free (Creamy Vanilla, French Chocolate,
    Strawberry),
Smooth & Dreamy Half Fat (Butter Pecan, Caramel Tracks,
    Chocolate (Chocolate Chip, Creamy, Dark Velvet), Mint
    Chocolate Chip, Rocky Road, Strawberry Cheesecake, Vanilla
    (Bean, Chocolate Strawberry, Creamy))
Snickers Caramel Swirl Chunk
Chapman's - Blueberry Cheesecake, Butterscotch Ripple, Canadian
    Vanilla Eh, Cherry Vanilla, Chocolate (& Vanilla, Caramel, Ripple),
    Dutch Chocolate, French Vanilla, Maple Twist, Mint Chip,
    Neapolitan, Orange Pineapple, Peppermint Stick, Raspberry
    Ripple, Rum & Raisin, Sorbet (Orange, Rainbow, Raspberry),
    Strawberry (Banana, Regular), Swiss Mocca, Tiger Tail, Vanilla,
    Vanilla Chip
Cool Fruits - Fruit Juice Freezers (Grape & Cherry, Sour Apple)
Double Rainbow Sorbet - Sorbet (Chocolate!!, Coconut!!,
    Lemon!!, Mango Tangerine!!, Raspberry!!)
Dove -
    All Pints *(Except Chocolate & Brownie Affair)*
    Dark Chocolate Ice Cream Bar w/(Almonds, Chocolate Ice
        Cream, Vanilla Ice Cream)
    Milk Chocolate Ice Cream Bar w/Vanilla Ice Cream, Miniature Ice
        Cream Bars

I

Dreyer's -

Fruit Bars (Acai Blueberry, Creamy Coconut, Grape, Lemonade, Lime, Orange & Cream, Pineapple, Pomegranate, Strawberry, Tangerine, Variety Pack (Lime, Strawberry, Wildberry), Variety Pack No Sugar Added (Black Cherry, Mixed Berry, Strawberry, Strawberry Kiwi, Tangerine & Raspberry))

Fun Flavors (Banana Split, Butter Pecan, Cherry Chocolate Chip, Dulce De Leche, Espresso Chip, Mango, Mocha Almond Fudge, Root Beer Float Limited Edition, Spumoni)

Grand (Chocolate (Chip, Regular), Double Vanilla, French Vanilla, Fudge Swirl, Mint Chocolate Chip, Neapolitan, Real Strawberry, Rocky Road, Vanilla (Bean, Chocolate, Regular))

Sherbet (Berry Rainbow, Orange Cream, Tropical Rainbow)

Slow Churned Rich & Creamy (Butter Pecan (No Sugar Added, Regular), Caramel Delight, Chocolate (Chip, Fudge Chunk, Regular), Coffee (No Sugar Added, Regular), French Vanilla (No Sugar Added, Regular), Fudge Tracks (No Sugar Added, Regular), Mint Chocolate Chip (No Sugar Added, Regular), Neapolitan (No Sugar Added, Regular), Peanut Butter Cup, Rocky Road, Strawberry, Take The Cake, Triple Chocolate No Sugar Added, Vanilla (No Sugar Added, Regular), Vanilla Bean (No Sugar Added, Regular))

Yogurt Blends (Black Cherry Vanilla Swirl, Cappucino Chip, Caramel Praline Crunch, Chocolate Vanilla Swirl, Peach, Strawberry, Tart Mango, Vanilla (Fat Free, Original))

Edy's -

Fruit Bars (Acai Blueberry, Creamy Coconut, Grape, Lemonade, Lime, Orange & Cream, Pineapple, Pomegranate, Strawberry, Tangerine, Variety Pack Lime, Strawberry, Wildberry, Variety Pack No Sugar Added (Black Cherry, Mixed Berry, Strawberry, Strawberry Kiwi, Tangerine & Raspberry))

Fun Flavors (Banana Split, Butter Pecan, Cherry Chocolate Chip, Dulce De Leche, Espresso Chip, Mango, Mocha Almond Fudge, Root Beer Float Limited Edition, Spumoni)

Grand (Chocolate (Chip, Regular), Coffee, Double Vanilla, French Vanilla, Mint Chocolate Chip, Neapolitan, Real Strawberry, Rocky Road, Vanilla (Bean, Chocolate, Regular))

Sherbet (Berry Rainbow, Orange Cream, Tropical Rainbow)

Slow Churned Rich & Creamy (Butter Pecan (No Sugar Added, Regular), Caramel Delight, Chocolate (Chip, Fudge Chunk, Regular), Coffee (No Sugar Added, Regular), French Vanilla (No Sugar Added, Regular), Fudge Tracks (No Sugar Added, Regular), Mint Chocolate Chip (No Sugar Added, Regular), Mocha Almond Fudge, Neapolitan (No Sugar Added, Regular), Peanut Butter Cup, Rocky Road, Strawberry, Take The Cake, Triple Chocolate No Sugar Added, Vanilla (No Sugar Added, Regular), Vanilla Bean (No Sugar Added, Regular))

Yogurt Blends (Black Cherry Vanilla Swirl, Cappucino Chip, Caramel Praline Crunch, Chocolate Vanilla Swirl, Peach, Strawberry, Tart Mango, Vanilla (Fat Free, Original))

Fla-Vor-Ice - Freezer Bars (Light, Regular, Sport, Tropical)

Food Club Brand -

Ice Cream (Butter Pecan, Cherry Vanilla, Chocolate, Moose Tracks, Neapolitan, Peach, Peppermint Stick, Strawberry, Vanilla)

Novelties (Banana Pop, Fudge Bar, Ice Cream Bar, Juice Pops, Junior Fudge Pop, Orange Cream Bars, Red White Blue Pops, Sundae Cups, Vanilla Cup)

Sherbet (Cherry Lemon, Lime, Orange, Pineapple, Rainbow, Raspberry, Triple Fruit)

Frootee Ice - Assorted Freezer Bars

Gaga - Sherbetter (Chocolate, Lemon, Orange, Rainbow, Raspberry)

Giant Brand -

Cups (Chocolate, Vanilla),

Light (Butter Pecan, Vanilla)

Natural (Butter Pecan, Chocolate, Chocolate Chip, Coffee, French Vanilla, Mint Chocolate Chip, Mocha Almond, Strawberry, Vanilla Bean, Vanilla Fudge Ripple)

Pops (Citrus, Junior, No Sugar Added Fudge, Orange Cream Bars, Twin)

Regular (Andes Creme De Menthe, Black Cherry, Black Raspberry, Butter Pecan, Butterscotch Ripple, Cherry Vanilla, Chocolate, Chocolate Marshmallow, Coffee, Mint Chocolate Chip, Moose Tracks, Peanut Butter Jumble, Strawberry, Toffee Crunch, Vanilla, Vanilla Fudge)

Sherbet (Lemon Lime, Orange, Pineapple, Rainbow, Raspberry)

GlutenFreeda ▲ - Ice Cream Cookie Sandwiches

Good Karma -

Chocolate Covered Bars (Chocolate Chocolate, Very Vanilla)

Organic Rice Divine (Banana Fudge, Carrot Cake, Chocolate Chip, Chocolate Peanut Butter Fudge, Coconut Mango, Key Lime Pie, Mint Chocolate Swirl, Mudd Pie, Very Cherry, Very Vanilla)

Haagen-Dazs -

Bars (Chocolate & Dark Chocolate, Coffee & Almond Crunch Snack Size, Vanilla & Almonds, Vanilla & Dark Chocolate, Vanilla & Milk Chocolate)

Five (Caramel, Coffee, Ginger, Lemon, Milk Chocolate, Mint, Passion Fruit, Strawberry, Vanilla Bean)

Frozen Yogurt (Coffee, Dulce De Leche, Peach, Tart Natural, Vanilla, Vanilla Raspberry Swirl, Wildberry)

Ice Cream (Banana Split, Butter Pecan, Cherry Vanilla, Chocolate (Chip, Peanut Butter, Regular), Coffee, Crème Brulée, Dulce De Leche, Green Tea, Java Chip, Mango, Mint Chip, Pineapple Coconut, Pistachio, Rocky Road, Rum Raisin, Strawberry, Vanilla (Bean, Chocolate Chip, Honey Bee, Regular, Swiss Almond), White Chocolate Raspberry Truffle)

Limited Edition (Amaretto Almond Crunch, Bananas Foster, Dark Chocolate Mint)

Sorbet (Chocolate, Cranberry Blueberry, Mango, Orchard Peach, Raspberry, Strawberry, Zesty Lemon)

Hannaford Brand -
> Assorted Pops (Citrus, Regular, Sugar Free)
> Bars (Artic, Fudge, Ice Cream, Orange Cream, Real Fruit)
> Black Cherry
> Butter Pecan
> Chocolate
> Chocolate Chip
> Churn Style Light (Black Raspberry, Butter Pecan, Chocolate, Vanilla)
> Frozen Yogurt (Black Cherry, Peach, Vanilla)
> Fudge Sticks (No Sugar Added, Regular)
> Heavenly Hash
> Maple Walnut
> No Sugar (Butter Pecan, Vanilla)
> Premium Moose Tracks (Caramel, Cherry, Mint, Original)
> Strawberry
> Strawberry Cheesecake
> Sundae Cups
> Three Flavors
> Tin Roof
> Vanilla (Chocolate, French, Fudge, Regular)

Hawaiian Punch - Freezer Bars

Hood -
> Bear Creek Caramel
> Boston Vanilla Bean
> Cape Cod Fudge Shop
> Frozen Novelty Items
>> Fudge Stix
>> Hoodsie (Cups, Pops 6 Flavor Assortment Twin Pops, Sundae Cups)
>> Ice Cream Bar
>> Kids Karnival
>> Orange Cream Bar
> Frozen Yogurt All Fat Free Varieties

Light (Butter Pecan, Chocolate Chip, Coffee, Maine Blueberry
& Sweet Cream, Martha's Vineyard Black Raspberry, Mint
Chocolate Chip, Moosehead Lake Fudge, Under The Stars,
Vanilla)
Mystic Lighthouse Mint
Red Sox (All Flavors)
Regular (Chocolate, Classic Trio, Creamy Coffee, Fudge Twister,
Golden Vanilla, Maple Walnut, Natural Vanilla Bean, Patchwork,
Strawberry)
Rhode Island Lighthouse Coffee
Sherbert (Black Raspberry, Orange, Rainbow, Wildberry)
Vermont Maple Nut
Horizon Organic - All Varieties
Hy-Vee -
Ice Cream Bars (Assorted Twin Pops, Fudge Bars (Fat Free,
No Sugar Added), Galaxy Reduced Fat (Orange, Regular),
Sundae Cups (Chocolate & Strawberry, Sherbet, Vanilla))
Ice Cream Cup Single Serve Chocolate Chip
Regular (Butter Crunch, Carmel Pecan, Cherry Nut (Light,
Regular), Chocolate (Chip (Light, Regular), Marshmallow,
Regular, Vanilla Flavored), Dutch Chocolate Light, Fudge
Marble, Lime Sherbet, Mint Chip, Neapolitan (Light, Regular),
New York Vanilla, Orange Sherbet, Root Beer Float, Star Tracks,
Strawberry, Tin Roof Sundae, Vanilla (Light, Regular))
Sherbet (Lime, Orange, Pineapple, Rainbow, Raspberry)
Icee - Freezer Bars
Icee Bits - Blue Raspberry, Cherry Burst, Cherry Cola
It's Soy Delicious - Almond Pecan ●, Awesome Chocolate ●, Black
Leopard ●, Carob Peppermint ●, Chocolate (Almond ●, Peanut
Butter ●), Espresso ●, Green Tea ●, Mango Raspberry ●, Pistachio
Almond ●, Raspberry ●, Tiger Chai ●, Vanilla Fudge ●, Vanilla ●
IttiBitz - Banana Split, Caramel 'N Fudge, Champions Chocolate,
Cotton Candy, Mint Chip, Neapolitan, Strawberry, Vanilla

Jamba - Novelty Bars (Coconut Pineapple Passion Smashin', Peach Blackberry Smash, Strawberry Lemonade Swirl, Vanilla Blueberry Pomegranate Perfection, Vanilla Strawberry Jubilation)

Jelly Belly - Freezer Bars/Pops

Kemps -

All American Pops

Bear Creek Caramel

Black (Jack Cherry, Raspberry Swirl)

Caramel (Cow Tracks, Fudge Cow Tracks)

Caribou (Blend, Coffee Caramel High Rise)

Cherry Fudge Chunk

Chocolate (Almond Cluster, Chip, Original)

Double Fudge Moose Tracks

Doubles

Ice Cream Nuggets (Caribou Blend, Mocha)

Family Size (Chocolate, Chocolate & Vanilla, Chocolate Chip, Chocolate Marshmallow, Chocolate Swirl, Mint Chocolate Chip, Neapolitan, New York Vanilla, Strawberry Swirl, Tin Roof Sundae)

Float Bars

Fat Free Frozen Yogurt (Black Raspberry, Caramel Praline Crunch, Chocolate, Key Lime, Peach, Strawberry Banana, Vanilla, Vanilla Pomegranate Swirl, Wild Blueberries 'N Sweet Cream, Wildberry Swirl)

Frozen Yogurt (Blueberry, Cherry Vanilla, Mango Peach, Mixed Berry Vanilla, Pomegranate Blueberry, Raspberry Vanilla, Strawberry, Vanilla)

Fudge (Bars, Jr.'s)

Gone Fishin'

Homemade Vanilla

Ice Cream (Bars, Cups Vanilla)

Juice Koolers

Light (Chocolate Chip, French Silk Chocolate, Mint Chocolate Chip, Neapolitan, Vanilla)

I

Maple Nut

Mint (Chocolate Chip, Cow Tracks)

Moo Jr.'s, Neapolitan

New York Vanilla Nuts To You

Old Fashioned (All Natural Vanilla, Butter Pecan, Chocolate Chip, French Vanilla, Homemade Vanilla, Maple Nut, New York Vanilla, Peppermint Bon Bon, Stawberries 'N Cream, Toasted Almond Fudge, Vanilla, Vanilla Custard)

Orange Cream (Bars, Dream)

Pecan Turtle Trail

Pink Peppermint

Pop Jr.'s

Premium Classics (100 Calorie Mini's Vanilla, Ice Cream Cups (Peanut Butter, Vanilla))

Raspberry Cow Tracks

Rocky Road

Sherbet (Lemon, Lime, Orange, Rainbow, Raspberry, Wild Strawberry)

Singles (Cherry Fudge Chunk, Cow Tracks Caramel, Frozen Yogurt Parfait (Strawberries 'N Cream, White Chocolate Raspberry, Wild Blueberry, Wildberry), Gone Fishing, Java Chunk, Mint Fudge Chunk, Pecan Turtle Trail)

Sneaker Doodle

Strawberry

Sugar Free Pop Jr.'s

Sundae Cups Chocolate & Strawberry Sauce

Timber Lodge Mint

Tin Roof Sundae

Toffee Bars

Tropical Pops

Turtle Tracks

Under The Stars Vanilla

Vanilla Bean

Kirkland Signature - Vanilla
Kool Pops - Freezer Bars
Lactaid - Butter Pecan, Chocolate, Strawberry & Cream, Vanilla
Larry & Luna's Coconut Bliss - Bars (Dark Chocolate Bars!, Naked
 Coconut Bars!), Cappuccino!, Cherry Amaretto!, Chocolate
 Hazelnut Fudge!, Chocolate Peanut Butter!, Dark Chocolate!,
 Mint Galactica!, Naked Almond Fudge!, Naked Coconut!,
 Pineapple Coconut!, Vanilla Island!
Living Harvest - Tempt Frozen Desserts (All Varieties)
Lowes Foods Brand -
 Bars (Fudge, Ice Cream, Orange Cream),
 Cups (Swirls, Vanilla)
 Lite (Chocolate, Neapolitan, Vanilla)
 Novelties Banana Jr. Pops
 Regular (Butter Pecan, Chocolate, French Vanilla, Fudge Swirl, Mint
  Chocolate Chip, Neopolitan, Vanilla (Bean, Original))
 Sherbet (Lime, Orange, Raspberry, Triple Threat)
Lucerne -
 Creamery Fresh Ice Cream (Black and White, Chocolate, Dutch
  Chocolate, Light Pecan, Light Vanilla, Mint Chocolate Chip,
  Rocky Road, Vanilla)
 Creamery Fresh Ice Cream Bars (Dutch Chocolate, Mint
  Chocolate Chip)
 Creamery Fresh Ice Cream Cups (Vanilla Cup, Butter Pecan)
 Regular (Chocolate, Chocolate Chip, French Vanilla, Golden Nut
  Sundae, Goo Goo Clusters, Mint Chip, Strawberry, Vanilla
  Low Fat)
Medifast - Soft Serve (Chocolate Mint ●, Coffee ●, Mango ●,
 Peanut Butter ●)
Meijer Brand -
 Awesome Strawberry
 Black Cherry
 Brr Bar
 Butter Pecan (Gold Georgian Bay, Lite No Sugar Added
  w/Splenda, Original)

Candy Bar Swirl

Carmel Pecan Fat Free No Sugar Added

Chocolate (Bordeaux Cherry, Carb Conquest, Chip, Double Nut
Chocolate, Mint, Original, Peanut Butter Fudge, Thunder)

Combo Cream

Cotton Candy

Dream Bars

Dulce De Leche

Fudge Bars (No Sugar Added, Original)

Fudge Swirl

Gold (Caramel Toffee Swirl, Peanut Butter Fudge Swirl, Peanut
Butter Fudge Tracks, Thunder Bay Cherry)

Heavenly Hash

Ice Cream Bars

Juice Stix

Mackinaw Fudge

Neapolitan (Lite, Original)

Novelties Gold Bar

Orange Glider

Party Pops (No Sugar Added Assorted, Orange/Cherry/Grape,
RB/B/BR)

Peppermint

Praline Pecan

Red White & Blue Pops

Scooperman

Sherbet (Cherry, Lemonberry Twist, Lime, Orange, Pineapple,
Rainbow, Raspberry)

Tin Roof

Toffee Bars

Twin Bars

Vanilla (Carb Conquest, Fat Free No Sugar Added w/Splenda,
Gold Victorian, Golden, Lite No Sugar Added w/Splenda,
Original))

Midwest Country Fare - Chocolate (Chip, Regular), Neapolitan, New York Vanilla, Vanilla (Lite, Regular)

Minute Maid - Orange/Cherry/Grape Juice Bars

Mr. Freeze - Freezer Bars Assorted

NadaMoo▲ - Creamy Coconut ●, Gotta Do Chocolate ●, Java Crunch ●, Lotta Mint Chip ●, Mmm...Maple Pecan ●, Vanilla...Ahhh ●

Natural Choice - Full Of Fruit Bars, Sorbets

North Star -
  Bars (Banana Creams, Dream, Fat Free Fudge, Fudge, Health Wise Fat Free No Sugar Added Fudge Bar, Ice Cream, Lotta, Premium English Toffee, Premium Old Recipe, Star Lite Reduced Fat)
  Lotta Pops (Bars, Cremes, Fruita, Fudge, Juice, Regular Pops, Sugar Free)
  Pops (Assorted Twin, Banana Twin, Blue Raspberry Twin, Cherry Twin, Health Wise Fat Free No Sugar Added, King Size Root Beer Float, Melon, Patriot)
  Specialty (Banana Blast, Frog Spit Turbo, King Size Root Beer Float, Totally Tubular Orange Sherbert Push Treat, Vanilla Slice)
  Sundae Ice Cream Cups (Chocolate, Chocolate Strawberry, Strawberry, Vanilla)

Otter Pops - Freezer Bars Regular

Philly Swirl - Fruit & Cream Stix, Fudge Swirl Stix, Original Swirl Stix, Philly Swirl Sorbet Italian Ice, Poppers, Sugar Free Swirl Stix

Pop Ice - Freezer Pops

Prairie Farms -
  Frozen Yogurt (Chocolate, Strawberry, Vanilla)
  Ice Cream (Chocolate (Chip, Fat Free, Regular), French Vanilla, Mint Chocolate Chip, No Sugar Added Vanilla)
  Old Recipe (Belgian Chocolate, Butter Pecan, French Vanilla, Sherbet (Lemon, Lime, Orange, Rainbow, Raspberry), Vanilla Regular)

Prestige - Chocolate, Chocolate Almond, Neapolitan, Strawberry, Vanilla

Publix -
Ice Cream (Chocolate (Marshmallow Swirl, Peanut Butter Swirl, Regular), Fudge Royal, Neapolitan, Vanilla, Vanilla Strawberry)
Low Fat Frozen Yogurt (Black Cherry, Butter Pecan, Chocolate, Neapolitan, Peach, Peanut Butter Cup, Strawberry, Vanilla, Vanilla Orange)
Low Fat Ice Cream (Chocolate, Fudge Royal, Neapolitan, Vanilla)
Novelties (Banana Pops, Fudge (Bar, Sundae Cups), Ice Cream Bar, Ice Cream Squares (Regular, Sugar Free), Ice Pops, Junior Ice Pops (All Flavors), No Sugar Added (Fudge Pops, Ice Cream Bars, Ice Pop), Red, White & Blue Junior, Toffee Bar, Twin Pops, Vanilla Cups)
Premium Ice Cream (Banana Split, Bear Claw, Black Jack Cherry, Butter Pecan, Cherry Nut, Chocolate (Almond, Cherish Passion, Cherry Passion, Chip, Regular, Trinity), Dulce De Leche, French Vanilla, Heavenly Hash, Mint Chocolate Chip, Neapolitan, Peanut Butter Goo Goo, Santa's White Christmas, Strawberry, Vanilla)
Premium Homemade (Butter Pecan, Chocolate Chip, Strawberry, Vanilla), Premium Light (Butter Pecan, Chocolate, Coffee Almond Fudge, Neapolitan, Strawberry, Vanilla)
Premium Limited Editon (Caramel Mountain Tracks, Egg Nog, Maple Walnut, Peppermint Stick, Rum Raisin)
Sherbet (Cool Lime, Exotic Fruit Medley, Peach Mango Passion, Rainbow Dream, Raspberry Blush, Sunny Orange (No Sugar Added, Regular), Tropic Pineapple)
Pure Market Express ▲ - Ice Cream (Cherry Chocolate Chip ●, Chocolate ●, Chocolate Fudge Brownie ●, Coffee ●, Cookie Dough●, Maple ●, Maple Nut ●, Mocha ●, Peanut Butter Cup●, Strawberry ●), Sorbet (Cherry ●, Lemon ●, Mango ●, Peach ●, Strawberry ●)

Purely Decadent -
Bars (Purely Vanilla ●, Vanilla Almond ●)
Dairy Free Ice Cream (Belgian Chocolate ●, Blueberry
Cheesecake ●, Cherry Nirvana ●, Chocolate Obsession ●,
Coconut Craze ●, Coconut Milk (Chocolate ●, Chocolate
Peanut Butter Swirl ●, Coconut ●, Mint Chip ●, Passionate
Mango ●, Vanilla Bean ●), Cookie Dough ●, Dulce De Leche ●,
Key Lime Pie ●, Mint Chip ●, Mocha Almond Fudge ●, Peanut
Butter Zig Zag ●, Pomegranate Chip ●, Praline Pecan ●, Purely
Vanilla ●, Rocky Road ●, Snickerdoodle ●, So Very Strawberry ●,
Turtle Trails ●)

Rice Dream - Non Dairy Frozen Desserts (Carob Almond !, Cocoa
Marble Fudge !, Neapolitan !, Orange Vanilla Swirl !, Strawberry !,
Vanilla !)

Safeway Select -
Churned (Butter Pecan, Caramel Caribou, Chocolate Moose
Tracks, Mint Chocolate Chip Light, Moose Tracks, Neapolitan,
Peppermint, Rocky Road, Strawberry, Vanilla Bean, Vanilla
Light), Dolce De Leche, Homestyle Vanilla, Mango, Pecan
Praline)
Premium (Black Walnut, Butter Pecan, Caribou Caramel,
Chocolate, French Vanilla, Neapolitan, Pecan Praline, Rocky
Road, Spumoni, Vanilla, White Chocolate Raspberry)
Regular (Fruit Bars (Lemonade, Lime, Strawberry), Moose Tracks
(Chocolate, Extreme))
Sherbet (Berry Patch, Key Lime, Mandarin Orange, Orange
Chocolate Chip, Pineapple Raspberry Orange, Strawberry Kiwi)

Slush Puppie - Freezer Bars Assorted
So Delicious - Coconut Water Sorbet (Hibiscus ●, Lemonade ●,
Mango ●, Raspberry ●)
So Delicious Coconut Milk - Bar (Coconut Almond, Vanilla)
So Delicious Dairy Free -
Kidz Assorted Fruit Pops ●

Organic (Butter Pecan ●, Chocolate (Peanut Butter ●, Velvet ●), Creamy Vanilla ●, Dulce De Leche ●, Mint Marble Fudge ●, Mocha Fudge ●, Neapolitan ●, Strawberry ●)

Organic Creamy Bars (Fudge Bar ●, Orange ●, Vanilla ●, Vanilla & Almonds ●)

Sugar Free Bar (Fudge, Vanilla)

Soda Pops - Freezer Bars (A & W, Crush, Dr. Pepper, Variety Pack)

Soy Dream - Non Dairy Frozen Desserts Butter Pecan !, French Vanilla !, Green Tea !, Mocha Fudge !, Vanilla (Fudge !, Regular !)

Spartan Brand - All American Cherry, Banana Split, Black Cherry, Butter Pecan, Golden Vanilla, Light Churn (Butter Pecan, Chocolate, Moose Tracks, Neapolitan, Peanut Butter Cup, Vanilla), Moose Tracks (Chocolate, Regular), Vanilla

Sweet Nothings - Non Dairy Bars (Fudge ●, Mango Raspberry ●)

The Skinny Cow - Low Fat Fudge Bars, Minis Fudge Bars

Tillamook - Old Fashioned Vanilla !!, Peppermint Candy !!

Trader Joe's -

Gone Bananas Chocolate Dipped Bananas

Ice Cream Bars (Blissful, Mango Vanilla, Mangolicious Fruit Blend, Raspberry Vanilla)

Sorbet (All Varieties)

Soy Creamy (Cherry Chocolate Chip, Organic Chocolate, Organic Vanilla)

Super Premium Ice Cream (Coffee Blast, French Vanilla, Mint Chocolate, Pumpkin, Ultra Chocolate)

WarHeads - Freezer Bars Extreme Sour

Wegmans Brand -

Black Raspberry

Chocolate (Marshmallow, Peanut Butter Swirl, Regular, Vanilla)

Extra Churned (Peanut Butter Swirl, Strawberry)

French (Roast Coffee, Vanilla)

Heavenly Hash

Ice Cream Bars (Cherry w/Dark Chocolate Fudge (Low Fat, No Sugar Added), Vanilla & Dark Chocolate Premium)

Ice Cream Cups (Orange Sherbert, Peanut Butter Candy, Peanut Butter Cup, Vanilla, Vanilla & Chocolate, Vanilla & Chocolate Swirl)

Ice Pops Twin Stick

Low Fat (Cappuccino Chip, Chocolate Indulgence, Creamy (Black Raspberry, Vanilla), Mint Chip, Pecan Praline, Raspberry Truffle, Vanilla)

Neapolitan

Orange Sherbert Cups

Peak Of Perfection (Black Cherry, Mango)

Peanut Butter (Chocolate Swirl, Cup, Sundae)

Premium (Butter Pecan, Chocolate, Chocolate Caramel, Coconut Mango, Creamy Caramel, Creme Brulee, French Roast, Jamocha Almond Fudge, Mint Chocolate Chip, Organic Dark Chocolate, Organic Mocha Java, Organic Vanilla, Peanut Butter & Jelly, Peanut Butter Cup, Pistachio, Rum Raisin, Strawberry, Vanilla)

Sorbet (Green Apple, Lemon, Pink Grapefruit, Raspberry), Strawberry, Vanilla (& Chocolate, Orange, Raspberry Sorbet, Regular)

Vanilla Pistachio

WholeSoy & Co. - All Frozen Yogurts

Winn & Lovett - Frozen Fruit Bars (Caribbean, Pina Colada, Raspberry, Strawberry)

Winn Dixie - Banana Pops, Classic (Chocolate, Neapolitan, Strawberry, Vanilla), Fudge Bars, Ice Cream Bars, Junior Pops, Orange Cream Bars

World's Fair - Butter Pecan, Chocolate, Neapolitan, Rocky Road, Vanilla (Light Creamy Churned, Regular)

Wyler's - Italian Ices (Freezer Bars)

Ice Cream Cones... see Cones

Ice Cream Toppings... see also Syrup

Giant Brand - Chocolate Syrup, Strawberry Syrup

Gordon Food Service - Syrup (Butterscotch, Hot Fudge Velvet, Mallow, Pineapple, Strawberry, Wild Cherry)

I

J

Hershey's - Chocolate Syrup (Lite, Regular, Special Dark)

Melissa's - Dessert Sauces (Caramel, Chocolate, Kiwi Lime, Mango, Raspberry, White Chocolate)

Smucker's -

Black Cherry

Magic Shell (Caramel, Cherry, Chocolate, Chocolate Fudge, Cupcake, Orange Creme)

Microwaveable Ice Cream Topping Hot Fudge

Plate Scrapers Dessert Topping (Caramel, Chocolate, Chocolate Fudge, Raspberry, Vanilla)

Special Recipe (Dark Chocolate, Hot Fudge, Milk Chocolate, Triple Berry)

Sugar Free (Caramel, Hot Fudge, Strawberry)

Sugar Free Sundae Syrup (Caramel, Chocolate)

Sundae Syrups (Butterscotch, Caramel, Chocolate, Strawberry)

Toppings (Andes Chocolate Mint, Apple Cinnamon, Butterscotch, Caramel, Chocolate Fudge, Hot Caramel, Hot Fudge, Marshmallow, Pecans In Syrup, Pineapple, Pumpkin Spice, Strawberry, Walnuts In Syrup)

Iced Tea/Iced Tea Mix... see Tea

Icing... see Baking Decorations & Frostings

Instant Coffee... see Coffee

J

Jalapenos

... *All Fresh Fruits & Vegetables Are Gluten-Free*

Chi-Chi's - Red

Dietz & Watson▲ - Sliced ●, Spread ●

Food Club Brand - Sliced

Great Value Brand (Wal-Mart) - Sliced Jalapenos En Rajas, Whole Jalapenos

Mezzetta - Deli Sliced (Hot Jalapeno Peppers, Tamed Jalapeno Peppers), Gourmet Deli (Sweet & Hot Jalapeno Pepper Rings, Tamed Diced Jalapeno Peppers, Tamed Fire Roasted Jalapeno Peppers w/Chipotle Peppers)

J

    Mt. Olive - Diced Jalapeno Peppers, Jalapeno Slices, Jalapeno Slices

    Old El Paso - Slices Pickled

    Ortega - Diced, Pickled Slices

    Safeway Brand - Sliced Regular

    Senora Verde - Jalapeno Slices

    Winn Dixie - Regular

Jalfrazi

    Seeds Of Change - Jalfrazi Sauce **!!**

Jam/Jelly

    Albertsons - All (Jam, Jellies, Preserves)

    Baxters - Conserve (Country Berry, Raspberry, Rhubarb & Ginger, Strawberry), Jelly (Cranberry, Mint, Red Currant), Marmalade (Lemon, Orange Lemon & Grapefruit, Seville Orange)

    Bionaturae - Organic Fruit Spread (Apricot, Bilberry, Peach, Plum, Red Raspberry, Sicilian Orange, Sour Cherry, Strawberry, Wild Berry, Wild Blackberry)

    Bramley's - Jellies & Preserves

    Eden Organic - Butter (Apple, Cherry)

    Fischer & Wieser -

        Jelly Texas (Mild Green Jalapeno, Red Hot Jalapeno)

        Marmalade (Apricot Orange, Whole Lemon Fig)

        Preserves (Old Fashioned Peach, Strawberry Rhubarb, Texas (Amaretto Peach Pecan, Jalapeach), Southern Style)

    Food Club Brand - Fun Stripes Peanut Butter (& Grape Jelly, & Strawberry Jelly), Grape Jam, Jelly (Apple, Grape, Strawberry), Preserves (Apricot, Blackberry Seedless, Marmalade, Peach, Red Raspberry, Strawberry)

    Full Circle - Apricot, Blueberry, Concord Grape, Raspberry, Strawberry

    Giant Brand -

        Apple Butter

        Jam Strawberry

        Jelly (Apple, Concord Grape, Currant, Mint, Strawberry)

Orange Marmalade

Preserves (Apricot, Blueberry, Cherry, Grape, Peach, Pineapple, Red Raspberry, Seedless Blackberry, Strawberry, Sugar Free (Apricot, Blackberry, Red Raspberry, Strawberry))

Spread (Apricot, Red Raspberry, Strawberry)

Squeezable (Grape Jelly, Strawberry Fruit Spread)

Gordon Food Service - Assorted (Reduced Calorie, Regular), Jelly (Grape, Mixed Fruit), Strawberry Jam

Hannaford Brand - Jelly (Apple, Currant, Grape, Strawberry), Orange Marmalade, Preserve (Apricots, Blueberry, Grape, Red Raspberry)

Hy-Vee - Jelly (Apple, Blackberry, Cherry, Concord Grape, Grape, Plum, Red Raspberry, Strawberry), Orange Marmalade, Preserves (Apricot, Cherry, Concord Grape, Peach, Red Raspberry, Strawberry)

Kirkland Signature - Organic Strawberry Spread

Kroger Brand - All Jams, Jellies, Preserves

Kroger Value - Grape, Strawberry Spread

Laura Lynn - Apricot Preserves, Grape Jam, Jelly (Apple, Grape), Orange Marmalade, Preserves (Apricot, Peach, Red Raspberry, Strawberry)

Lowes Foods Brand - Grape Jam, Jelly (Apple, Grape), Strawberry Preserves

Meijer Brand -

Fruit Spread (Apricot, Blackberry Seedless, Red Raspberry, Strawberry)

Grape (Jam, Jelly)

Preserves (Apricot, Blackberry Seedless, Marmalade Orange, Peach, Red Raspberry, Red Raspberry w/Seeds, Strawberry)

Nature's Promise - Organic Fruit Spread (Raspberry, Strawberry), Organic Grape Jelly

O Organics - Preserves (Apricot, Blackberry, Blueberry, Raspberry, Strawberry)

Oskri Organics - Preserves (Apricot, Cranberry, Nectarine, Peach, Pear, Plum, Raspberry), Spread (Date, Fig, Sesame)

J

Peanut Butter & Co. - Awesome Apricot Preserves, Gorgeous Grape Jelly, Rip Roaring Raspberry Preserves, Seriously Strawberry Jam

Polaner▲ - All (Jam, Jellies, Preserves)

Publix - All (Jam, Jellies, Preserves)

Safeway Brand - All (Jams, Jellies, Preserves)

Safeway Select - All (Jams, Jellies, Preserves)

Santa Cruz - Fruit Spread (All Varieties)

Shiloh Farms - Apple Butter

Simply Enjoy - Preserves (Balsamic Sweet Onion, Blueberry, Raspberry Champagne Peach, Spiced Apple, Strawberry), Red Pepper Jelly, Roasted Garlic & Onion Jam

Smucker's - All (Fruit Butter, Jams, Jellies, Low Sugar, Marmalades, Orchard's Finest Preserves, Organic, Preserves, Simply Fruit, Squeeze, Sugar Free w/NutraSweet, Sugar Free w/Splenda)

Spartan Brand - Grape Jam, Jelly (Apple, Currant, Grape, Strawberry), Orange Marmalade, Preserves (Apricot, Blackberry, Cherry, Peach, Red Raspberry, Strawberry)

Stop & Shop Brand -
Concord Grape Jelly (Spreadable, Squeezable)
Jelly (Apple, Currant, Mint)
Orange Marmalade
Preserves (Apricot, Grape, Peach, Pineapple, Red Raspberry, Seedless Blackberry, Strawberry)
Spread (Apricot, Blueberry, Strawberry)
Squeezable Grape Jelly
Sugar Free Preserves (Apricot, Blackberry, Red Raspberry, Strawberry)

Taste Of Inspiration - All Flavors **!**

Trader Joe's -
Organic Fruit Spread (Blueberry, Strawberry, Superfruit),
Organic Preserves Reduced Sugar (Blackberry**!!**, Blueberry**!!**, Raspberry**!!**, Strawberry**!!**)
Preserves (Apricot**!!**, Blackberry**!!**, Blueberry**!!**, Boysenberry**!!**, Raspberry**!!**)

Walden Farms - Spread (Apple Butter, Apricot, Blueberry, Grape, Orange, Raspberry, Strawberry)

Wegmans Brand -
Fruit Spread (Apricot/Peach/Passion Fruit, Blueberry/Cherry/Raspberry, Raspberry/Strawberry/Blackberry, Strawberry/Plum/Raspberry, Sugar Free Raspberry/Wild Blueberry/Blackberry)
Jelly (Apple, Cherry, Concord Grape, Currant, Mint, Red Raspberry, Strawberry)
Nature's Marketplace Organic Fruit Spread (Jammin' Red Raspberry, Jammin' Strawberry)
Preserves (Apricot, Cherry, Concord Grape, Peach, Pineapple, Red Raspberry, Seedless Blackberry, Strawberry)
Sugar Free Fruit Spread (Apricot/Peach/Passion Fruit, Raspberry/Wild Blueberry/Blackberry, Strawberry/Plum/Raspberry)

Welch's - All (Jams, Jellies, Preserves)

Winn Dixie - All (Jams, Jellies, Preserves)

Jello... see Gelatin

Jerky/Beef Sticks

Blackwing - Organic Beef Jerky Piedmontese (Original, Peppered), Organic Buffalo Jerky (Original, Peppered)

Buffalo Guys - Buffalo Jerky (Mild, Old Style)

Dietz & Watson▲ - Dried Beef●

Gary West - All Certified Angus Beef Steak Strips *(Except Teriyaki)*, All Original Steak Strips *(Except Teriyaki)*, Buffalo & Elk Strips, Silver Fork Natural Steak Strips

Hormel - Dried Beef

Hy-Vee - Original Jerky

Lowes Foods Brand - Beef Jerky (Honey BBQ, Original, Peppered)

Lowrey's - Beef Jerky

Old Wisconsin - Snack Bites (Beef, Pepp, Turkey), Snack Sticks (Beef, Beef Sausage & Cheddar, Pepp, Turkey)

Organic Prairie - Organic Beef Jerky 2 oz. (Prairie Classic, Smoky Chipotle, Spicy Hickory)

J
K

Shelton's - Beef Jerky, Turkey Jerky (Hot Turkey, Regular)
Wellshire Farms - Snack Sticks (Hot N' Spicy!!, Matt's Beef
Pepperoni!!, Turkey Tom Tom!!)

Juice Mix... see Drink Mix
Juice... see Drinks/Juice

K

Kale
... *All Fresh Fruits & Vegetables Are Gluten-Free*
Pictsweet - Cut Leaf

Kasha
Bob's Red Mill▲ - Organic
Shiloh Farms - Organic!!
Wolff's - Regular

Kefir
Lifeway▲ - All Varieties, ProBugs (All Varieties)
Nancy's - All Cultured Dairy & Soy Products
Trader Joe's - Regular

Ketchup
Albertsons
Annie's Naturals - Organic!!
Bakers & Chefs - Fancy Ketchup
Food Club Brand - Regular, Squeeze, Upside Down Bottle
Full Circle - Regular
Gordon Food Service - Tomato (Bottle, Can, Packet)
Great Value Brand (Wal-Mart) - Regular
Hannaford Brand - Regular
Heinz - Easy Squeeze Regular, Hot & Spicy, Hot & Spicy Kick'rs,
No Salt Added, Organic, Organic Tomato, Reduced Sugar, Regular
Hy-Vee - Regular, Squeezable Thick & Rich Tomato, Thick &
Rich Tomato
Kroger Value
Kurtz - Regular
Lowes Foods Brand - Squeeze Bottle

Meijer Brand - Regular, Squeeze, Tomato Organic
Midwest Country Fare - Regular
Nature's Basket - Organic
O Organics - Regular
Organicville - Organic ●
Publix - Regular
Publix GreenWise Market - Organic
Safeway Brand - Regular
Spartan Brand - Regular
Trader Joe's - Organic
Walden Farms - Regular
Wegmans Brand - Organic, Regular
Westbrae - Unsweetened
Winn Dixie - Regular
Woodstock Farms - Organic

Kielbasa... see Sausage

Kipper Snacks
Crown Prince - Naturally Smoked (Natural, Regular)
Ocean Prince - In Mustard, Naturally Smoked

Kiwi
*... *All Fresh Fruits & Vegetables Are Gluten-Free*

Kohlrabi
*... *All Fresh Fruits & Vegetables Are Gluten-Free*

Korma
Amy's - Indian Vegetable !
Seeds Of Change - Korma Sauce ! !
Sharwood's - Korma
Tasty Bite - Vegetable Korma !

L

Lamb
*... *All Fresh Meat Is Gluten-Free (Non-Marinated, Unseasoned)*
Kirkland Signature - Fresh Rib Roast
Sweet Bay - All Fresh Lamb
Trader Joe's - Fresh All Natural, Seasoned Rack Of Lamb

L

Lasagna
>**Amy's** - Gluten Free Garden Vegetable **!**
>**Conte's Pasta** - Cheese ●, Meat ●, Vegetable ●

Lasagna Noodles... see Pasta

Leeks
>... *All Fresh Fruits & Vegetables Are Gluten-Free*

Lemonade... see Drinks/Juice

Lemons
>... *All Fresh Fruits & Vegetables Are Gluten-Free*
>**Nuts Online** - Dried ●
>**Trader Joe's** - Lemon Curd

Lentils... see also Beans
>**GoGo Rice** - On The Go Cooked Rice Bowls Tasty & Healthy Harvest
>**Tasty Bite** - Bengal **!**, Jodphur **!**, Lentil Magic **!**, Madras **!**, Snappy Soya **!**
>**Trader Joe's** - Curried Lentils w/Basmati Rice, Steamed Lentils

Lettuce
>... *All Fresh Fruits & Vegetables Are Gluten-Free*

Licorice... see Candy/Candy Bars

Limes
>... *All Fresh Fruits & Vegetables Are Gluten-Free*

Liquid Aminos
>**Bragg** - Liquid Aminos
>**Marigold** - Liquid Aminos

Liverwurst
>**Dietz & Watson** ▲ - Liverwurst ●
>**Five Star Brand** - Natural Casing Braunschweiger (Chubs, Regular)
>**Jones Dairy Farm** - Chub Braunschweiger Liverwurst (Bacon & Onion ●, Light ●, Mild & Creamy ●, Original ●), Chunk Braunschweiger (Light ●, Original ●), Sliced Braunschweiger (Cracker Size ●, Sandwich Size ●)
>**Kayem** - Old World Style
>**Old Wisconsin** - Spreadable Pate (Black Pepper, Onion & Parsley, Original)
>**Wellshire Farms** - Liverwurst **! !**

Lobster
... *All Fresh Seafood Is Gluten-Free (Non-Marinated, Unseasoned)
Lunch Meat... see Deli Meat

Macaroni & Cheese
Amy's - Rice Mac & Cheese!, Rice Macaroni w/Non Dairy Cheeze!
Annie's - Rice Pasta & Cheddar!!
DeBoles - Elbow Style Paste & Cheese ●, Shells & Cheese ●
Gluten Free & Fabulous▲ - Macaroni & Cheese ●
Ian's - Wheat Free Gluten Free Mac & No Cheese
Mrs. Leeper's - Mac & Cheese Dinner
Namaste Foods▲ - Say Cheez
Pastariso▲ - Dolphin Rice Macaroni & Yellow Cheese ●, Elephant
  Rice Macaroni & White Cheese ●, Gorilla Rice Mini Shells & White
  Cheese ●, Rhino Rice Mini Shells & Yellow Cheese ●
Pastato▲ - Potato (Bobcat Mini Shells & Yellow Cheddar Cheese ●,
  Orangutan Mac & White Cheddar Cheese ●, Panda Mac & Yellow
  Cheddar Cheese ●, Tiger Mini Shells & White Cheddar Cheese ●)
Road's End Organics - Dairy Free Organic Mac & Chreese
  Alfredo Style, Dairy Free Organic Penne & Chreese
  Cheddar Style
Trader Joe's - Rice Pasta & Cheddar
Macaroons... see Cookies
Mackerel
... *All Fresh Fish Is Gluten-Free (Non-Marinated, Unseasoned)
Bumble Bee - Jack Mackerel
Chicken Of The Sea - All Mackerel Products
Crown Prince - Fillet Of Mackerel In Soybean Oil, Jack
  Mackerel In Water
Mahi Mahi
... *All Fresh Fish Is Gluten-Free (Non-Marinated, Unseasoned)
Mandarin Oranges
... *All Fresh Fruits & Vegetables Are Gluten-Free
Albertsons - Regular

M

Del Monte - Canned/Jarred Fruit (All Varieties), Fruit Snack Cups (Metal, Plastic)

Dole - All Fruits (Bowls *(Except Fruit Crisps)*, Canned, Dried, Frozen, Jars)

Food Club Brand - In Lite Syrup

Great Value Brand (Wal-Mart) - Plastic Cups In Light Syrup

Hy-Vee - Fruit Cups (Light Syrup, Orange Gel), Light Syrup, Mandarin Oranges

Kroger Brand - Fruit (Canned, Cups)

Lowes Foods Brand - In Lite Syrup

Meijer Brand - Light Syrup

Native Forest - Organic Mandarins

Publix - In Gel, In Light Syrup

Spartan Brand - Canned, Fruit Cups

Trader Joe's - In Light Syrup

Wegmans Brand - Regular, Whole Segment In Light Syrup

Winn Dixie - Regular

Mango

... *All Fresh Fruits & Vegetables Are Gluten-Free*

C & W - All Plain Frozen Fruits

Del Monte - Canned/Jarred Fruit (All Varieties), Fruit Snack Cups (Metal, Plastic)

Giant Brand - Frozen

Gluty Free - Dried (Diced ●, Organic ●, Regular ●, Unsulphured ●)

Meijer Brand - Frozen (Chunks, Sliced)

Native Forest - Organic Mango Chunks

Nuts Online - Dried Mango (Diced ●, Less Sugar Added ●, Organic ●, Regular ●, Simply ●)

Stop & Shop Brand - Frozen

Trader Joe's - Frozen (Mango Chunks, Sweet Mango Halves), Mango On Sticky Rice, Mangolicious Fruit Blend

Winn Dixie - Frozen Mango Chunks

Woodstock Farms - Organic Frozen Mango

Maple Syrup... see **Syrup**

Maraschino Cherries... see **Cherries**

Margarine... see Spread and/or Butter

Marinades

    A.1. - Chicago Steakhouse, Classic, New York Steakhouse

    Adolph's - Marinade In Minutes (Meat**!!**, Meat Sodium Free**!!**)

    Annie's Naturals - Baja Lime**!!**

    Consorzio - 10 Minute Marinade (Lemon Pepper, South Western w/Smoked Chipotles), Roasted Garlic & Balsamic

    Drew's - 10 Minute Marinades (Buttermilk Ranch, Honey Dijon, Italian Garlic Vinaigrette, Kalamata Olive & Caper, Poppy Seed, Raspberry, Roasted Garlic & Peppercorn, Romano Caesar, Rosemary Balsamic, Smoked Tomato)

    Food Club Brand - 30 Minute Marinades (Herb & Garlic, Lemon Pepper, Mesquite), Black Peppercorn Marinade Mix, Italian Herb Marinade Mix, Seasoning Mix (Black Peppercorn Marinade, Italian Herb Marinade Mix)

    Giant Brand - Lemon Pepper

    House Of Tsang - Japanese Steakhouse Marinade, Sweet & Sour Marinade

    Hy-Vee - Citrus Grill, Herb & Garlic, Lemon Pepper, Mesquite

    Jack Daniel's EZ Marinader - Honey Teriyaki, Slow Roasted Garlic & Herb, Steakhouse

    Ken's Steak House - Buffalo Wing Sauce, Herb & Garlic

    Kroger Brand - Bourbon Peppercorn, Caribbean Jerk, Chipotle, Grill Time (Chipotle, Mesquite, Southwest), Herb & Garlic, Lemon Pepper, Mesquite, Tequila Lime

    Lawry's - Baja Chipotle**!!**, Caribbean Jerk**!!**, Havana Garlic & Lime**!!**, Herb & Garlic**!!**, Lemon Pepper**!!**, Louisiana Red Pepper**!!**, Mesquite**!!**, Tuscan Sun Dried Tomato**!!**

    Lea & Perrins - White Wine

    McCormick -

        Grill Mates Marinade Packets (25% Less Sodium Montreal Steak, Baja Citrus, Chipotle Pepper, Garlic Herb & Wine, Mesquite, Mojito Lime, Montreal Steak, Peppercorn & Garlic, Southwest, Tomato Garlic & Basil)

M

Mexican Fiesta

Marinade Mix (Caribbean Citrus Seafood, Lemon Pepper Seafood)

Meijer Brand - Garlic & Herb, Lemon Pepper, Mesquite

Moore's Marinade - Original, Teriyaki

Mr. Spice Organic - Sauce & Marinade (Garlic Steak, Ginger Stir Fry, Honey BBQ, Honey Mustard, Hot Wing, Indian Curry, Sweet & Sour, Thai Peanut)

Mrs. Dash - Garlic Lime, Lemon Herb Peppercorn, Mesquite Grille, Southwestern Chipotle, Spicy Teriyaki, Zesty Garlic Herb

Newman's Own - Herb & Roasted Garlic, Lemon Pepper, Mesquite w/Lime

Safeway Select - Buffalo Wing, Caribbean Jerk, Lemon Garlic

San-J - Gluten Free (Sweet & Tangy ●, Szechuan ●, Teriyaki ●, Thai Peanut ●)

Sweet Baby Ray's - Buffalo Wing Sauce, Herb & Garlic, Steakhouse

Taste Of Inspiration - Roasted Garlic **!**, Steak House **!**, Texas Tumbler **!**

Weber Grill Creations - Chipotle Marinade

Wegmans Brand - Chicken BBQ, Citrus Dill, Fajita, Greek, Honey Mustard, Italian, Lemon & Garlic, Mojo, Peppercorn, Rosemary Balsamic, Santa Fe Medium, Steakhouse Peppercorn, Tangy, Zesty (Savory, Thai)

Wild Thymes - Chili Ginger Honey, New Orleans Creole

Winn Dixie - Mojo

Wright's - Liquid Smoke (Hickory Seasoning, Mesquite)

Marmalade... see Jam/Jelly

Marsala

Wegmans Brand - Mushroom Marsala Sauce

Marshmallow Dip

Marshmallow Fluff - Original, Raspberry, Strawberry

Walden Farms - Calorie Free Marshmallow Dip

Marshmallows

Albertsons - Mini, Regular

AllerEnergy▲ - Marshmallow Creme, Regular

Eylon - Natural Vanilla (Mini, Regular)
Food Club Brand - Mini, Regular
Ginger Evans - Regular
Gordon Food Service - Regular, Mini
Great Value Brand (Wal-Mart) - Marshmallows (Flavored, Miniature, Regular)
Hannaford Brand - Miniature, Regular
Hy-Vee - Colored Marshmallows, Miniatures, Regular
Jet-Puffed - FunMallows, Miniatures, Regular, StrawberryMallows, SwirlMallows
Kroger Brand - Colored, Cream, Large, Miniature
Laura Lynn - Regular
Lowes Foods Brand - Mini, Regular
Manischewitz - Regular
Marshmallow Fluff - Original, Raspberry, Strawberry
Meijer Brand - Mini, Mini Flavored, Regular
Publix - Regular
Safeway Brand - Large, Mini
Spartan Brand - Miniature, Regular
Winn Dixie - Miniature, Regular

Masala
    A Taste Of India - Masala Rice & Lentils
    Ethnic Gourmet - Chicken
    Lightlife - Indian Veggie Masala
    Loyd Grossman - Tikka Masala
    Seeds Of Change - Tikka Masala ! !
    Sharwood's - Black Pepper, Saag, Spicy Tikka, Tikka
    Tasty Bite - Channa !
    Trader Joe's - Channa, Masala Simmer Sauce ! !

Mashed Potatoes
    Albertsons - Instant (Creamy Butter, Four Cheese, Roasted Garlic)
    Alexia Foods - Red Potatoes w/Garlic & Parmesan !, Yukon Gold Potatoes & Sea Salt !
    Edward & Sons - Organic (Chreesy, Home Style, Roasted Garlic)

M

Giant Eagle Brand - Side Dishes (Garlic, Home Style, Loaded, Sweet, White Cheddar, Yukon Gold)

Hy-Vee - Four Cheese, Real Russet, Roasted Garlic, Sour Cream & Chive

Kroger Brand - Plain Instant, Refrigerated, Three Cheese

Kroger Value - Frozen

Laura Lynn - Herb & Garlic, Regular, Roasted Garlic, Sour Cream & Chives

Meijer Brand - Instant

Nasoya - Dijon Style, Fat Free, Original

Ore-Ida - Steam N' Mash (Cut Russet Potatoes, Cut Sweet Potatoes, Garlic Seasoned Potatoes)

Potato Buds▲ - Gluten Free 100% Real Potatoes

Reser's - Creamy

Safeway Brand - Instant (Regular, Roasted Garlic)

Spartan Brand - Bag (Buttery Homestyle, Four Cheese, Fully Loaded), Box (Butter & Herb, Creamy Butter, Instant, Roasted Garlic, Sour Cream & Chives)

Trader Joe's - Garlic

Winn Dixie - Frozen Homestyle Mashed

Mayonnaise

Albertsons - Regular

Bakers & Chefs - Extra Heavy

Best Foods - All (Canola, Light, Low Fat, Real), w/Lime Juice

Boar's Head - All Varieties

Cains - All Natural, Fat Free, Kitchen Recipe, Light

Dietz & Watson▲ - Mixed Pepper ●, Sandwich Spread ●, Sweet Red Pepper ●

Follow Your Heart - Vegenaise (Grapeseed Oil, High Omega 3 Expeller Pressed, Organic, Original, Reduced Fat)

Food Club Brand - Light, Regular, Salad Dressing (Light Whipped, Regular)

Gordon Food Service - Regular

Great Value Brand (Wal-Mart) - Regular

Hannaford Brand - Lite, Regular, Squeeze
Hellmann's - Canola, Light, Olive Oil Mayo Dressing, Real,
   Reduced Fat
Hy-Vee - Regular, Squeezable
Kroger Brand - Classic, Lite
Kroger Value
Laura Lynn - Fat Free, Regular
Lowes Foods Brand - Regular, Southern Style, Squeeze Bottle
Mayo Gourmet - Smoky Bacon
Meijer Brand - Lite, Regular
Miracle Whip - Free, Light, Regular
Nasoya - Nayonaise (Dijon Style, Fat Free, Original)
Naturally Delicious - Regular
Olde Cape Cod - Regular
Portmann's - Light Mayonnaise, Regular, Sandwich Spread
Publix - Regular
Royal Food Products - Garden Fresh (Heavy Duty, Regular),
   Gourmet Choice, Royal Deluxe
Safeway Brand - Light, Regular
Safeway Select - Whipped Dressing
Simply Delicious - Organic Mayonnaise (Garlic, Original)
Smart Balance - Omega Plus Light
Spartan Brand - Jar, Regular Squeeze
Spectrum - Artisan Organic (Dijon, Olive Oil, Roasted Garlic,
   Wasabi), Canola (Light Eggless Vegan, Regular), Organic (Omega 3
   w/Flax Oil, Regular), Squeeze Bottle Canola (Light Eggless Vegan,
   Regular), Organic
Tiger Tiger - May O (Original!, w/Garlic!, w/Sweet Chili!, w/
   Tikka!, w/Wasabi!)
Trader Joe's - Real!!, Reduced Fat!!, Wasabi Mayo
Walden Farms - Mayo
Wegmans Brand - Classic, Light
Winn Dixie - Light, Regular

M Meals

A Taste Of China - Szechuan Noodles

A Taste Of India - Quick Meals (Masala Rice & Lentils, Spiced Rice w/Raisins)

A Taste Of Thai - Quick Meals (Coconut Ginger Noodles, Pad Thai Noodles, Peanut Noodles, Red Curry Noodles, Yellow Curry Noodles)

Adolph's - Meal Maker Beef Stew**!!**

Amy's - Kids Meals Baked Ziti**!**

Asian Helper▲ - Gluten Free (Beef Fried Rice, Chicken Fried Rice)

Celiac Specialties▲ - Frozen Meals (Butter Noodles, Chicken Parmesan, Lasagna, Lasagna Wraps, Mac & Cheese, Spaghetti & Meatballs)

Chi-Chi's - Fiesta Plates (Creamy Chipotle Chicken, Salsa Chicken, Savory Garlic Chicken)

Dinty Moore - Microwave Meals (Rice w/Chicken, Scalloped Potatoes & Ham)

Ethnic Gourmet - Chicken Biryani, Chicken Korma, Chicken Tandoori w/Spinach, Chicken Tikka Masala, Eggplant Bhartha, Palak Paneer, Shahi Paneer, Vegetable Korma

Food Club Brand - Dinner Taco Kit

Free Choice Foods▲ -
Chickpea & Potato Curry w/Roasted Peanuts ●
Chili Non Carne ●
Creole Red Bean Jambalaya Rice & Bean Mix ●
Cuban Style Black Beans & Rice ●
Hearty Vegetable Stew w/Buckwheat & Quinoa ●
Middle Eastern Lentil Pilaf w/Cashews & Raisins ●
Quinoa Lentil Pilaf w/Almonds & Raisins ●
Quinoa Vegetable Pilaf ●
Red Quinoa & Black Bean Salad Starter ●
Taboule Style Quinoa Salad Starter ●
Tuscan Style White Beans & Rice Mix ●
Wild Rice Pilaf Mix w/Roasted Pecans ●

Garden Of Eatin' - Yellow Corn Taco Dinner Kit

Giant Eagle Brand - Broccoli Rice & Cheese Casserole

Gluten Free Cafe - Asian Noodles ●, Fettuccini Alfredo ●, Homestyle Chicken & Vegetables ●, Lemon Basil Chicken ●, Pasta Primavera ●, Savory Chicken Pilaf ●

Glutino ▲ - Frozen Meals (Chicken Penne Alfredo, Chicken Ranchero, Pad Thai w/Chicken, Penne Alfredo, Pomodoro Chicken)

Hamburger Helper ▲ - Gluten Free Cheesy Hashbrowns

Hormel - Compleats Santa Fe Style Chicken, Compleats Microwave 10 oz. Meals (Chicken & Rice, Santa Fe Chicken & Rice)

Ian's - Wheat Free Gluten Free (Mac & Meat Sauce, Mac & No Cheese)

Kid's Kitchen - Beans & Wieners

Lightlife - Indian Veggie Masala, Zesty Mexican

Mayacamas - Skillet Toss (Black Olive Pesto, Dried Tomato, Garden Style, Green Olive Pesto, Mushroom Sauce, Seafood Recipe, Spicy Style)

Mixes From The Heartland ▲ - Meal Mix (Baked Chicken Salad ●, BBQ Beef & Pasta ●, Beef Skillet ●, Cheeseburger Pie ●, Garden Meat Loaf ●, Green Chili ●, Mexican Chicken N' Rice ●, Mexican Rice Bake ●, Mexican Style Casserole ●, Noodle Casserole ●, Sausage Casserole ●, Southwest Potato Casserole ●, Sweet Corn Casserole ●, Taco Rice Skillet ●, Tex Mex Meat Loaf ●, Texas Bean Bake ●, Texas Goulash ●, Tuna Casserole ●)

Mrs. Leeper's - Beef (Lasagna Dinner, Stroganoff Dinner), Cheeseburger Mac Dinner, Chicken Alfredo Dinner, Creamy Tuna Dinner, Mac & Cheese Dinner

My Own Meals - Beef Stew, Chicken & Black Bean, Mediterranean Chicken Meal, My Kind Of Chicken, Old World Stew

Namaste Foods ▲ - Pasta Meals (Pasta Pisavera, Say Cheez, Taco)

Old El Paso - Dinner Kit (Stand N' Stuff Taco, Taco)

Orgran ▲ - Pasta Ready Meal (Tomato & Basil, Vegetable Bolognese), Spaghetti In A Can

Ortega - Dinner Kit (12 Count Taco, 18 Count Taco, Pizza Grande)

Pure Market Express ▲ - Baked Macaroni & Cheese ●, Black Bean Burgers ●, Garlic Alfredo Pasta ●, Hemp Tabouli ●, Lasagna ●, Pad Thai Kit ●, Portabella Herb Steak & Red Pepper Corn Salsa ●, Ravioli ●, Salmon & Hollandaise ●, Stir Fry Less Sauce ●, Tostadas ●, Walnut Pesto Pasta w/Shrimp Bites Kit ●

Sharwood's - Vegetable Curry

Simply Enjoy - Butter Chicken, Pad Thai w/Chicken, Tikka Masala

Smart Ones - Frozen Entrees (Broccoli & Cheddar Potatoes, Cranberry Turkey Medallions, Creamy Tuscan Chicken, Fiesta Chicken, Grilled Chicken In Garlic Herb Sauce, Home Style Chicken, Honey Dijon Chicken, Lemon Herb Chicken Piccata, Santa Fe Rice & Beans)

Tambobamba - Mojo Bowls (Brazilian Rice & Beans, Caribbean Rice & Beans, Peruvian Rice & Beans)

Tasty Bite - Agra Peas & Greens !, Aloo Palak !, Bombay Potatoes !, Channa Masala !, Chunky Chickpeas !, Jaipur Vegetables !, Kashmir Spinach !, Kerala Vegetables !, Madras Lentils !, Mushroom Takatak !, Paneer Makhani !, Punjab Eggplant !, Zesty Lentils and Peas !

Thai Kitchen - Microwave Rice Noodles & Sauce (Ginger & Sweet Chili, Original Pad Thai, Thai Basil & Chili), Noodle Carts (Pad Thai, Thai Peanut), Stir Fry Rice Noodles (Lemongrass & Chili, Original Pad Thai, Thai Peanut)

Trader Joe's - All Indian Fare Meals, Chicken Tandoori Rice Bowl, Chicken Tikka Masala, Peruvian Style Chimichurri Rice w/Vegetables !!, Roasted Poblano Peppers w/Shrimp Rice & Cheese

Tre Bella Foods - Silly Fusilli

Meatballs

Aidells - Buffalo Style, Chipotle, Sun Dried Tomato & Parmesan Cheese

Al Fresco - Tomato & Basil Chicken Meatballs

Andrea's Fine Foods ▲ - Meatballs

Tre Bella Foods - Gluten Free Turkey Mini Meatballs

Melon
... *All Fresh Fruits & Vegetables Are Gluten-Free*

Milk
Albertsons - 1%, 2%, Instant & Powdered (All Varieties), Evaporated, Fat Free, Half & Half, Lactose Free (Reduced Fat, w/Calcium), Sweetened Condensed

Borden Eagle Brand - Condensed Milk (Fat Free, Low Fat, Sweetened)

Carnation - Evaporated (Fat Free, Low Fat, Regular, Regular w/Vitamin D), Instant Non Fat Dry, Sweetened Condensed Milk

Coburn Farms - Evaporated, Evaporated Filled, Sweetened Condensed

Couburn Farms - Evaporated

Dairy Ease - Lactose Free Milk

Dari Free - Non Dairy Milk Alternative (Chocolate, Original)

Food Club Brand - 1%, 1% Chocolate, 2%, Buttermilk (Fat Free, Whole), Chocolate, Condensed Milk, Evaporated Fat Free, Evaporated Milk Regular, Half & Half (Fat Free, Regular), Instant (Pouches, Regular), Lactose Free (2%, No Fat, Whole), Skim, Whole Chocolate

Friendship - Light Buttermilk

Garelick Farms - Chug (1% Low Fat Milk, Low Fat Chocolate, TruMoo Chocolate, TruMoo Strawberry, Whole Milk), Cultured Low Fat Buttermilk, Flavored (Over the Moon Chocolate, TruMoo Chocolate, TruMoo Coffee, TruMoo Strawberry), Fresh (Half & Half, Light Cream), Ultra Pasteurized (Fat Free Half & Half, Half & Half, Light Cream), Ultra-Pasteurized Heavy Cream, White (1% Low Fat, 2% Reduced Fat, Fat Free, Over the Moon 1% Low Fat, Over The Moon Fat Free, Skim & More, Whole)

Giant Brand - 1% Buttermilk, 1% Low Fat Chocolate, Instant Non Fat Dry, Lactose Free (Skim, w/Added Calcium, Whole)

Giant Eagle Brand - Heavy Cream

Great Value Brand (Wal-Mart) - Evaporated Milk, Evaporated Skimmed, Fat Free Half & Half, Fat Free Sweetened Condensed, Half & Half, Lactose Free (Fat Free, Reduced Fat, Vitamin D), Organic (Fat Free, Reduced Fat, Vitamin D), Sweetened Condensed

Hannaford Brand - All Regular, Condensed, Evaporated, Half & Half, Instant

HealthMarket - Organic (1% Low Fat, 2% Reduced Fat, Skim, Whole)

Hood - All Chocolate (All Sizes, Full Fat, Low Fat), All Creams, All Fluid Milk, Buttermilk, Calorie Countdown (All Varieties)

Horizon Organic - All Varieties

Hy-Vee - ½%, 1% Low Fat, 2% Reduced Fat, Chocolate Soy, Enriched (Original Rice, Vanilla Rice), Evaporated, Fat Free (Evaporated, Skim), Instant Non Fat Dry, Original Soy, Refrigerated Soy (Chocolate, Original, Vanilla), Skim, Sweetened Condensed, Vanilla Soy, Vitamin D

Kemps - All Varieties

Kirkland Signature - 2%, Fat Free, Low Fat (Organic, Regular)

Kroger Brand - Instant Chocolate Milk, Liquid, Powdered

Kroger Value - Evaporated

Lactaid - All Varieties

Laura Lynn - Evaporated, Half & Half, Instant Dry, Lactose Reduced, Sweetened Condensed

Living Harvest - Tempt Hempmilk (All Varieties)

Lowes Foods Brand - Half & Half, Half & Half Fat Free

Lucerne - Buttermilk (Fat Free, Low Fat, Regular), Chocolate, Half & Half, Lactose Free (All Varieties)

Meijer Brand - ½% Low Fat, 1% Low Fat, 2% Reduced Fat, Chocolate (1% Low Fat, Regular), Evaporated (Lite Skimmed, Small, Tall), Fat Free, Instant, Lactose Free Milk (2% w/Calcium, Fat Free w/Calcium), Milk Sweetened Condensed, Strawberry Milk, Ultra Pasteurized Heavy Half & Half, Vitamin D

Nature's Promise - Organic (Fat Free, Low Fat, Reduced Fat, Whole)

Nesquik - Ready To Drink (All Flavors)

O Organics - All Varieties

Organic Valley - Buttermilk, Chocolate, Eggnog, Fat Free, Half & Half, Lactose Free, Low Fat 1%, Powder (Buttermilk Blend, Non Fat Dry Milk), Reduced Fat 2%, Shelf Stable Liters (Chocolate 2%, Half & Half, Whole), Shelf Stable Single Serves (Chocolate, Low Fat, Strawberry, Vanilla)

Pacific Natural Foods - Hemp Milk (Original, Vanilla), Organic (2% Reduced Fat, Fat Free)

Pet - Evaporated, Fat Free Evaporated Milk

Prairie Farms - Flavored Milk (1% Chocolate, 1% Strawberry, 1% Vanilla, 2% Chocolate, Chocolate), Half & Half (Fat Free, Ultra Pasteurized), Regular Egg Nog, White Milk (1% Low Fat, 2% Low Fat, 2% Reduced Fat, Fat Free)

Private Selections - Condensed, Evaporated

Publix - Chocolate, Evaporated, Fat Free (Plus, Regular), Instant Non Fat Dry, Low Fat (Chocolate, Regular), Reduced Fat, Sweetened Condensed, Whole

Publix GreenWise Market - Organic Milk (Fat Free, Reduced Fat, Whole)

Pure Market Express▲ - Brazil Nut Milk●

Safeway Brand - Buttermilk, Fat Free, Half & Half (Reduced Fat, Regular), Lactose Free (Fat Free, Whole), Whole

Shamrock Farms - Buttermilk 1% Lowfat, Flavored Mmmmilk (Cafe Mocha, Chocolate, Dulce De Leche, No Sugar Added Low Fat 1% Chocolate, Strawberry, Vanilla, Whole Chocolate), Organic (1% Low Fat, 2% Reduced Fat, Fat Free, Whole), Regular (Low Fat 1% Chocolate, Whole), Regular Mmmmilk (1% Low Fat, 2% Reduced Fat, Fat Free, Fat Free Plus Calcium, Whole), Rockin' Refuel (Chocolate, Strawberry, Vanilla), Shamrockers (Chocolate, White)

Simply Smart - Chocolate Fat Free, Half & Half Fat Free, Milk (Fat Free, Low Fat)

Smart Balance - Fat Free (Antioxidant Vitamins C & E, Heart Right, Lactose Free Omega 3 & Vitamin E, Omega 3 & Vitamin E), Low Fat

Spartan Brand - Country Fresh (1% Chocolate, 1% Low Fat, 2% Reduced Fat, Skim, Whole), Half & Half, Instant Powdered, Sweetened Condensed

Stop & Shop Brand - Half & Half (Fat Free, Pasteurized, Ultra Pasteurized), Lactose Free (Calcium Fortified Fat Free, Whole), Low Fat, Skim, Whole

Wegmans Brand - 1% (Low Fat, Regular), 2% (Reduced Fat, Regular), Evaporated (Fat Free, Regular, Vitamin D), Fat Free Skim (Regular, Rich Calcium Fortified), Half & Half (Fresh, Grade A Ultra Pasteurized), Heavy Cream, Lactose Free (Fat Free, Low Fat, Reduced Fat, Regular), Low Fat Chocolate, Organic (1%, 2%, Fat Free, Reduced Fat, Vitamin D), Sweetened Condensed, Vitamin A & D Added, Vitamin D

Winn Dixie - Evaporated, Fat Free, Instant Nonfat Dry, Low Fat (1%, 2%), Organic (1% Low Fat, 2% Low Fat, Fat Free, Whole), Soy (Chocolate, Plain, Unsweetened, Vanilla), Sweetened & Condensed, Whole

Woodstock Farms - Organic Milk (1% Low Fat, 2% Reduced Fat, Fat Free Skim, Whole)

Yoo-Hoo - All Varieties

Millet

Arrowhead Mills - Hulled Millet, Millet Flour

Bob's Red Mill▲ - Flour, Grits/Meal, Hulled Millet

Gluty Free - Organic ●

GoGo Rice - On The Go Cooked Rice Bowls (Exotic & Spicy Thai Peanut, Sweet & Mild Hawaiian)

Mints

Altoids - Curiously Strong Mints Large Tin (Cinnamon, Crème De Menthe, Peppermint, Wintergreen)

Doublemint - Mintcreme, Wintercreme

Eclipse - All Flavors

Lowes Foods Brand - Starlight Mints

Safeway Brand - Star Light

St. Claire's Organics - Organic (Peppermint, Spearmint, Wintermint), Premium

Vermints - Cafe Express, Chai, Cinnamint, Gingermint, Peppermint, Wintermint

Miso

Eden Organic - Organic Miso (Genmai, Shiro)

Edward & Sons - Miso Cup Savory Soup w/Seaweed South River Azuki Bean**!!**, Chick Pea**!!**, Dandelion Leek**!!**, Garliced Pepper**!!**, Golden Millet**!!**, Hearty Brown Rice**!!**, Sweet Tasting Brown Rice**!!**, Sweet White**!!**

Mixed Fruit

*... *All Fresh Fruits & Vegetables Are Gluten-Free*

C & W - All Plain Frozen Fruits & Medleys

Del Monte - Canned/Jarred Fruit (All Varieties), Fruit Snack Cups (Metal, Plastic)

Dole - All Fruits (Bowls *(Except Fruit Crisps)*, Canned, Dried, Frozen, Jars *(Except Real Fruit Bites)*)

Food Club Brand - Bowls In Light Syrup (Mixed Fruit w/Cherries, Regular, Tropical), Canned X Treme Cherry, Chunky Mixed Fruit In Juice, Frozen Berry Medley, Frozen Mixed Fruit

Giant Brand - Frozen Berry Medley, Regular

Great Value Brand (Wal-Mart) - Canned (Fruit Cocktail, No Sugar Added Fruit Cocktail, Triple Cherry Fruit Mix In Natural Flavored Cherry, Tropical Fruit Salad In Light Syrup & Fruit Juices), Frozen Berry Medley, Frozen Strawberries Peaches Pineapples & Mangoes, Plastic Cups (Cherry Fruit Mix, No Sugar Added Mixed, Regular, Tropical)

Hannaford Brand - All (Canned, Frozen)

Hy-Vee - Fruit Cups (Mixed, Tropical), Mixed Fruit (Lite Chunk, Regular)

Kroger Value - All Fresh Fruit Canned

Laura Lynn - Canned

Lowes Foods Brand - Canned Fruit Cocktail (In Heavy Syrup, In Juice)

Meijer Brand - Frozen Tropical Fruit Blend, Mixed Fruit (Individually Quick Frozen, Regular)

Publix - Canned (Chunky Mixed Fruit In Heavy Syrup, Fruit Cocktail In Heavy Syrup, Lite Chunky Mixed Fruit In Pear Juice, Lite Fruit Cocktail In Pear Juice), Frozen

S&W - All Canned/Jarred Fruits

Spartan Brand - Frozen (Berry Medley, Mixed Fruit), Fruit Cups, In Lite Syrup

Stop & Shop Brand - Fruit Mix In Heavy Syrup, Mixed Fruit, Very Cherry Fruit Mix In Light Syrup

Trader Joe's - Frozen (Berry Medley, Fancy Berry Medley)

Wegmans Brand - Fruit Cocktail (In Heavy Syrup, In Pear Juice, Regular)

Winn Dixie - Canned Chunky Mixed Fruit (Heavy Syrup, Light Syrup), Frozen (Berry Medley, Mixed Fruit), Fruit Cocktail (Heavy Syrup, Light Syrup)

Woodstock Farms - Organic Tropical Delight Mix, Tropical Fruit Mix

Mixed Vegetables

*... *All Fresh Fruits & Vegetables Are Gluten-Free*

Albertsons - Frozen *(Except Sweet Onion Rounds)*

Birds Eye - All Plain Frozen Vegetables

C & W - All Plain Frozen Vegetables

Del Monte - All Canned Vegetables

Food Club Brand - Canned Mixed Vegetables, Frozen Fiesta, Mixed Vegetables, Steamin' Easy (California Style, Florentine Style, Mixed Vegetables, Peas & Carrots), Stir Fry

Freshlike - Frozen Plain Vegetables

Full Circle - Organic Frozen 4 Vegetable Blend

Giant Brand - Frozen (Broccoli Cauliflower & Pepper Mix, Broccoli Corn & Red Peppers Mix, Country Blend, Green Beans & Wax Beans, Japanese Stir Fry Blend, Latino Blend, Mixed Vegetables, Peas & Diced Carrots, Stew Vegetables, Stir Fry), Frozen Petite (Ranchero Blend, Soup Mix Vegetables)

Grand Selections - Frozen Vegetables (Caribbean Blend, Normandy Blend, Riviera Blend)

Green Giant - Frozen Garden Vegetable Medley Seasoned, Mixed Vegetables, Simply Steam (Baby Vegetable Medley, Garden Vegetable Medley), Valley Fresh Steamers Mixed Vegetables

Hannaford Brand - All Frozen

Hy-Vee - Canned Mixed Vegetables, Frozen (California Mix,

Country Trio, Fiesta Blend, Italian Blend, Mixed Vegetables, Oriental Vegetables, Stew Vegetables, Winter Mix)

Kirkland Signature - Frozen (Normandy Style Vegetable Blend, Stir Fry Vegetable Blend)

Kroger Brand - All Plain Vegetables (Canned, Frozen)

Kroger Value - All Plain Vegetables (Canned, Frozen)

Laura Lynn - 2lb. Frozen Vegetables *(Except Breaded Okra, Hushpuppies)*, Mixed Vegetables (No Salt, Regular)

Lowes Foods Brand - Frozen (California Blend, Fajita Blend, Italian Blend, Mixed Vegetables, Peking Stir Fry, Vegetables For Soup)

Meijer Brand - Canned Mixed, Frozen (California Style, Fiesta, Florentine Style, Italian, Mexican, Mixed Vegetables (Organic, Regular), Oriental, Parisian Style, Stew Mix, Stir Fry)

Mezzetta - California Hot Mix, Chicago Style Italian Sandwich Mix (Hot Giardiniera, Mild Giardiniera), Italian Mix Giardiniera, Mexi Mix Hot N' Spicy

Midwest Country Fare - Canned, Frozen (California Blend, Mixed Vegetables, Winter Mix)

Nuts Online - Simply Organic Mixed Veggies Freeze Dried Vegetables ●

O Organics - Frozen (California Style Vegetables, Mixed Vegetable Blend)

Pictsweet -
All Plain Frozen Vegetables
Baby California
Baby Mixed Vegetables
Cracked Pepper Seasoned (Okra & Squash, Seasoned Summer Vegetables)
Fiesta Chicken & Rice
Grilled Chicken w/Summer Vegetables
Ground Peppercorn Seasoned Garden Vegetables
Seasoned Corn & Black Beans
Seasoning Blend
Spring Vegetables

M

Publix - Canned, Frozen Blends (Alpine, California, Del Oro, Gumbo, Italian, Japanese, Mixed Vegetable, Oriental, Peas & Carrots, Roma, Soup Mix w/Tomatoes, Succotash)

S&W - All Canned Vegetables

Safeway Brand - Frozen Blends (Asian Style, California Style, Santa Fe Style, Stew Vegetables, Stir Fry, Tuscan Style Vegetables, Winter Blend), Mixed Vegetables (Canned, Frozen)

Spartan Brand - Canned Mixed Vegetables, Frozen (Baby Corn Blend, Baby Pea Blend, California Vegetables, Fiesta Vegetables, Italian Vegetables, Mixed Vegetables, Oriental Vegetables, Pepper Stir Fry, Stew Mix Vegetables, Vegetables For Soup, Winter Blend)

Stop & Shop Brand - Blend (Country, Latino), Mixed Vegetables (No Salt Added, Regular), Stew Vegetables

Tasty Bite - Jaipur Vegetables!, Kerala Vegetables!, Vegetable Korma!

Trader Joe's - Frozen Harvest Hodgepodge!!, Frozen Organic Foursome

Wegmans Brand - Mix (Santa Fe, Southern, Spring)

Winn Dixie - Canned No Salt Added, Frozen Mixed Vegetables (Organic, Regular)

Woodstock Farms - Organic Frozen Mixed Vegetables

Mochi

Grainaissance - Cashew Date, Chocolate Brownie, Original, Pizza, Raisin Cinnamon, Sesame Garlic, Super Seed

Molasses

Brer Rabbit - Molasses (Blackstrap, Full Flavor, Mild)

Grandma's - Original, Robust

Oskri Organics - Regular

Mousse

Orgran▲ - Chocolate Mousse Mix

Muffins/Muffin Mix

1-2-3 Gluten Free▲ - Meredith's Marvelous Muffin/Quickbread Mix●

Andrea's Fine Foods▲ - Banana, Blueberry, Carrot Spice, Chocolate Chunk, Pumpkin

M

Augason Farms - Gluten Free Muffin Mix (Almond Poppy Seed ●, Blueberry ●, Raspberry ●, Western Scone ●)

Authentic Foods ▲ - Blueberry Muffin Mix, Chocolate Chip Muffin Mix

Bi-Aglut - Cocoa Muffin w/Milk Filling, Grandula Cream Filled, Margherita Muffin, Sugar Free Apricot, Yoghurt Raisin

Breads From Anna ▲ - Pancake & Muffin Mix (Apple, Cranberry, Maple)

Breakaway Bakery ▲ - Muffin Batter (Banana ●, Coffee Cake ●, Pumpkin ●)

Canyon Bakehouse ▲ - Cranberry Crunch Muffins

Cause You're Special ▲ - Classic Muffin & Quickbread Mix, Lemon Poppy Seed Muffin Mix, Sweet Corn Muffin Mix

Celiac Specialties ▲ - Mini Lemon Poppy Muffins, Mini Pumpkin Chocolate Muffins, Pumpkin Muffins

El Peto ▲ - Muffin Mix, Muffins (Apple & Spice, Blueberry, Chocolate Chip, Cranberry, Lemon Poppy Seed, Tropical Delight, Whole Grain Banana, Whole Grain Carrot, Whole Grain Raisin)

Ener-G ▲ - Brown Rice English Muffins w/Flax, English Muffins

Flax4Life ▲ - Flax Muffins (Chunky Chocolate Chip ●, Faithfully Carrot Raisin ●, Hawaiian Pineapple Coconut ●, Tantalizing Cranberry & Orange ●, Wild Blueberry ●)

Flour Nut - Muffin Mix (Austin's Maple Cinnamon, Maple Walnut)

Foods By George ▲ - Muffins (Blueberry, Cinnamon Currant English, Corn, English, No Rye)

Gifts Of Nature ▲ - Mix (Basic, Cinnamon Spice, Cranberry Orange, Vanilla Poppy Seed)

Gluten Free Life ▲ - Apple Pie, Blueberry, Carrot Cake, Chocolate Chip, The Ultimate Gluten Free Cake Muffin & Brownie Mix

Gluten Free Mama ▲ - Mama's Scone Mix ●

Gluten Free Pantry ▲ - Muffin & Scone Mix

Gluten-Free Creations ▲ - Chocolate Zucchini ●, Cinnamon Rolls ●, Cranberry Orange Pecan ●, English Muffins ●, Lemon Poppyseed ●

Gluten-Free Essentials▲ - Lemon Poppy Seed Bread & Muffin Mix ●, Spice Cake & Muffin Rich ●

Glutino▲ - Premium English Muffins

Grandma Ferdon's▲ - Muffins (Banana ●, Corn ●, Pumpkin ●)

Heaven Mills▲ - Muffins (Blueberry ●, Carrot ●, Chocolate Chip ●, Cinnamon ●)

Hodgson Mill▲ - Gluten Free Apple Cinnamon Muffin Mix

Katz Gluten Free▲ - Honey Muffins ●

King Arthur Flour▲ - Gluten Free Muffin Mix ●

Kinnikinnick▲ - Cornbread & Muffin Mix, Jumbo Muffin Chocolate Lovers, Jumbo Muffins (Harvest Crunch, Lemon Poppy Seed), Muffin Mix, Regular Muffins (Blueberry, Carrot, Chocolate Chip), Tapioca Rice English Muffin

Kneaded Specialties▲ - Banana Muffins ●, Blueberry Streusel ●, Double Chocolate Chip Banana ●, Raspberry Swirl ●, Vegan Pumpkin ●, Vegan Very Berry ●

Longevity Bean Muffins - Muffins (Almond, Banana, Blueberry, Cherry, Cinnamon, Cranberry, Original)

Marion's Smart Delights▲ - Cookie & Muffin Mix ●

Midge's Muffins - Banana, Blueberry, Cherry Apple, Chocolate Chip, Cranberry, Pumpkin

Mixes From The Heartland▲ - Streusel Muffin Mix (Apple Cinnamon ●, Blueberry ●, Cranberry ●, Raspberry ●, Spring ●)

Mrs. Crimble's - Chocolate Chip, Muffin Mix

Namaste Foods▲ - Muffin Mix, Sugar Free

Only Oats - Muffin Mix (Cinnamon Spice ●, Decadent Chocolate ●)

Orgran▲ - Muffin Mix (Chocolate, Lemon & Poppyseed)

Pamela's Products▲ - Cornbread and Muffin Mix

Quejos▲ - Non Dairy Muffins (Chocolate Chip Banana, Cranberry Banana, Hemp Heart Banana)

Really Great Food Company▲ - Muffin Mix (Apple Spice, Cornbread, English, Maple Raisin, Sweet, Vanilla)

Silly Yak Bakery - CFGF Muffins (Apple ●, Apple Sorghum ●, Blueberry Rice ●, Blueberry Sorghum ●, Carrot Raisin Sorghum ●, Peach Rice ●, Raspberry Rice ●)

Skye Foods - Muffins (Blueberry ●, Chocolate Chunk ●)

The Cravings Place ▲ - Create Your Own

The Grainless Baker ▲ - Muffins (Banana Walnut, Blueberry, Chocolate Chip, Corn, Sampler, Seasonal (Pumpkin, Zucchini))

Udi's Gluten Free Foods ▲ - Gluten Free Muffins (Blueberry, Double Chocolate, Lemon Streusel)

Whole Foods Market Gluten Free Bakehouse ▲ - Muffins (Blueberry, Cherry Almond Streusel, Lemon Poppyseed, Morning Glory)

Mushrooms

*... *All Fresh Fruits & Vegetables Are Gluten-Free*

Albertsons - Pieces & Stems (No Salt, Regular)

Birds Eye - All Plain Frozen Vegetables

Cara Mia - Marinated

Eden Organic - Maitake Dried, Shiitake (Dried Sliced, Dried Whole)

Food Club Brand - Canned (Pieces & Stems, Whole, Whole Sliced)

Fungus Among Us - All Dried

Great Value Brand (Wal-Mart) - Canned Mushrooms (Pieces & Stems, Sliced)

Green Giant - Canned Mushrooms (Pieces & Stems, Sliced, Whole)

Hannaford Brand - Stems & Pieces (No Salt, Regular)

Hy-Vee - Sliced, Stems & Pieces

Ka-Me - Stir Fry !, Straw Mushrooms !

Kroger Value - All Plain Vegetables Canned

Laura Lynn - All Mushrooms

Lowes Foods Brand - Canned Sliced, Jar Sliced

Meijer Brand - Canned (Sliced, Whole), Canned Stems & Pieces (No Salt, Regular)

Midwest Country Fare - Mushrooms & Stems (No Salt Added, Regular)

Native Forest - Organic Pieces & Stems

Nuts Online - Simply Mushrooms Freeze Dried Vegetables ●

Pennsylvania Dutchman - Chunky Style Portabella, Sliced, Stems & Pieces, Whole

Publix GreenWise Market - Portabella, Regular

M

Safeway Brand - Canned Button Sliced

Spartan Brand - Buttons Sliced, Canned Buttons Whole, No Salt Added Pieces & Stems, Pieces & Stems

Trader Joe's - Marinated w/Garlic

Wegmans Brand - Button, Pieces & Stems, Sliced

Woodstock Farms - Organic Frozen (Mixed, Shiitake)

Mustard

Albertsons - Dijon, Regular

Annie's Naturals - Organic (Dijon!!, Honey!!, Horseradish!!, Yellow!!)

Best Foods - Dijonnaise, Honey

Boar's Head - All Varieties

Bone Suckin' Sauce - Regular, Sweet & Hot

Di Lusso - Chipotle, Cranberry Honey, Deli Style, Dijon, Honey Sweet & Hot, Jalapeno

Dietz & Watson▲ - Champagne Dill ●, Chipotle ●, Cranberry Honey ●, Jalapeno ●, Smoky Chipotle ●, Spicy Brown ●, Sweet & Hot ●, Wasabi ●, Whole Grain Dijon ●, Yellow ●

Dorothy Lane Market - Champagne, Classic Dijon, Honey

Eden Organic - Organic (Brown, Yellow)

Emeril's - Dijon, Kicked Up Horseradish, New York Deli Style, Smooth Honey, Yellow

Fischer & Wieser - Smokey Mesquite, Sweet Heat

Food Club Brand - Creamy Dijon, Dijon, Honey, Horseradish, Regular, Spicy Brown

French's - Classic Yellow, Honey, Honey Dijon, Horseradish, Spicy Brown

Frontera - Chipotle Honey Mustard Grilling Sauce

Full Circle - Organic (Spicy Brown, Yellow)

Giant Brand - Dijon (Creamy, Regular, Tarragon), Grainy (Old, Raspberry), Honey, Yellow

Gordon Food Service

Great Value Brand (Wal-Mart) - All Natural Yellow, Coarse Ground, Dijon, Honey, Southwest Spicy, Spicy Brown

mustard

M

Grey Poupon - Country Dijon, Deli, Dijon, Harvest Coarse Ground, Hearty Spicy Brown, Mild & Creamy, Savory Honey

Hannaford Brand - Dijon, Honey, Spicy Brown, Yellow

Heinz - Deli, Dijon, Honey, Spicy Brown, Yellow

Hellmann's - Deli Brown, Dijonnaise, Honey

Hy-Vee - Dijon, Honey, Regular, Spicy Brown

Jack Daniel's - Hickory Smoke, Honey Dijon, Horseradish, Old No. 7, Spicy Southwest, Stone Ground Dijon

Kroger Brand - Honey, Horseradish, Regular, Spicy Brown

Kurtz - Honey Mustard, Spicy Brown, Yellow

Laura Lynn - All Varieties

Lou's Famous - Organic Horseradish

Meijer Brand - Dijon Squeeze, Honey Squeeze, Horseradish Squeeze, Hot & Spicy, Salad Squeeze, Spicy Brown Squeeze

Midwest Country Fare - Yellow

Mr. Spice Organic - Honey Mustard Sauce & Marinade

O Organics - Dijon

Olde Cape Cod - All Varieties

Publix - Classic Yellow, Deli Style, Dijon, Honey, Spicy Brown

Publix GreenWise Market - Creamy Yellow, Spicy Yellow, Tangy Dijon

Royal Food Products - Gourmet Choice Honey Dijon, Royal Deluxe (Dijon Honey, Honey), Slender Select Fat Free

Ruth's Hemp Power - Hemp & Honey Mustard

Safeway Brand - Coarse Ground Dijon, Dijon, Honey Mustard, Spicy Brown, Stone Ground Horseradish, Sweet & Spicy, Yellow

Safeway Select - Stoneground w/Horseradish

Spartan Brand - Deli Style w/Horseradish, Dijon, Honey, Southwestern Sweet & Hot, Yellow

Stop & Shop Brand - Creamy Dijon, Deli, Dijon, Honey, Old Grainy, Raspberry Grainy, Spicy Brown, Tarragon Dijon, Yellow

Taste Of Inspiration - Cranberry!, Honey!, Maine Maple!, Raspberry!, Roasted Garlic!

Texas Pete - Honey Mustard

M
N

Trader Joe's - Dijon**!!**, Organic Yellow**!!**
Wegmans Brand - Dijon (Honey, Traditional, Whole Grain),
   Horseradish, Smooth & Tangy, Spicy Brown, Yellow
Winn Dixie - Dijon, Honey, Horseradish, Spicy Brown, Yellow
Woodstock Farms - Organic (Dijon, Stoneground, Yellow)

N

Neufchatel... see Cream Cheese
Noodles... see also Pasta
   A Taste Of Thai - Rice Noodles (Pad Thai For Two, Regular, Thin,
      Vermicelli Rice, Wide)
   Annie Chun's - Rice Noodles (Maifun Brown, Pad Thai Brown Rice)
   Grandma Ferdon's▲ - Chow Mein ●
   Manischewitz - Passover Noodles
   Mixes From The Heartland▲ - Noodle Mix (Pesto ●, Plain ●,
      Spinach ●)
   Seitenbacher - Gluten Free Rigatoni, Gourmet Noodles Gluten Free
      Golden Ribbon
   Thai Kitchen - Instant Rice Noodle Soup (Bangkok Curry, Garlic &
      Vegetable, Lemongrass & Chili, Thai Ginger), Rice Noodle Carts
      (Pad Thai, Thai Peanut), Rice Noodles (Stir Fry Rice Noodles, Thin
      Rice Noodles), Stir Fry Rice Noodle Meal Kit (Lemongrass & Chili,
      Original Pad Thai, Thai Peanut), Take Out Boxes (Ginger & Sweet
      Chili, Original Pad Thai, Thai Basil & Chili)
   Trader Joe's - Rice Noodles
Nut Beverages
   Blue Diamond - Almond Breeze (Chocolate, Original, Vanilla),
      Almond Breeze Unsweetened (Chocolate, Original, Vanilla),
      Refrigerated Almond Breeze (Chocolate, Original, Unsweetened
      Vanilla, Vanilla)
   MimicCreme - Sugar Free Sweetened, Sweetened, Unsweetened
   Pacific Natural Foods - Almond (Chocolate, Unsweetened Original,
      Unsweetened Vanilla), Hazelnut Chocolate, Low Fat Almond
      (Original, Vanilla), Original Hazelnut
Nut Butter... see Peanut Butter

Nutritional Supplements

Boost - High Protein Powder

Boost Drink - Kid Essentials (All Varieties), Boost Plus (All Varieties), Glucose Control (All Varieties), High Protein (All Varieties), Original (All Varieties)

Carnation - All Instant Breakfast *(Except Chocolate Malt)*

Ensure - All Liquid Products

Fruit Advantage - Dietary Supplement (All Varieties)

Glucerna - All Shakes

Hy-Vee - Nutrional Supplement (Chocolate (Plus, Regular), Strawberry (Plus, Regular), Vanilla (Plus, Regular))

MLO - Brown Rice Protein Powder

Meijer Brand -
Diet Quick Extra Thin (Chocolate, Strawberry, Vanilla)
Gluco Burst (Artic Cherry, Chocolate Diabetic Nutrional Drink, Strawberry DND, Vanilla DND)

Nutripals - Balanced Nutrition Drinks (Chocolate, Strawberry, Vanilla)

Pedialyte - Freezer Pops**!**, Hospital Sized Bottles, One Liter Bottles, Powder Packs, Single Juice Boxes**!**

Pediasure - Drinks (Banana Cream, Berry Cream, Chocolate, Strawberry, Vanilla, Vanilla w/Fiber), Sidekicks (All Varieties)

Ruth's Hemp Power - Organic Hemp Protein Powder (E3 Live & Maca, Hemp Protein Power, Hemp w/Sprouted Flax & Maca)

Safeway Brand - All Flavors Of Nutritional Shakes (Plus, Regular)

Salba - Ground Salba Seed ●, Salba Seed Oil Gelcaps ●, Salba Seed Oil ●, Whole Salba Seed ●

Worldwide Pure Protein - Shake (Banana Cream, Frosty Chocolate, Strawberry Cream, Vanilla Cream)

Nuts

Albertsons - Cashews (Halves & Pieces, Lightly Salted, Whole), Mixed Nuts (Deluxe, Lightly Salted, Regular), Peanuts (Dry Roasted, Dry Roasted Unsalted, Lightly Salted, Lightly Salted Party, Party)

Back To Nature - Sea Salt Roasted California Almonds, Sea Salt Roasted Cashew Almond Pistachio Mix, Sea Salt Roasted Jumbo

N

Cashews, Tuscan Herb Roasts, Unroasted Unsalted California Almonds, Unroasted Unsalted Walnuts

Blue Diamond -
Almonds (100 Calorie Packs (Cinnamon Brown Sugar, Dark Chocolate, Lightly Salted, Sea Salt, Whole Natural)
Bold Flavors (Blazin' Buffalo Wing, Carolina Barbeque, Chocolate Mint, Cinnamon Brown Sugar, Habanero BBQ, Jalapeno Smokehouse, No Salt, Salt N' Vinegar, Sea Salt)
Cooking & Baking (Sliced, Slivered, Whole)
Oven Roasted (Butter Toffee, Dark Chocolate, Honey Roasted)
Traditional Flavors (Honey Roasted, Lightly Salted, Roasted Salted, Smokehouse, Whole Natural)

Don Enrique's - Chile Pistachio

Eden Organic - Tamari Dry Roasted Almonds

Emerald -
Cocoa Roasted Walnuts**!!**
Dry Roasted Lightly Salted Peanuts
Glazed Pecans
Glazed Walnuts (Apple Cinnamon, Butter Toffee, Original)
On The Go Canisters (Cashews Halves & Pieces, Cocktail Peanuts, Deluxe Mix Nuts, Dry Roasted Almonds, Dry Roasted Peanuts, Whole Cashews)

FritoLay - Almonds Roasted**!!**, Deluxe Mixed Nuts**!!**, Honey Roasted Peanuts**!!**, Hot Peanuts**!!**, Praline Pecans**!!**, Salted Cashews**!!**, Salted Peanuts**!!**, Whole Cashews**!!**

Giant Brand - Pistachios

Gluty Free -
Almonds (Blanched Whole ●, No Shell Raw Organic ●, Organic Dark Chocolate ●, Raw (In Shell ●, No Shell ●), Salted ●, Sliced Natural ●, Sliced ●, Slivered ●, Tamari ●, Unsalted ●)
Blanched Hazelnuts/Filberts ●
Brazil Nuts (In Shell ●, No Shell Raw Organic ●, Raw (No Shell ●, Pieces ●), Salted ●, Unsalted ●)
Cashews (Raw ●, Raw Organic ●, Raw Organic Pieces ●, Raw

Pieces ●, Salted ●, Unsalted ●)

Cilantro Lime Pistachios & Pepitas ●

Hazelnuts (In Shell ●, No Shell Raw ●, Raw Organic No Shell ●, Salted ●, Unsalted ●)

Macadamia Nuts (Raw ●, Raw Organic ●, Raw Pieces ●, Salted ●, Unsalted ●)

Mixed Nuts In Shell ●

Peanuts (Blanched ●, Cajun Salted In Shell ●, In Shell Salted ●, No Shell Salted Organic ●, No Shell Salted ●, Raw (In Shell ●, Redskin ●, Spanish ●), Raw Organic (In Shell ●, No Shell ●), Roasted (In Shell ●, In Shell Organic ●), Salted Jumbo No Shell ●, Unsalted Jumbo No Shell ●, Unsalted No Shell ●, Unsalted Organic No Shell ●, Wild Organic Jungle ●)

Pecans (Hard Shell ●, No Shell Raw Organic ●, Paper Shell ●, Raw (No Shell ●, Pieces ●), Salted ●, Unsalted ●)

Pignolia Nuts (In Shell Raw ●, Mediterranean ●, No Shell Raw Organic ●)

Pistachios (In Shell Salted Organic ●, In Shell Salted ●, No Shell Raw Organic ●, No Shell Salted ●, Raw (In Shell ●, No Shell ●), Red ●, Siirt Turkish ●, Sweet & Spicy Chipotle ●, Unsalted (In Shell ●, No Shell ●), Unsalted Organic In Shell ●)

Walnuts (In Shell ●, Raw (Halves No Shell ●, No Shell ●, Pieces ●), Raw Organic (No Shell ●, Pieces ●), Salted ●, Unsalted ●)

Gordon Food Service - Dry Roasted Peanuts

Just Almonds - All Varieties

Katy Sweet▲ - Nuts (Bar B Que ●, Double Chip Chocolate Nuts ●, Glazed Pecans ●, Holy Mole ●, Pecan Krunch ●, Pecan Quartets ●, Peppered Pecans ●, Roasted & Salted Pecans ●, Smokin' Chipotle Pecans ●, Sugar & Spice Pecans ●)

Kirkland Signature - Pecans, Pistachios, Walnuts

Kroger Brand - All Baking Varieties, Cashews (Lightly Salted, Salted), Mixed (Deluxe, Lightly Salted, Natural, Unsalted w/Peanuts), Peanuts (Honey Roasted, In Shell (Raw, Salted, Unsalted), Lightly Salted, Salted, Salted Spanish, Unsalted), Salted Pistachios

N

Laura Lynn - Almonds (Roasted, Smoked), Cashew Halves, Deluxe Mixed Nuts, Dry Roast Nuts, Light Salt (Cashews, Dry Roast Nuts, Mixed Nuts, Peanuts), Mixed Nuts, Peanuts (Honey Roast, Party, Spanish), Unsalted Dry Roast Nuts, Whole Cashews

Mareblu Naturals▲ -
  Crunch Bags (Almond ●, Cashew ●, Cashew Coconut ●, CranMango Cashew ●, Dark Chocolate Almond ●, Pecan Cinnamon ●, Pecan Cranberry Cinnamon ●)
  Dry Roasted Nuts (Almonds ●, Cashews ●, Pistachios ●)
  Glazed Whole Nuts Pecans w/Cranberry & Cinnamon ●
  Trail Mix Crunch Bags (Blueberry Pomegranate ●, Cranberry Pomegranate ●, Cranblueberry ●, Cranstrawberry ●, Pecan ●, Pistachio ●)

Meijer Brand - Almonds (Blanched Sliced, Blanched Slivered, Natural Sliced, Slivered, Whole), Blanched (Regular, Slightly Salted), Butter Toffee, Cashews (Halves w/Pieces, Halves w/ Pieces Lightly Salted, Whole), Dry Roasted (Lightly Salted, Regular, Unsalted), Honey Roasted, Hot & Spicy, Mixed (Deluxe, Lightly Salted, Regular), Nut Topping, Peanuts, Pecan (Chips, Halves), Pine, Spanish, Walnuts (Black, Chips, Halves & Pieces)

Nut Harvest - Lightly Roasted Almonds **!!**, Sea Salted Whole Cashews **!!**

Nuts Online -
  Almonds (Organic (Blanched ●, Dry Roasted Salted ●, Natural Sliced ●, Natural Slivered ●, Raw No Shell ●, Roasted Unsalted ●), Organic Dark Chocolate Covered ●, Organic Milk Chocolate Covered ●, Raw (In Shell ●, No Shell ●), Roasted (Salted ●, Unsalted ●), Sliced Natural ●, Sliced ●, Slivered ●, Sprouted ●, Tamari ●, Whole Blanched ●)
  Brazil Nuts (In Shell ●, No Shell ●, Organic Raw No Shell ●, Pieces ●, Roasted (Salted ●, Unsalted ●))
  Cashews (Organic (Pieces ●, Raw ●), Pieces ●, Raw ●, Roasted (Salted ●, Unsalted ●), Salted Organic Dry Roasted ●, Supreme Raw ●, Supreme Roasted (Salted ●, Unsalted ●), Thai Coconut

Curry ●), Cilantro Lime Pistachios & Pepitas ●

Hazelnuts (Blanched ●, Organic Raw No Shell ●)

Hazelnuts/Filberts (In Shell ●, Raw No Shell ●, Roasted (Salted ●, Unsalted ●))

Macadamia Nuts(In Shell ●, Organic ●, Pieces ●, Raw ●, Roasted (Salted ●, Unsalted ●))

Mixed Nuts In Shell ●

Peanuts (Blanched ●, Cajun Roasted Salted In Shell ●, In Shell (Jumbo Raw ●, Jumbo Roasted ●), Organic Dry Roasted (Salted No Shell ●, Unsalted No Shell ●), Organic Raw (In Shell ●, No Shell ●), Organic Roasted (In Shell ●, Salted In Shell ●), Organic Wild Jungle ●, Raw Redskin ●, Raw Spanish ●, Roasted Salted In Shell ●, Roasted Super Jumbo Virginia (Salted No Shell●, Unsalted No Shell ●), Roasted Virginia (Salted No Shell ●, Unsalted No Shell ●), Super Jumbo Blanched ●)

Pecans (Georgia Raw No Shell ●, Hard Shell ●, Organic (Pieces ●, Raw No Shell ●), Paper Shell ●, Pieces ●, Roasted (Salted ●, Unsalted ●))

Pine Nuts (Mediterranean Pignolias ●, Organic Raw No Shell ●, Pignolias ●, Raw In Shell ●)

Pink Salt & Cracked Pepper Mixed Nuts & Seeds ●

Pistachios (Chili Lime ●, Dry Roasted (Salted ●, Unsalted ●), Organic Raw No Shell ●, Raw (In Shell ●, No Shell ●), Red ●, Roasted (Salted In Shell ●, Salted No Shell ●, Unsalted In Shell ●, Unsalted No Shell ●), Roasted Organic (Salted In Shell ●, Unsalted In Shell ●), Sweet & Spicy Chipotle ●, Turkish Siirt ●)

Raw Cacao (Almonds & Raisins ●, Brazil Nuts & Mulberries ●)

Rosemary Garlic Pistachios & Almonds ●

Sesame Teriyaki Almonds & Cashews ●

Walnuts (Black ●, English (Halves Raw No Shell ●, In Shell, Raw No Shell ●), Maple Mesquite Pod ●, Organic (Pieces ●, Raw No Shell ●), Pieces ●, Roasted Salted ●)

White Chocolate Chip Almonds Cashews & Cacao Nibs ●

N Planters -

    Almonds (Chocolovers, Dry Roasted)

    Baking (Almond (Slices, Slivers, Whole), Black Walnuts, Pecan (Chips, Halves, Pieces), Walnut Pieces), Cashews Chocolate Lovers, Halves & Pieces, Halves & Pieces Lightly Salted, Jumbo, Whole (Honey Roasted, Lightly Salted, Regular)

    Flavor Grove

      Almonds (Chili Lime, Cracked Pepper w/Onion & Garlic, Sea Salt & Olive Oil)

      Cashews (Chipotle, Sea Salt & Cracked Pepper)

    Mixed (Cashew Lovers, Deluxe (Lightly Salted, Regular), Honey Roasted, Lightly Salted, Macadamia Lovers, Pecan Lovers, Pistachio Lovers, Regular, Select (Cashews Almonds & Pecans, Macadamia Cashew & Almonds), Unsalted)

    Nut-rition (Almonds, Antioxidant, Digestive Health, Heart Healthy, South Beach Diet Recommended)

    Peanuts (Cocktail (Honey Roasted, Lightly Salted, Regular, Unsalted), Dry Roasted (Honey Roasted, Lightly Salted w/Sea Salt, Unsalted, w/Sea Salt), Kettle Roasted, Redskin Spanish)

Private Selections - Cashews, Macadamia, Mixed, Pecans, Praline Pecans, Select Brand Mixed, Shell Pistachios

Sabritas - Picante Peanuts!!, Salt & Lime Peanuts!!

Safeway Brand - Baking (Almonds, Pecan, Walnut)

Shiloh Farms - Whole Almonds!!

Spartan Brand - Cashews (Halves w/Pieces, Whole), Mixed (Fancy w/Macadamias, Nature, w/Peanuts), Peanuts Blanched Roasted, Butter Toffee, Dry Roasted (Lightly Salted, No Salt, Regular), Honey Roasted

Sunkist - Pistachios (Dry Roasted, Kernels)

Trader Joe's - All Raw & Roasted Nuts, Cinnamon Almonds, Marcona Almonds

True North - Clusters (Almond!!, Almond Pecan Cashew!!, Pecan Almond Peanut!!), Lightly Roasted Almonds/Pistachios/Walnuts & Pecans!!

Wegmans Brand -
> Cashews (Salted, Unsalted)
> Dry Roasted (Macadamias Salted, Seasoned Sunflower Kernels)
> Honey Roasted Whole Cashews
> Party Peanuts (Roasted Lightly Salted, Salted)
> Peanuts (Salted In Shell, Unsalted In Shell)
> Peanuts Dry Roasted (Lightly Salted, Seasoned, Unsalted)
> Pine Nuts Italian Classics
> Roasted (Almonds Salted, Cashews Halves & Pieces Salted, Deluxe Mixed Nuts w/Macadamias Salted, Jumbo (Cashew Mix w/Almonds Pecans & Brazils, Cashews), Mixed Nuts w/Peanuts Lightly Salted, Party Mixed Nuts w/Peanuts Salted, Party Peanuts (Lightly Salted, Salted), Spanish Peanuts Salted, Virginia Peanuts Salted, Whole Cashews (Salted, Unsalted))
> Virginia Peanuts Chocolate Covered

Winn & Lovett - Cinnamon Toasted Almonds, Coconut Almonds, Macadamia Nut Crunch, Pecan Praline

Woodstock Farms -
> Organic Nuts
>> Almonds Milk Chocolate
>> Almonds (All About, Chocolate w/Evaporated Cane Juice, Cocoa Dusted Dark Chocolate, Non Pareil Supreme, Roasted & No Salt, Roasted & Salt, Tamari, Thick Slice, Yogurt Covered w/Evaporated Cane Juice)
>> Brazil
>> Cashew (Large Whole, Large Whole Roasted & Salted)
>> Deluxe Mixed Nuts Roasted & Salted
>> Extra Fancy Mixed Nuts Roasted & Salted
>> Hazelnut Filberts
>> Honey Roasted Peanuts
>> Organic Brazil
>> Organic Nuts (Almonds Dark Chocolate, Brazil, Cashew (Large Whole, Large Whole Roasted & Salted, Pieces), Pecan Halves, Pine, Pistachios (No Salt, Roasted & Salt), Soy Nuts (No Salt, Roasted), Walnuts Halves & Pieces)

N

O

Pecan Halves
Pine
Soynuts Roasted (No Salt, Regular)
Walnuts Halves & Pieces

O

Oatmeal

GlutenFreeda▲ - Instant Oatmeal (Apple Cinnamon w/Flax, Banana Maple w/Flax, Maple Raisin w/Flax, Natural)

PrOatina Gluten Free - Gluten Free Oat Bran ●, Gluten Free Old Fashioned Oatmeal ●

Pure Market Express▲ - French Toast Oatmeal ●

Oats

Augason Farms - Gluten Free Regular Rolled Oats ●

Bob's Red Mill▲ - Gluten Free Quick Rolled Oats, Gluten Free Rolled Oats, Gluten Free Steel Cut Oats

Celiac Specialties▲ - Oats

Chateau Cream Hill Estates - Lara's Rolled Oats ●

Gifts Of Nature▲ - Old Fashioned Rolled Oats, Whole Oat Groats

Gluten Free Oats▲ - Old Fashioned Rolled Oats ●

Gluty Free - Steel Cut ●

Montana Monster Munchies - Whole Grain (Quick Oats ●, Rolled Oats)

Montina▲ - Rolled Oats ●

Only Oats - Oat Flakes (Quick ●, Regular ●), Steel Cut Oat Pearls ●

Tom Sawyer▲ - Gluten Free

Oil

Albertsons - Canola Oil, Olive Oil, Peanut, Vegetable

Annie's Naturals - Olive Oil (Basil!!, Dipping!!, Roasted Pepper!!), Olive Oil Extra Virgin Roasted Garlic!!

Bakers & Chefs - 100% Pure Clear Frying Oil, 100% Pure Peanut Oil, 100% Pure Vegetable Oil

Bertolli - Olive Oil (Classico, Extra Light, Extra Virgin)

Bionaturae - Organic Extra Virgin Olive Oil

O

Bragg - All Varieties

Carapelli - Olive Oil

Consorzio - Olive Oil (Basil, Cilantro, Roasted Garlic, Roasted Pepper, Rosemary)

Crisco - Canola w/Omega 3DHA, Frying Blend, Natural Blend, Olive (100% Extra Virgin, Light Tasting, Pure), Pure (Canola, Corn, Peanut, Vegetable)

Eden Organic - Olive Oil Spanish Extra Virgin, Organic (Hot Pepper Sesame Oil, Safflower Oil, Sesame Oil Extra Virgin, Soybean Oil), Toasted Sesame Oil

Filippo Berio - Extra Virgin Olive

Food Club Brand - Canola, Canola & Vegetable Blend, Corn, Olive, Peanut, Vegetable

Foods Alive - Organic (Hemp, High Lignan Golden Flax)

Full Circle - Canola, Organic Extra Virgin Olive Oil

Fungus Among Us - Certified Organic Olive Infused w/White Truffle

Giant Brand - Blended, Canola, Grill Spray, Olive Oil (Extra Light, Pure), Peanut, Soybean

Gordon Food Service - Pure Olive Oil

Grand Selections - 100% Pure & Natural Olive Oil, Extra Virgin Olive Oil, Olive Oil Lemon

Great Value Brand (Wal-Mart) - Canola Oil Blend, Olive Oil (Extra Light, Extra Virgin), Pure Oil (Canola, Corn, Vegetable), Pure Olive Oil

Hannaford Brand - Canola Oil, Corn Oil, Olive (Extra Virgin, Extra Virgin Imported, Light Pure), Vegetable Oil

Hollywood - Enriched (Canola, Expeller Pressing Safflower, Gold Peanut)

House Of Tsang - Oil (Hot Chili Sesame, Mongolian Fire, Sesame, Wok)

Hy-Vee - 100% Pure Oil (Canola, Corn, Vegetable), Natural Blend Oil

Ka-Me - Pure Sesame **!**

Kirkland Signature - Canola, Peanut, Pure Olive, Soybean, Vegetable

Kroger Brand - Blended, Canola, Corn, Olive, Peanut, Spray (Butter, Canola, Olive, Vegetable), Sunflower, Vegetable

Laura Lynn - Blended, Canola, Corn, Peanut, Vegetable

Lee Kum Kee - Oil (Blended Sesame, Chili, Pure Sesame, Sesame Flavored Seasoning)

Living Harvest - Hemp Oil

Lowes Foods Brand - 100% Pure, Canola, Corn, Extra Virgin, Peanut, Vegetable

Manischewitz - Vegetable

Manitoba Harvest - Hemp Seed Oil (Organic, Regular)

Mazola - Canola Oil, Corn Oil, Corn Oil Plus, Olive Oil (Extra Virgin, Pure), Vegetable Plus

Meijer Brand -
    Blended Canola/Vegetable
    Canola
    Corn
    Oil Olive Infused (Garlic & Basil Italian, Roasted Garlic Italian, Spicy Red Pepper Italian)
    Olive 100% Pure Italian Classic
    Extra Virgin (Italian Classic, Regular)
    Italian Select Premium Extra Virgin
    Milder Tasting
    Regular
    Peanut
    Sunflower
    Vegetable

Member's Mark - 100% Pure Olive Oil

Mezzetta - Extra Virgin Olive Oil

Midwest Country Fare -
    100% Pure Vegetable Oil
    Vegetable Oil

Newman's Own Organics - Extra Virgin Olive Oil

Nutiva - Organic (Extra Virgin Coconut Oil, Hemp Oil)

Nuts Online - Organic Hemp Oil ●

O

O Organics - Extra Virgin Olive
Odell's - Popcorn Popping Oil
OmegaMontana - Virgin Camelina Oil ●
Oskri Organics -
    Extra Virgin Olive Oil
    Flaxseed Oil
    Grapeseed Oil
    Omega 3 Olive Oil
    Sesame Seed Oil
Peter Paul - Virgin Coconut
Phildesco - Virgin Coconut
Planters - Peanut
Private Selections - All Varieties, Organic Sprays (Canola, Olive)
Publix - Canola, Corn, Olive, Peanut, Vegetable
Ruth's Hemp Power - Hemp
Safeway Brand - Canola, Corn, Peanut, Vegetable
Safeway Select - Olive Oil (Extra Light, Extra Virgin, Regular)
Salad Dressing - 100% Pure Vegetable Oil
Santa Barbara Olive Co. - Chili, Cuvee 60/40 Blend, Geno's Garlic
    Nectar, Olive Oil (Chili Fajita, Extra Virgin), Rosemary
Simply Enjoy -
    Extra Virgin Olive Oil
        Flavored (Basil, Garlic, Lemon, Orange, Pepper)
        Regional (Apulian, Sicilian, Tuscan, Umbrian)
Smart Balance - Cooking, Olive Oil (Extra Virgin, Light Taste, Pure)
Spartan Brand - Blended, Canola, Corn, Olive (Extra Virgin, Pure),
    Vegetable
Star - Extra Light Olive, Extra Virgin Garlic Olive, Extra Virgin Olive,
    Originale Garlic Olive, Originale Olive, Special Reserve Organic
    Extra Virgin Olive
Stop & Shop Brand - Blended, Canola, Corn, Extra Light Olive,
    MiCasa (Corn, Vegetable), Pure Olive, Soybean, Vegetable
Tassos - Olive Oil (Extra Virgin, Fine, Organic Extra, Peza Crete Extra)
Toscano - Extra Virgin Olive

Trader Joe's - All Varieties
Tropical Traditions - Organic Virgin Palm Oil
Wegmans Brand -
  Basting w/Garlic & Herbs
  Canola
  Corn
  Extra Virgin (Black Truffle, Campania Style, Olive, Sicilian Lemon,
    Sicilian Style, Tuscany Style)
  Grapeseed
  Mild Olive
  Organic (Extra Virgin, High Oleic Sunflower Oil, Sunflower Oil)
  Peanut
  Pumpkin Seed
  Pure Olive
  Submarine Sandwich
  Vegetable
Winn & Lovett - Olive Oil (Balsamic, Extra Virgin, Garlic,
  Mediterranean, Roasted Garlic, Zesty Italian)
Winn Dixie - Canola, Corn, Olive, Peanut, Vegetable

Okra

*... *All Fresh Fruits & Vegetables Are Gluten-Free*

Food Club Brand - Frozen Okra (Cut, Whole)
Giant Brand - Frozen Whole
Meijer Brand - Frozen (Chopped, Whole)
Mezzetta - Hors D'Oeuvres Gourmet, Marinated Hot
Mt. Olive - Mild Okra
Pictsweet - All Plain Vegetables (Frozen), Cracked Pepper Seasoned
  Okra & Squash
Publix - Frozen (Cut, Whole Baby)
Safeway Brand - Frozen
Spartan Brand - Cut, Whole
Trappey's - Cocktail Okra
Winn Dixie - Frozen (Cut, Diced, Whole)

Olive Oil... see Oil

Olives

O

B&G - Black, Green

Di Lusso - Green Ionian, Mediterranean Mixed, Pitted Kalamata

Food Club Brand - Chopped, Manzanilla Stuffed, Pitted, Queen Stuffed, Salad Sliced, Sliced

Giant Brand - Queen (Plain, Stuffed), Stuffed Manzanilla

Great Value Brand (Wal-Mart) - California Chopped Ripe, California Medium Pitted Ripe, California Sliced Ripe, Jumbo Pitted Ripe, Large Pitted Ripe, Minced Pimento Stuffed Manzanilla, Sliced Salad

Hannaford Brand - Pitted Ripe (Extra Large, Large, Medium, Small), Sliced Ripe, Sliced Salad, Stuffed (Manzanilla, Queen)

Hy-Vee - Chopped Ripe, Manzanilla Olives, Medium Ripe Black, Queen, Ripe Black (Jumbo, Large), Sliced (Ripe Black, Salad)

Krinos - Imported (Black, Green Cracked, Kalamata Olives)

Kroger Brand - Green Pimento Stuffed, Not Stuffed Green, Not Stuffed Black

Kurtz - Salad Olives, Small Pitted Black Olives, Spanish Olives

Laura Lynn - All Olives (Green, Ripe)

Lowes Foods Brand - Chopped Ripe, Manzanilla Stuffed, Pitted (Jumbo, Large, Medium, Small), Plain Queen, Salad Sliced, Sliced (Buffet Ripe, Ripe)

Meijer Brand - Manzanilla Stuffed (Placed, Thrown, Tree), Queen (Stuffed Placed, Whole Thrown), Ripe (Large, Medium, Pitted Jumbo, Pitted Small, Sliced), Salad, Salad Sliced

Mezzetta -
  Calamata Greek
  Castelvetrano Whole Green
  Colossal Spiced Sicilian
  Fancy Colossal Green
  Garlic (Original, Queen)
  Home Style Cured Pitted
  Jalapeno Garlic (Original, w/Minced Pimento)
  Marinated Cracked Deli

O

Mediterranean Nicoise Style

Napa Valley Bistro (Applewood Smoked Olives, Garlic Stuffed Olives, Italian Olive Antipasto, Jalapeno Stuffed Olives, Olive Medley, Pitted Kalamata Olives, Roasted Garlic Stuffed Olives)

Organics (Pitted Kalamata, Whole Kalamata)

Pitted Calamata

Salad

Sliced Calamata

Spanish (Colossal Queen w/Minced Pimento, Manzanilla w/ Minced Pimento, Queen Martini In Dry Vermouth)

Stuffed Olives (Anchovy, Bleu Cheese, Garlic, Greek Style Feta Cheese, Jalapeno)

Midwest Country Fare - Large Ripe Black, Sliced Ripe Black

Peloponnese - Antipasto Party, Country Gourmet Mixed, Cracked Gourmet Green, Halved Kalamata Gourmet Black, Ionian Gourmet Green, Kalamata Olive Spread, Pitted Kalamata Gourmet Black

Private Selections - All Varieties

Publix - Colossal, Green, Large, Ripe, Small

Safeway Brand - All Varieties

Santa Barbara Olive Co. - Bleu Cheese Stuffed, Canned (#10, Green, Jumbo, Large, Medium), Sun Dried (Black, Organic California, Pitted Black)

Spartan Brand - Manzanilla, Queen, Ripe Pitted Olives (Jumbo, Large, Medium, Sliced Salad, Small), Sliced Spanish Salad

Star - Manzanilla Spanish Olives Stuffed w/Pimento, Queen Spanish Olives Stuffed w/Pimento, Spanish Salad Olives, Stuffed Cannonballs

Stop & Shop Brand - Manzanilla Olives (Sliced, Stuffed), Pitted Black Ripe Olives Chopped, Stuffed Queen, Whole & Sliced (Jumbo, Large, Medium, Small)

Tassos - Black Olives In Extra Virgin Olive Oil & Red Wine, Blonde Olives In Extra Virgin Olive Oil & Red Wine, Evian Olives In Sea Salt Brine, Kalamata In Tassos Extra Virgin Olive Oil & Red Wine

Gluten-Free Dining Out

Nationwide restaurant chains offering gluten-free menus:

Austin Grill
Bertucci's Italian Restaurant
Biaggi's Ristorante Italiano
Bonefish Grill
Bugaboo Creek Steak House
Carino's Italian
Carrabba's Italian Grill
Charlie Brown's Steakhouse
Cheeseburger In Paradise Bar & Grill
Claim Jumper Restaurants
Daily Grill
Fire Bowl Café
Fleming's Prime Steakhouse & Wine Bar
Garlic Jim's Famous Gourmet Pizza
Lee Roy Selmon's
Legal Sea Foods Restaurant & Oyster Bar
Mama Fu's Asian House
Mitchell's Fish Market
Ninety Nine 99
Old Spaghetti Factory
Outback Steakhouse
P.F. Chang's China Bistro
Pei Wei Asian Diner
Pizza Fusion
The Melting Pot
Village Tavern
Weber Grill Restaurant
Wildfire Steaks, Chops & Seafood
Z' Tejas Southwestern Grill

Gluten-Free Resources

1-2-3 Gluten Free
These award-winning, great-tasting baking mixes, made in a dedicated gluten-free and allergen-free U.S. facility (certified gluten-free, kosher) are versatile, make large amounts and are available at stores nationwide and www.123glutenfree.com.

Bakery On Main
Bakery On Main started in the bakery of our natural foods market in Glastonbury, Connecticut. Founder Michael Smulders listened to his Celiac customers complain about the taste of many gluten free foods. He made it his mission to create products that were good for them but taste like they aren't. www.bakeryonmain.com

Bard's Tale Beer
Bard's Beer is America's first gluten-free sorghum beer and the only beer brewed with 100% malted sorghum to provide traditional beer flavor and aroma. Visit www.bardsbeer.com or call 877-440-2337.

Breads From Anna
All Breads From Anna® mixes are gluten, soy, rice and nut free, several are also corn, dairy and yeast free. Unique - because of a smooth, non-grainy texture, high in protein and fiber and an outstanding taste!

Ener-G Foods
Since 1962 Ener-G Foods has met the challenging requirements for diet restricted consumers. We offer over 150 wheat-free, gluten-free, dairy-free, nut-free, kosher certified baked goods, flours, and mixes. www.ener-g.com

Enjoy Life
Our whole business is making smile-good foods that keep people's insides happy. That's why our foods are Gluten-Free and free of the 8 most common allergens, so everyone can EAT FREELY! www.enjoylifefoods.com

Gluten Free Sensations
We've made it our mission to simplify your gf-life. It tastes like the 'real' thing because it IS the real thing!
Enter "gfpromo123" for 10% off your online order.
www.glutenfreesensations.com

Gluten-Free Living
Gluten-Free Living is the only magazine necessary for a gluten-free lifestyle, bringing you the latest on gluten-free ingredients, labeling, recipes, nutrition, new products and more. www.glutenfreeliving.com

Jones Dairy Farm
From all natural sausage and Canadian bacon to hams, bacon and braunschweiger, Jones Dairy Farm has a 120-year heritage of producing a wide variety of delicious gluten-free products. Visit www.jonesdairyfarm.com

Kettle Cuisine
Experience Kettle Cuisine's all natural, gluten free soups, chilis and chowders. These chef inspired varieties deliver restaurant quality taste without anything artificial. Look for Kettle Cuisine in the natural food freezer.
www.kettlecuisine.com

Kirkman
KIRKMAN® is the leading manufacturer of nutritional supplements for individuals with food allergies, special dietary requirements and environmental sensitivities. All Kirkman's products are gluten and casein free.
www.kirkmanlabs.com

Pamela's Products
Pamela's Products offers the highest quality, gluten-free foods. Our award winning products have been setting the standard in great tasting gluten-free food since 1988. Find us online at www.pamelasproducts.com.

riceworks
It isn't just what we put into our whole grain brown rice crisps that make them perfect for snacking. It's what we leave out. Like artificial flavors, preservatives and gluten. So the gourmet flavor of Sweet Chili, Salsa Fresca or Sea Salt comes through in every crispy crunch. 6 great flavours.
www.riceworks.com

San-J
Pour on the flavor with San-J! Our delectable and all-natural Asian cooking sauces, salad dressings and Organic Wheat Free Tamari are certified gluten free by the Gluten Free Certification Organization. www.san-j.com

Simply Organic
Simply Organic offers six irresistible gluten-free baking mixes: Banana Bread, Carrot Cake, Chai Spice Scone, Cocoa Brownie, Cocoa Cayenne Cupcake and Pancake. Available at Natural Food and Grocery outlets. www.simplyorganicfoods.com

simplyrice
The simplyrice™ brand is a "perfectly clean", natural, organic, gluten-free whole grain crisp that is preservative free, contains no trans fats – it is as simple as the four ingredients used to make it: brown jasmine rice flour, sunflower oil, sea salt and ginger powder. All organic and the taste is great. www.simplyrice.ca

Woodchuck Cider
Woodchuck Hard Cider is handcrafted in small batches at our cidery nestled within the Green Mountains of Vermont. Made with a unique combination of nature's best ingredients, Woodchuck is easy to drink with a variety of styles from sweet to dry. www.woodchuck.com

Helpful Gluten-Free Tips

✓ Never lick envelopes when closing letters. The adhesive on envelopes may contain gluten.

✓ Make sure your pet food is gluten-free. Most dog and cat food contains wheat flour. Pets can easily pass on gluten to their owners through close contact.

✓ Speak with your pharmacist to make sure your prescription medication is gluten-free.

✓ Always use cosmetics that are gluten-free, such as lipstick, eye shadow and blush.

✓ Double check to make sure your shampoo and conditioner are gluten-free. Using ones that contain gluten can cause irritation to the skin, scalp, eyes, as well as, may be ingested by accident.

✓ Make sure your dentist and hygienist are aware of your sensitivity to gluten.

Vinegar, Stuffed Almond In Sea Salt Brine

Trader Joe's - Colossal Olives Stuffed w/(Garlic Cloves, Jalapeño Peppers), Pitted Kalamata, Stuffed Queen Sevillano

Wegmans Brand - Greek Mix, Kalamata (Pitted, Whole), Pitted Ripe (Colossal, Extra Large, Medium), Sliced Ripe, Spanish (Manzanilla, Queen, Salad), Stuffed w/(Almonds, Blue Cheese, Garlic, Red Peppers)

Winn Dixie - Green (All Varieties), Ripe (All Varieties)

Onions

... *All Fresh Fruits & Vegetables Are Gluten-Free*

Birds Eye - All Plain Frozen Vegetables

C & W - All Plain Frozen Vegetables

Food Club Brand - Frozen Diced

Lowes Foods Brand - Frozen Diced

Meijer Brand - Frozen Chopped

Mezzetta - Hors D' Oeuvres Onions, Imported Cocktail Onions

Ore-Ida - Chopped Onions

Publix - Frozen Diced

Star - Imported Cocktail Onions, Imported Hors D' Oeuvres Onions

Trader Joe's - Frozen Peeled and Ready To Use Pearl Onions

Wegmans Brand - Whole Onions In Brine

Winn Dixie - Frozen Pearl Onions

Orange Juice... see Drinks/Juice

Oranges

... *All Fresh Fruits & Vegetables Are Gluten-Free*

Nuts Online - Dried Fruit Organic Dried Oranges ●

Sunkist

Oyster Sauce

Choy Sun - Oyster Flavored Sauce (Glass Bottles & Metal Cans)

Panda Brand - Lo Mein Oyster Flavored Sauce, Oyster Flavored Sauce *(Green Label Only)*

Wok Mei - All Natural Oyster Flavored

O Oysters

P   ... *All Fresh Seafood Is Gluten-Free (Non-Marinated, Unseasoned)*

Bumble Bee - Fancy Smoked, Fancy Whole, Fancy Whole

Chicken Of The Sea - Smoked In Oil, Whole

Crown Prince - Fancy Whole Smoked In Cottonseed Oil, Natural Smoked Oysters In Olive Oil, Natural Whole Boiled In Water Whole Boiled

Great Value Brand (Wal-Mart) - Canned Smoked Oysters

Ocean Prince - Fancy Whole Smoke In Cottonseed Oil, Whole Boiled

Trader Joe's - Whole Smoked Oysters In Olive Oil

P

Pancakes/Pancake Mix & Waffles/Waffle Mix

1-2-3 Gluten Free▲ - Allie's Awesome Buckwheat Pancake Mix●

Andrea's Fine Foods▲ - Pancake Mix

Arnel's Originals - Pancake Mix

Arrowhead Mills - Gluten Free Pancake & Waffle Mix, Wild Rice Pancake & Waffle Mix

Augason Farms - Gluten Free (Blueberry Pancake Mix●, Buttermilk Pancake ●)

Authentic Foods▲ - Pancake & Baking Mix

Better Batter - Pancake & Biscuit Mix

Bisquick▲ - Pancake & Baking Mix

Bob's Red Mill▲ - Gluten Free Pancake Mix

Breads From Anna▲ - Pancake & Muffin Mix (Apple, Cranberry, Maple)

Breakaway Bakery▲ - Pancake Batter ●

Cause You're Special▲ - Hearty Pancake & Waffle Mix

Celiac Specialties▲ - Pancake Mix (Buttermilk, Flaxseed, Plain)

Cherrybrook Kitchen - Gluten Free Chocolate Chip Pancake Mix (*Box Must Say Gluten Free*), Gluten Free Pancake Mix (*Box Must Say Gluten Free*)

El Peto▲ - Pancake Mix, Waffles (Belgium, Belgium Milk Free Corn Free)

Food-Tek Fast & Fresh▲ - Minute Waffle Mix

Full Circle - Gluten Free Waffle & Pancake Mix

Gifts Of Nature▲ - Pancake & Waffle Mix

Gluten Free Mama▲ - Mama's Pancake Mix ●

Gluten Free Pantry▲ - Brown Rice Pancake Mix

Gluten Free Sensations▲ - Pancake & Waffle Mix

Gluten-Free Creations▲ - Buckwheat Pancake Mix ●, Mighty Mesquite Pancake Mix ●

Gluten-Free Essentials▲ - Pancake & Waffle Mix ●

Grandma Ferdon's▲ - Pancake/Waffle Mix ●, Waffles ●

Hodgson Mill▲ - Gluten Free Pancake & Waffle Mix w/Flaxseed

Hol Grain▲ - Pancake & Waffle Mix ●

King Arthur Flour▲ - Gluten Free Pancake Mix ●

Kinnikinnick▲ - Homestyle Waffles (Cinnamon & Brown Sugar, Original), Pancake & Waffle Mix

Larrowe's - Instant Buckwheat Pancake Mix

Laurel's Sweet Treats▲ - Bulk Pancake Mix, Pancake & Waffle Mix

Linda's Gourmet Latkes - Potato Pancake Latkes

Little Bay Baking - All Purpose Breakfast Mix ●, Waffle & Donut Hole Mix ●

Manischewitz - Pancake Mix (Potato, Sweetened Potato)

Maple Grove Farms Of Vermont - Gluten Free Pancake Mix !

Mixes From The Heartland▲ - Pancake Mix (Apple Cinnamon ●, Blueberry ●, Country ●, Cranberry ●)

Mrs. Crimble's - Pancake Mix

Namaste Foods▲ - Waffle & Pancake Mix

Nature's Path - Frozen Organic Waffles (Buckwheat Wildberry !, Homestyle Gluten Free !, Mesa Sunrise Omega 3 !)

Nuts Online - Gluten Free Pancake Mix ●

Only Oats - Whole Oat Pancake Mix ●

Orgran▲ - Apple & Cinnamon Pancake Mix, Buckwheat Pancake Mix

Pamela's Products▲ - Baking & Pancake Mix

Pure Market Express▲ - Blueberry Pancake Dippers w/Honey ●

P

Really Great Food Company▲ - Pancake Mix (Brown Rice Flour, Classic, Jumbo Classic)

Ruby Range - Southwest Pancakes Gluten Free Baking Mix ●

Silly Yak Bakery - GF Flap Jack Mix

Simply Organic▲ - Pancake & Waffle Mix

Sylvan Border Farm - Pancake & Waffle Mix

The Cravings Place▲ - All Purpose

Trader Joe's - Gluten Free Homestyle Pancakes, Gluten Free Pancake & Waffle Mix, Wheat Free Toaster Waffles **!!**

Van's Natural Foods - Gluten & Wheat Free Waffles Minis Totally Natural **!**, Totally Natural **!**, Wheat & Gluten Free Waffles (Apple Cinnamon **!**, Blueberry **!**, Buckwheat w/Berries **!**, Flax **!**)

Paneer

Amy's - Indian Mattar Paneer (Light In Sodium **!**, Regular **!**), Indian Palak Paneer **!**, Indian Paneer Tikka **!**

Tasty Bite - Paneer Makhani **!**, Peas Paneer **!**

Trader Joe's - Paneer Tikka Masala **!!**

Papaya

... *All Fresh Fruits & Vegetables Are Gluten-Free*

Gluty Free - Dried (Chunks ●, Diced ●, Natural ●, Regular ●)

Native Forest - Organic Papaya Chunks

Nuts Online - Dried Fruit (Chunks ●, Diced ●, Dried ●, Natural ●, Organic ●)

Woodstock Farms - Organic Frozen Papaya Chunks, Spears Low Sugar Unsulphured

Paprika... see Seasonings

Parmesan Cheese... see Cheese

Pasta

Allegaroo - Chili Mac, Spaghetti, Spyglass Noodles

Ancient Harvest Quinoa - Elbows, Garden Pagodas, Linguine, Rotelle, Shells, Spaghetti, Veggie Curls

Andean Dream - Quinoa (Fusilli, Macaroni, Spaghetti)

Annie Chun's - Rice Noodles (Maifun Brown, Pad Thai Brown Rice)

Aproten - Bucatini, Fettuccine, Linguine, Spaghetti, Tagliatelle

Beretta - Gluten Free Rice Pasta (Fusilli, Penne, Spaghetti)

Bi-Aglut - Bucatini, Ditalini, Egg Pasta (Lasagne, Sedani, Tagliatelle), Fusilli, Gemmini, Maccheroncini, Micron, Penne, Pipe, Sedani, Spaghetti, Stelline

Bionaturae▲ - Organic Gluten Free (Elbow ●, Fusilli ●, Penne ●, Spaghetti ●)

Conte's Pasta - Cheese Stuffed Shells ●, Gnocchi ●, Pierogies (Potato Cheese Onion ●, Potato Onion ●), Ravioli (Cheese ●, Cheese Spinach ●)

Cornito - Elbow Macaroni, Mystic Flames Noodles, Rainbow Rotini, Rigatoni (Penne), Rotini, Sea Waves (Mini Lasagna), Spaghetti

DeBoles -
  Corn Pasta (Elbow Style ●, Spaghetti ●)
  Gluten Free Multi Grain Pasta (Penne ●, Spaghetti ●)
  Gluten Free Rice Pasta (Angel Hair ●, Angel Hair & Golden Flax ●, Elbow Style Pasta & Cheese ●, Fettucini ●, Lasagna ●, Penne ●, Spaghetti ●, Shells & Cheddar ●, Spirals ●, Spirals & Golden Flax ●)

Eden Organic - Bifun, Kuzu, Mung Bean

Ener-G▲ - White Rice (Lasagna, Macaroni, Small Shells, Spaghetti, Vermicelli)

Gillian's Foods▲ - Fetuccini, Fusilli, Penne, Spaghetti

Glutano▲ - Fusilli, Penne, Spaghetti

Grandma Ferdon's▲ - Brown Rice (Chow Mein Noodles ●, Elbows ●, Fettuccini ●, Lasagna ●, Spaghetti ●)

Hodgson Mill▲ - Gluten Free Brown Rice (Angel Hair, Elbow, Lasagna, Linguine, Penne, Spaghetti)

Jovial▲ - Brown Rice (Capellini ●, Caserecce ●, Fusilli ●, Penne Rigate ●, Spaghetti ●)

Le Veneziane - Anellini, Ditalini, Eliche, Fettucce, Penne, Pipe Rigate, Rigatoni, Spaghetti

Lundberg▲ - Organic Brown Rice Pasta (Elbow, Penne, Rotini, Spaghetti)

Manischewitz - Passover Noodles

P

Mixes From The Heartland▲ - Pasta Mix (Penne ●, Shells ●,
Spaghetti ●)

Mrs. Leeper's -
Corn Pasta (Elbows, Rotelli, Spaghetti, Vegetable Radiatore)
Dinners (Beef Lasagna, Beef Stroganoff, Cheeseburger Mac,
Chicken Alfredo, Creamy Tuna, Mac & Cheese)
Rice Pasta (Alphabets, Elbows, Kids Shapes, Penne, Spaghetti,
Vegetable Twists)

Namaste Foods▲ - Pasta Meals (Pasta Pisavera, Say Cheez, Taco)

Notta Pasta - Fettuccine, Linguine, Spaghetti, Vermicelli

Orgran▲ -
Buontempo Rice Pasta (Penne, Shells, Spirals)
Canned (Alternative Grain Spaghetti, Spaghetti In Tomato Sauce,
Spirals In Tomato Sauce)
Corn & Spinach Rigati
Corn & Vegetable Pasta Shells
Corn Pasta Spirals
Essential Fibre (Penne, Spirals)
Garlic & Parsley Rice Pasta Shells
Italian Style Spaghetti
Pasta & Sauce Tomato Basil
Pasta Ready Meals (Tomato & Basil, Vegetable Bolognese)
Rice & Corn (Herb Pasta, Macaroni, Mini Lasagne Sheets, Penne,
Risoni Garlic Herb, Spaghetti, Spirals, Tortelli, Vegetable Animal
Shapes, Vegetable Corkscrews)
Rice & Millet Spirals
Rice Pasta Spirals
Super Grains Multigrain Pasta (w/Amaranth, w/Quinoa)
Tomato & Basil Corn Pasta
Vegetable Rice (Penne, Spirals)

Pastariso▲ -
All Natural Rice Pasta (Brown Rice Elbows ●, Brown Rice
Penne ●, Brown Rice Rotini ●, Brown Rice Spaghetti ●)

Organic Brown Rice Pasta (Angel Hair ●, Elbows ●, Fettuccine ●, Lasagna ●, Linguine ●, Penne ●, Rotini ●, Spaghetti ●, Spinach Spaghetti ●, Vegetable Rotini ●, Vermicelli ●)

Pastato▲ - Fortified Potato Pasta (Elbows ●, Shells ●, Spaghetti ●)

Rizopia -

Brown Rice Pasta (Elbows, Fettuccine, Fusilli, Lasagne, Penne, Shells, Spaghetti, Spirals)

Organic Brown Rice Pasta (Elbows, Fantasia, Fettuccine, Fusilli, Penne, Spaghetti)

Organic Wild Rice (Elbows, Fusilli, Penne, Radiatore, Shells, Spaghetti)

Spinach Brown Rice Spaghetti

Vegetable Brown Rice Fusilli

White Rice Spaghetti

Rustichella - Gluten Free Pasta (Corn Fusillotti, Corn Spaghetti, Rice Penne, Rice Spaghetti)

Sam Mills - Corn Pasta (Conchiliette, Cornetti Rigati, Fusilli, Lasagna, Penne Rigate, Rigatoni, Tubetti Rigati)

Schar▲ - Anellini, Fusilli, Multigrain Penne Rigate, Penne, Spaghetti, Tagliatelle

Seitenbacher - Gluten Free Rigatoni, Gourmet Noodles Gluten Free Golden Ribbon

Tinkyada▲ -

Brown Rice (Elbows, Fettuccini, Fusilli, Grand Shells, Lasagne, Little Dreams, Penne, Shells, Spaghetti, Spinach Spaghetti, Spirals, Vegetable Spirals)

Organic Brown Rice (Elbows, Lasagne, Penne, Spaghetti, Spirals), White Rice Spaghetti

Trader Joe's - All Organic Brown Rice Pasta, Rice Pasta & Cheddar, Rice Sticks Rice Pasta

Westbrae - Corn Angel Hair Pasta

Wild Wood - PastaSlim (Spaghetti ●, Spinach Fettuccini ●)

Pasta Sauce... see Sauces

P Pastrami

    Boar's Head - All Varieties

    Carl Buddig - Deli Cuts, Extra Thin Original, Original

    Castle Wood Reserve - Deli Meat Turkey Pastrami

    Dietz & Watson▲ - Pastrami Brisket ●, Spiced Beef Pastrami ●

    Eckrich - Deli Meat Pastrami

    Hormel - Bread Ready

    Hy-Vee - Thin Sliced

    Jennie-O Turkey Store - Refrigerated Dark Turkey

    Kayem - Extra Lean Black, New England Red, New York Style Black

    Meijer Brand - Sliced Chipped Meat

    Perdue - Deli Dark Turkey Pastrami Hickory Smoked

    Wellshire Farms - Brisket ‼, Navel, Round ‼, Sliced Beef ‼

Pastry Mix

    Mrs. Crimble's - Pastry Mix

    Orgran▲ - All Purpose

Pate

    Kootenay Kitchen - Vege Pate (Curry, Herb, Jalapeno)

    Old Wisconsin - Spreadable Pate (Black Pepper, Onion & Parsley, Original)

    Tartex -

        Cremisso (Champignon, Chardonnay Cote D'Or, Delicacy, Exquisite, Green Pepper, Herbs, Horseradish Apple, Hungarian, Mediterrana, Mexicana, Olivera, Peppers Chili, Pesto, Pomodoro D'Italia, Provence Herbs, Ratatouille, Shiitake, Tomato Basil, Truffle Champagne, Zucchini Curry)

        Organic Pate In Tubes (Chilli, Classic, Green Olive, Herb & Garlic, Herbs, Mushroom, Roasted Onion & Pink Peppercorn, Sundried Tomato)

        Pate (Chanterelle Mushroom, Grilled Aubergine, Porcini Mushrooms & Cranberry)

        Pate Creme (Basil, Italian Olives, Rocket & Mustard, Sundried Tomato & VanDouvan)

Pea Pods... see Peas

Peaches

*... *All Fresh Fruits & Vegetables Are Gluten-Free*

Albertsons - All Canned Peaches, Frozen

C & W - All Plain Frozen Fruits

Del Monte - Canned/Jarred Fruit (All Varieties), Fruit Snack Cups Metal, Plastic

Dole - All Fruits (Bowls *(Except Fruit Crisps)*, Canned, Dried, Frozen, Jars *(Except Real Fruit Bites)*), Fruit Parfait Peaches & Creme

Food Club Brand - Frozen Peaches Sliced, Fruit Cups Diced Peaches, Halves In Heavy Syrup, Sliced In Heavy Syrup, Sliced In Juice

Giant Brand - Canned (In Heavy Syrup, In Pear Juice, Yellow Cling), Frozen

Gluty Free - Dried White ●, Dried ●

Gordon Food Service - Chunk Bite Sized In Juice, Diced, Sliced

Great Value Brand (Wal-Mart) - Frozen, No Sugar Added Yellow Cling Peaches (Halves In Pear Juice from Concentrate, Sliced), Yellow Cling Sliced Peaches In Heavy Syrup

Hy-Vee - Diced, Diced Fruit Cups, Halves, Lite (Diced, Halves, Slices), Peaches In Strawberry Gel, Slices

Kirkland Signature - Sliced

Kroger Brand - Fruit (Canned, Cups)

Kroger Value - All Fresh Fruit Canned

Laura Lynn - Canned

Lowes Foods Brand - Slices (In Heavy Syrup, In Juice)

Meijer Brand - Cling Halves (In Heavy Syrup, In Juice Lite, In Pear Juice Lite), Cling Sliced (In Heavy Syrup, In Juice, In Pear Juice Lite), Frozen (Organic, Sliced), Yellow Sliced In Heavy Syrup

Midwest Country Fare - Lite Peaches (Halves, Slices), Slices, Yellow Cling Halves In Light Syrup, Slices (In Heavy Syrup, In Light Syrup)

Native Forest - Organic Sliced Peaches

Nuts Online - Dried Fruit (Diced ●, Dried ●, Natural ●, Organic ●, Simply ●, White ●)

Publix - Canned (Lite Yellow Cling Peaches in Pear Juice Halves & Slices, Yellow Cling Peaches In Heavy Syrup Halves & Slices), Frozen Sliced Peaches

P

S&W - All Canned/Jarred Fruits

Safeway Brand - Canned Peaches (Halves, Halves Lite, Sliced, Sliced Lite), Frozen

Spartan Brand - Cling Halves (Heavy Syrup, Lite Syrup), Cling Slices (Heavy Syrup, Lite Syrup), Diced (Heavy Syrup, Lite Syrup), Frozen, Fruit Cups

Wegmans Brand - Halved Yellow Cling, Sliced Yellow Cling (In Heavy Syrup, In Light Syrup Raspberry Flavored, Regular)

Winn Dixie - Frozen Sliced, Yellow Cling Halves & Slices (Heavy Syrup, Light Syrup)

Woodstock Farms - Organic Frozen Peach Slices

Peanut Butter... (includes Nut Butter)

Albertsons - Creamy, Crunchy

Arrowhead Mills - Almond Butter Creamy, Cashew Butter Creamy, Organic Valencia Peanut Butter (Creamy, Crunchy), Valencia Peanut Butter (Creamy, Crunchy)

Bell Plantation - PB2 Powdered (Chocolate ●, Original ●)

Blue Diamond - Almond Butter (Homestyle (Creamy, Crunchy, Honey), Ready Spread (Creamy, Crunchy, Honey))

Earth Balance▲ - Natural Almond Butter Creamy, Natural Peanut Butter (Creamy, Crunchy)

Emmy's Organics▲ - Raw (Cashew, Macadamia Cashew)

Food Club Brand - Creamy (Reduced Fat, Regular), Crunchy, Fun Stripes Peanut Butter (& Grape Jelly, & Strawberry Jelly), Reduced Sugar

Full Circle - Organic Creamy

Giant Brand - All Natural, Creamy, Crunchy, No Added Salt, Reduced Fat, Regular

Gluty Free -
Almond Butter (Crunchy ●, Raw Organic (Crunchy ●, Smooth ●), Smooth ●)
Cashew Butter Organic Smooth ●
Peanut Butter Organic (Crunchy ●, Smooth ●)
Sunflower Butter Organic ●

Great Value Brand (Wal-Mart) - Peanut Butter (Creamy, Crunchy)

Hannaford Brand - Creamy, Crunchy, No Salt Creamy, Reduced Fat Creamy

Hy-Vee - Creamy, Crunchy, Reduced Fat

I.M. Healthy - Soy Nut Butter (Chocolate, Honey (Chunky, Creamy), Original (Chunky, Creamy), Unsweetened (Chunky, Creamy))

Jif - Creamy, Creamy Omega 3, Extra Crunchy, Jif To Go, Natural (Creamy, Crunchy), Peanut Butter & Honey, Reduced Fat Creamy, Reduced Fat Crunchy, Simply Jif

Kirkland Signature - Organic Creamy

Kroger Brand - Creamy, Crunchy, Just Right (Creamy, Crunchy), Reduced Fat (Creamy, Crunchy), Roasted Peanuts & Honey (Creamy, Crunchy)

Laura Lynn - Peanut Butter & Grape Jelly Spread, Peanut Butter & Strawberry Jelly Spread

Lowes Foods Brand - Creamy, Crunchy

MaraNatha -
 All Natural Almond Butter (Hint Of Salt (Creamy, Crunchy), Natural (Honey, No Salt Creamy, No Salt Crunchy, Raw), No Stir (Creamy, Crunchy))
 Dark Chocolate Almond Spread
 Dark Chocolate Peanut Spread
 Natural Cashew Butter
 Organic Almond Butter (Raw (No Salt Creamy, No Salt Crunchy), Roasted (No Salt Creamy, No Salt Crunchy))
 Peanut Butter (All Varieties)
 Sunflower Seed Butter

Meijer Brand - Creamy, Crunchy, Natural (Creamy, Crunchy)

Midwest Country Fare - Creamy, Crunchy

Nature's Basket - Creamy, Creamy w/No Salt Added, Crunchy

Nature's Promise - Cashew Butter, Organic Almond Butter (Crunchy, Salted, Smooth, Unsalted), Organic Peanut Butter (Crunchy, Salted, Smooth, Unsalted)

P

Nuts Online - Almond Butter Organic (Raw Crunchy ●, Roasted Smooth ●), Roasted Crunchy ●, Roasted Smooth ●, Almond Paste ●, Hazelnut Praline Paste ●, Organic Peanut Butter (Crunchy Unsalted ●, Smooth Unsalted ●), Organic Sunflower Butter ●, Pistachio Nut Paste ●, Roasted Smooth Organic Cashew Butter ●

O Organics - Old Fashioned (Creamy, Crunchy)

Panner - Creamy, Crunchy, PB & J Grape, PB & J Strawberry

Peanut Butter & Co. - Cinnamon Raisin Swirl, Crunch Time, Dark Chocolate Dreams, Mighty Maple, Old Fashioned Crunchy, Old Fashioned Smooth, Smooth Operator, The Bee's Knees, The Heat Is On, White Chocolate Wonderful

Peanut Delight - Creamy, Crunchy

Private Selections - Organic (Creamy, Crunchy)

Publix - All Natural (Creamy, Crunchy), Creamy, Crunchy, Deli Fresh Ground, Reduced Fat Spread (Creamy, Crunchy)

Safeway Brand - Creamy, Crunchy, Reduced Fat (Creamy, Crunchy)

Santa Cruz - All Varieties

Skippy - Creamy, Extra Crunchy Super Chunk, Natural (Creamy, Super Chunk), Reduced Fat (Creamy, Super Chunk), Roasted Honey Nut (Creamy, Super Chunk)

Smart Balance - Rich Roast (Chunky, Creamy)

Smucker's▲ - Goober (Grape, Strawberry), Natural (Chunky, Creamy, Honey, No Salt Added Creamy, Reduced Fat Creamy), Organic (Chunky, Creamy)

Spartan Brand - Crunchy, Peanut Spread, Smooth

Stop & Shop Brand - All Natural Smooth Peanut Butter (No Added Salt, Reduced Fat, Regular), Peanut Butter (Creamy, Crunchy, Smooth)

Sunland - Organic Peanut Butter (Creamy Cherry Vanilla, Creamy Dark Chocolate, Creamy Valencia, Crunchy Chipotle Chile, Crunchy Valencia, Italian Thai Ginger & Red Pepper)

Trader Joe's -
Almond Butter (Creamy w/Salt, Crunchy Unsalted, Raw Crunchy Unsalted)

Better N' Peanut Butter
Organic Creamy **!**
Organic Crunchy **!**
Salted (Creamy **! !**, Crunchy **! !**)
Sunflower Seed Butter
Unsalted (Creamy **! !**, Crunchy **! !**)
Tropical Traditions - Coconut Peanut Butter
Walden Farms - Creamy Peanut Spread Sugar Free
Wegmans Brand - Natural Peanut Butter (Creamy, Crunchy),
Organic (Creamy, Crunchy), Organic No Stir (Creamy, Crunchy),
Peanut Butter (Creamy, Crunchy, Reduced Fat Creamy)
Winn Dixie - Creamy, Crunchy
Woodstock Farms -
Non Organic Nut Butters (Almond Butter (Crunchy Unsalted,
Smooth Unsalted), Cashew Butter Unsalted, Raw Almond,
Tahini Unsalted))
Organic Nut Butters (Almond Butter (Crunchy Unsalted, Smooth
Unsalted), Classic Peanut Butter (Crunchy Salted, Smooth
Salted), Easy Spread Peanut Butter (Crunchy Salted, Crunchy
Unsalted, Smooth Salted, Smooth Unsalted), Peanut Butter
(Crunchy Salted, Crunchy Unsalted, Smooth Salted, Smooth
Unsalted), Raw Almond, Tahini Unsalted)

Peanut Sauce
A Taste Of Thai - Peanut Satay Sauce, Peanut Sauce Mix
Lee Kum Kee - Satay Sauce
Mr. Spice Organic - Thai Peanut Sauce & Marinade
Thai Kitchen - Peanut Satay

Peanuts... see Nuts

Pears
... *All Fresh Fruits & Vegetables Are Gluten-Free*
Albertsons - Canned
Del Monte - Canned/Jarred Fruit (All Varieties), Fruit Snack Cups
(All Varieties)
Dole - All Fruits (Bowls *(Except Fruit Crisps)*, Canned, Dried, Frozen,
Jars *(Except Real Fruit Bites)*)

P

Food Club Brand - Bartlett Canned Halves

Full Circle - Organic (Halves In Juice, Sliced In Juice)

Giant Brand - Canned Bartlett Halves (In Heavy Syrup, In Juice, In Light Syrup, In Pear Juice, w/Splenda)

Gluty Free - Dried ●

Gordon Food Service - Bite Sized In Juice, Sliced

Great Value Brand (Wal-Mart) - Bartlett Pears In Heavy Syrup (Halves, Sliced), No Sugar Added Bartlett Chunky Mixed Fruits, Pear Halves In Pear Juice From Concentrate & Water

Hy-Vee - Bartlett Pears (Halves, Sliced), Diced Bartlett Pears Cups, Lite Pears

Kroger Brand - Fruit (Canned, Cups)

Laura Lynn - Canned Pears

Lowes Foods Brand - Halves (In Heavy Syrup, In Juice)

Meijer Brand - Halves (Heavy Syrup, In Juice, In Juice Lite, Lite), Slices (Heavy Syrup, In Juice Lite)

Midwest Country Fare - Bartlett Pear Halves In Light Syrup

Native Forest - Organic Sliced Asian Pears

Nuts Online - Dried Fruit (Diced ●, Dried ●, Natural ●, Organic ●, Simply ●)

Publix - Canned Bartlett Pears In Heavy Syrup (Halves, Slices), Lite Bartlett Pear Halves In Pear Juice

S&W - All Canned/Jarred Fruits

Safeway Brand - Canned Pears (Halves, Halves Lite, Sliced, Sliced Lite)

Spartan Brand - Fruit Cups, Halves (Heavy Syrup, Lite Syrup), Slices (Heavy Syrup, Lite Syrup)

Stop & Shop Brand - Bartlett Pear Halves (Heavy Syrup, Light Syrup, Pear Juice, w/Splenda)

Wegmans Brand - Halved (In Heavy Syrup, In Pear Juice From Concentrate), Sliced (In Heavy Syrup, In Pear Juice From Concentrate)

Winn Dixie - Bartlett Halves & Slices (Heavy Syrup, Light Syrup)

Peas

... *All Fresh Fruits & Vegetables Are Gluten-Free

Albertsons - All Plain Vegetables Canned & Frozen

Birds Eye - All Plain Frozen Vegetables

Bush's Best - Black Eye, Crowder, Field Peas w/Snaps, Purple Hull

C & W - All Plain Frozen Vegetables

Del Monte - All Canned Vegetables

Food Club Brand -

Canned (Black Eyed Peas, Blended, Peas & Sliced Carrots, Small, Sweet)

Dried Peas (Blackeyed, Green Split)

Frozen (Black Eyed Peas, Green Peas, Green Petite, Steamin' Easy Green Peas, Sugar Snap)

Freshlike - Select Petite Sweet Peas, Sweet Peas & Carrots, Tender Garden

Full Circle - Organic (Frozen Peas, Sweet Peas)

Giant Brand - Canned (Black Eyed Peas, Sweet), Frozen (Peas & Diced Carrots, Sugar Snap, Sweet), Frozen Petite (No Salt Added, Regular)

Gluty Free - Freeze Dried ●, Fried Green ●

Grand Selections - Frozen (Petite Green, Sugar Snap)

Great Value Brand (Wal-Mart) - Canned (Blackeye Peas, No Salt Added Sweet Peas, Peas & Carrots, Sweet Peas), Microwaveable Plastic Cups Sweet Peas

Green Giant - Canned Sweet Peas, Frozen Baby Sweet Peas & Butter Sauce, Simply Steam (Baby Sweet Peas, Sugar Snap Peas), Sweet Peas, Valley Fresh Steamers (Select Baby Sweet Peas, Select Sugar Snap Peas, Sweet Peas)

Hannaford Brand - No Salt, Petite, Sweet

HealthMarket - Organic Sweet

Hy-Vee - Black Eyed, Dry Green Split, Frozen Sweet, Steam In A Bag Frozen Peas, Sweet

Kroger Brand - All Plain Vegetables (Canned, Frozen)

Kroger Value - All Plain Vegetables (Canned, Frozen)

P

Laura Lynn - Canned Blackeye Peas, Sweet Peas, Tiny June Peas

Lowes Foods Brand - Frozen (Black Eyed, Crowder, Field Peas, Green, Peas & Carrots, Tiny Peas), Peas, Split Green Peas

Meijer Brand - Canned (Blackeye, Peas & Sliced Carrots, Small, Sweet, Sweet No Salt, Sweet Organic), Frozen Peas (Chinese Pea Pods, Green, Green Petite, Organic Green, Peas & Sliced Carrots)

Midwest Country Fare - Frozen Green, Sweet

Nature's Promise - Organic Sweet

Nuts Online - Fried Green Peas ●, Simply Peas Freeze Dried Vegetables ●

O Organics - Frozen Sweet Peas

Pictsweet - All Plain Vegetables (Frozen)

Private Selections - All Plain Vegetables Frozen

Publix - Canned Sweet Peas (Regular, Small), Frozen (Blackeye, Butter, Crowder, Field Peas w/Snap, Green, Original, Petite, Purple Hull)

Publix GreenWise Market - Organic Canned Sweet Peas

S&W - All Canned Vegetables

Safeway Brand - Frozen, Steam In Bag

Safeway Select - Frozen (Blackeyed, Green, Peas & Carrots, Petite), Steam In Bag (Peas & Onions, Petite Green, Pod)

Spartan Brand - Canned (Green, Peas & Carrots, Sweet), Dried (Blackeyed, Green Split), Frozen (Blackeyed, Peas & Sliced Carrots, Petite, Plain, Sugar Snap, w/Snaps)

Tasty Bite - Agra Peas & Greens **!**

Trader Joe's - Frozen (Organic Naturally Sweet, Petite Peas)

Wegmans Brand - Black-Eyed, Petite In Butter Sauce, Regular (Sweet Canned, Sweet Frozen), Small Sweet, Sugar Snap Frozen, Sweet No Salt Added, Sweet Petite Frozen, w/Pearl Onions Frozen

Westbrae - Sweet Peas

Winn Dixie - Canned Green Peas (Large, Medium, No Salt Added, Small, Tiny), Frozen (Field w/Snaps, Green, Organic Green, Peas & Carrots, Petite Green, Purple Hull)

Woodstock Farms - Organic Frozen (Green Peas, Peas & Carrots, Petite Peas, Sugar Snap)

Pectin
>   **Certo** - Premium Liquid Fruit Pectin

Pepper Rings
>   **B&G** - Hot Pepper Rings
>   **Food Club Brand** - Banana Peppers Hot Rings
>   **Meijer Brand** - Banana Pepper Rings Hot, Mild
>   **Mezzetta** - Deli Sliced (Hot Pepper Rings, Mild Pepper Rings), Gourmet Deli (Mild Rosemary & Garlic Pepper Rings, Sweet & Hot Jalapeno Pepper Rings)
>   **Mt. Olive** - Hot Banana Pepper Rings
>   **Publix** - Banana Pepper Rings Mild
>   **Spartan Brand** - Hot, Pepper Rings Mild

Pepperoni...see Sausage

Peppers
>   *... *All Fresh Fruits & Vegetables Are Gluten-Free*
>   **B&G** - Giardiniera, Hot Cherry Peppers (w/Oregano & Garlic, Red & Green, Regular), Hot Chopped Roasted, Hot Jalapenos, Pepperoncini, Roasted (w/Balsamic Vinegar, w/Oregano & Garlic), Sandwich Toppers (Hot Chopped Peppers, Hot Peppers, Sweet Bell Bepper, Sweet Pepper), Sweet (Red, Salad w/Oregano & Garlic)
>   **Birds Eye** - All Plain Frozen Vegetables
>   **C & W** - All Plain Frozen Vegetables
>   **Cara Mia** - Piquillo Peppers
>   **Di Lusso** - Roasted Red
>   **Dietz & Watson▲** - Pepperoncini ●, Sliced Jalapeno ●, Sweet Roasted Red Pepper ●
>   **Earthbound Farm** - Organic Bell
>   **Food Club Brand** - Banana Peppers Mild, Frozen Green Pepper Diced, Pepperoncini
>   **Giant Brand** - Frozen Chopped Green
>   **Hannaford Brand** - Whole Pepperoncini
>   **Heinz** - All Varieties

P

Hy-Vee - Diced Green Chilies, Green Salad Pepperoncini, Hot Banana Peppers, Mild Banana Peppers, Salad Peppers, Sliced Hot Jalapenos, Whole Green Chilies

La Victoria - Diced Jalapenos, Nacho Jalapenos Sliced

Meijer Brand - Frozen Green Peppers Chopped

Melissa's - Fire Roasted Sweet Bell

Mezzetta -

Deli Sliced (Hot Jalapeno Peppers, Roasted Sweet Bell Pepper Strips, Sweet Bell Pepper Sandwich Strips, Tamed Jalapeno Peppers)

Deli Style (Sweet Bell Pepper Relish, Zesty Bell Pepper Relish Hot)

Garlic & Dill Golden Peperoncini

Golden Pepperoncini

Gourmet Deli (Roasted Red Bell Pepper & Caramelized Onions, Tamed Diced Jalapeno Peppers, Tamed Fire Roasted Jalapeno Peppers w/Chipotle Pep, Tri Color Roasted Bell Pepper Strips)

Habanero Peppers

Hot (Banana Wax Peppers, Cherry Peppers, Chili Peppers, Chili Peppers Mexican Style En Escabeche, Jalapeno Peppers En Escabeche, Serrano Chili Peppers)

Italian Wax Peppers

Organics (Fire Roasted Red Bell Peppers, Sliced Hot Jalapeno Peppers)

Roasted (Bell Peppers, Marinated Yellow & Red Sweet Peppers, Yellow & Red Sweet Peppers)

Sweet (Banana Wax Peppers, Cherry Peppers)

Tamed Jalapeno Peppers En Escabeche

Mt. Olive - Diced Jalapeno Peppers, Jalapeno Slices, Jalapeno Slices Pepper PAK, Marinated Roasted Red Peppers, Mild Banana Pepper Rings, Pepperoncini, Roasted Red Peppers, Sliced Pepperoncini, Sweet 'N Hot Salad Peppers, Sweet Salad Peppers

Nuts Online - Simply Red Peppers Freeze Dried Vegetables ●

Peloponnese - Florina Whole Sweet Peppers

Peppadew - Goldew, Peppadew Hot, Peppadew Mild

Pictsweet - Chopped Green
Publix - Frozen Green Peppers Diced
Safeway Select - Fire Roasted, Frozen Pepper Strips
Spartan Brand - Jalapeno
Star - Greek Pepperoncini
Stop & Shop Brand - Chopped Green
Trader Joe's -
   Artichoke Red Pepper Tapenade**!!**
   Fire Roasted Red (Regular, Sweet & Yellow)
   Frozen Fire Roasted Bell Peppers & Onions**!!**
   Frozen Melange A Trois
   Marinated Red
   Red Pepper Spread w/Garlic & Eggplant
Trappey's - Banana Peppers, Cherry Peppers, Hot Jalapenos, Peppers In Vinegar, Tempero Peppers, Torrido Peppers
Vlasic - All Varieties
Wegmans Brand - Clean and Cut Peppers & Onions (Diced, Sliced), Pepper & Onions Mix, Roasted Red Peppers Whole
Winn Dixie - Pepperoncini, Sliced Banana Peppers
Woodstock Farms - Organic Frozen Tri Colored Peppers

Pesto

Classico - All Varieties
Fischer & Wieser - Cilantro Pepito, Sicilian Tomato
Mezzetta - Napa Valley Bistro Homemade Style Basil Pesto
Santa Barbara - Basil, Chipotle Basil, Spinach Cilantro, Sun Dried Tomato
Santa Barbara Olive Co. - Chunky Olive
Sauces 'N Love - Mint Pesto, Pesto, Pink Pesto
Scarpetta - Pesto, Pink Pesto
Trader Joe's - Pesto Alla Genovese Basil Pesto

Picante Sauce

Albertsons - Medium, Mild
Chi-Chi's
Hy-Vee - Hot, Medium, Mild
Winn Dixie - Medium, Mild

P Pickles

Albertsons - All Varieties

B&G - Bread & Butter, Dill, Hamburger Dill, Kosher Dill (Gherkins, Original), NY Deli Dill, Pickle In A Pouch, Sandwich Toppers (Bread & Butter, Hamburger Dill, Kosher Dill, N Y Deli, Polish Dill), Sweet (Gherkins, Mixed)

Boar's Head - All Varieties

Dietz & Watson ▲ - Kosher Spear ●, New Half Sours ●, Sour Garlic ●

Food Club Brand - All Varieties

Full Circle - Kosher Baby Dill, Sweet Bread & Butter

Giant Brand - Sweet Whole Midgets

Gordon Food Service - Dill (Chips, Kosher (Sliced, Spears, Whole), Sliced), Sweet (Butter Chips, Gherkins, Sliced)

Great Value Brand (Wal-Mart) - Bread & Butter, Dill Spears, Hamburger Dill Chips, Kosher Baby Dill, Kosher Dill Spears, Sweet (Gherkin, Pickle Relish), Whole Dill, Whole Sweet

Hannaford Brand - Bread & Butter (Chips, Sandwich Slices), Dill Relish, Hot Dog Relish, Kosher (Baby Dills, Dill, Dill Sandwich Slices, Dill Spears, Petite), Polish Dill Spears, Sour Dill, Sugar Free Bread & Butter (Chips, Spears), Sugar Free Sweet Gherkins, Sweet (Gherkins, Midgets, Mixed Chips, Relish, Relish Squeeze)

Heinz - All Varieties

Hy-Vee -

　　Bread & Butter (Sandwich Slices, Sweet Chunk Pickles, Sweet Slices)

　　Cocktail Dills

　　Dill (Kosher Sandwich Slices, Relish)

　　Dill Pickles

　　Fresh Pack Kosher Baby Dills

　　Hamburger Dill Slices

　　Kosher (Baby Dills, Dill Spears)

　　Polish Dill (Pickles, Spears)

　　Refrigerated Kosher Dill (Halves, Sandwich Slices, Spears, Whole Pickles)

Special Recipe (Baby Dills, Bread & Butter Slices, Hot & Spicy Zingers, Hot & Sweet Zinger Chunks, Jalapeno Baby Dills, Sweet Garden Crunch)

Sweet Gherkins

Whole (Dill, Sweet)

Zesty (Kosher Dill Spears, Sweet Chunks)

Kroger Brand - All Varieties

Kroger Value - All Varieties

Kurtz - Bread & Butter, Hamburger Dill Slices, Kosher Dill Spears, Sweet, Whole Dill

Laura Lynn - All Pickles

Lowes Foods Brand - Bread & Butter Chips, Dill (Hamburger, Kosher, Kosher Spears), Kosher (Baby Dill, Sandwich Slices), Sweet Midgets, Sweet Salad Cubes

Meijer Brand - Bread & Butter Chips (Regular, Sugar Free), Sandwich Slice, Dill (Hamburger, Kosher (Baby, Spears, Whole), Polish, Sandwich Slice Polish, Spears (No Garlic, Polish, Zesty), Whole), Kosher (Baby Dill, Sandwich Slices, Whole), Sweet (Gherkin, Midgets, Sugar Free)

Mezzetta - Whole Kosher Style Dill Pickles

Midwest Country Fare - Dill, Hamburger Dill Pickle Slices, Kosher Dill, Whole Sweet

Mrs. Renfro's - Green Tomato Pickles

Mt. Olive -

Bread & Butter (Chips, Sandwich Stuffers, Spears)

Dills (Jumbo, Large, Original, Thin)

Hamburger Dill Chips

Hot Sauce Flavored Kosher Baby Dills

Jalapeno Flavored (Baby Dills, Dill Spears, Kosher Dill Spears)

Kosher (Baby Dills, Dill Chips, Dill Hamburger Stuffers, Hamburger Dill Chips, Hot 'N Spicy Dills, Petite Dills, Zesty Garlic Dills)

No Sugar Added (Bread & Butter Chips, Bread & Butter Sandwich Stuffers, Bread & Butter Spears, Sweet Gherkins, Sweet Petites PicklePak)

P

Petite Snack Crunchers (Hot Sauce Flavored Kosher Dill, Kosher Dills, Sweet Petite)

PicklePak (Hamburger Dill Chips, Kosher Dill Petites, Sweet Petites)

Polish (Dill Spears, Kosher Dills)

Sour

Sweet (Gerkins, Midgets, Mixed, Pickles)

Publix - All Varieties

Safeway Brand - All Varieties

Spartan Brand - Bread & Butter Slices (Sandwich, Sweet), Kosher Dill (Baby, Slices (Hamburger, Sandwich), Spears, Whole), Polish Dill (Spears, Whole), Sweet (Gherkin Whole, Slices, Whole)

Trader Joe's - Organic (Kosher Sandwich Pickles, Sweet Butter Pickles)

Vlasic - All Varieties

Wegmans Brand - Hamburger Dill Slices, Kosher Dill (Baby Dills, Halves, Mini, Sandwich Slices, Spears, Spears Reduced Sodium, Whole), Polish Dill (Spears, Whole), Sweet (Gherkins, Midgets), Sweet Bread & Butter Chips (No Salt Added, Regular), Sweet Sandwich Slices

Winn Dixie - Dill (All Varieties), Sweet Pickles (All Varieties), Sweet Relish

Woodstock Farms - Organic Kosher Dill (Baby, Sliced, Whole), Sweet Bread & Butter

Pie

Amy's - Mexican Tamale Pie!, Shepherd's Pie (Light In Sodium!, Regular!)

Cedarlane - Three Layer Enchilada Pie

Ceres Kitchen▲ - Banana Cream, Blueberry, Chocolate, Coconut Cream, Key Lime, Lemon Meringue

El Peto▲ - Apple, Blueberry, Cherry, Peach, Strawberry Rhubarb, Walnut

Fabe's Bakery - 8" Gluten Free Vegan (Apple Pie ●, Pumpkin Pie ●), Mini Gluten Free Vegan (Apple Pie ●, Pumpkin Pie ●)

Gillian's Foods▲ - Apple, Pumpkin

Grandma Ferdon's▲ - Apple (Crisp ●, Pie ●), Peach ●, Pumpkin ●
Pure Market Express▲ - Apple Pie ●, Banana Cream Pie ●, Pumpkin Pie ●
Silly Yak Bakery - GF Pastry (Apple Turnover ●, Blueberry Turnover ●, Gluten Free Cherry Turnover ●, Raspberry Turnover ●), GF Pie (Apple ●, Apple Caramel Pie ●, Apple Crisp Pie ●, Blackberry ●, Blueberry ●, Cherry ●, Cherry Crisp ●, Dutch Apple ●, Peach ●, Peach Pecan ●, Pecan ●, Pumpkin ●)
Skye Foods - Pie Tarts (Apple ●, Cherry ●, Pumpkin ●)
Trader Joe's - Shepherd's Pie Beef
Whole Foods Market Gluten Free Bakehouse▲ - Apple, Cherry, Peach, Pumpkin, Southern Pecan

Pie Crust/Pie Crust Mix
Andrea's Fine Foods▲ - Pie Crust
Arnel's Originals - Pie Crust Mix
Augason Farms - Gluten Free Pie Crust Mix ●
Authentic Foods▲ - Pie Crust Mix
Breads From Anna▲ - Piecrust Mix
Cause You're Special▲ - Homestyle Pie Crust
Ceres Kitchen▲ - Pie Crust
El Peto▲ - Perfect Pie Crust Mix, Pie Crust, Pie Dough
Gillian's Foods▲ - Pie Shell
Gluten Free Mama▲ - Mama's Pie Crust Mix ●
Gluten Free Pantry▲ - Perfect Pie Crust
Gluten-Free Creations▲ - Graham Cracker Crumb Mix ●
Grandma Ferdon's▲ - Frozen 8" Crust w/Tin ●, Pie Crust Mix ●
Kinnikinnick▲ - Pastry & Pie Crust Mix
Mixes From The Heartland▲ - Impossible Coconut Pie Mix ●, Pie Crust Mix ●
Really Great Food Company▲ - Flaky Pie Crust Mix
Silly Yak Bakery - GF Pie Crust Mix
The Grainless Baker▲ - Pie Crust
Whole Foods Market Gluten Free Bakehouse▲ - Pie Crust Mix

P Pie Filling

Comstock - All Varieties

Fischer & Wieser - Fredericksburg Golden Peach, Harvest Apple & Brandy Pie

Food Club Brand - Apple, Blueberry, Cherry, Peach, Very Cherry

Giant Brand - Canned Blueberry Fruit, Cherry (Lite, Regular), Spiced Apple

Gold Leaf - Apple, Blueberry, Cherry, Peach

Great Value Brand (Wal-Mart) - Apple, Blueberry, Cherry, No Sugar Added (Apple, Cherry)

Hy-Vee - More Fruit Pie Filling/Topping (Apple, Cherry)

Jell-O -

Regular Cook N' Serve (Banana Cream, Butterscotch, Chocolate (Fudge, Regular), Coconut Cream, Fat Free Tapioca, Lemon, Vanilla)

Regular Instant Pudding & Pie Filling (Banana Cream, Butterscotch, Cheesecake, Chocolate (Caramel Chip, Fudge, Mint Chip, Regular), Coconut Cream, Devil's Food, French Vanilla, Lemon, Pistachio, Pumpkin Spice, Vanilla (Chocolate Chip, Regular), White Chocolate)

Sugar Free Fat Free Cook N' Serve (Chocolate, Vanilla)

Sugar Free Fat Free Instant Pudding & Pie Filling (Banana Cream, Butterscotch, Cheesecake, Chocolate, Lemon, Pistachio, Vanilla, White Chocolate)

Kroger Brand - Canned Pie Filling

Lowes Foods Brand - Apple, Blueberry, Cherry

Lucky Leaf - Apple, Apricot, Banana Crème, Blueberry, Cherries Jubilee, Cherry, Chocolate Crème, Coconut Crème, Dark Sweet Cherry, Key Lime Pie Crème, Lemon, Lemon Crème, Lite (Apple, Cherry), Peach, Pineapple, Premium (Apple, Blackberry, Blueberry, Cherry, Red Raspberry), Raisin, Strawberry

Meijer Brand - Apple, Blueberry, Cherry, Cherry Lite, Peach

Midwest Country Fare - Apple, Cherry

Musselman's - Apple, Apricot, Banana Crème, Blackberry, Blueberry, Cherries Jubilee, Cherry, Chocolate Crème, Coconut Crème, Dark Sweet Cherry, Key Lime Crème Pie, Lemon, Lemon Crème, Lite Apple, Lite Cherry, Peach, Pineapple, Raisin, Strawberry, Strawberry Glaze, Supreme Blueberry & Crème, Supreme Cherries & Crème, Supreme Peaches & Crème, Vanilla Crème

My T Fine - Chocolate, Lemon, Vanilla

Nuts Online - Filling (Almond ●, Chocolate ●, Cinnamon ●, Poppy Seed ●)

Private Selections - All Varieties

Spartan Brand - Apple, Blueberry, Cherry (Lite, Regular), Pumpkin

Wilderness - All Varieties

Winn Dixie - Apple, Blueberry, Cherry

Pilaf

Trader Joe's - Thai Style Lime, Wild & Basmati Rice Pilaf

Pimentos

Meijer Brand - Pieces, Sliced

Pineapple

... *All Fresh Fruits & Vegetables Are Gluten-Free

Albertsons - All Varieties

Del Monte - Canned/Jarred Fruit (All Varieties), Fruit Snack Cups (Metal, Plastic)

Dole - All Fruits (Bowls *(Except Fruit Crisps)*, Canned, Dried, Frozen, Jars *(Except Real Fruit Bites)*), Fruit Parfait Pineapple & Creme

Food Club Brand - Chunks, Crushed, Sliced, Tidbits (In Juice, In Lime Jel)

Giant Brand - Frozen

Gluty Free - Dried (Diced ●, Natural ●, Organic ●, Regular ●)

Great Value Brand (Wal-Mart) - Chunks, Pineapple In Unsweetened Pineapple Juice (Crushed, Slices, Tidbits), Plastic Cups Tidbits

Hy-Vee - Chunk, Crushed, In Lime Gel, Sliced, Tidbit Fruit Cup

Kroger Brand - Fruit (Canned, Cups)

Laura Lynn - Canned

Lowes Foods Brand - Chunks In Juice, Crushed In Juice, Sliced In Juice

P

Meijer Brand - Chunks (Heavy Syrup, In Juice), Crushed (Heavy Syrup, In Juice), Frozen Chunks, Sliced In (Heavy Syrup, Juice)

Midwest Country Fare - Chunks, Crushed, Slices, Tidbits

Native Forest - Organic (Chunks, Crushed, Slices)

Nuts Online - Dried Fruit (Chunks ●, Diced ●, Dried ●, Natural ●, Organic ●, Organic Chunks ●, Simply ●)

Publix - All Varieties

Safeway Brand - Chunks, Crushed, Sliced

Spartan Brand - Chunks, Crushed, Sliced, Tidbits

Stop & Shop Brand - Frozen Pineapple

Trader Joe's - Frozen Pineapple Tidbits

Wegmans Brand - Chunk In Heavy Syrup, In Pineapple Juice (Chunk, Crushed, Sliced, Tidbits)

Winn Dixie - Chunks, Crushed, Sliced, Tidbits

Pistachio Nuts... see Nuts

Pizza

Against The Grain Gourmet - 12" (Pesto, Three Cheese/Tomato)

Amy's - Rice Crust Pizza (Cheese!, No Cheese Roasted Vegetable, Non Dairy Cheese!, Non Dairy Spinach!, Roasted Vegetable)

Andrea's Fine Foods▲ - Cheese, Pepperoni, Sausage, Spinach Artichoke

Celiac Specialties▲ - French Bread Pizza, Pizza (12" Pizza, 6" Pizza)

Ceres Kitchen▲ - Cheese, Garlic Chicken, Kaua'i, Pepperoni & Cheese, Supreme, Vegetarian Combo

Conte's Pasta - Margherita ●, Mushroom Florentine ●

Di Manufacturing - 12" Gluten Free Pizza (Pepperoni ●, Sausage ●, Three Cheese ●)

Everybody Eats▲ - Tomato Mozzarella Pizza

Foods By George▲ - Cheese Pizza

Gluten Free & Fabulous▲ - Cheese ●, Pepperoni ●, Pesto Margherita ●, Spinach Feta ●, Vegetable Margherita ●

Glutino▲ - Frozen Pizza (3 Cheese Pizza w/Brown Rice Crust, Barbeque Chicken, Duo Cheese, Pepperoni, Spinach & Feta, Spinach Soy Cheese w/Brown Rice Crust)

Ian's - Wheat Free Gluten Free Recipe French Bread Soy Cheese
Miller's Gluten Free Foods▲ - Frozen Thin Crust (Pepperoni, Plain)
Pure Market Express▲ - Pepperoni Pizza ●, Sausage Pizza ●

Pizza Crust/Pizza Mix

Against The Grain Gourmet - 12" Crust
Andrea's Fine Foods▲ - Pizza Crust (12", 6")
Arrowhead Mills - Gluten Free Pizza Crust Mix
Augason Farms - Gluten Free Pizza & Foccacia Dough Mix ●
Authentic Foods▲ - Pizza Crust Mix
Bob's Red Mill▲ - GF Pizza Crust Mix
Bready - Gluten Free Pizza Dough ●
Cause You're Special▲ - Famous Pizza Crust Mix
Celiac Specialties▲ - 12" Pizza Crust, 6" Casein Free Pizza, 6" Pizza Crust
Chebe▲ - Pizza Frozen Dough ●, Pizza Mix ●
Dad's▲ - Gluten Free Pizza Crust
Domata - Gluten Free Pizza Crust ●
El Peto▲ - Pizza Crust (Basil, Millet, White)
Ener-G▲ - Rice Pizza Shell (10", 6"), Yeast Free Rice Pizza Shell (10", 6")
Everybody Eats▲ - Pizza Shells
Foods By George▲ - Pizza Crusts
Food-Tek Fast & Fresh▲ - Dairy Free Minute Pizza Crust Mix
French Meadow Bakery - Gluten Free Pizza Crust ●
Gifts Of Nature▲ - French Bread & Pizza Crust Mix
Gillian's Foods▲ - Deep Dish Pizza Crust, Pizza Dough Mix
Gluten Free Pantry▲ - French Bread & Pizza Mix
Gluten-Free Creations▲ - Italian Seasoned Crust ●, Simply Pizza Crust Mix ●, Simply Pizza Crust ●
Glutino▲ - Premium Pizza Crust
Gourmet Parlor Pizza - Gluten Free (Cheese ●, Pepperoni ●, Sausage Pepperoni ●)
Grandma Ferdon's▲ - 10" Pizza Crust ●, 6" Cheese Pizza ●, Pizza Crust Mix ●
Heaven Mills - Pizza Crust

P

Hodgson Mill▲ - Gluten Free Pizza Crust Mix

Katz Gluten Free▲ - Pizza Crust ●

King Arthur Flour▲ - Gluten Free Pizza Crust Mix ●

Kinnikinnick▲ - Pizza Crust (10", Personal Size), Pizza Crust Mix

Kneaded Specialties▲ - Pizza Crust ●

Laurel's Sweet Treats▲ - Pizza Dough Mix

Namaste Foods▲ - Pizza Crust Mix

O'Doughs Bakery▲ - Pizza Kit (Flax ●, White ●)

Orgran▲ - Pizza & Pastry Multi Mix

PaneRiso▲ - White Rice Pizza Crust ●

Quejos▲ - Cheese Thin Crust Pizza Shells, Non Dairy Thin Crust Pizza Shells

Really Great Food Company▲ - French Bread/Pizza Crust, Pizza Crust Mix

Rose's Bakery▲ - Pizza Crusts (14", 9", Parbaked)

Rustic Crust▲ - Gluten Free Napoli Herb Pizza Crust ●

Schar▲ - Pizza Crusts

Silly Yak Bakery - CFGF 8-inch Pizza Crusts ●, GF (8" Pizza Crust ●, Gourmet Pizza Party ●)

Still Riding Pizza - Gluten Free Pizza Crust

The Grainless Baker▲ - 8" Shell

Udi's Gluten Free Foods▲ - Gluten Free Pizza Crust

Whole Foods Market Gluten Free Bakehouse▲ - Pizza Crust

Pizza Sauce... see also Sauces

Contadina - Flavored w/Pepperoni, Four Cheese, Original

Eden Organic - Organic Pizza Pasta Sauce

Food Club Brand - Pizza Sauce

Hannaford Brand

Hy-Vee

Lowes Foods Brand

Mantia's - Regular

Meijer Brand

Ragu - Homemade Style, Pizza Quick Traditional

Sauces 'N Love - Marinara & Pizza Sauce

Spartan Brand - w/Basil
Trader Joe's - Fat Free**!!**
Wegmans Brand - Chunky
Winn Dixie

Plum Sauce
Sharwood's
Wok Mei - All Natural Plum

Plums
... *All Fresh Fruits & Vegetables Are Gluten-Free
Giant Brand - Canned Whole In Heavy Syrup
Gluty Free - Dried Pluots ●
Kirkland Signature - Pitted Dry Plums
Safeway Brand
Stop & Shop Brand - Whole Plums In Heavy Syrup
Winn Dixie - Canned Whole Plums

Polenta
Beretta - Gran Polenta Express
Bob's Red Mill▲ - Gluten Free Corn Grits/Polenta
Food Merchants Brand - Ancient Harvest Basil & Garlic, Chili &
   Cilantro, Mushroom & Onion, Quinoa Heirloom Red & Black, Sun
   Dried Tomato & Garlic, Traditional Italian
Melissa's - Organic (Italian Herb, Original, Sun Dried Tomato)
San Gennaro Foods - Basil & Garlic, Sundried Tomato & Garlic,
   Traditional
Trader Joe's - Organic Polenta

Pomegranate
Trader Joe's - Frozen Pomegranate Seeds

Pop... see Soda Pop/Carbonated Beverages

Popcorn
Albertsons - Microwavable (Butter, Kettle, Light Butter, Movie
   Theater Butter), Yellow
Better Made Snack Foods - All Varieties, Caramel Corn
   (All Varieties)
Cape Cod - Sweet Cream Butter, White Cheddar

P

Chester's - Butter Flavored Puffcorn Snacks**!!**, Cheddar Cheese Flavored**!!**, Cheese Flavored Puffcorn Snacks**!!**

Cracker Jack - Original Caramel Coated Popcorn & Peanuts**!!**

Deep River Snacks - Sharp White Cheddar Popcorn

Eden Organic - Organic Yellow Popping Kernels

Farmer Steve's - Organic Microwave, Super Pop Kernels

Food Club Brand - Butter Crazy Lite, Popcorn Microwave (Butter (Light, Regular), Butter Crazy, Natural (Lite, Regular))

Full Circle - Organic Microwave (Butter, Natural)

Giant Brand - Microwave Butter (94% Fat Free, Light, Movie Theater, Regular, Sweet & Buttery), Kettle Corn, Natural Light, White Cheddar, Yellow

Gordon Food Service - Buttery, Cheese

Great Value Brand (Wal-Mart) - Yellow Popping Corn

Hannaford Brand - Microwavable (Butter, Fat Free Butter, Kettle, Light Butter, Natural)

Herr's - Light, Original, White Cheddar Ranch

Hy-Vee - Microwave (94% Fat Free Butter, Butter, Caramel Fresh Pop, Cheese, Extra Butter (Lite, Regular), Kettle, Light Butter, Lightly Salted, Natural Flavor, No Salt, Regular, White Cheddar), Regular (White, Yellow)

Jolly Time - Kernel Corn (American's Best, Organic Yellow, White, Yellow), Microwave (America's Best, Better Butter, Blast O Butter (Light, Minis, Regular), ButterLicious (Light, Regular), Crispy N White (Light, Regular), Healthy Pop (Butter Flavor, Caramel Apple, Crispy White Naturally Flavored, Kettle Corn, Regular), KettleMania, Mallow Magic, Sassy Salsa, Sea Salt & Cracked Pepper, The Big Cheez, White & Buttery)

Kroger Brand - 94% Fat Free, Butter, Kettle, Movie Theater Butter, Natural, Plain Popcorn Kernels (White, Yellow)

Laura Lynn - All Items

LesserEvil - Kettle Corn (Black & White**!!**, Class Kettle**!!**, Maple Pecan**!!**)

Lowes Foods Brand - Microwave (Butter, Butter 94% Fat Free, Extra Butter, Light Butter Mini Bags, Light Natural, Natural), Popcorn (Butter Flavor, White Cheddar Flavor), Yellow Bag

Meijer Brand - Microwave (75% Fat Free Butter, 94% Fat Free, Butter (GP, Regular), Extra Butter (GP, Lite, Regular), Hot N' Spicy, Kettle Sweet & Salty, Natural Lite), Regular (White, Yellow)

Mini Pops▲ - Popped Sorghum (Baby White Cheddar ●, Hot N' Chilly Chili ●, Itsy Bitsy Chili Cheese ●, Little Lemon Pepper ●, Petite Plain ●, Subatomic Sea Salt ●)

Newman's Own - Microwave (100 Calorie Natural Mini Bags, 94% Fat Free, Butter (Boom, Light, Low Sodium, Reduced Sodium, Regular), Natural, Tender White Kernels Natural), Regular Raw Popcorn

Newman's Own Organics - Microwave Pop's Corn (Butter Flavored, Light Butter Flavored, No Butter/No Salt 94% Fat Free)

O Organics - Microwave Popcorn (Butter Flavor, Regular)

Odell's - Movie Theatre Popcorn Kit

Old Dutch - Caramel Corn, Cheddar Cheese, Gourmet White, Northern Lights Fat Free Caramel Corn, White Cheddar

Pirate's Booty - Aged White Cheddar, Barbeque, Sour Cream & Onion, Veggie

Pop Secret - Microwave (1 Step Cheddar, 1 Step White Cheddar, Butter (94% Fat Free, Regular), Cheddar, Extra Butter, Homestyle, Jumbo Pop (Butter, Movie Theater Butter), Kettle Corn, Light Butter, Movie Theater Butter)

Publix - Microwave (Butter, Kettle, Light Butter, Movie Theater, Natural)

Safeway Brand - Kettle, Microwave (All Varieties), White, Yellow

Skeete & Ike's - Organic (BBQ!!, Kettle Corn!!, Sea Salt!!, White Cheddar!!)

Smart Balance - Light Butter, Light Butter Mini Bags, Smart Movie Style, Smart 'N Healthy

Smartfood - Cranberry Almond Flavored Popcorn Clusters!!, White Cheddar Cheese Flavored (Reduced Fat!!, Regular!!)

P

Snyder's Of Hanover - Butter Flavored Popcorn

Spartan Brand - Extra Butter, Microwave (Butter, Kettle, Lite Butter, Lite Extra Butter, Natural, Regular), White, Yellow

Stop & Shop Brand - Microwave Popcorn (94% Fat Free Butter, Butter (Flavored, Light), Kettle Corn, Movie Theatre Butter Flavored, Natural Light, Sweet & Buttery) Yellow Popcorn Kernels

Trader Joe's - Cranberry Nut Clusters, Fat Free Caramel, Gourmet White, Kettle, Lite Popcorn 50% Less Salt, Microwave (94% Fat Free, Natural Butter), Organic w/Olive Oil **!**, White Cheddar

UTZ - Popcorn (Butter, Cheese, White Cheddar)

Wegmans Brand - Microwave (94% Fat Free Butter Flavor, Butter Flavor, Kettle Corn, Light Butter Flavor, Movie Theater Butter, Organic), Regular Yellow

Winn Dixie - Microwavable (Butter, Double Butter, Light Butter, Natural), Yellow

Wise - Popcorn (Hot Cheese, Original Butter Flavored, Reduced Fat Butter Flavored, Reduced Fat White Cheddar Flavored, White Cheddar Flavored)

Pork

... *All Fresh Meat Is Gluten-Free (Non-Marinated, Unseasoned)*

Always Tender - Flavored Fresh Pork (Apple Bourbon, Bourbon Maple, Brown Sugar Maple, Citrus, Honey Mustard, Lemon Garlic, Mediterranean, Mesquite, Olive Oil, Onion Garlic, Original, Peppercorn, Portabella Mushroom, Roast Flavor, Sun Dried Tomato), Non Flavored Fresh Pork

Coleman's Natural Foods - Hampshire Chops ●, Loin ●, Ribs (Baby Back ●, St. Louis ●), Tenderloins ●

Dietz & Watson ▲ - Boneless Pork Chops w/Natural Juices ●, Canadian Center Cut Spare Ribs ●, Cuban Roast Pork ●, Italian Style Roast Pork ●, Panchetta Sweet ●, Pork Cello Butt ●, Roast Sirloin Of Pork ●, Souse Roll ●, Spiced Luncheon Meat ●

Farmer John - California Natural Pork (Boneless Loin, Ground Pork, Spareribs, Tenderloins)

Farmland - Sliced Salt Pork Belly, Smoked Pork Jowl

Giant Eagle Brand - Baby Back Ribs w/BBQ Sauce, Shredded w/BBQ Sauce

Gordon Food Service - Pureed Pork w/Broth

Hormel - Pickled (Pigs Feet, Pork Hocks, Tidbits), Pork Roast Au Jus Fully Cooked Entrée

Jones Dairy Farm -

All Natural

Hearty Pork Sausage Links ●

Light Pork Sausage & Rice Links ●

Little Link Pork Sausage ●

Maple Sausage Links ●

Original Pork Roll Sausage ●

Pork Sausage Patties ●

Golden Brown All Natural Fully Cooked

Maple Sausage (Links ●, Patties ●)

Mild Sausage (Links ●, Patties ●)

Pork & Uncured Bacon Sausage Links ●

Sausage & Rice Links ●

Spicy Sausage Links ●

Kirkland Signature - Fresh Sirloin Tip Roast, Smoked Pulled

Lloyd's - Babyback Pork Ribs (w/Honey Hickory BBQ Sauce, w/ Original BBQ Sauce), Shredded Pork In (Honey Hickory BBQ Sauce, Original Barbecue Sauce)

Organic Prairie - Fresh Organic (Ground Pork 1 lb., Pork Chops, Pork Loin, Pork Loin Roast), Frozen Organic Pork Chops

Publix - All Natural Fresh Pork, Fresh Ground (Hot, Mild, Sage)

Saz's - Barbecue Pork Meat Tub, Barbecued Baby Back Ribs

Trader Joe's - BBQ Pulled Pork In Spicy BBQ Sauce, Fresh All Natural, Refrigerated Baby Back Pork Ribs

Wegmans Brand - Canned Pork & Beans In Tomato Sauce

Potato Chips... see Chips

Potato Crisps... see Crisps

Potato Puffs... see Snacks

P Potatoes

... *All Fresh Fruits & Vegetables Are Gluten-Free

Albertsons -
Canned (Sliced, Whole)
Frozen (French Fries (Crinkle Cut, Regular, Shoestring), Hash Browns
Southern, Potato Rounds Tator Tots)

Alexia Foods -
Crispy Potatoes w/Seasoned Salt Waffle Fries!
Julienne Fries (Spicy Sweet Potato!, Sweet Potato!, w/Sea Salt
Yukon Gold!)
Mashed Potatoes Yukon Gold Potatoes w/Sea Salt!
Olive Oil (& Sea Salt Oven Fries!, Parmesan & Roasted Garlic Oven
Reds!, Rosemary & Garlic Oven Fries!)
Organic (Classic Oven Crinkles!, Oven Crinkles Onion & Garlic!,
Oven Crinkles Salt & Pepper!, Seasoned Salt Hashed Browns!,
Yukon Gold (Julienne Fries w/Sea Salt!, w/Seasoned Salt Potato
Nuggets!))

Andrea's Fine Foods▲ - Hash Brown Potato Casserole

Dr. Praeger's - Potato Littles!

Dinty Moore - Microwave Meals Scalloped Potatoes & Ham

Food Club Brand -
Canned (Diced, Green Beans & Potatoes, Sliced, Whole)
Frozen (Crinkle Cut Fries, French Fries, Hashbrowns (Dried, Patties,
Shredded, Southern Style), Steak Fries, Tater Treats)
Instant Mashed Potatoes

Giant Brand -
Canned (No Salt Added, Whole)
Frozen (French Fries (Crinkle Cut, Crispy, Extra Crispy Crinkle,
Shoestring, Steak Fries, Straight Cut), Hash Browns (O'Brien,
Shredded, Southwestern Style), Puffs w/Onions)

Gordon Food Service - Hash Browns (Shredded (Regular, Supreme),
Skillet), Granules No Milk, Natural Cubes, Rounds, Tater Puffs
Triangles

Great Value Brand (Wal-Mart) - Canned (Diced, Sliced, Whole New),
Instant Regular

Hannaford Brand -
    Frozen (Crinkle Cut Fries, Crispy Crowns, Hash Browns (Country, Patties, Southern Style), Shoestring Fries, Steak Style Fries, Straight Cut Fries, Tasty Taters)
    Instant (Butter, Butter & Herb, Four Cheese, Regular, Roasted Garlic)

Hy-Vee -
    Canned (Sliced, Whole)
    Frozen (Country Style Hash Brown Potatoes, Crinkle Cut Fries, Criss Cut Potatoes, Curly Cut, Potatoes O'Brien, Regular, Shoestring, Steak Fries)

Ian's - Alphatots

Jimmy Dean - Breakfast Skillets (Bacon, Ham, Sausage)

Kroger Brand - Frozen (Crinkle Fries, Crispy Stix, Extra Crispy Crinkle Fries, French Fries, Hash Brown Patties, Hash Browns (Country Style, Southern Style), O'Brien, Shoestring Fries, Steak Fries, Tater Bites, Tater Rounds, Twice Baked, Wedges, Instant, Three Cheese)

Laura Lynn - All Frozen Potatoes *(Except Seasoned Fries)*, Cut Sweet Potatoes, Sliced, Whole

Linda's Gourmet Latkes - Potato Pancake Latkes

Lowes Foods Brand -
    Canned Sweet Potatoes Cut
    Frozen (French Fries (Crinkle Cut, Shoestring, Steak Cut), Hash Browns (Country Style, Regular), Tater Treats)
    Instant Mashed

Meijer Brand -
    Canned White (Sliced, Whole)
    Frozen French Fries (Crinkle Cut, Original, Quickie Crinkles, Shoestring, Steak Cut)
    Frozen Hash Browns (Original, Shredded, Southern Style, Western Style)
    Frozen Potatoes (Crinkle Cut, Hash Browns, Tater Tots)

Midwest Country Fare - Whole White Potatoes

Nuts Online - Simply Potatoes Freeze Dried Vegetables ●

P   **Ore-Ida -**

Cottage Fries

Country Inn Creations (Peppers & Onion Hash Browns, Savory Seasoned Hash Browns)

Country Style Steak Fries

Crispers

Easy Fries Golden Crinkles

Extra Crispy (Fast Food Fries, Golden Crinkles, Seasoned Crinkles)

Golden (Crinkles, Fries, Twirls)

Hash Browns (Country Style, Golden Patties, Southern Style, Toaster)

Pixie Crinkles

Potatoes O'Brien

Roasted (Garlic & Parmesan, Original)

Shoestrings

Steak Fries

Steam N' Mash (Cut Russet Potatoes, Cut Sweet Potatoes, Garlic Seasoned)

Sweet Potato Fries

Tater Tots (ABC, Extra Crispy, Mini, Onion)

Waffle Fries

Zesties

Zesty Twirls

Potato Buds▲ - Gluten Free 100% Real Potatoes

Publix -

Canned White

Deli Side Dishes Garlic Redskin Smashed Potatoes

Frozen (Crinkle Cut Fries, Fast Food Fries, Golden Fries, Southern Style Hash Browns, Steak Fries, Tater Bites)

Instant (Garlic, Regular)

Potato Salad (Homestyle, New York Style, Southern Style)

S&W - All Canned Vegetables

Safeway Brand - Frozen (Crinkle Cut, French Fries Classic, Mashed), Instant Mashed Potatoes (Regular, Roasted Garlic), Shoestring, Steak Cut, Twice Baked (Cheddar, Sour Cream & Chives)

Sharwood's - Bombay Potatoes, Saag Aloo
Shiloh Farms - Potato Flakes!!
Signature Cafe - Side Dish (Broccoli Cheddar Au Gratin, Creamy Mashed, Red Skin Garlic Mashed)
Smart Ones - Frozen Entrees Broccoli & Cheddar Potatoes
Spartan Brand -
  Canned White (Sliced, Whole)
  Frozen (Fries (Crinkle Cut, Extra Crispy Fast, French Fried, Steak), Hash Browns (O'Brien, Patties, Shredded, Southern Style), Tater Puffs), Mashed Potatoes (Bag (Buttery Homestyle, Four Cheese, Fully Loaded), Box (Butter & Herb, Creamy Butter, Instant, Roasted Garlic, Sour Cream & Chives))
Stop & Shop Brand - Cut Sweet Potatoes In Light Syrup, French Fries (Crinkle Cut, Straight Cut), Fries (Crispy, Extra Crispy Crinkle Cut, Shoestring, Steak), Frozen Natural Wedges Potatoes, Latkes, Puffs w/Onions, Shredded Hash, Southwestern Style Hash Browns, Twice Baked Potatoes (Butter, Cheddar Cheese, Sour Cream & Chive), Whole Potatoes (No Added Salt, Regular)
Tasty Bite - Aloo Palak!, Bombay!, Mushroom Takatak!
Trader Joe's - Frozen Crinkle Wedge Potatoes, Frozen Mashed Potatoes, Garlic Mashed Potatoes
Wegmans Brand - Frozen (Crinkle Cut, Steak Cut, Straight Cut, Tater Puffs), Frozen Hash Browns (Country Style, Hash Browns O'Brien, Regular), White Potatoes (Sliced, Whole Peeled)
Winn Dixie - Canned (Diced White, No Salt Added White, Sliced White, Sweet, Whole White), Frozen (O'Brien, Potato Crowns, Southern Style Hashbrowns, Tater Puffs), Instant (Regular, Roasted Garlic)
Woodstock Farms - Organic Frozen (Crinkle Cut Oven Fries, Shredded Hash Browns, Tastee Taters)
Preserves... see Jam/Jelly
Pretzels
  Barkat - Pretzels (Regular, Sesame, Sticks)
  Better Balance - Cinnamon Toast Pretzel Sticks, Golden Butter Twists, Jalapeno Honey Mustard Pretzel Sticks, Original Sticks

P

Dutch Country - Soft Pretzel Mix

Ener-G▲ - Crisp Pretzels, Sesame Pretzel Rings, Wylde Pretzels (Poppy Seed, Regular, Sesame)

Glutano▲ - Pretzels

Glutino▲ - Family Bag (Sticks, Twists), Pretzels (Chocolate Covered, Yogurt Covered), Sesame Ring, Snack Pack, Sticks, Twists, Unsalted Twists

Snyder's Of Hanover - Gluten Free Sticks ●

Protein

Beneprotein - Resource Beneprotein Instant Protein Powder **! !**

Bob's Red Mill▲ - Hemp Protein Powder, Soy Protein Powder, TSP Textured Soy Protein, TVP Textured Vegetable Protein

CalNaturale Svelte▲ - Sustained Energy Protein Drink (Cappuccino ●, Chocolate ●, French Vanilla ●, Spiced Chai ●)

Gluty Free - Organic Hemp Protein Powder ●

Growing Naturals - Rice Protein Isolate Powder (Chocolate, Original, Vanilla)

Living Harvest - Organic Hemp Protein Powder (All Varieties)

MLO - Brown Rice Protein Powder

Nutiva - Hemp Protein Shake (Amazon Acai, Berry Pomegrate, Chocolate), Protein Powder (Hemp, Hemp & Fiber)

Nuts Online - Organic Hemp Protein Powder ●

Ruth's Hemp Power - Powders (Regular, w/Maca & E3Live, w/ Sprouted Flax & Maca)

Safeway Brand - Plus Nutritional Shakes (All Flavors), Regular (All Flavors)

Trader Joe's - All Protein Powders *(Except Whey Quick Dissolve)*

Worldwide Pure Protein - Shake (Banana Cream, Frosty Chocolate, Strawberry Cream, Vanilla Cream)

Protein Shakes... see Protein and/or Shakes

Prunes

Gluty Free - Dried Pluots ●, Jumbo ●, Organic Pitted ●, Pitted ●

Great Value Brand (Wal-Mart) - Pitted Prunes

Meijer Brand - Pitted (Canister, Carton)

Nuts Online - Dried Fruit Plums (Angelino ●, Jumbo ●, No Pit ●, October Sun ●, Organic Angelino ●, Organic No Pit ●), Pluots ●

Spartan Brand - Prunes Pitted

Pudding

Albertsons - Cups (Butterscotch, Chocolate, Tapioca, Vanilla)

Bakers & Chefs - Chocolate, Vanilla

Bi-Aglut - Apple Banana Bisconttino, Cocoa Dessert, Pear & Rice, Vanilla Dessert

Echo Farms - All Puddings

Food Club Brand -

Cook & Serve (Butterscotch, Chocolate, Vanilla)

Instant (Chocolate, Banana Cream, Coconut Cream, French Vanilla, Lemon, Pistachio, Sugar Free (Butterscotch, Chocolate, Vanilla), Vanilla)

Pudding Cups (Banana, Butterscotch, Chocolate, Fat Free Chocolate, Tapioca, Vanilla)

Refrigerated Packs (Chocolate, Chocolate Vanilla Swirl (Fat Free, Regular), Vanilla)

Giant Brand - Chocolate Fudge, Chocolate Vanilla (Fat Free, Regular), Pudding Mix (Butterscotch, Chocolate, Tapioca), Refrigerated Chocolate (Fat Free, Regular), Rice Pudding

Ginger Evans - Instant (Chocolate, Vanilla)

Gordon Food Service - Mix (Butterscotch, Chocolate, Rice, Tapioca, Vanilla)

Great Value Brand (Wal-Mart) -

Instant Pudding

Banana Cream Regular

Chocolate (Regular, Sugar Free)

French Vanilla (Regular, Sugar Free)

Pistachio Regular

Vanilla Regular

Hannaford Brand -

All Fat Free

All Sugar Free

P

Pudding Cook & Serve (Chocolate, Vanilla)
Pudding Instant (Banana Cream, Butterscotch, Chocolate, Pistachio, Vanilla)
Pudding Snacks (Banana, Butterscotch, Chocolate, Fudge, Tapioca, Vanilla)
Refrigerated Dessert Cups (All Fat Free, All Regular)
Hy-Vee -
Cooked Pudding (Chocolate, Vanilla)
Instant Pudding (Butterscotch, Chocolate (Fat Free/Sugar Free, Regular), Lemon, Pistachio, Vanilla (Fat Free/Sugar Free, Regular))
Pudding Cups (Butterscotch, Chocolate (Fat Free, Fudge, Regular), Strawberry Banana, Tapioca, Vanilla)
Jell-O -
Regular Cook N' Serve (Banana Cream, Butterscotch, Chocolate (Fudge, Regular), Coconut Cream, Fat Free Tapioca, Lemon, Vanilla)
Regular Instant Pudding & Pie Filling (Banana Cream, Butterscotch, Cheesecake, Chocolate (Caramel Chip, Fudge, Mint Chip, Regular), Coconut Cream, Devil's Food, French Vanilla, Lemon, Pistachio, Pumpkin Spice, Vanilla (Chocolate Chip, Regular), White Chocolate)
Sugar Free Fat Free Cook N' Serve (Chocolate, Vanilla)
Sugar Free Fat Free Instant Pudding & Pie Filling (Banana Cream, Butterscotch, Cheesecake, Chocolate, Lemon, Pistachio, Vanilla, White Chocolate)
Kozy Shack - All Varieties *(Except Soy)*
Kroger Brand - Boxed, Snack Cups
Laura Lynn - Pudding RTE Dairy All Items
Medifast - Banana ●, Chocolate ●, Vanilla ●
Meijer Brand -
Cook & Serve (Butterscotch, Chocolate, Vanilla)
Instant
Banana Cream

Butterscotch (Fat Free, Sugar Free)
Chocolate (Fat Free, Sugar Free)
Vanilla (Fat Free, Sugar Free))
Instant Pudding & Pie Filling (Chocolate, Coconut Cream, French
Vanilla, Pistachio, Vanilla)
Premium (Chocolate Peanut Butter, French Vanilla, Orange
Dream)
Snack (Banana, Butterscotch, Chocolate (Fat Free, Fudge, Regular),
Multi Pack Chocolate & Vanilla, Tapioca, Vanilla)
Mixes From The Heartland▲ - Pudding Mix (Apple Cinnamon
Rice ●, Chocolate Delight ●)
Mori-Nu - Mates Pudding Mix (Chocolate, Vanilla)
My T Fine - Chocolate, Lemon, Vanilla
Publix - Chocolate, Fat Free (Chocolate, Chocolate Vanilla Swirl),
Rice, Sugar Free Chocolate Vanilla Swirl, Tapioca
Royal - All Instant Varieties, Cook & Serve (Chocolate, Vanilla)
Safeway Brand - Snack Cups (All Flavors)
Spartan Brand -
Cook & Serve (Chocolate, Vanilla)
Instant (Banana Cream, Butterscotch, Chocolate (Regular, Sugar
Free), French Vanilla, Pistachio, Vanilla (Regular, Sugar Free))
Snack (Butterscotch, Chocolate, Tapioca, Vanilla)
Stop & Shop Brand -
Butterscotch
Chocolate (Fudge, Instant Pudding & Pie Filling, Regular, Sugar
Free Instant), Fat Free (Chocolate, Chocolate/Vanilla)
Instant Low Calorie Vanilla Pudding & Pie Mix
Refrigerated (Chocolate, Chocolate/Vanilla)
Rice
Tapioca
Vanilla
Tayloe's - Chocolate, Vanilla
Trader Joe's - Puddings (Chocolate, Rice, Tapioca)

P

Q

Wegmans Brand -
   Chocolate (Fat Free, Regular, Sugar Free)
   Chocolate Vanilla Swirl (Fat Free, Regular, Sugar Free)
   Homestyle (Chocolate, Rice, Tapioca)
   Vanilla (Fat Free, Regular, Sugar Free)
ZenSoy - All Pudding Varieties

Pumpkin
   ... *All Fresh Fruits & Vegetables Are Gluten-Free*
   Hy-Vee - Canned Pumpkin
   Libby's - Canned (100% Pure Pumpkin, Easy Pumpkin Pie Mix)
   Meijer Brand - Canned
   Nuts Online - Pumpkin Seed Powder ●
   Spartan Brand - Canned
   Wegmans Brand - Solid Pack

Puppodums
   Sharwood's - Indian Puppodums (Crushed Garlic & Coriander,
      Garlic & Coriander, Plain, Red Chilli & Cumin, Spicy)

Q

Queso
   Chi-Chi's - Con Queso
   Eat Smart - Naturals Salsa Con Queso
   Fischer & Wieser - Queso Starter
   Food Club Brand - Salsa Con Queso
   Great Value Brand (Wal-Mart) - Jalapeno Mexican Style Queso Dip,
      White Salsa Con Queso
   Lowes Foods Brand - Salsa Con Queso
   Taco Bell - Black Bean Con Queso, Chili Con Queso w/Beef, Salsa
      Con Queso (Medium, Mild)
   Tostitos - Monterey Jack Queso!!, Salsa Con Queso!!
   Trader Joe's - Queso Cheese Dip!
   Winn Dixie - Salsa Con Queso

Quiche
   Andrea's Fine Foods▲ - Ham & Swiss, Spinach & Chedder

Quinoa

Ancient Harvest Quinoa - Inca Red Quinoa, Quinoa Flakes, Quinoa Flour, Quinoa Pasta (Elbows, Garden Pagodas, Linguine, Rotelle, Shells, Spaghetti, Veggie Curls), Traditional Quinoa Grain

Arrowhead Mills - Quinoa

Arzu - Chai ●, Original ●, Southwest ●

Gluten Free & Fabulous ▲ - Bon Appetit! Quinoa w/Marinara ●

Gluty Free - Organic ●

GoGo Rice - Organic Steamed Quinoa Bowls Regular

Seeds Of Change - Amantani Whole Grain Blend Quinoa & Wild Rice **!!**, Cuzco Whole Grain Quinoa Blend **!!**

Shiloh Farms - Quinoa **!!**, Quinoa Flakes **!!**, Red Quinoa **!!**

Trader Joe's - Organic Quinoa

R

Radishes

... *All Fresh Fruits & Vegetables Are Gluten-Free

Raisins

Albertsons - Regular

Food Club Brand - Chocolate Covered

Full Circle - Organic (Canister, Regular)

Gluty Free - Crimson ●, Dark ●, Flame ●, Golden ●, Organic (Dark Chocolate ●, Milk Chocolate ●), Organic ●, Thompson Seedless ●

Great Value Brand (Wal-Mart) - 100% Natural California Sun Dried Raisins

Hannaford Brand

Hy-Vee - California Sun Dried Raisins Regular

Kroger Brand

Kroger Value

Lowes Foods Brand - Canister, Seedless Carton

Meijer Brand - Canister, Seedless Carton

Nuts Online - Crimson ●, Dark ●, Jumbo (Flame ●, Golden ●, Golden Flame ●, Thompson Seedless ●), Midget ●, Organic (Dark Chocolate Covered ●, Milk Chocolate Covered ●), Organic ●

R   O Organics

Private Selections - Organic

Publix - Raisins

Spartan Brand

Sun-Maid - Raisins (Baking, Golden, Natural California, Regular), Zante Currants

Wegmans Brand - Seedless

Woodstock Farms - Chocolate w/Evaporated Cane Juice, Organic Chocolate (Dark w/Evaporated Cane Juice, Milk w/Evaporated Cane Juice), Jumbo Flame, Jumbo Thompson, Select Thompson, Raisin Mania, Yogurt Raisins w/Evaporated Cane Juice

Raspberries

*... *All Fresh Fruits & Vegetables Are Gluten-Free*

C & W - All Plain Frozen Fruits

Food Club Brand - Frozen Red

Full Circle - Frozen Organic

Giant Brand - Frozen (In Syrup, Plain)

Gluty Free - Dried Red ●

Great Value Brand (Wal-Mart) - Frozen Red

Hy-Vee - Frozen Red

Meijer Brand - Frozen (Organic, Regular), Red Individually Quick Frozen

Nuts Online - Dried Fruit (Dried Red ●, Organic Red ●, Simply ●)

Publix - Frozen

Safeway Brand - Frozen Red

Spartan Brand - Frozen Red

Stop & Shop Brand - Frozen, In Syrup

Trader Joe's - Frozen Organic, Frozen

Wegmans Brand - Regular, w/Sugar

Winn Dixie - Frozen Red

Woodstock Farms - Organic Frozen Red

Ravioli

Conte's Pasta - Cheese ●, Spinach & Cheese ●

Everybody Eats ▲ - Beef, Cheese, Chicken, Spinach Ricotta

Philadelphia Gluten Free Ravioli Pasta Company - Cheese & Spinach Mini ●, Rice Breaded Cheese & Spinach ●, Rice Breaded Cheese ●, Spinach ●, Traditional Cheese ●, Traditional Mini ●

Star Ravioli - Gluten Free Cheese Ravioli

Refried Beans... see Beans

Relish

Albertsons - Sweet

B&G - Dill, Hamburger, Hot Dog, India, Sweet

Cains - All Varieties

Food Club Brand - All Varieties

Full Circle - Sweet

Giant Brand - Dill, Sweet

Gordon Food Service - Dill, Sweet

Great Value Brand (Wal-Mart) - Sweet Pickle Relish

Hannaford Brand - Dill Relish, Hot Dog Relish, Sweet (Relish, Relish Squeeze)

Heinz - All Varieties

Hy-Vee - Dill, Squeeze Sweet, Sweet

Kurtz - Sweet Relish

Lowes Foods Brand - Regular, Sweet Pickle

Meijer Brand - Dill Relish, Sweet Relish Sugar Free

Mezzetta - Deli Style (Sweet Bell Pepper Relish, Zesty Bell Pepper Relish Hot)

Midwest Country Fare - Sweet Pickle

Mrs. Renfro's - Corn, Hot Chow Chow, Hot Tomato, Mild Chow Chow, Mild Tomato

Mt. Olive - Dill Relish, Dill Salad Cubes, Hot Dog Relish, Sweet Green Salad Cubes, Sweet India Relish, Sweet Relish, Sweet Salad Cubes

Spartan Brand - Dill, Sweet

Trader Joe's - Organic Sweet!!

Vlasic - All Varieties

Wegmans Brand - Dill, Hamburger, Hot Dog, Sweet

Winn Dixie - Sweet Relish

Woodstock Farms - Organic (Spicy Chipotle Sweet, Sweet Relish)

R Ribs

... *All Fresh Meat Is Gluten-Free (Non-Marinated, Unseasoned)

Kirkland Signature - Fresh Spare Ribs

Saz's - Barbecued Baby Back Ribs

Trader Joe's - Baby Back Pork Ribs

Rice

A Taste Of India - Masala Rice & Lentils, Spiced Rice w/Raisins

A Taste Of Thai - Rice (Coconut Ginger, Garlic Basil, Jasmine, Soft Jasmine, Yellow Curry)

Albertsons - Boil In A Bag, Brown, White (Instant, Regular)

Annie Chun's - Sprouted Brown Rice, Sticky White Rice

Arrowhead Mills - Brown Basmati, Long Grain Brown

Beretta - Carnaroli Chef, Carnaroli Rice, Superfino Arborio Rice

Dinty Moore - Microwave Meal Rice w/Chicken

Eden Organic - Organic Canned (Curried Rice & Lentils, Mexican Rice & Black Beans, Moroccan Rice & Garbanzo Beans, Rice & Cajun Small Red Beans, Rice & Caribbean Black Beans, Rice & Garbanzo Beans, Rice & Lentils, Rice & Pinto Beans, Rice & Kidney Beans, Spanish Rice & Pinto Beans)

Fantastic World Foods - Arborio, Basmati, Jasmine

Food Club Brand - Instant Rice (All Plain Varieties), Long Grain

Full Circle - Organic (Basmati Brown, Basmati White, Long Grain Brown, Long Grain White)

Giant Brand - Instant (Brown, White)

Gluten-Free Essentials▲ - Side Kicks (Exotic Curry●, Italian Herb & Lemon ●, Southwest Chipotle & Lime ●)

GoGo Rice -

Brown Rice w/Thai Curry Sauce

Harvest

On The Go Cooked Rice Bowls (Exotic & Spicy Thai Peanut, Sweet & Mild Hawaiian, Tasty & Healthy Harvest, Zesty & Spicy Mexican Green)

Organic Rice Medley w/Wild Rice

Organic Steamed Rice Bowls (Brown, White)

Organic White Rice
Sprouted Brown
Golden Star - Jasmine Rice
Goose Valley - Family Blend (Basmati & Wild Rice Fusion ●, Brown & Wild Rice Fusion ●), Family Reserve (Certified Organic Wild Rice●, Natural Wild Rice ●)
Gordon Food Service - Long Grain & Wild Mix, Mexican
Great Value Brand (Wal-Mart) - Boil In Bag, Brown, Enriched Long Grain Parboiled Rice
Hannaford Brand - Enriched Long Grain, Frozen Steam In Bag White Rice, Instant
Hormel - Compleats Microwaveable Meals (Chicken & Rice, Santa Fe Chicken & Rice)
Hy-Vee - Boil In Bag Rice, Enriched Extra Long Grain (Instant, Regular), Extra Long Grain, Instant Brown, Natural Long Grain Brown, Spanish
Konriko ▲ - Brown Rice (Hot N' Spicy ●, Original ●), Wild Pecan Rice (Box Regular ●, Burlap Bag Regular ●)
Kroger Brand - 90 Second Rice (Garden Vegetable, Red Beans, Roasted Chicken, Whole Grain Brown), Boil N' Bag (Brown, White), Instant (Brown, White), Original (Brown, White)
Laura Lynn - Boil N' Bag, Flavored Rice All Items, Instant, Long Grain White
Lotus Foods - Bhutanese Red, Brown Kalijira, Forbidden, Madagascar Pink, Organic (Brown Jasmine, Forbidden, Jade Pearl, Jasmine, Mekong Flower), Volcano
Lowes Foods Brand - Boil N' Bag, Instant (Brown, White)
Lundberg ▲ - All Varieties
Meijer Brand - Brown, Instant (Boil In Bag, Brown), Long Grain, Medium Grain
Midwest Country Fare - Pre Cooked Instant Rice
Minute Rice - Brown, Premium, Ready To Serve Rice (Brown & Wild, Chicken Flavor, Spanish, White, Whole Grain Brown, Yellow), Steamers (Spanish, White, Whole Grain Brown), White

R

Mixes From The Heartland▲ - Instant Rice Mix (White ●, Wild ●)

Nishiki - Sushi Rice

O Organics - Long Grain (Brown, Thai Jasmine)

Ortega - Yellow Rice Mix, Spanish Rice Mix

Publix - Long Grain (Brown, Enriched), Medium Grain White, Pre Cooked Instant (Boil In Bag, Brown, White), Yellow Rice Mix

Pure Market Express▲ - Basil Fried Rice ●, Spanish Rice ●

Royal - Basmati Rice

Safeway Brand - Brown, Instant, Long Grain, Rice Pouch Gently Milled Bran Rice, White

Seeds Of Change -
   Amantani Whole Grain Blend Quinoa & Wild Rice**!!**
   Cuzco Whole Grain Quinoa Blend**!!**
   Havana Cuban Style Whole Grain Rice & Beans**!!**
   Microwaveable (Dharamsala Aromatic Indian Rice Blend**!!**, Rishikesh Whole Grain Brown Basmati Rice**!!**, Tapovan White Basmati Rice**!!**)
   Velleron French Style Herb Whole Grain Blend**!!**

Shiloh Farms - Basmati Rice**!!**, California Wild Rice**!!**, Long Grain Brown Rice**!!**, Short Grain Brown Rice**!!**

Signature Cafe - Side Dish Parmesan Risotto

Smart Ones - Frozen Entrees Santa Fe Rice & Beans

Spartan Brand - 4% Broken Long Grain, Instant (Boil In Bag, Brown Box, Regular Box)

Stop & Shop Brand - Instant Brown, Organic Long Grain Brown & White, Simply Enjoy (Butter Chicken, Pad Thai w/Chicken, Tikka Masala)

Success - Boil In Bag Rice (Jasmine, White, Whole Grain Brown)

Tambobamba - Mojo Bowls (Brazilian Rice & Beans, Caribbean Rice & Beans, Peruvian Rice & Beans), Side Dishes (Cuban Black Beans & Rice, Jamaican Rice & Beans, Mexican Rice & Beans)

Tasty Bite - Basmati**!**, Brown Rice (Garlic**!**, Regular**!**), Ginger Lentil**!**, Jasmine**!**, Jasmine Green Energy**!**, Long Grain**!**, Mexican Fiesta**!**, Tandori Pilaf**!**, Tehari Herb**!**

R

Thai Kitchen - Jasmine Rice Mixes (Green Chili & Garlic, Jasmine Rice, Lemongrass & Ginger, Roasted Garlic & Chili, Spicy Thai Chili, Sweet Chili & Onion, Thai Yellow Curry)

Trader Joe's -
Biryani Curried Rice, Curried Lentils w/Basmati Rice**!!**
Frozen (Chicken Tandoori Rice Bowl, Peruvian Style Chimichurri w/Vegetables)
Organic (All Varieties)
Organic Fully Cooked Brown Rice, Roasted Poblano Peppers w/ Shrimp Rice & Cheese
Thai Style Lime Rice Pilaf, Wild & Basmati Rice Pilaf

Uncle Ben's -
Boil In Bag
Fast & Natural Instant Brown Rice
Instant Rice
Natural Whole Grain Brown Rice
Original Converted Brand Rice
Ready Rice (Original Long Grain Rice 8.8 oz. & 14.8 oz., Whole Grain Brown Rice)

Wegmans Brand - Arborio (Italian Style, Regular), Basmati, Boil In Bag, Enriched (Long, Long Grain White, Medium), Instant (Brown, Regular), Jasmine, Long Grain (Brown, White), Medium Grain White

Rice Beverages

Full Circle - Organic (Original, Vanilla)

Good Karma - Original Ricemilk (Chocolate, Original, Unsweetened, Vanilla)

Grainaissance - Almond Shake, Amazing Mango, Banana Appeal, Chocolate (Almond, Chimp, Cool Coconut), Gimme Green, Go (Go Green, Hazelnuts), Oh So Original, Rice Nog, Tiger Chai, Vanilla (Gorilla, Pecan Pie)

Growing Naturals - Rice Milk (Creamy Vanilla, Silky Smooth Original, Velvety Chocolate)

Nature's Promise - Ricemilk (Plain, Vanilla)

R

    Pacific Natural Foods - Low Fat Plain, Low Fat Vanilla

    Rice Dream - Refrigerated & Shelf Stable Rice Beverages (All Varieties)

    Trader Joe's - Rice Milk

    Wegmans Brand - Organic (Original, Vanilla)

Rice Cakes

    Eco-Farmed - Buttery Caramel

    Giant Brand - Multigrain Unsalted, Plain Unsalted, Sour Cream & Onion

    Hannaford Brand - Apple Cinnamon, Caramel Corn, Lightly Salted, Multi Grain, White Cheddar

    Hy-Vee - Caramel, Lightly Salted, White Cheddar

    Lundberg▲ - Eco Farmed Brown Rice (Apple Cinnamon, Lightly Salted, Toasted Sesame), Honey Nut, Salt Free, Sesame Tamari, Organic Brown Rice Lightly Salted, Caramel Corn, Cinnamon Toast, Flax w/Tamari, Koku Seaweed, Mochi Sweet, Rice w/Popcorn, Salt Free, Sesame Tamari, Sweet Green Tea w/Lemon, Tamari w/ Seaweed, Wild Rice

    Mrs. Crimble's - Apple, Caramel, Chocolate Coated, Honey, Slightly Salted, Unsalted, Yoghurt Coated

    Publix - Lightly Salted, Mini (Caramel, Cheddar, Ranch), Unsalted, White Cheddar

    Quaker - Apple Cinnamon**!**, Butter Popcorn**!**, Caramel Corn**!**, Chocolate**!**, Lightly Salted**!**, Unsalted**!**, White Cheddar**!**

    Spartan Brand - Caramel, Salt Free, White Cheddar

    Stop & Shop Brand - Rice Cakes (Multigrain Unsalted, Plain Salted, Plain Unsalted, Sesame Unsalted, Sour Cream & Onion, White Cheddar)

    Trader Joe's - Lightly Salted Rice Cakes**!!**

Rice Noodles... see Noodles and/or Pasta

Rice Vinegar... see Vinegar

Risotto

    Lundberg▲ - Eco Farmed (Butternut Squash, Cheddar Broccoli, Creamy Parmesan, Garlic Primavera, Italian Herb), Organic (Alfredo, Florentine, Tuscan, Wild Porcini Mushroom)

Roast Beef... see Beef

Rolls... see Bread

Rum

... *All Distilled Alcohol Is Gluten-Free[2]*

Rutabaga

... *All Fresh Fruits & Vegetables Are Gluten-Free*

S

Salad

... *All Fresh Fruits & Vegetables Are Gluten-Free*

Earthbound Farm - American Salad, Baby Arugula, Baby Arugula Blend, Baby Lettuces, Baby Romaine, Baby Spinach, Baby Spinach Blend, Baby Spinach Salad Kit, Bibb Lettuce Leaves, Butter Lettuce Leaves, California Blend, Fancy Romaine Salad, Fresh Herb Salad, Fresh Spinach, Frisée, Frisée Blend, Harvest Blend, Hearts Of Romaine, Heirloom Lettuce Leaves, Iceberg Lettuce, Italian Salad, Mâche, Mâche Blend, Mixed Baby Greens, Mixed Baby Greens Salad Kit, Romaine Hearts, Romaine Salad, Spring Mix, Washed & Trimmed Romaine Heart Leaves

Hy-Vee - American Blend, Chopped Romaine, Cole Slaw, European Blend, Garden, Garden Supreme, Italian Blend, Riveria Blend, Shredded Lettuce, Spring Mix

Mixes From The Heartland▲ - Pasta (Corn ●, Cucumber Dill●, Dilled●)

Publix - Classic Blend, Cole Slaw Blend, Deli Pre Made Salads (Carrot & Raisin, Chicken, Chicken Tarragon, Egg, Ham, Marshmallow Delight), European Blend, Italian Blend, Packaged Blends, Romaine Lettuce Heart, Spinach

Publix GreenWise Market - Organic Salad Baby (Arugula, Lettuce, Mixed Greens, Romaine, Spinach), Fresh Herb, Romaine Hearts

Pure Market Express▲ - Broccoli Salad ●, Salad Kit (Big Greek ●, Caesar Salad ●), Thai Salad ●

Trader Joe's - Baby Spinach Salad, Chef, Chicken Salad Wine Country w/Cranberries & Pecans, Classic Greek, Cobb, Egg White**!!**, Eggless Egg, Garden, Gorgonzola Walnut, Greek, Grilled Chicken w/ Orange Vinaigrette, Marinated Bean, Powerhouse Salad

S Salad Dressing

    A Taste Of Thai - Peanut Salad Dressing Mix

    Albertsons - Blue Cheese, Caesar, Ranch, Raspberry Vinaigrette, Thousand Island, Zesty Italian

    Annie's Naturals

      Natural Dressings

        Artichoke Parmesan!!

        Balsamic Vinaigrette!!

        Basil & Garlic!!

        Caesar!!

        Cowgirl Ranch!!

        Fat Free

          Mango Vinaigrette!!

          Raspberry Balsamic Vinaigrette!!

        Lemon & Chive!!

        Lite Herb Balsamic!!

        Lite Vinaigrette

          Honey Mustard!!

          Raspberry!!

        Roasted Red Pepper Vinaigrette!!

        Tuscany Italian!!

      Organic

        Buttermilk!!

        Caesar!!

        Cowgirl Ranch!!

        Creamy Asiago Cheese!!

        French!!

        Green Garlic!!

        Green Goddess!!

        Maple Ginger!!

        Oil & Vinegar!!

        Papaya Poppy Seed!!

        Thousand Island!!

Vinaigrette
 Balsamic!!
 Pomegranate!!
 Red Wine & Olive Oil!!
 Roasted Garlic!!
 Sesame Ginger w/Chamomile!!
Bakers & Chefs - French, Ranch
Big Y - Lite (French, Italian, Ranch, Thousand Island), Regular (Creamy French, Italian, Ranch, Thousand Island)
Boar's Head - All Varieties
Bragg - Organic (Ginger & Sesame, Vinaigrette)
Briannas -
 Classic Buttermilk Ranch,
 Dijon Honey Mustard
 New American
 Rich (Poppy Seed, Santa Fe Blend)
 True Blue Cheese
 Vinaigrette (Blush Wine, Champagne Caper, Real French)
 Zesty French
Cains -
 Fat Free
  Caesar
  Honey Dijon
  Italian
  Peppercorn Ranch,
  Vinaigrette Blush Wine
 Light
  Caesar
  French
  Italian
  Ranch
  Vinaigrette (Blush Wine, Raspberry)
 Regular
  Blue Cheese

S

Creamy Caesar
French (Original, Zesty Tomato & Onion)
Italian (Bellisimo, Cheese Trio, Country, Creamy, Original, Robust)
Peppercorn Parmesan
Ranch (Chipotle, Deluxe Buttermilk, Original, w/Bacon)
Vinaigrette (Balsamic, Raspberry Country)
White Balsamic w/Honey

Cardini's -
Aged Parmesan Ranch
Caesar (Fat Free, Light, Original)
Honey Mustard
Italian
Vinaigrette (Balsamic, Light Balsamic, Light Caesar, Light Greek, Pear, Raspberry Pomegranate)

Consorzio - Fat Free (Mango, Raspberry & Balsamic, Strawberry & Balsamic), Honey Mustard, Italian, Parmesan & Romano Caesar

Drew's -
Buttermilk Ranch
Garlic Italian Vinaigrette
Honey Dijon
Kalamata Olive & Caper
Poppy Seed
Raspberry
Roasted Garlic & Peppercorn
Romano Caesar
Rosemary Balsamic
Smoked Tomato

El Torito - Cilantro Pepita

Emeril's - Caesar, Vinaigrette (Balsamic, House Herb, Italian, Raspberry Balsamic)

Fischer & Wieser - Citrus Herb & Truffle Oil Vinaigrette, Creamy Garlic & Chile, Original Roasted Raspberry Chipotle Vinaigrette, Southwestern Herb & Tomato Vinaigrette, Spicy Lime & Coriander, Sweet Corn & Shallot

Follow Your Heart -
- Fresh & Naturals
  - Caesar w/Aged Parmesan,
  - Creamy Garlic
  - Honey Mustard
  - Lemon Herb
  - Low Fat Ranch
  - Sesame (Dijon, Miso)
  - Spicy Southwestern Ranch
  - Thousand Island
  - Vegan Caesar
- Organic
  - Balsamic Vinaigrette
  - Chipotle Lime Ranch
  - Chunky Bleu Cheese
  - Creamy (Caesar, Miso Ginger, Ranch)
  - Italian Vinaigrette

Food Club Brand -
- Blue Cheese
- California French
- Classic Caesar
- Fat Free (California French, French, Italian, Ranch)
- French
- Italian
- Lite (Ranch, Thousand Island)
- Peppercorn Ranch
- Ranch
- Ranch Dressing Mix
- Thousand Island
- Western Style

Foods Alive - Organic Golden Flax Oil (Mike's Special, Sweet & Sassy, Sweet Mustard), Organic Hemp Oil Sweet & Sassy

Fosse Farms ▲ - Blackberry ●, Cranberry ●, Marionberry ●, Organic (Blackberry ●, Cranberry ●, Provencal ●, Raspberry ●), Raspberry ●

S

Full Circle - Organic (Balsamic Vinaigrette, Caesar, French, Honey Mustard, Italian, Ranch, Thousand Island)

Giant Brand -

Creamy (French, Italian)

Fat Free (Italian, Ranch)

Lite (Italian, Ranch)

Reduced Fat Raspberry Vinaigrette

Regular (Blue Cheese, Caesar, French, Italian, Ranch, Raspberry Vinaigrette, Thousand Island w/Bacon, Vinaigrette Balsamic)

Spicy Sweet French

Girard's -

Apple Poppyseed

Caesar

Champagne

Creamy Balsamic

Honey Dijon Peppercorn

Light (Caesar, Champagne, Raspberry)

Olde Venice Italian

Original French

Peach Mimosa

Raspberry

Romano Cheese Italian

Spinach

Vinaigrette (Blue Cheese, Greek, Lite Balsamic, White Balsamic)

Gordon Food Service - Packets (1000 Island, Buttermilk Ranch, French, Italian, Salad)

Hannaford Brand - Bacon Ranch, Balsamic Vinaigrette (Light, Regular), Chunky Blue Cheese, Creamy (Dill, Italian, Ranch), Deluxe French, Fat Free (California French Style, Raspberry Vinaigrette, Sweet Herb Vinaigrette, Zesty Italian), Honey Dijon, Light (Caesar, Italian, Ranch), Old World Greek, Peppercorn Ranch, Ranch Lite, Robust Italian, Thousand Island, Vidalia Onion

HealthMarket - Organic (Balsamic, Creamy Caesar, Honey Mustard, Raspberry Vinaigrette)

Henri's - Classic Cream Garden Ranch, Fat Free Honey Mustard, Fat Free Italian, Original French

Hy-Vee -

Dressing (Bacon Ranch, Buttermilk Ranch, French, Italian, Peppercorn Ranch, Ranch, Raspberry Vinaigrette, Thousand Island, Zesty Italian)

Light Dressing (Italian, Ranch, Thousand Island)

Light Salad Dressing (French, Italian, Ranch, Thousand Island)

Squeezable Salad Dressing

Ken's Steak House -

Chef's Reserve

Blue Cheese w/Gorgonzola,

Creamy (Balsamic w/Honey, Greek w/Fresh Oregano)

Farm House Ranch w/Buttermilk

French w/Applewood Smoke Bacon

Golden Vidalia Onion

Honey Dijon

Italian w/Garlic & Asiago Cheese

Ranch

Russian

Fat Free Dressings (Raspberry Pecan, Sun Dried Tomato)

Healthy Options Caesar Vinaigrette

Light Options

Honey (Dijon, French)

Italian w/Romano & Red Pepper

Olive Oil & Vinegar

Parmesan & Peppercorn

Ranch

Raspberry Walnut

Vinaigrette (Balsamic, Caesar, Sweet Vidalia Onion)

Lite Accents Vinaigrette (Balsamic, Honey Mustard, Italian, Mixed Berry, Raspberry Walnut)

Lite Dressings

Balsamic & Basil

S

    Caesar
    Chunky Blue Cheese
    Country French w/Vermont Honey
    Creamy (Caesar, Parmesan w/Cracked Peppercorn)
    Honey Mustard
    Italian
    Northern Italian
    Ranch
    Raspberry (Pomegranate, Walnut)
    Sun Dried Tomato
    Sweet Vidalia Onion
    Vinaigrette (Balsamic, Olive Oil, Red Wine)

Regular
    Balsamic & Basil
    Caesar
    Christo's Yasou Greek
    Chunky Blue Cheese
    Country French w/Vermont Honey
    Creamy (Balsamic, Caesar, French, Italian, Parmesan
       w/Cracked Peppercorn)
    Greek
    Honey Mustard
    Italian (& Marinade, Three Cheese, w/Aged Romano)
    Ranch (Buttermilk, New & Improved, Peppercorn, Regular)
    Red Wine Vinegar & Olive Oil
    Russian
    Sweet Vidalia Onion
    Thousand Island
    Zesty Italian

Kraft -
    Balsamic Vinaigrette
    Caesar (Vinaigrette w/Parmesan, w/Bacon)
    Catalina
    Classic (Caesar, Italian Vinaigrette)

Creamy (French, Italian, Poppyseed)
Free (Caesar Italian, Catalina, Classic Caesar, French, Honey
    Dijon, Italian, Ranch, Zesty Italian)
Greek Vinaigrette
Honey Dijon
Light (Balsamic Vinaigrette, Balsamic Vinaigrette w/Parmesan
    & Asiago, Creamy French Style, Done Right Red Wine
    Vinaigrette, Raspberry Vinaigrette, Sicilian Roasted Garlic
    Balsamic Vinaigrette, Thousand Island, Three Cheese Ranch)
Ranch (Buttermilk, Garlic, Light, Light Three Cheese,
    Peppercorn, Regular, w/Bacon)
Roasted Red Pepper Italian w/Parmesan
Roka Blue Cheese
Special Collection Parmesan Romano
Sun Dried Tomato Vinaigrette
Sweet Honey Catalina
Tangy Tomato Bacon
Thousand Island (Regular, w/Bacon)
Tuscan House
Vidalia Onion Vinaigrette w/Roasted Red Pepper
Zesty Italian

Kroger Brand -
Balsamic Vinaigrette
California (French, Honey French)
Chunky Bleu Cheese
Classic Whip (Lite, Regular)
Cole Slaw Dressing
Creamy (Buttermilk, Cucumber, French, Garlic Ranch, Italian,
    Ranch)
Fat Free (Creamy Ranch, Zesty Italian)
Greek
Lite (Avocado Ranch, Creamy Ranch, Southwest Ranch)
Olive Oil & Vinegar
Peppercorn Ranch

S

Poppy Seed
Red Wine Vinegar & Oil
Roasted Red Pepper Vinaigrette
Russian
Sun Dried Tomato Vinaigrette
Sweet & Sour
Thousand Island
Zesty Italian

Kroger Value - Italian, Ranch, Thousand Island

Laura Lynn -
Buttermilk
California (French, Honey French)
Chunky Blue Cheese
Creamy (Cucumber, Italian)
French
Garlic Ranch
Italian (Fat Free, Regular)
Peppercorn Ranch
Poppyseed
Ranch (Fat Free, Lite, Regular)
Ranch Dressing Mix
Red Wine Vinegar & Oil
Salad Dressing
Thousand Island
Zesty Italian

Lily's Gourmet Dressings - Balsamic Vinaigrette, Northern Italian,
Poppyseed, Raspberry Walnut Vinaigrette

Litehouse -
Bleu Cheese (Bacon, Big, Chunky, Lite, Original, Yoghurt w/Kefir)
Caesar (Chunky Garlic, Parmesan, Regular, Yoghurt w/Kefir)
Coleslaw (Regular, w/Pineapple)
Creamy Cilantro
Honey Mustard

Lite
>   1000 Island
>   Caesar
>   Coleslaw
>   Honey Dijon Vinaigrette

Organic
>   Balsamic Vinaigrette
>   Caesar
>   Raspberry Lime Vinaigrette

Pear Gorgonzola

Poppyseed

Ranch (Buttermilk, Homestyle, Jalapeno, Lite, Lite Salsa, Organic, Regular, Yoghurt w/Kefir)

Raspberry Walnut Vinaigrette

Spinach Salad

Sweet & Sour

Sweet French

Thousand Island

Vinaigrette (Balsamic, Bleu Cheese, Garlic, Harvest Cherry, Huckleberry, Pomegranate Blueberry, Red Wine Olive Oil, Zesty Italian)

White Balsamic

Lowes Foods Brand - Chunky Blue Cheese, Creamy Caesar, French, Italian (Fat Free, Regular, Spicy), Ranch (Lite, Regular), Thousand Island

Maple Grove Farms Of Vermont -

All Natural
>   Asiago & Garlic
>   Blueberry Pomegranate
>   Champagne Vinaigrette
>   Ginger Pear
>   Maple Fig
>   Strawberry Balsamic

Balsamic Maple

S

Fat Free
- Cranberry Balsamic
- Greek
- Honey Dijon
- Lime Basil
- Poppyseed
- Vinaigrette (Balsamic, Raspberry)

Honey Mustard (Lite, Regular)
Lite Caesar
Organic
- Italian Herb
- Sweet Onion
- Vinaigrette (Balsamic, Dijon, Raspberry)

Parmesan & Pepper
Ranch
Sugar Free
- Italian Balsamic
- Vinaigrette (Balsamic, Raspberry)

Sweet 'N Sour

Marzetti -
Refrigerated Dressings
- Asiago Peppercorn
- Blue Cheese (Bistro, Chunky, French, Light Chunky, Organic, The Ultimate)
- Caesar (Light Supreme, Organic, Supreme)
- Honey Balsamic
- Honey Dijon (Light, Regular)
- Honey French (Light, Regular)
- Organic Parmesan Ranch
- Poppyseed
- Ranch (Classic, Light Classic)
- Slaw (Lite, Regular)
- Sweet Italian
- Thousand Island

Ultimate Gorgonzola
Venice Italian
Vinaigrette (Balsamic, Light Balsamic, Light Caesar, Light
    Raspberry Cabernet, Roasted Garlic Italian, Strawberry
    Chardonnay, White Balsamic)
Shelf Stable
  Asiago Peppercorn
  Caesar Creamy
  Country French
  Honey Balsamic
  Honey Dijon (Fat Free, Mustard)
  Italian (Creamy, Fat Free, House, Regular, w/Blue Cheese
      Crumbles)
  Poppyseed
  Potato Salad
  Ranch (Aged Parmesan, Regular)
  Slaw (Lite, Low Fat, Original)
  Sweet & Sour (Fat Free, Regular)
  Sweet Vidalia
  Thousand Island
  Venice Italian
  Vinaigrette (Balsamic, Blue Cheese Italian, Light Balsamic,
      Organic Balsamic, Peppercorn, Strawberry)
Midwest Country Fare - French, Italian, Ranch, Thousand Island
Miracle Whip - Free, Lite, Regular
Naturally Delicious - Light (Blush Wine, Italian, Raspberry), Regular
    (Balsamic, Blue Cheese, Chipotle Ranch, French, Honey Mustard,
    Italian, Peppercorn Parmesan)
Nature's Basket - Balsamic Vinaigrette, Italian, Ranch, Raspberry
    Vinaigrette, Roasted Red Pepper Vinaigrette, Sesame Ginger
    Vinaigrette
Newman's Own -
  Lighten Up Light
    Balsamic Vinaigrette
    Caesar

S

    Cranberry Walnut
    Honey Mustard
    Italian
    Lime Vinaigrette
    Raspberry Walnut
    Red Wine Vinegar & Olive Oil
    Roasted Garlic Balsamic
    Sun Dried Tomato Italian
Organic
    Light Balsamic Vinaigrette
    Tuscan Italian
Regular
    Balsamic Vinaigrette
    Caesar
    Creamy (Caesar, Italian)
    Greek Vinaigrette
    Olive Oil & Vinegar
    Parisienne Dijon Lime
    Parmesan & Roasted Garlic
    Poppy Seed
    Ranch
    Red Wine Vinegar & Olive Oil
    Southwest
    Three Cheese Balsamic Vinaigrette
    Two Thousand Island
Salad Mist (Balsamic, Italian)
Olde Cape Cod - Lite Caesar, Honey French, Sundried Tomato, Sweet & Sour Poppyseed, Vinaigrette (Blush Wine, Raspberry), Regular (Balsamic (Original, w/Olive Oil), Chipotle Ranch, Honey Dijon, Parmesan & Peppercorn, Poppyseed (Lemon, Orange), Vinaigrette (Lemon & Mint w/Green Tea, Zesty Mango))
Oliv - Vinaigrette (Aged Balsamic, Herbs De Provence, Sundried Tomato & Garlic, White Balsamic)

Organicville - Organic (French •, Herbs De Provence •, Miso Ginger •, Non Dairy Ranch •, Olive Oil & Balsamic •, Orange Cranberry •, Pomegranate •, Sesame (Goddess •, Tamari •), Sundried Tomato & Garlic •, Tarragon Dijon •)

Pfeiffer - Blue Cheese, Caesar, California French, Cole Slaw, French, Garden Ranch, Honey Dijon, Italian (Creamy, Regular, Roasted Garlic, Zesty Garlic), Ranch (Light, Regular), Sweet & Sour, Thousand Island (Light, Regular), Vinaigrette (Balsamic, Red Wine)

Portmann's - Buttermilk Ranch, Light Italian, Light Ranch, Spoonable Salad Dressing, Sweet & Saucy French, Thousand Island, Traditional Italian

Private Selections - Creamy Balsamic, Creamy Ceaser, Herb Ranch, Poppy Seed, Raspberry Vinaigrette, Sweet Onion

Publix - Balsamic Vinaigrette, California French, Chunky Blue Cheese, Creamy Parmesan, Italian (Fat Free, Regular), Lite (Caesar, Honey Dijon, Ranch, Raspberry Walnut), Ranch, Thousand Island (Fat Free, Regular), Zesty Italian

Ring Bros Marketplace - All Varieties *(Except Blue Cheese)*

Royal Food Products -

Garden Fresh

Bleu Cheese (Pourable, Regular, San Francisco Style)

Cole Slaw (Regular, Special)

French (Red, Regular)

Italian (Creamy, Golden)

Ranch/Buttermilk

Thousand Island

White (Salad Dressing, Whipped Salad Dressing)

Gourmet Choice

Balsamic Herb Vinaigrette

California Raspberry Vinaigrette

Caribbean Thousand Island

Classic Caesar

French

Original Recipe Chunky Bleu Cheese

    Poppy Seed
    Ranch/Buttermilk (Chipotle, Classic)
    Sweet Garden Italian
    Sweet N' Creamy Poppy Seed
  Royal Deluxe
    Caesar (Creamy, Regular)
    Chunky Bleu Cheese
    Cole Slaw (Regular, w/Celery Seed)
    French (Island Honey, Red, Red Ranch, Regular)
    Italian (Creamy, Creamy Garlic, Golden, Oil & Vinegar, Reduced
      Calorie, Regular, Seperating)
    Parmesan Pepper
    Ranch/Buttermilk (Ranch Style, Red Ranch, Shelf Stable)
    Raspberry Vinaigrette
    Sweet & Sour Cole Slaw
    Thousand Island
    White Majestic Blend
  Slender Select
    French (Fat Free Red, Reduced Calorie Red)
    Italian
    Ranch/Buttermilk (Fat Free, Reduced Calorie)
Ruth's Hemp Power - Balsamic Hemp
Safeway Brand - 1000 Island (Fat Free, Regular), Creamy Italian,
  Italian (Light, Regular), Ranch (Light, Regular, w/Bacon)
Safeway Select - Basil Ranch, Blue Cheese, Garlic Caesar, Jalapeno
  Ranch, Olive Oil & Balsamic Vinaigrette, Parmesan & Herb,
  Raspberry Vinaigrette, Tuscan Basil Herb
San-J - Gluten Free Asian Dressing (Tamari Ginger ●, Tamari Peanut ●,
  Tamari Sesame ●)
Seeds Of Change - Balsamic Vinaigrette ❗❗, French Tomato ❗❗, Greek
  Feta Vinaigrette ❗❗, Italian Herb Vinaigrette ❗❗, Roasted Red Pepper
  Vinaigrette ❗❗
Spartan Brand - Blue Cheese, French, Italian (Lite, Regular, Zesty),
  Ranch (Lite, Peppercorn, Regular), Squeeze, Thousand Island

Spectrum - Premium Organic Dressing (Prevencal Garlic Lover's, Rocky Mountain Ranch)

Stop & Shop Brand - Balsamic Vinaigrette, Blue Cheese, Caesar, French (Creamy, Regular), Italian (Creamy, Fat Free, Lite), Ranch (Fat Free, Regular), Raspberry Vinaigrette, Thousand Island

Taste Of Inspiration - House!, Mandarin Orange!, Wild Maine Blueberry!

Teresa's Select Recipes - Asiago Pepper Crème, Blackberry Poppyseed, Lite Honey Dijon, Melon Cucumber, Raspberry White Balsamic, Vinaigrette (Berry Lavender, Blueberry Pomegranate, Sun Dried Tomato, Vidalia Onion)

Trader Joe's -
Dressings Balsamic Vinaigrette (Fat Free!!, Organic!!, Regular!!)
Organic Red Wine & Olive Oil Vinaigrette!!
Raspberry Low Fat!!
Romano Caesar!!
Tuscan Italian w/Balsamic Vinegar!!
Refrigerated Dressings Organic Red Wine & Olive Oil Vinaigrette!!

Walden Farms -
Single Serve Packets
Creamy Bacon
Honey Dijon
Italian
Ranch
Thousand Island
Sugar Free No Carb
Asian
Bacon Ranch
Balsamic Vinaigrette
Blue Cheese
Caesar
Coleslaw
Creamy (Bacon, Italian)

French
Honey Dijon
Italian (Regular, w/Sun Dried Tomato)
Ranch
Raspberry Vinaigrette
Russian
Sweet Onion
Thousand Island
Zesty Italian

Wegmans Brand -
Basil Vinaigrette
Caramelized Onion & Bacon
Cracked Pepper Ranch Dressing
Creamy (Curry & Roasted Red Pepper, Italian, Ranch)
Fat Free (Parmesan Italian, Red Wine Vinegar, Roasted Red Pepper)
Light (Garlic Italian, Golden Caesar, Italian, Parmesan Peppercorn Ranch, Ranch, Thousand Island)
Organic (Balsamic w/Garlic Chunks, Creamy Caesar, Honey Mustard, Italian, Raspberry Vinaigrette, Sun Dried Tomato Vinaigrette)
Parmesan Italian
Roasted Sweet Red Bell Pepper & Garlic
Sun Dried Tomato Vinaigrette
Tarragon Vinaigrette
Thousand Island (Light, Regular)
Three Spice Garden French
Traditional Italian

Wild Thymes - Salad Refresher (Black Currant, Mango, Meyer Lemon, Morello Cherry, Passion Fruit, Pomegranate, Raspberry, Tangerine), Vinaigrette (Fig Walnut, Mandarin Orange Basil, Mediterranean Balsamic, Parmesan Walnut Caesar, Raspberry Pear Balsamic, Roasted Apple Shallot, Tahitian Lime Ginger, Tuscan Tomato Basil)

Winn & Lovett - Jalapeno Ranch, Manadarin Poppyseed, Parmesan Peppercorn Ranch, Three Cheese Italian, Vadalia Onion

Winn Dixie - Balsamic Vinaigrette, California French, Chunky Blue Cheese, Creamy (French, Ranch), Fat Free (Italian, Ranch, Thousand Island), Garden Ranch, Honey Dijon, Italian (Lite, Regular, Robust, Zesty), Thousand Island

Wish-Bone - Balsamic Oil & Herbs, Balsamic Vinaigrette, Blue Cheese (Chunky, Fat Free), Deluxe French (Low Fat, Regular), Italian (Fat Free, Light, Regular, Robusto), Ranch (Light, Regular), Raspberry Hazelnut Vinaigrette, Salad Spritzers Vinaigrette (Italian, Ranch), Western

Salami... see Sausage

Salmon

... *All Fresh Fish Is Gluten-Free (Non-Marinated, Unseasoned)

Bumble Bee - Blueback, Keta, Pink, Premium Wild Pink, Prime Fillet Atlantic, Prime Fillet Salmon Steaks Lemon & Dill, Red, Smoked Salmon Fillets In Oil

Chicken Of The Sea - All Salmon Products

Crown Prince - Natural (Alaskan (Coho Alder Wood Smoked, Pink Salmon), Skinless & Boneless Pacific Pink Salmon)

Food Club Brand - Pink

Great Value Brand (Wal-Mart) - Canned Alaskan Pink Salmon

Henry & Lisa's - 4 oz Wild, Battered Salmon Filets, Canned Wild Alaskan Pink

Hy-Vee - Frozen

Kirkland Signature - Fresh Atlantic, Frozen Alaskan Fillets, Sockeye (Canned, Frozen Fillets)

Kroger Brand - Canned

Morey's - Marinated Salmon (Garlic Cracked Pepper, Lemon Dill, Seasoned Grill), Smoked Salmon (Nuggets, Whole Wild Keta, Wild Keta Portions)

Publix - Coho Salmon Fillets, Sockeye Salmon Fillets

Pure Market Express▲ - Salmon ●

Trader Joe's - Pink Salmon Skinless Boneless, Premium Salmon Patties!!, Salmon Burger, Smoked Salmon

S Salsa

Albertsons - Chunky (Medium, Mild)

Amy's - Organic (Black Bean & Corn!, Medium!, Mild!, Spicy Chipotle!)

Bone Suckin' Sauce - Hot, Regular

Bravos - Hot, Medium, Mild, Spicy Salsa Con Queso

Chi-Chi's - Con Queso, Fiesta, Garden, Natural, Original

Dave's Gourmet - Insanity Salsa

Dei Fratelli - Black Bean 'N Corn Medium, Casera (Medium Hot, Mild), Chipotle Medium, Original (Medium, Mild)

Drew's - Organic (Black Bean Cilantro & Corn Medium, Chipotle Lime Medium, Double Fire Roasted Medium, Hot, Medium, Mild)

Eat Smart - Naturals (Garden Style Sweet, Salsa Con Queso)

Emeril's - Gaaahlic Lovers Medium, Kicked Up Chunky Hot, Original Recipe Medium, Southwest Style Medium

Fischer & Wieser - Artichoke & Olive, Black Bean & Corn, Chipotle & Corn, Cilantro & Olive, Das Peach Haus Peach, Havana Mojito, Hot Habanero, Salsa A La Charra, Salsa Verde Ranchera, Timpone's Organic Salsa Muy Rica

Food Club Brand - Corn & Black Bean (Medium, Mild), Medium, Mild, Mild Picante, Think & Chunky (Medium, Mild)

Frontera - Gourmet Mexican Salsa (Chipotle, Corn & Poblano, Double Roasted, Guajillo, Habanero, Jalapeno Cilantro, Mango Key Lime, Medium Chunky Tomato, Mild Chunky Tomato, Red Pepper & Garlic, Roasted Tomato, Spanish Olive, Tomatillo)

Full Circle - Organic (Medium, Mild)

Giant Brand - Hot, Medium, Mild, Regular

Gordon Food Service - Chunky

Green Mountain Gringo▲ - All Varieties

Hannaford Brand - Con Queso Medium, Medium, Mild, Southwestern (Medium, Mild)

HealthMarket - Organic (Medium, Mild, Pineapple)

Herdez - Salsa Casera

Herr's - Chunky (Medium, Mild)

Hy-Vee - Salsa Con Queso Medium, Thick & Chunky (Hot, Medium, Mild)

Kirkland Signature - Organic Medium

Kroger Brand - Picante Sauce (Hot, Medium, Mild), Thick & Chunky (Hot, Medium, Mild), Traditional (Hot, Medium, Mild), Verde, Viva (Medium, Mild), Viva Con Queso (Monterey Jack & Salsa, Salsa & Cheese)

La Victoria - Cilantro (Medium, Mild), Jalapena Extra Hot (Green, Red), Salsa Ranchera Hot, Suprema (Medium, Mild), Thick 'N Chunky (Medium, Mild), Verde (Medium, Mild), Victoria Hot

Laura Lynn - All Picante

Litehouse - Medium

Lowes Foods Brand - Salsa Con Queso, Thick & Chunky (Medium, Mild)

Meijer Brand - Original (Hot, Medium, Mild), Restaurant Style (Hot, Medium, Mild), Santa Fe Style (Medium, Mild), Thick & Chunky (Hot, Medium, Mild)

Melissa's - Salsa Casera

Mezzetta - California Habanero Salsa Twist & Shout

Miguel's - Black Bean & Corn, Chipotle, Medium, Mild, Roasted Garlic

Mixes From The Heartland▲ - Mix (Corn & Tomato ●, Garden ●, Kick N Hot ●, Sun Dried Tomato ●, Tex Mex ●)

Mrs. Renfro's - Black Bean, Chipotle Corn, Garlic, Green, Mild, Peach, Raspberry Chipotle, Roasted

Nature's Basket - Black Bean & Corn, Hot, Medium, Mild, Pineapple

Nature's Promise - Organic Chipotle (Medium, Mild)

Newman's Own - All Natural (Hot, Medium, Mild), Black Bean & Corn, Farmer's Garden, Mango, Peach, Pineapple, Roasted Garlic, Tequila Lime

O Organics - Chipotle, Chunky Bell Pepper, Fire Roasted Tomato, Mild

Old Dutch - Restaurante Salsa (Medium, Mild)

Old El Paso - Cheese 'N Salsa (Medium, Mild), Salsa Thick N' Chunky (Hot, Medium, Mild)

On The Border - Hot, Medium, Mild

Organicville - Medium ●, Mild ●, Pineapple ●

Ortega - Black Bean & Corn, Garden Vegetable (Medium, Mild), Original (Medium, Mild), Picante (Hot, Medium, Mild), Roasted Garlic, Salsa Con Queso, Salsa Verde, Thick & Chunky (Medium, Mild)

Pace - Black Bean & Roasted Corn, Chunky (Medium, Mild), Picante Sauce (Extra Mild, Hot, Medium, Mild), Pico De Gallo, Pineapple Mango Chipotle, Thick & Chunky (Extra Mild, Hot, Medium, Mild), Verde

Private Selections - Authentic Restaurant Style, Black Beans & Corn, Cilantro, Fire Roasted, Green Chile, Peach Mango, Peppery Sweet Corn, Tart Lime

Publix - All Natural (Hot, Medium, Mild)

Publix GreenWise Market - Organic (Medium, Mild)

Pure Market Express ▲ - Red Pepper ●, Sassy ●

Safeway Select - 3 Bean Medium, Chipotle Medium, Fiesta Fajita, Garlic Lovers, Peach Pineapple Medium, Roasted Tomato Medium, Southwest (Hot, Medium, Mild), Verde Medium

Salpica - Chipotle Garlic, Cilantro Green Olive, Fall Harvest, Grilled Pineapple Key Lime, Habanero Lime, Mango Peach, Roasted Corn & Bean, Rustic Tomato, Spring Break, Summer Of Love, Tomato Jalapeno

Santa Barbara - Black Bean & Corn, Garden Style, Grilled Pineapple Chipotle, Habanero Lime, Hot, Mango & Peach, Medium, Mild, Pico De Gallo, Roasted (Chili, Garlic, Tomatillo), Taquera, Texas Style

Senora Verde - Salsa Con Queso

Signature Cafe - Creamy Tomatillo w/Avocado, Fresca, Triple Roasted, Verde

Simply Enjoy - Black Bean & Corn, Peach Mango, Pineapple Chipotle, Raspberry Chipotle, Tequila Lime

Stop & Shop Brand - Hot, Medium, Mild, Simply Enjoy Salsa (Black Bean & Corn, Peach Mango, Pineapple Chipotle, Tequila Lime)

Taco Bell - Black Bean Con Queso, Chili Con Queso w/Beef, Salsa Con Queso (Medium, Mild), Thick 'N Chunky (Medium, Mild)

Tostitos - All Natural Chunky (Hot!!, Medium!!, Mild!!), Restaurant Style!!, Salsa Con Queso!!

Trader Joe's - 3 Pepper, Authentica!!, Chunky, Corn & Chili Tomatoless!!, Double Roasted!!, Fire Roasted Tomato!!, Fresh (All Varieties)!!, Black Bean & Roasted Corn!!, Garlic Chipotle!!, Hot & Smoky Chipotle, Pineapple!!, Spicy Smoky Peach, Verde!!

UTZ - Mt. Misery Mike's Salsa Dip, Sweet Salsa Dip

Wegmans Brand - Hot, Medium, Mild, Organic (Hot, Mango, Medium, Mild), Roasted (Chipotle, Salsa Verde, Sweet Pepper, Tomato), Santa Fe Style

Winn Dixie - Hot, Medium, Mild, Salsa Con Queso

Wise - Medium, Mild

Salt

Albertsons - Iodized, Regular

Giant Brand - Iodized, Plain

Gluty Free - Citric Acid ●

Gordon Food Service - Salt Packet

Great Value Brand (Wal-Mart) - Iodized, Plain

Hannaford Brand - Iodized, Regular

Kroger Brand

Lawry's - Seasoned!!

Manischewitz

Marcum Spices - Iodized Salt, Sea Salt, Seasoned Salt

Meijer Brand - Iodized, Plain

Morton - Coarse Kosher Salt, Iodized Table Salt, Lite Salt Mixture, Plain Table Salt, Salt Substitute, Sea Salt (Coarse, Fine)

No Salt - Salt Substitute

Nuts Online - Citric Acid ●

Odell's - Popcorn Salt

Private Selections - Mediterranean Sea Salt

Publix

Safeway Brand - Iodized, Plain, Rock

Spartan Brand - Garlic, Iodized, Plain

Stop & Shop Brand - Iodized Salt, Plain

The Vegetarian Express - All Purpose Veggie Salt!

S

Victoria Gourmet - Sea Salt (Anglesey, Australian Flake, Celtic, Trapani)

Wegmans Brand - Iodized, Plain, Sea Salt (Coarse Crystals, Fine Crystals)

Sandwich Meat... see Deli Meat

Sardines

... *All Fresh Fish Is Gluten-Free (Non-Marinated, Unseasoned)

Bumble Bee - In Hot Sauce, In Mustard, In Oil, In Water

Chicken Of The Sea - All Sardine Varieties

Crown Prince - Crosspacked Brisling In Olive Oil, In Water, One Layer Brisling (In Mustard, In Oil/No Salt Added, In Soybean Oil, In Tomato), Skinless & Boneless (In Olive Oil, In Soybean Oil), Two Layer Brisling (In Olive Oil, In Soybean Oil)

Giant Brand - Portuguese

Ocean Prince - In (Louisiana Hot Sauce, Mustard, Tomato Sauce, Water), Lightly Smoked (In Oil, With Green Chilies), Premium Skinless & Boneless In Oil

Port Side - Canned Sardines In Soybean Oil

Trader Joe's - Skinless Boneless Sardines In Olive Oil

Sauces... (includes Marinara, Pasta, Tomato, Misc.)

A Taste Of Thai - Curry Paste (Green, Panang, Red, Yellow), Fish Sauce, Garlic Chili Pepper, Pad Thai, Peanut Satay, Peanut Sauce Mix, Sweet Red Chili

Ah So - Original Chinese BBQ For Pork/Chicken & Barbecue, Smokey Chinese BBQ

Albertsons - Pasta (Four Cheese, Garden Vegetable, Meat, Mushroom, Tomato & Garlic & Onion, Traditional)

Amy's - Organic Low Sodium Marinara!, Organic Family Marinara (Light In Sodium!, Regular!), Organic Tomato Basil (Light In Sodium!, Regular!)

Baxters - Bramley Apple Sauce, Mint Sauce

Bertolli - Alfredo, Five Cheese, Marinara w/Burgundy Wine, Mushroom Alfredo, Tomato & Basil, Vidalia Onion w/Roasted Garlic, Vodka

Black Horse - Apricot Sauce, Chili Verde Sauce, Marionberry Pepper Sauce, Raspberry Mustard Sauce, Savory Sauce, Spicy Sauce

Bove's Of Vermont - All Natural (Basil, Marinara, Mushroom & Wine, Roasted Garlic, Sweet Red Pepper, Vodka), Organic (Basil, Vodka)

Capa Di Roma - Arrustica, Fresh Basil, Marinara, Roasted Garlic

Choy Sun - Oyster Flavored Sauce (Glass Bottles & Metal Cans)

Cielo - Vegan (Arrabiata, Classic, Pizza)

Classico -
  Alfredo Sauce (All Varieties)
  Bruschetta (All Varieties)
  Pesto (All Varieties)
  Red Sauce
    Cabernet Marinara w/Herbs
    Caramelized Onion & Roasted Garlic
    Fire Roasted Tomato & Garlic
    Florentine Spinach & Cheese
    Four Cheese
    Italian Sausage w/Peppers & Onions
    Marinara w/Plum Tomatoes
    Mushroom & Ripe Olives
    Organic (Spinach & Garlic, Tomato Herbs & Spices)
    Roasted Garlic
    Spicy Red Pepper
    Spicy Tomato (& Basil, & Pesto)
    Sun Dried Tomato
    Tomato & Basil
    Traditional Sweet Basil
    Triple Mushroom
    Vodka Sauce

Contadina -
  Pizza (Flavored w/Pepperoni, Four Cheese, Original)
  Pizza Squeeze, Sauce (Extra Thick & Zesty, Regular, w/Garlic & Onion, w/Italian Herbs)
  Sweet & Sour Sauce

S

Cuisine Sante▲ - Brown Sauce Mix●

Daddy Sam's - Bar B Que Sawce (Medium Ginger Jalapeno, Original), Salmon Glaze

Dave's Gourmet - Pasta Sauce Butternut Squash, Organic (Red Heirloom, Roasted Garlic & Sweet Basil, Spicy Heirloom Marinara), Wild Mushroom

Dei Fratelli - Pizza Sauce, Presto (Italian Dip, Pizza Sauce), Sloppy Joe, Tomato

Del Monte - All Tomato Products *(Except Spaghetti Sauce Flavor)*

Di Lusso - Buffalo Wing Sauce, Sweet Onion Sauce

Dietz & Watson▲ - Hoagie Dressing ●, Sweet Vidalia Onions In Sauce ●

Dorothy Lane Market - Original Marinara

Eden Organic - Apple Cherry Sauce, Apple Strawberry Sauce, Spaghetti Sauce (Organic, Organic No Salt Added)

Emeril's - Pasta Sauce (Cacciatore Dinner, Eggplant & Gaaahlic, Home Style Marinara, Kicked Up Tomato, Roasted (Gaahlic, Red Pepper), Sicilian Gravy, Three Cheeses, Tomato & Basil, Vodka)

Ethnic Gourmet - Simmer Sauce (Bombay Curry, Calcutta Masala, Delhi Korma, Punjab Saag Spinach)

Ferratto's - Pasta Sauce (Four Cheese, Tomato Basil)

Fischer & Wieser -

    Especial Pasilla Chile

    All Purpose Vegetable & Meat Marinade

    Asian Wasabi Plum

    Charred Pineapple Bourbon

    Chipotle Sauce (Blackberry, Blueberry, Original Roasted Raspberry, Plum Chipotle BBQ, Pomegranate & Mango)

    Granny's Peach 'N' Pepper Pourin'

    Mango Ginger Habanero

    Mom's (Artichoke Heart & Asiago Cheese, Garlic & Basil, Martini, Puttanesca, Special Marinara, Spicy Arrabbiata)

    Mom's Organic (Roasted Pepper, Traditional)

    Papaya Lime Serrano

Steak & Grilling
Sweet & Savory Onion Glaze
Sweet Sour & Smokey Mustard Sauce
Food Club Brand -
Cheddar Cheese Sauce
Pasta Sauce (Chunky Garden Style, Chunky Tomato Garlic Onion, Mushroom, Plain, Traditional, w/Meat)
Spaghetti Sauce (Four Cheese, Garden Vegetable, Garlic & Herb, Garlic & Onion, Meat, Mushroom, Regular, Robust Parmesan & Romano, Traditional)
Frank's RedHot - Chile 'N Lime, Original, Sweet Chili, Wings (Buffalo, Hot Buffalo, Sweet Heat BBQ), Xtra Hot
Frontera -
Barbeque Sauce (Original Sweet & Smoky, Roasted Chipotle Pineapple, Texas Black Pepper)
Cocktail & Ceviche Sauce (Cilantro Lime, Tomato Chipotle)
Cooking Sauce (Red Chile & Roasted Garlic, Roasted Garlic & Chipotle, Roasted Tomato & Cilantro)
Enchilada Sauce Classic Red Chile
Grilling Sauce (Chipotle Honey Mustard, Red Pepper Sesame)
Hot Sauce (Chipotle, Habanero, Jalapeno, Red Pepper)
Taco Sauce (Chipotle Garlic, Roasted Tomato)
Full Circle - Organic Pasta Sauce (Parmesan Cheese, Portabella Mushroom, Roasted Garlic, Tomato Basil), Organic Tomato Sauce
Full Flavor Foods - Sauce Mix (Alfredo ●, Cheese ●, Vegetarian Mushroom ●)
Fungus Among Us - Truffle Gatherers
Giant Brand - Strawberry Syrup
Gordon Food Service - Barbeque (Dip Cup, Original, Pit Style, Sweet), California Tomato, Marinara (Dip Cup, Regular), Spaghetti Sauce, Sweet & Savory
Hannaford Brand - Cranberry Sauce, Four Cheese, Hot Sauce, Mushroom & Olive, Mushroom & Onion, Onion & Garlic, Roasted Garlic, Sloppy Joe Sauce, Sweet Pepper & Onion, Taco Sauce,

S

Tartar Sauce, Tomato, Tomato & Basil, Tomato Onion & Garlic, Traditional

Hargis House - Sloppy Joe Sauce

HealthMarket - Mushroom Onion, Organic Tomato Basil, Vegetable

House Of Blues - Bayou Heat Hot Sauce

Hy-Vee - Spaghetti Sauce (3 Cheese, Garden, Mushroom, Traditional, w/Meat), Tomato Sauce

Ka-Me - Duck!, Fish!, Hot Mustard!, Sriracha!, Sweet Chili!

Katy Sweet▲ - Saucy Stuff (Caramel ●, Praline ●)

Kroger Brand -
Extra Hot
Hot
Pasta
Chunky (Green Pepper, Mushroom)
Homestyle (Beef, Parmesan & Romano, Tomato w/Basil)
Original (Beef, Mushroom, Six Cheese, Traditional)
Pesto Sauce Blend Mix
Pizza (Parlor, Pepperoni, Traditional)
Spaghetti (Thick & Zesty, w/Mushrooms)
Sweet & Sour

Kroger Value - Pasta (Four Cheese, Garlic & Herb, Meat Flavored, Mushroom)

Kurtz - Steak Sauce

Las Palmas - Red Chile, Red Enchilada

Laura Lynn - Chili, Elmer Ingle 1922

Lee Kum Kee - Satay, Shrimp

Lowes Foods Brand - Spaghetti Sauce (Traditional, w/Meat, w/Mushrooms), Tomato

Mantia's - Pasta Sauce (Flavored w/Meat, Mushroom, Traditional), Pizza Sauce

Mayacamas -
Gourmet Sauce Hollandaise
Pasta Sauce Mix (Alfredo, Chicken Fettuccine, Creamy Clam, Creamy Pesto, Peppered Lemon, Pesto), Skillet Toss Mix (Black

Olive Pesto, Dried Tomato, Garden Style Recipe, Green Olive Pesto, Mushroom Sauce, Seafood Pasta Recipe, Spicy Pasta Recipe)

McCormick - Marinade Mix (Caribbean Citrus Seafood, Lemon Pepper Seafood)

Meijer Brand -
Extra Chunky Spaghetti Sauce (3 Cheese, Garden Combo, Garlic & Cheese, Mushroom & Green Pepper)
Pasta Sauce Select (Four Cheese, Marinara, Mushroom & Olive, Onion & Garlic, Original)
Regular Spaghetti Sauce (Plain, w/Meat, w/Mushroom)
Tomato Sauce (Organic, Regular)

Mezzetta - Napa Valley Bistro Pasta Sauce (Arrabbiata, Artichoke Marinara, Artichoke Parmesan Marinara, Creamy Marinara, Creamy Vodka Style Marinara, Fire Roasted Marinara, Homemade Style Marinara, Porcini Mushroom, Puttanesca, Roasted Garlic, Tomato Basil)

Midwest Country Fare - Spaghetti Sauce (All Natural Garlic & Onion, Four Cheese, Garden Vegetable, Garlic & Herb, Mushroom, Traditional), Tomato Sauce

Moore's Marinade - Buffalo Wing, Honey BBQ Wing, Original Marinade

Mr. Spice Organic - Sauce & Marinade (Garlic Steak, Ginger Stir Fry, Honey BBQ, Honey Mustard, Hot Wing, Indian Curry, Sweet & Sour, Thai Peanut)

Nature's Basket - Organic (Marinara, Roasted Garlic, Three Cheese, Tomato Basil, Vodka Cream), Tomato Sauce

Nature's Promise - Organic Pasta Sauce (Garden Vegetable, Original, Parmesan)

Newman's Own -
Alfredo
Cabernet Marinara
Fire Roasted Tomato & Garlic
Five Cheese

S

Fra Diavolo
Italian Sausage & Peppers
Marinara (Regular, w/Mushroom)
Organic (Marinara, Tomato Basil, Traditional Herb)
Pesto & Tomato
Roasted (Garlic, Garlic & Peppers, Garlic Alfredo)
Sockarooni
Sweet Onion & Roasted Garlic
Tomato Basil Bombolina
Vodka

O Organics - Marinara, Mushroom, Roasted Garlic, Tomato Basil

Olde Cape Cod - Grilling Sauce (Chipotle, Cranberry, Honey Orange, Lemon Ginger, Sweet & Bold)

Panda Brand - Lo Mein Oyster Flavored Sauce, Oyster Flavored Sauce *(Green Label Only)*

Para Micasa - Adobo (Pepper, Regular)

Patsy's Pasta Sauce - Marinara, Tomato Basil

Portmann's - Seafood Cocktail Sauce, Seafood Tartar Sauce, Sweet & Sour Sauce

Prego -
Chunky Garden (Combo, Mushroom & Green Pepper, Mushroom Supreme w/Baby Portobello, Tomato Onion & Garlic)
Flavored w/Meat
Fresh Mushroom
Heart Smart (Mushroom, Onion & Garlic, Ricotta Parmesan, Roasted Red Pepper & Garlic, Traditional)
Italian Sausage & Garlic, Marinara
Mushroom & Garlic
Roasted (Garlic & Herb, Garlic Parmesan)
Three Cheese
Tomato Basil Garlic
Traditional

Private Selections - Pasta (Artichoke Bruschetta, Basil Pesto, Bolognese & Arrabbiata, Creamy Alfredo, Tomato Bruschetta)

Publix - Garden Style, Meat Flavored, Mushrooms, Parmesan & Romano, Tomato Garlic & Onion, Tomato Sauce, Traditional

Pure Market Express▲ - Pasta Sauce (Creamy Garlic Dill ●, Garlic Alfredo ●, Spicy Peanut ●)

Ragu -

    Cheesy (Classic Alfredo, Double Cheddar, Light Parmesan Alfredo, Roasted Garlic Parmesan)

    Chunky (Garden Combination, Mama's Special Garden, Mushroom & Green Pepper, Roasted Red Pepper & Onion, Sundried Tomato & Sweet Basil, Super Chunky Mushroom, Super Vegetable Primavera, Tomato Garlic & Onion)

    Light (Tomato & Basil, No Sugar Added Tomato & Basil)

    Old World Style (Flavored w/Meat, Marinara, Mushroom, Sweet Tomato Basil, Tomato & Mozzarella, Traditional)

    Organic (Garden Veggie, Traditional)

    Pizza (Homemade Style, Pizza Quick Traditional)

    Robusto (7 Herb Tomato, Chopped Tomato Olive Oil & Garlic, Parmesan & Romano, Roasted Garlic, Sauteed Onion & Garlic, Sauteed Onion & Mushroom, Six Cheese, Sweet Italian Sausage & Cheese)

Rao's Specialty Foods - Homemade (Arrabbiata, Cuore DiPomodoro, Marinara, Puttanesca, Roasted Eggplant, Southern Italian Pepper & Mushroom, Vodka), Pizza Sauce

S&W - Homestyle

Safeway Brand - Sloppy Joe

Safeway Select - Gourmet Dipping Sauces (Honey Mustard, Sweet & Sour), Pasta Sauce (Arrabiatta, Artichoke Pesto, Four Cheese, Garlic Basil, Marinara, Mushroom/Onion, Roasted Onion & Garlic, Spicy Red Bell Pepper, Sun Dried Tomatoes & Olives), Taco Sauce (Green, Red)

Salpica - Texas Picante

San-J - Gluten Free (Asian BBQ ●, Sweet & Tangy ●, Szechuan ●, Teriyaki ●, Thai Peanut ●)

Santa Barbara Olive Co. - Pasta Sauce (Roasted Garlic, Wine & Mushroom)

S

Sauces 'N Love -
Chimichurri (Cilantro, Traditional Parsley)
Original Sauces (Arrabbiata, Barely Bolognese, Fresh Marinara
& Pizza, Pommodoro & Basilico, Puttanesca, Sugo Rosa, Tuscan
Vodka)

Scarpetta - Arrabbiata, Barely Bolognese, Bruschetta Toppings
(Tomato & Artichoke, Tomato & Capers), Fresh Marinara & Pizza
Sauces, Puttanesca, Tomato & Arugula, Tuscan Vodka

Seeds Of Change -
Indian Simmer Sauce (Jalfrezi**!!**, Korma**!!**, Madras**!!**, Tikka
Masala**!!**)
Madras Sauce**!!**
Pasta Sauce (Arrabiatta Di Roma**!!**, Marinara di Venezia**!!**,
Romagna Three Cheese**!!**, Tomato Basil Genovese**!!**, Tuscan
Tomato & Garlic**!!**, Vodka Americano**!!**)

Senora Verde - Taco Sauce (Medium, Mild)

Sharwood's - Balti, Bhuna, Cantonese Curry, Goan Vindaloo, Jalfrezi,
Korma, Madras, Pineapple & Coconut, Plum Sauce, Rogan Josh,
Saag Masala, Spicy Tikka Masala, Thai Mussaman Curry, Thai
Yellow Curry, Tikka Masala, Two Step (Coconut & Curry Biryani,
Mint & Coriander Biryani, Tomato & Cumin Biryani)

Simply Boulder - Culinary Sauce (Coconut Peanut ●, Honey Dijon ●,
Lemon Pesto ●, Pineapple Ginger ●, Truly Teriyaki ●)

Simply Enjoy - Pasta Sauce (Fra Diavolo, Marinara, Roasted Garlic,
Sicilian Eggplant, Tomato Basil, Vodka)

Spartan Brand - Chili, Pizza Sauce, Sloppy Joe, Spaghetti Sauce
(Traditional, w/Meat, w/Mushroom), Tomato Sauce

Steels Gourmet - Agave Teriyaki (Regular, Wasabi), Hoisin, Mango
Curry, Sweet & Sour

Stop & Shop Brand - Simply Enjoy Sauce (Fra Diavolo, Marinara,
Roasted Garlic, Sicilian Eggplant, Tomato Basil, Vodka), Tomato
Sauce (No Added Salt, Regular)

Stubb's - Bar-B-Q Sauce (Hickory Bourbon ●, Honey Pecan ●, Mild ●,
Original ●, Smokey Mesquite ●, Spicy ●)

Sweet Baby Ray's -
> Dipping Sauce (Creamy Buffalo Wing, Honey Mustard, Ray's Signature)
> Grilling Sauce (Maple & Brown Sugar, Original)
> Marinade & Sauce (Buffalo Wing Sauce, Steakhouse)

Taste Of Inspiration - Barbeque (Maple Chipotle!, Spicy Mango!, Wild Maine Blueberry!), Grilling (Caribbean Mango!, Chipotle!, Sweet Apple!)

Tasty Bite - Simmer (Good Korma!, Pad Thai!, Rogan Josh!, Satay Partay!, Tikka Masala!)

Texas Pete - Buffalo Wing, Garlic Hot Sauce, Hotter Hot Sauce, Original Hot Sauce, Pepper, Seafood

Thai Kitchen - 10 Minute Simmer Sauce (Green Curry, Panang Curry, Red Curry, Yellow Curry), Original Pad Thai, Peanut Satay, Premium Fish Sauce, Spicy Thai Chili, Sweet Red Chili

The Ginger People - Ginger Lemon Grass!, Ginger Wasabi!, Hot Ginger Jalapeno!, Sweet Ginger Chili!, Thai Green Curry!

Trader Joe's -
> Organic
>> Chocolate Midnight Moo!!
>> Marinara Sauce (No Salt Added!!, Regular!!),
>> Red Wine & Olive Oil Vinaigrette!!
>> Spaghetti Sauce!!
>> Tomato Basil Marinara!!
>> Vodka Sauce!!
>
> Regular
>> Arrabiata!!
>> Bruschetta
>> Cacciatore Simmer
>> Chili Pepper!!
>> Curry Simmer!!
>> Italian Sausage
>> Masala Simmer!!
>> Pizza Fat Free!!

S

Roasted Garlic Marinara
Rustico
Thai Curry (Red**!!**, Yellow**!!**)
Three Cheese
Tomato Basil (Marinara**!!**, Pasta Sauce)
Traditional Marinara**!!**
Tuscano Marinara Low Fat**!!**
Whole Peeled Tomatoes w/Basil

Walden Farms - Alfredo, Marinara, Scampi

Wegmans Brand -

Bruschetta Topping (Artichoke Asiago, Roasted Red Pepper, Traditional Tomato)
Chunky (Marinara Pasta Sauce, Pizza Sauce)
Four Cheese
Horseradish Cream
Italian Classics (Arrabbiata, Basil Pesto, Bolognese, Diavolo Sauce, Marinara, Mushroom Marsala, Portabello Mushroom, Puttanesca, Sun Dried Tomato, Tomato w/Italian Sausage, Vodka Sauce)
Lemon & Caper Sauce
Lemon Butter
Mustard
Organic Pasta Sauce (Marinara, Roasted Garlic, Tomato Basil)
Prepared Horseradish
Remoulade
Roasted (Garlic Pasta, Sweet Red Pepper)
Smooth Marinara
Tomato (& Basil, Regular)
White Clam Sauce

Wild Thymes - Dipping Sauce (Indian Vindaloo, Moroccan Spicy Pepper, Thai Chili Roasted Garlic)

Wild Wood - Aioli Zesty Garlic

Winn Dixie - Classic (Fra Diavolo, Home Style, Marinara, Tomato Basil), Garden Combination, Garlic & Onion, Meat, Mushroom,

Parmesan & Romano, Pizza Sauce, Select Receipe (Double Garlic, Peppers & Onions), Tomato Sauce, Traditional

Woodstock Farms - Organic Sauce Original, Organic Tomato Sauce (No Salt, Original)

Sauerkraut

B&G

Boar's Head

Cortland Valley Organic

Dietz & Watson▲ - ●

Eden Organic - Organic

Flanagan - Krrrrisp Kraut (Bavarian, Regular)

Food Club Brand - Canned, In Bag

Giant Brand - Canned

Great Value Brand (Wal-Mart) - Canned

Hannaford Brand

Krrrrisp Kraut

Laura Lynn

Meijer Brand

S&W - All Canned Vegetables

Safeway Brand

Silver Floss

Spartan Brand

Wegmans Brand

Willie's

Sausage

Abraham - Diced Prosciutto

Aidells -

Apricot Ginger Breakfast Links

Artichoke & Garlic

Burmese Curry

Cajun Style Andouille

Chicken & Apple Breakfast Links (Minis, Regular)

Habanero & Green Chile

Italian Style w/Mozzarella Cheese

Mango (Breakfast Links, Regular)
Maple & Smoked Bacon Breakfast Links
Organic (Andouille, Chicken & Apple, Spinach & Feta, Sun
    Dried Tomato, Sweet Basil & Roasted Garlic)
Pesto
Portobello Mushroom
Roasted (Garlic & Gruyere Cheese, Pepper w/Corn)
Smoked Chorizo
Spinach & Feta
Sun Dried Tomato & Mozzarella
Whiskey Fennel

Al Fresco -
Chicken Sausage
Breakfast Sausages (Apple Maple, Country Style, Wild
    Blueberry)
Dinner Sausage Fully Cooked (Buffalo Style, Chipotle Chorizo,
    Roasted Garlic, Roasted Pepper & Asiago, Spicy Jalapeno,
    Spinach & Feta, Sundried Tomato, Sweet Apple, Sweet Italian
    Style)
Fresh Dinner Sausages (Buffalo Style, Sweet Apple, Sweet Italian
    Style)

Albertsons - Beef Smoked, Polska Kielbasa, Smoked

Applegate Farms -
Genoa Salami (Hot, Organic, Regular)
Natural Uncured Hot Dogs (Beef, Big Apple, Chicken, Turkey)
Organic Sausages (Andouille, Chicken & Apple, Fire Roasted Red
    Pepper, Smoked Pork Andouille, Smoked Pork Bratwurst,
    Smoked Pork Kielbasa, Spinach & Feta, Sweet Italian)
Organic Uncured Hot Dogs (Beef, Chicken, Stadium Style, The
    Great Organic, Turkey)
Pancetta
Pepperoni
Sopressata (Hot, Regular)
The Greatest Little Organic Smokey Pork Cocktail Franks
Turkey Salami

Armour - 1877 (Hard Salami, Reduced Fat Hard Salami), Cotto Salami, Deli Sandwich Style Pepperoni, Hard Salami, Hickory Smoked Summer Sausage, Novara Hard Salami, Pepperoni (Italian Style, Turkey), Smoked Sausage Beef, Beef Mesquite, Bun-Length (Beef, Cheddar, Fresh Bratwurst, Italian, Jalepeno & Cheddar, Polish), Cheese, Jalepeno & Cheddar, Original w/Skin, Polska Kielbasa, Skinless Beef, Skinless Cheese, Skinless Original, Skinless Polska Kielbasa, Summer Sausage

Boar's Head - All Varieties

Busseto - Coppa (Dry, Hot), Dry Salami (Black Pepper, Italian, Rosette De Lyon), Herbs De Providence, Pepper Coated Salami, Premium Genoa Salami

Butcher's Cut - Beef Smoked Sausage, Bratwurst, Breakfast, Bun Length (Beef Franks, Meat Franks), Italian Sausage (Mild, Regular), Jumbo Franks (Chicken, Pork, Turkey), Polska Kielbasa

Butterball -
Premium Turkey Franks (Bun Size, Jumbo, Regular)
Turkey Sausage
    Dinner (Polska Kielbasa, Smoked)
    Fresh (Bratwurst, Breakfast, Hot Italian, Sweet Italian)
Smoked (Cheddar, Hot, Regular)

Canino's - Bratwurst ●, Breakfast Sausage ●, German Brand Sausage ●, Hot Chorizo ●, Hot Italian Sausage ●, Mild Italian Sausage ●, Polish Sausage ●, Spicy Cajun Style Sausage ●, Sweet Italian Sausage ●

Castle Wood Reserve - Deli Meat (Genoa Salami, Hard Salami)

Coleman's Natural Foods -
All Natural Uncured (Beef Hot Dog ●, Beef/Pork Franks ●), Chicken Sausage (Mild Italian ●, Spicy Andouille ●, Spicy Chipotle ●, Spicy Chorizo ●, Spicy Italian ●, Spinach & Feta Cheese ●, Sun Dried Tomato & Basil ●)
Fully Cooked Bratwurst ●
Organic Chicken Sausage (Mild Italian ●, Spinach & Feta ●, Sun Dried Tomato & Basil ●, Sweet Apple ●)
Polish Kielbasa ●

S

Columbus Salame - Deli Meat (All Varieties), Salame (All Varieties)
Di Lusso - Beef Summer
Dietz & Watson▲ -
    Abruzzese (Hot ●, Sweet ●)
    Baby Genoa (Pepper Salame ●, Salame ●)
    Beef Hot ●,
    Beef Franks (Deli ●, Foot Long ●, Frankfurters ●, Gourmet Lite ●
        Mini Cocktail ●, New York Brand ●, New York Griddle ●)
    Beef Franks New York Deli *(Except Fat Free And Gourmet Lite)*●
    Beef Summer Sausage ●
    Beerwurst ●
    Black Forest (Bauernwurst ●, Bratwurst ●, Cooked Fresh Liver
        Ring ●, Hungarian Brand Bratwurst ●, Wieners ●)
    Black Forest Wieners ●
    Blood Kiska ●
    Blutwurst ●
    Bologna (Beef ●, Regular ●, Ring ●)
    Cacciatore ●
    Capocolla (Hot ●, Sweet ●)
    Cheddarwurst ●
    Cheese Franks w/Bacon ●
    Chicken (Andouille ●, Brats ●, Buffalo Style ●, Italian ●, Jerk ●, Pepper
        & Onion Sausage ●)
    Cooked Salami ●
    Deli Franks ●
    Deluxe Loaf ●
    Gourmet Lite Franks ●
    Honey Roll ●
    Italian ●
    Jalapeno Peppers Cheese Franks ●
    Knockwurst ●
    Krakow ●
    Landjaeger ●
    Lunch Roll ●

Mini Chorizo ●
Mortadella (Regular ●, w/Pistachios ●)
Natural Casing Knockwurst ●
Olive Loaf ●
P & P Loaf ●
Pancetta ●
Panino (Buffalo Cheese ●, Pizzaz ●, Proseiutto ●, Salame ●, Toasted Onion Cheese ●)
Pepper Loaf ●
Pepperoni ●
Pickle & Pimiento Loaf ●
Polska Kielbasa ●
Pork Roll Grillin' Links ●
Salame (Hard ●, Hot & Zesty ●, Milano Paper Wrap ●, Mini ●)
Smoked (Hot ●, Mild ●)
Sopressata (Hot ●, Sweet ●)
South Philly Style Pepper & Onion ●
Super Franks ●
Twin Stick Pepperoni ●
Eckrich -
Angus Beef
Beef Franks (Jumbo, Regular)
Breakfast Smoky Links (Beef, Cheese, Jalapeno & Cheddar, Lite, Maple, Original)
Bun Length Original
Country Fresh Roll Sausage
Deli Meat (Hard Salami (Reduced Fat, Regular), Pepperoni Regular, Regular Summer Sausage, Salami (Cotto, Genoa))
Franks (Bun Sized Beef, Jumbo Cheese, Regular Lite)
Grillers Smoked Sausage (Cheese, Original, Polish)
Li'l Smokies
Lunch Meat
Pepperoni, Salami (Cotto, Hard)
Original Meat Franks (Bun Sized, Franks, Jumbo)

S

Polska Kielbasa
Skinless Turkey
Smoked Sausage (Beef, Regular)
XL Skinless Angus Beef

Empire Kosher - Chicken Franks, Roll (Turkey Bologna, Turkey Salami), Turkey Franks

Fairgrounds - Hot Dogs w/Chicken & Pork, Jumbo Hot Dogs

Farmer John -

Breakfast Sausage Links & Patties (Old Fashioned Maple Skinless, Original Roll, Original Skinless, Premium PC Links Lower Fat, Premium Sausage Patties Lower Fat)

California Natural Chicken Sausage (Chicken Brat Smoked, Mango & Habanero Smoked)

Dinner Sausage (Beef Rope, Classic Polish, Hot Louisiana Smoked, Jalapeno Pepper Premium Smoked, Mild Jalapeno Pepper Premium Rope, Premium Beef Rope, Red Hots Extra Hot Premium Smoked)

Franks & Wieners Classic Beef Franks (Regular, w/Sharp Cheddar Cheese), Dodger Dogs, Premium Beef Franks, Premium Jumbo Beef Franks, Premium Jumbo Meat Wieners, Premium Meat Wieners, Lemon Cracked Pepper Chicken Smoked

Five Star Brand - Beef Franks Mild, Bratwurst, Cooked Salami, Garlic Knockwurst, German Franks (Hot, Mild), Head Cheese, Jumbo Beef Wieners, Natural Casing Less Salt Kielbasa, Pepperoni Sticks, Prasky, Beef Wieners, Wieners (Low Salt, Regular), Skinless Beef Kielbasa, Slovenian Franks, Smoked Bratwurst

Fratelli Beretta - Big Sopressata, Bresaola, Cacciatorino, Coppa, Dry Sausage, Milano, Mortadella, Nostrano, Pancetta, Sopressata

Garrett County Farms - Andouille Sausage!, Chorizo Sausage!, Franks (4XL Big Beef!, Chicken!, Old Fashioned Beef!, Original Deli!, Premium Beef!, Turkey!), Kielbasa (Polska!, Turkey!), Sliced Beef (Bologna!, Salami!), Sliced Uncured Pepperoni!

Giant Eagle Brand -

Breakfast Sausage (Fully Cooked Patties, Links (Brown & Serve, Maple, Original))

Patties Original
Roll (Hot, Regular, Sage)
Polska Kielbasa (Beef, Links, Pork & Beef)
Pork & Beef Smoked Sausage
Smoked Sausage Links (Cheese, Chili, Cheese & Onion, Jalapeno & Cheese)

Gordon Food Service -
Franks (3 Meat (Cocktail, Classic, Footlong), Beef & Pork (Coney, Natural, Regular), Beef (Angus, Mini, Regular))
Sausage Links (Buffet (Coarse, Regular), Cheddar & Peppercorn, Cooked (Skinless, w/Casing, Zesty), Italian Link, Maple (Cooked Skinless, Regular), Kielbasa, Polish, Pork (Pure, Skinless), Smokey)
Sausage Patties (Cooked, Maple, Regular)
Smoked (Cocktail, Regular, Rope)

Great Value Brand (Wal-Mart) - Breakfast (Beef Breakfast Patties, Fully Cooked Pork Links, Fully Cooked Turkey Breakfast Patties, Maple Pork Patties, Original Pork Patties), Canned Vienna Sausage

Habbersett - Pork Sausage (Hearty Link, Links), Pork Sausage Roll, Quick 'N Easy (Sausage Links, Sausage Patties)

Hannaford Brand - Hot Dogs (Beef Franks, Weiners), Pepperoni

Hans All Natural - Breakfast Links (Organic Chicken ●, Skinless Chicken ●), Chicken Sausage (Spinach & Feta ●, Spinach Fontina & Garlic ●, Sun Dried Tomato Provolone ●)

Hargis House - Chicken Vienna

Heaven Mills▲ - Kishka (Cholent ●, Vegetable ●)

Hebrew National - Franks Quarter Pound Beef

Hertel's - All Original Fresh Sausages (*Except British Bangers*)

Hillshire Farms -
Cheddar Wurst
Links (Beef Hot, Beef Smoked, Cheddar Wurst, Hot, Hot & Spicy Italian Smoked, Polska Kielbasa, Smoked Bratwurst)
Lit'l (Beef Franks, Polskas, Smokies (Beef, Cheddar, Regular, Turkey Breast), Wieners))

S

Polska Kielbasa (Beef, Lite, Regular, Turkey)
Smoked Bratwurst
Smoked Sausage (Beef, Hardwood Chicken, Hot, Italian Style, Lite, Regular, Turkey)
Summer Sausage (Beef, Regular, Yard O Beef)

Honeysuckle White -
Hardwood Smoked Turkey Franks
Hickory Smoked Cooked Turkey Salami
Turkey Sausage
    Breakfast (Links, Patties)
    Chipotle Seasoned Links
    Fully Cooked Smoked (Chipotle, Original Links, Original Rope, Polish Rope)
    Italian (Hot Links, Sweet Links)
    Mild Italian Roll
    Poblano Pepper Links
    Tomato & Garlic Links
    Traditional Bratwurst

Hormel -
Bread Ready (Deli Pastrami, Hard Salami)
Crumbled
Hard Salami
Little Sizzlers (Links, Patties)
Natural Choice (Hard Salami, Pepperoni)
Pepperoni
Smokies
Turkey Pepperoni
Wranglers Franks (Beef, Cheese, Smoked)

Hy-Vee - Beef, Beef Summer, Cooked Salami, Little Smokies (Beef, Regular), Pepperoni, Summer Sausage, Thin Sliced Pastrami

Ian's - Wheat Free Gluten Free Recipe Popcorn Turkey Corn Dogs

Jennie-O Turkey Store -
Breakfast Lover's Turkey Sausage
Extra Lean Smoked Turkey Sausage (Kielbasa, Regular)

Fresh
> Breakfast Sausage (Maple Links, Mild Links, Mild Patties)
> Dinner Sausage (Hot Italian, Lean Turkey Bratwurst, Sweet Italian)
> Lean Turkey Patties
Frozen Fully Cooked Sausage (Links, Patties)
Turkey Franks

Jimmy Dean -
> Fully Cooked Crumbles (Hot Hearty, Original Hearty, Turkey Hearty)
> Fully Cooked Links (Maple, Original, Turkey)
> Fully Cooked Patties (Hot, Maple, Original, Sandwich Size, Turkey)
> Heat 'N Serve Sausage Patties
> Heat 'N Serve Sausage Links (Hot, Maple, Regular)
> Maple Fresh Sausage (Links, Patties)
> Original Fresh Sausage (Links, Patties)
> Pork Roll Sausage (All Natural Regular, Hot, Italian, Light, Maple, Mild Country, Regular, Sage)

Johnsonville -
Beddar w/Cheddar
BOLD (Beef Hot Links, Chili Cheese, Jalapeno & Cheese),
Bratwurst (Beef, Cheddar, Hot 'N Spicy, Original, Patties, Smoked, Stadium Style)
Breakfast (Brown Sugar & Honey Links, Mild Country Sausage Roll, Original (Links, Patties), Vermont Maple Syrup (Links, Patties), Wisconsin Cheddar Cheese Links)
Chorizo
Irish O'Garlic
Italian Ground Sausage (Hot, Mild, Sweet)
Italian Links (Four Cheese, Hot, Mild, Sweet)
New Orleans
Polish
Sausage Roll (Hot, Regular)

S

Smoked Turkey

Summer Sausage (Beef, Deli Bites (Beef, Original, Salami),
Garlic, Old World, Original)

Turkey w/Cheddar

Jones Dairy Farm -

All Natural (Hearty Pork Sausage Links ●, Light Pork Sausage &
Rice Links ●, Little Link Pork Sausage ●, Maple Sausage Links ●,
Original Pork Roll Sausage ●, Pork Sausage Patties ●)

Golden Brown All Natural Fully Cooked

Beef Links ●

Maple Sausage (Links ●, Patties ●)

Mild Sausage (Links ●, Patties ●)

Pork & Uncured Bacon Links ●

Sausage & Rice Links ●

Spicy Links ●

Turkey Links ●

Kayem - Bratwurst (Cheddar, Original), Franks Beef Fenway Style,
Beef Hot Dogs, Beef Minis, Fenway Style, Hot Dogs, Jumbo Beef
Hot Dogs, Jumbo Hot Dogs, Lower Sodium Hot Dogs, Minis, Old
Tyme (Natural Casing, Natural Casing Beef, Natural Casing Reds),
Skinnies, Kielbasa (Fresh, Old World Style, Polish), Natural (4
Pepper Hot Italian, Sweet Italian)

Kroger Brand -

Hot Dogs, Links (Maple Flavored Breakfast, Seasoned Brown Sugar
& Honey)

Maple Flavored Pork Sausage Patties

Pepperoni (Regular, Turkey)

Salami (Hard Sliced, Italian Dry Sliced)

Vienna (Barbecue, Chicken, Original)

Kroger Value - Cooked Salami, Country, Hot Dogs, Old Fashioned
Loaf, P&P Loaf, Smoked Sausage

Lightlife - Tofu Pups

Lou's Famous - Chicken Sausage (Aged Provolone, Apple, Artichoke
& Calamata, Feta Cheese & Spinach, Peppers & Onion, Roasted
Red Pepper & Garlic, Spicy Italian, Sundried Tomato)

Malone's - Vienna Sausages

Maluma - All Bison Sausage

Member's Mark - Chicken Sausage (Gourmet Chicken & Apple, Mozzarella & Roasted Garlic, Spinach Asiago, Sundried Tomato w/Provolone Cheese)

Mulay's - Ground Sausage (Breakfast ●, Mild Italian ●, Original ●, Original Italian ●), Links (Breakfast ●, Killer Hot ●, Mild Italian ●, Original ●, Original Italian ●)

Nature's Promise - Chicken (Mild Italian, Spiced Apple, Spinach & Feta, Sun Dried Tomato & Basil), Pork (Italian Spicy, Red Pepper & Provolone)

Old Wisconsin -
    Grilling Sausages (Festive Bratwurst, Natural Casing Wieners, Polish Kielbasa, Smoked Sausage w/Cheddar)
    Hand Tied Summer Sausage (Beef, Beef Garlic, Garlic, Original)
    Liver Sausage
    Snack Bites (Beef, Pepp, Turkey)
    Snack Sticks (Beef, Beef Sausage & Cheddar, Pepp, Turkey)
    Summer Sausage (Beef, Beef Garlic, Garlic, Original, Party)

Organic Prairie -
    Frozen Organic (Beef Hot Dogs, Bratwurst, Breakfast Sausage, Brown N Serve Breakfast Links, Italian Sausage)
    Organic Pork Fresh (Classic Hot Dogs, Sliced Pepperoni)
    Organic Poultry Fresh (Chicken Hot Dogs, Turkey Hot Dogs)

Oscar Mayer -
    Beef Franks (Bun Length, Classic, Light, Premium)
    Cheese Dogs
    Premium Franks (Beef & Cheddar, Jalapeno & Cheddar)
    Salami (Cotto, Deli Fresh Beef, Hard)
    Summer Sausage (Beef, Regular)
    Turkey Franks (Bun Length, Cheese Franks, Classic)
    Variety Pak Bologna/Ham/Salami
    Wieners (98 % Fat Free, Bun Length, Classic, Light, Premium)
    XXL Hot Dogs (Deli Style Beef, Hot & Spicy, Premium Beef)

S

Perdue - Deli Turkey (Bologna, Salami), Turkey Sausage Seasoned
Fresh Lean (Hot Italian, Sweet Italian)

Primo - Hot Italian, Mild Italian, Old World Bratwurst

Primo Naturale -
Chorizo (Sliced Dried, Stick Dried)
Chub Salami (Genoa, Original, w/Black Pepper, w/Herbs)
Pepperoni (Pillow Pack, Sliced Dried, Stick, Whole Large Diameter)
Sliced Salami (Hard, Original, Premium Genoa, w/Black Pepper,
w/Herbs)
Sopressata (Sliced, Sticks, Whole)
Whole Chorizo
Whole Salami (Black Pepper, Genoa, Hard, Herb, Original)

Primo Taglio - Pepperoni, Salami (Cervelat, Genoa, Peppered
Coated w/Gelatin & Black Pepper), Sopressata

Private Selections - Bratwurst (Cheddar, Hot Italian, Mild Italian,
Sausage, Sweet Italian), Frozen Mild Country Patties, Maple
Flavored Links

Publix - Beef Hot Dogs, Deli Pre Pack Sliced Hard Salami Reduced
Fat, Franks (Beef, Jumbo Beef, Jumbo Meat, Meat), Fresh (Bratwurst,
Chorizo, Italian (Hot, Mild), Turkey Italian (Hot, Mild)), Pepperoni

Pure Market Express▲ - Sausage ●

Rocky Jr. - Rocky Dogs Uncured Chicken Hot Dog ●

Safeway Brand - Beef Franks, Bratwurst, Hot Dogs, Pepperoni, Polish

Safeway Select - Country Pork (Hot, Regular), Italian, Regular Hot Dogs

Shelton's -
Franks (Smoked Chicken, Smoked Turkey, Uncured Chicken)
Turkey Sausage (Breakfast, Italian, Patties)
Turkey Sticks (Pepperoni, Regular)
Uncured Turkey

Smithfield -
Breakfast Sausage (Hot Pork Roll, Mild Pork Roll, Pork Links, Pork
Patties)
Smoked Sausage
Hickory Smoke Loops (Hickory Smoke, Beef, Polska, Original)
Links (Hot, Regular, w/Cheese)

S

Spartan Brand - Hot, Mild
Sweet Bay - All Fresh Sausage
Thumann's - All Varieties ●
Trader Joe's - All Sausage, Sliced Prosciutto, Uncured All Beef Hot Dogs
Wegmans Brand -
 Beef Hot Dogs Skinless
 Cocktail Hot Dogs Skinless Frankfurters
 Pepperoni Italian Style (Regular, Sliced, Tangy With A Hint Of Red
  Pepper)
 Red Hot Dogs Skinless (Lite, Regular)
 Uncured Skinless (Beef Hot Dogs, Hot Dogs)
Wellshire Farms -
 Beef Franks Hot Dogs (4XL Big**!!**, The Old Fashioned**!!**, The
  Premium**!!**)
 Cheese Franks**!!**
 Cocktail Franks**!!**
 Frozen
  Chicken Apple Sausage (Links**!!**, Patties**!!**)
  Original Breakfast Sausage (Links**!!**, Patties**!!**)
  Sunrise Maple Sausage (Links**!!**, Patties**!!**)
  Turkey (Burgers**!!**, Maple Sausage Links**!!**, Maple Sausage
   Patties**!!**)
 Morning Maple Turkey Breakfast Link Sausage**!!**
 Polska Kielbasa**!!**
 Pork Andouille Sausage**!!**
 Pork Sausage (Chorizo**!!**, Linguica**!!**)
 Sliced (Beef Pepperoni**!!**, Beef Salami**!!**)
 The Original Deli Franks**!!**
 Turkey
  Andouille Sausage**!!**
  Dinner Link Sausage Mild Italian Style**!!**
  Franks**!!**
  Kielbasa**!!**
  Tom Toms (Hot & Spicy**!!**, Original**!!**)

S

Winn Dixie - Hot Dogs (Chicken, Jumbo Beef, Meat Franks, Turkey, w/Cheese & Chicken), Pepperoni, Smoked Sausage (Hot, Original, Polish, Polish Kielbasa, Turkey, w/Cheddar Cheese)

Scallops

... *All Fresh Seafood Is Gluten-Free (Non-Marinated, Unseasoned)*

Whole Catch - Sea Scallops

Scones/Scone Mix

Breakaway Bakery▲ - Lemon Raisin Scone Dough ●, Orange Cranberry Scone Dough ●

Cause You're Special▲ - English Scone Mix

Gluten Free Mama▲ - Mama's Scone Mix ●

Gluten Free Pantry▲ - Muffin & Scone Mix

Silly Yak Bakery -

GF Scone Mix●

GF Scones (Almond Joy ●, Apple Walnut ●, Apricot ●, Blackberry ●, Blueberry ●, Cherry Chocolate ●, Chocolate Raspberry ●, Coffee Chocolate Chip ●, Cranberry Orange ●, Lemon Blueberry ●, Lemon Cream ●, Lemon Poppy Seed ●, Maple Walnut ●, Mixed Berry ●, Oatmeal Blueberry ●, Oatmeal Raisin ●, Peach ●, Peanut Butter Chocolate ●, Pineapple Coconut ●, Pumpkin ●, Raspberry ●)

Simply Organic▲ - Chai Spice Scone Mix

Whole Foods Market Gluten Free Bakehouse▲ - Scones (Almond, Cranberry Orange)

Seafood Sauce ... see also Cocktail Sauce

Food Club Brand - Cocktail Sauce

Frontera - Cocktail & Ceviche Sauce (Cilantro Lime, Tomato Chipotle)

Giant Brand - Seafood Cocktail Sauce

Heinz - Cocktail Sauce

Kroger Brand - Cocktail Sauce

Laura Lynn - Cocktail

Mayacamas - Seafood Pasta Skillet Toss Mix

McCormick -
  Cajun
  Lemon Butter Dill (Fat Free, Regular)
  Lemon
  Herb
  Mediterranean
  Original Cocktail Sauce
  Santa Fe Style
  Scampi
Safeway Brand - Cocktail
Simply Delicious - Organic Seafood Sauce w/Lemon
Spartan Brand - Cocktail Sauce
Stop & Shop Brand - Seafood Cocktail Sauce
Texas Pete - Seafood Cocktail
Trader Joe's - Seafood Cocktail Sauce**!!**
Walden Farms
Seasoning Packets... see Seasonings
Seasonings
  Accent - Flavor Enhancer (All Varieties)
  Adolph's - Original Tenderizer**!!**, Tenderizer Seasoned w/Spices**!!**
  Albertsons - Bay Leaves, Black Pepper, Chili Powder, Cinnamon,
    Garlic Powder, Garlic Salt, Ginger, Nutmeg, Onion, Onion Powder,
    Paprika, Parsley Flakes, Seasoned Salt
  American Natural & Organic Spices -
    Natural (Adobo Seas Sf ●, All Purpose ●, Allspice Ground ●, Allspice
      Whole ●, Anise Ground ●, Anise Star Whole ●, Anise Whole●,
      Annatto Ground ●, Annatto Seed ●, Apple Pie Spice ●,
      Arrowroot●, Baharat Sf ●, Barbeque Sf ●, Basil ●, Beef Burger
      Sf●, Bouquet Garni Sf ●, Cajun Seasoning ●, Caraway Seeds ●,
      Cardamom Decorticated ●, Cardamom Ground ●, Cardamom
      Pods Green ●, Cayenne Pepper ●, Celery Ground ●, Celery Salt●,
      Celery Seeds●, Chicken Kabob Sf ●, Chili Ancho Ground ●, Chili
      California Ground ●, Chili Chipotle Ground Chili Con Carne
      Sf●, Chili Guajillo Ground ●, Chili Habanero Ground ●, Chili

S

Jalapeno Ground ●, Chili New Mexico Ground ●, Chili Pepper Crushed●, Chili Pepper Whole ●, Chili Powder ●, Chimichurri Seas Sf ●, Chinese Five Spice Sf ●, Chives ●, Cilantro Flakes ●, Cinnamon Ground ●, Cinnamon Sticks ●, Cloves Ground ●, Cloves Whole●, Coriander Ground ●, Coriander Seeds ●, Cream Of Tartar ●, Cumin Ground ●, Cumin Seed Whole ●, Curry Powder Hot ●, Curry Powder Salt Free ●, Curry Powder ●, Curry Thai Red Salt Free ●, Dill Seed ●, Dill Weed ●, Dukka Seasoning●, Epazote ●, Fajita Seasoning Sf ●, Fennel Ground ●, Fennel Seeds●, Fenugreek (Ground ●, Seeds ●), Fines Herbes Sf ●, Fish Grill & Broil Sf ●, Flaxseed ●, French Four Spice Sf ●, Galangal●, Garam Masala ●, Garlic (Bread ●, Granulates ●, Herbs ●, Minced●, Pepper ●, Sliced●, Toasted ●), Ginger Ground ●, Greek Seasoning Sf ●, Gumbo File ●, Harisa Sf ●, Herbs De Provence●, Horseradish Powder ●, Italian Seasoning ●, Jerk Seasoning Sf●, Juniper Berries●, Lamb Seasoning Sf ●, Lavender ●, Lemon (Grass ●, Peel●, Pepper ●), Mace Ground ●, Marjoram (Ground●, Whole●), Meatloaf Seasoning Sf ●, Mediterranean Seas Sf●, Mexican Seasoning Sf ●, Mint (Peppermint ●, Spearmint ●), Mulling Spice Blend ●, Mustard (Ground ●, Seeds Brown ●, Seeds Yellow ●), Nigella Seed ●, Nutmeg (Ground ●, Whole●), Onion Granulates●, Orange Peel ●, Oregano (Ground●, Mediterranean●, Mexican ●)

Organic (Allspice (Ground ●, Whole ●), Almond Extract ●, Anise Star Whole ●, Basil ●, Bay Leave Whole ●, Cajun Seasoning ●, Caraway Seeds ●, Cardamom (Green ●, Ground ●, Original●), Cayenne Pepper ●, Celery Seeds ●, Chili (Ancho Ground ●, Chipotle Ground ●, Pepper Crush ●, Powder ●), Chinese Five Spice ●, Cinnamon (Ground ●, Sticks ●), Cloves (Ground ●, Whole ●), Coriander (Ground ●, Seeds ●), Cumin Ground ●, Cumin Seeds Whole ●, Curry (Powder ●, Thai Herb ●), Dill Weed●, Fennel Seeds ●, Garam Masala ●, Garlic Granulates ●, Ginger Ground ●, Herbs De Provence ●, Italian Season ●, Juniper Berries ●, Lemon Extract ●, Marjoram Whole ●, Melange Pepper●,

Mexican Seasoning ●, Mustard (Ground ●, Seed Brown ●, Seed Yellow ●), Nutmeg (Ground ●, Whole ●), Onion Granulates ●, Orange Extract ●, Oregano Mediterranean ●, Panch Phoron Sf ●, Paprika (Regular ●, Smoked ●), Parsley ●, Pasta Spaghetti Sf ●, Pepper Black Long ●, Pepper Ground (Black ●, White ●), Peppercorn (Black ●, Green ●, Melange ●, Melody ●, Pink ●, Szechuan ●, White ●), Pickling Seasoning ●, Pizza Spice Sf ●, Poppy Seeds ●, Pork Chop Sf ●, Poultry Seasoning ●, Pumpkin Pie Spice ●, Rosemary Whole ●, Saffron ●, Sage (Ground ●, Rubbed ●, Whole ●), Sesame (Seed Black ●, Seed White ●), Tarragon ●, Thyme ●, Turmeric ●, Vanilla Extract ●), Ras El Hanout Sf ●, Rib Eye Steak Sf ●, Rice Seasoning Sf ●, Rosemary (Ground●, Whole ●), Safflower ●, Saffron ●, Sage (Ground ●, Rubbed ●, Whole ●), Sambal Ulek Sf ●, Savory Ground ●, Savory ●, Sesame Seed (Black ●, White ●), Shawarma Seas Sf ●, Shish Kabob Sf ●, Shrimp/Crab Gr&Bl Sf ●, Sumac ●, Taco Seasoning Sf ●, Tandoori Masala Sf ●, Tarragon ●, Thai Spice Blend Sf ●, Thyme Ground●, Thyme ●, Tsatsiki Greek Yogurt ●, Turmeric ●, Vanilla (Bean ●, Extract ●), Vegetable Seas Sf ●, Vindaloo Seasoning Sf ●, Wasabi Powder Sf ●, Zatar Sf ●

Arora Creations - Organic Seasoning Packets (Bhindi Masala, Chicken Tikka Masala, Goan Shrimp Curry, Gobi, Punjabi Chole, Rajmah, Tandoori Chicken), Regular Seasoning Packets (Bhindi Masala, Chicken Tikka Masala, Goan Shrimp Curry, Gobi, Punjabi Chole, Rajmah, Tandoori Chicken)

Bone Suckin' Sauce - Seasoning & Rub (Hot, Regular)

Bragg - Sea Kelp Delight, Sprinkle Seasoning

Cali Fine Foods▲ - Gourmet Seasoning Packets (Dill Delight ●, Garlic Gusto ●, Herb Medley ●, Spicy Fiesta ●, Sweet & Spicy BBQ●)

Chef Paul Prudhommes Magic - All Seasoning Blends *(Except Breading Magic & Gumbo Gravy Magic)*

Chi-Chi's - Fiesta Restaurante Seasoning Mix

Dave's Gourmet - Insanity Spice

Dorothy Lane Market - Grilling & Seasoning Rub

S

Durkee - All Food Coloring, All Liquid Extracts, All Liquid Flavorings, All Pepper Black/White, Allspice, Alum, Anise Seed, Apple Pie Spice, Arrowroot, Basil, Bay Leaves, Caraway Seed, Cardamom, Cayenne Pepper, Celery Flakes, Celery Seed, Chicken & Rib Rub, Chicken Seasoning, Chili Powder, Chives, Cilantro, Cinnamon, Cloves, Coriander, Crazy Dave's Lemon Pepper, Crazy Dave's Pepper & Spice, Crazy Dave's Salt & Spice, Cream Of Tartar, Crushed Red Pepper, Cumin, Curry Powder, Dill Seed/Weed, Fennel, Garlic Minced, Garlic Pepper, Garlic Powder, Garlic Salt, Ginger, Hickory Smoke Salt, Italian Seasoning, Jamaican Jerk Seasoning, Lemon & Herb, Lemon Peel, Lemon Pepper, Lime Pepper, Mace, Marjoram, Meat Tenderizer, Mint Leaves, Mr. Pepper, MSG, Mustard, Nutmeg, Onion Minced, Onion Powder, Onion Salt, Orange Peel, Oregano, Oriental 5-Spice, Paprika, Parsley, Pepper Green Bell, Pickling Spice, Pizza Seasoning, Poppy Seed, Poultry Seasoning, Pumpkin Pie Spice, Rosemary, Rosemary Garlic Seasoning, Sage, Salt Free Garden Seasoning, Salt Free Garlic & Herb, Salt Free Lemon Pepper, Salt Free Original All Purpose Seasoning, Salt Free Vegetable Seasoning, Seasoned Pepper, Sesame Seed, Six Pepper Blend, Smokey Mesquite Seasoning, Spaghetti/Pasta Seasoning, Spicy Spaghetti Seasoning, Steak Seasoning, Tarragon, Thyme, Turmeric

Durkee California Style Blends - Garlic Powder, Garlic Salt, Onion Powder, Onion Salt

Emeril's - Bam It Salad Seasoning, Essence (Bayou Blast, Garlic Parmesan, Italian, Original, Southwest), Rub (Chicken, Steak, Turkey), Rubs (Fish, Rib)

Food Club Brand - Allspice Whole, Alum Granulated, Cajun Spice, California Style (Garlic Powder, Garlic Salt, Onion Powder), Cayenne Pepper, Celery Salt, Chili Powder (Regular, Texas Style), Chives Chopped, Cilantro Leaves, Cinnamon (& Sugar, Ground, Sticks), Cumin Ground, Curry Powdered, Dill Weed, Fried Chicken Spice, Garlic (Bread Spice Sprinkle, Minced, Pepper, Powder, Salt), Grilling Seasoning (Chicken, Seafood, Steak), Grinder

(Black Pepper, Pepper Medley, Sea Salt), Italian Seasoning, Meat Tenderizer (Non Seasoned, Seasoned, Unseasoned), Mustard (Ground, Seed), Nutmeg Ground, Onion (Chopped, Minced, Powder), Oregano Leaves, Paprika, Parsley Flakes, Pepper Black, Pepper & Lemon Seasoning, Peppercorns, Pickling Spice, Pumpkin Pie Spice, Red Crushed Pepper, Rosemary, Salad Seasoning w/Cheese, Salt (Iodized, Plain, Seasoned), Seasoning Mix (Alfredo Sauce, Spaghetti Sauce w/Mushrooms, Taco), Thyme (Crushed, Ground), Turmeric Ground

Full Circle - All Varieties

Gaylord Hauser - Spice Garden Herbs & Spices (All Varieties), Spike Magic (5 Herb, Garlic, Hot N Spicy, Onion, Original, Salt Free, Vegit)

Grandma Ferdon's ▲ - Caraway Seeds ●, Chili Powder ●, Garlic Flakes ●, Ground (Allspice ●, Black Peppercorns ●, Cinnamon ●, Cloves ●, Coriander ●, Ginger ●, Nutmeg ●), Italian ●, Lemon Peel Granules ●, Onion Flakes ●, Onion Powder ●, Paprika ●, Pure Spices Basil Leaves ●, Taco Seasoning Mix ●, Whole Marjoram ●, Whole Thyme ●,

Hannaford Brand - Basil Leaves, Bay Leaves, Celery Salt, Chili Powder, Crushed Red Pepper, Garlic Powder, Garlic Salt, Ground Black Pepper, Ground Cinnamon, Ground Ginger, Ground Mustard, Ground Nutmeg, Minced Onion, Oregano Leaves, Paprika, Taco Seasoning Mix

Hy-Vee - Basil Leaf, Bay Leaves, Black Pepper, Chicken Grill Seasoning, Chili Powder, Chopped Onion, Dill Weed, Garlic Powder, Garlic Salt, Grinders (Black Peppercorn, Peppercorn Melange, Sea Salt), Ground Cinnamon, Ground Cloves, Ground Mustard, Iodized Salt, Italian Seasoning, Lemon Pepper, Meat Tenderizer, Oregano Leaf, Paprika, Parsley Flakes, Plain Salt, Red Crushed Pepper, Rosemary, Salt & Pepper Shaker, Seasoned Salt, Steak Grilling Seasoning, Thyme

Kirkland Signature - California Garlic, Chopped Onion, Cinnamon, Garlic Salt, Malabar Black Pepper, Organic No Salt, Sea Salt

S

(Mediterranean Grinder, Pure), Sweet Mesquite, Tellicherry Pepper (Grinder, Whole Peppercorns)

Kernel Season's - Popcorn Seasoning (Barbecue, Butter, Cajun, Chili Lime, Jalapeno, Nacho Cheddar, Parmesan & Garlic, Ranch, Sour Cream & Onion, White Cheddar)

Konriko▲ - Chipotle All Purpose Seasoning ●, Creole Seasoning ●

Kootenay Kitchen - Traditional Gomashio

Kroger Brand - Popcorn (Nacho Cheese, White Cheddar), Seasoning Mixes (Chicken, Enchilada, Guacamole, Pork Chop, Stir Fry Oriental, Swiss Steak, Taco)

Kroger Value - All Varieties

Laura Lynn - Black Pepper, Steak Seasoning

Lawry's - Garlic Pepper **!!**, Garlic Powder **!!**, Garlic Salt **!!**, Lemon Pepper **!!**, Salt Free 17 **!!**, Seasoned Pepper **!!**, Seasoned Salt (25% Less Sodium **!!**, Black Pepper **!!**, Regular **!!**)
Seasoning Mixes (Chicken Fajitas **!!**, Chicken Taco **!!**, Chimichurri Burrito Casserole **!!**, Extra Thick & Rich Spaghetti Sauce **!!**, Fajitas **!!**, Guacamole **!!**, Mediterranean Sundried Tomato & Garlic Chicken **!!**, Original Style Spaghetti Sauce **!!**, Sloppy Joes **!!**, Tenderizing Beef Marinade **!!**)

Litehouse - Dried (Basil, Chives, Cilantro, Dill, Garlic, Italian Herb Blend, Mushrooms, Oregano, Parsley, Poultry Herb Blend, Red Onion, Salad Herb Blend, Spring Onion)

Lowes Foods Brand - Black Pepper, Chili Powder, Cinnamon Ground, Garlic Powder, Paprika, Salt & Pepper Shaker Set, Steak Seasoning

Marcum Spices - Barbeque Pork Seasoning Mix, Basil, Bay Leaves, Black Peppercorn, Chicken Seasoning, Chili Powder, Chili Seasoning Mix, Cinnamon Sugar, Coarse Ground Black Pepper, Crushed Oregano, Crushed Red Pepper, Cumin, Garlic Pepper, Garlic Powder, Garlic Salt, Iodized Salt, Italian Seasoning, Lemon Pepper, Minced Onion, Onion Powder, Paprika, Parsley Flakes, Pure Ground Black Pepper, Pure Ground Cinnamon, Sea Salt, Seasoned Meat Tenderizer, Seasoned Salt, Soul Seasoning, Steak Seasonings, Taco Seasoning Mix, Whole Peppercorns

Mayacamas - Chicken BBQ, Curry Blend, Salad Delight, Savory Salt

McCormick -

Bag 'N Season (Chicken, Herb Roasted Pork Tenderloin, Pork Chops, Swiss Steak)

Blends (Bon Appetite, Cajun Seasoning, Celery Salt, Chinese Five Spice, Cocoa Chili, Curry Powder, Garam Masala, Garlic Salt, Greek Seasoning, Herbes De Provence, Hot Madras Curry Powder, Jamaican Jerk, Lemon & Pepper, Mediterranean Spiced Sea Salt, Poultry Seasoning, Poultry Seasoning, Red Curry Powder)

Gourmet Collection

100% Organic (Basil Leaves, Cayenne Red Pepper, Celery Seed, Chinese Ginger, Coarse Ground Black Peppercorn, Crushed Red Pepper, Crushed Rosemary, Curry Powder, Dill Weed, Fennel Seed, Garlic Powder, Ground Cloves, Ground Coriander Seed, Ground Cumin, Ground Mustard, Ground Nutmeg, Ground White Pepper, Herbes De Provence, Italian Seasoning, Marjoram Leaves, Oregano Leaves, Paprika, Parsley Flakes, Poppyseed, Rosemary Leaves, Rubbed Sage, Saigon Cinnamon, Sesame Seed, Tellicherry Black Peppercorns, Thyme Leaves, Turkish Basil Leaves)

Spices (California Lemon Peel, Caraway Seed, Cardamom Seed, Celery Seed, Chevril Leaves, Chipotle Chili Pepper, Chopped Chives, Cilantro Leaves, Cinnamon Stick, Coarse Ground Black Peppercorn, Coriander Seed, Cracked Black Pepper, Cream Of Tartar, Crushed Red Pepper, Crushed Rosemary, Crystallized Ginger, Cumin Seed, Cumin Seed, Diced Jalapeno Pepper, Dill Seed, Dill Weed, Fennel Seed, Garlic Powder, Green Peppercorns, Ground Allspice, Ground Cardamom, Ground Cayenne Red Pepper, Ground Cloves, Ground Coriander Seed, Ground Cumin, Ground Ginger, Ground Mace, Ground Marjoram, Ground Mediterranean Oregano, Ground Mustard, Ground Nutmeg, Ground Savory, Ground Thyme, Ground Turmeric, Ground White

Pepper, Italian Seasoning, Lemongrass, Madagascar Vanilla
Beans, Marjoram Leaves, Mediterranean Oregano Leaves,
Mexican Oregano Leaves, Mexican Style Chili Powder, Mint
Flakes, Onion Powder, Paprika, Parsley Flakes, Peppercorn
Melange, Poppyseed, Roasted Ground Coriander, Roasted
Ground Cumin, Roasted Ground Ginger, Roasted Saigon
Cinnamon, Rosemary Leaves, Rubbed Sage, Sage Leaves,
Saigon Cinnamon, Sesame Seed, Sicilian Sea Salt, Smoked
Paprika, Spanish Saffron, Tarragon Leaves, Tellicherry Black
Peppercorns, Thyme Leaves, Toasted Sesame Seed, Valencia
Orange Peel, Wasabi Powder, Whole Allspice, Whole Cloves,
Whole Nutmeg, Yellow Mustard Seed)

Grill Mates Marinade Packets (Brown Sugar Bourbon, Mexican
Fiesta)

Grill Mates Dry Rub (Applewood, Chicken, Pork, Seafood, Steak,
Sweet & Smoky)

Grill Mates Grinders (Montreal Chicken, Montreal Steak)

Grill Mates Seasoning Blends (25% Less Sodium Montreal
Chicken, 25% Less Sodium Montreal Steak, Barbecue, Garlic &
Onion Medley, Hamburger, Lemon Pepper w/Herbs, Mesquite,
Montreal Chicken, Montreal Steak, Roasted Garlic & Herb,
Smokehouse Maple, Spicy Montreal Steak)

Pure Orange

Roasting Rub (Cracked Peppercorn Herb, French Herb,
Savory Herb)

Seafood Rubs (Herb w/Lemon, Sweet Citrus & Spice Salmon)

Seafood Steamers (Garlic Butter, Lemon Garlic, Shrimp &
Crab Boil)

Seasoning Packets (Creamy Garlic Alfredo Sauce, Enchilada
Sauce Mix, Fajitas, Guacamole, Hickory Barbeque Buffalo
Wings, Honey Barbeque Chicken Glaze, Italian-Style Spaghetti,
One Dish (Homestyle Chicken & Mushroom, Salsa Chicken &
Rice), Pesto, Salsa, Sloppy Joes, Taco (30% Less Sodium, Chicken,
Hot, Mild, Original), Tex Mex Chili, Thick & Zesty Spaghetti
Sauce)

Slow Cookers (Barbeque Pulled Pork, Chicken Noodle Soup, Chili, Italian Herb Chicken)

Spices (Alum, Anise Seed, Apple Pie Spice, Basil Leaves, Bay Leaves, Black Peppercorns, Caraway Seed, Celery Flakes, Celery Salt, Celery Seed, Chives, Chopped Onions, Cilantro Leaves, Cinnamon Sticks, Cinnamon Sugar, Coarse Ground Black Pepper, Cream Of Tartar, Crushed Red Pepper, Cumin Seed, Curry Powder, Dill Seed, Dill Weed, Fennel Seed, Garlic & Italian Herb, Garlic Powder, Garlic Salt, Garlic w/Extra Virgin Olive Oil, Ground Allspice, Ground Black Pepper, Ground Cinnamon, Ground Cloves, Ground Cumin, Ground Ginger, Ground Mace, Ground Marjoram, Ground Mustard, Ground Nutmeg, Ground Oregano, Ground Red Pepper, Ground Sage, Ground Thyme, Ground White Pepper, Hot Mexican Style Chili Powder, Hot Shot Black & Red Pepper Blend, Italian Seasoning, Marjoram Leaves, Minced Garlic, Minced Onions, Mixed Pickling Spice, Mustard Seed, Onion Powder, Onion Salt, Oregano Leaves, Paprika, Parsley Flakes, Poppy Seed, Poultry Seasoning, Pumpkin Pie Spice, Roasted Garlic Blend, Rosemary Leaves, Rubbed Sage, Sesame Seed, Sliced Garlic, Smokehouse Ground Black Pepper, Tarragon Leaves, Texas Style Chili Powder, Thyme Leaves, Turmeric, Whole Allspice, Whole Cloves, Whole Mexican Oregano)

Veggie Steamers (Cheddar Cheese, Garlic & Basil)

Meijer Brand - Black Pepper, Chili Powder, Cinnamon, Garlic Powder, Garlic Salt, Mild Taco Seasoning Packet, Minced Onion, Onion Salt, Oregano Leaves, Paprika, Parsley Flakes, Seasoned Salt, Spaghetti Mix, Taco Seasoning Packet

Melissa's - Garlic In Pure Olive Oil

Midwest Country Fare - Chili Powder, Chopped Onion, Cinnamon, Garlic Powder, Garlic Salt, Ground Black Pepper, Italian, Onion Powder, Parsley Flakes, Pure Ground Black Pepper, Season Salt

Morton - Canning & Pickling Salt, Garlic Salt, Hot Salt, Lite Salt Mixture, Nature's Seasons Seasoning Blend, Popcorn Salt, Salt &

S

Pepper Shakers, Sausage & Meat Loaf Seasoning, Seasoned Salt, Smoke Flavored Sugar Cure, Sugar Cure, Tender Quick

Mrs. Dash - Caribbean Citrus, Extra Spicy, Fiesta Lime, Garlic & Herb, Grilling Blend (Chicken, Hamburger, Steak), Italian Medley, Lemon Pepper, Onion & Herb, Original Blend, Southwest Chipotle, Table Blend, Tomato Basil Garlic

Nantucket Off-Shore - Garden, Rub (Bayou, Dragon, Mt. Olympus, Nantucket, Prairie, Pueblo, Rasta, Renaissance), Shellfish Boil, St. Remy

Nielsen-Massey - Madagascar Bourbon Pure Vanilla Powder ●

Nuts Online - Chamomile Flowers ●, Garam Masala ●, Ground Sumac ●, Hibiscus Flowers ●, Mahlab ●, Mixed Syrian Spices ●, Spearmint ●, Whole Licorice Root ●

O Organics - Basil Leaves, Bay Leaves, Cayenne Peppers, Chili Powder, Ground Cinnamon, Ground Cloves, Ground Cumin, Ground Nutmeg, Paprika

Old Bay - 30% Less Sodium, Blackened Seasoning, Garlic & Herb, Lemon & Herb, Original, Rub, Seafood Steamer

Ortega - Guacamole Mix, Taco Seasoning Mix (40% Less Sodium, Chipotle, Hot & Spicy, Jalapeno & Onion, Original)

Para Micasa - Minced Garlic In Water

Polaner ▲ - Ready To Use Wet Spices (All Varieties)

Private Selections - All Varieties, Rubs (Asian, Kicked Up Poultry, Peppercorn, Sweet & Spicy)

Publix - Adobo Seasoning w/o Pepper, Adobo Seasoning w/Pepper, Black Pepper, Chili Powder, Cinnamon, Garlic Powder, Garlic Powder w/Parsley, Garlic Salt, Ground Cumin, Ground Ginger, Ground Red Pepper, Italian Seasonings, Lemon & Pepper, Minced Onion, Onion Powder, Paprika, Parsley Flakes, Salt, Seasoned Salt, Taco Seasoning Mix, Whole Basil Leaves, Whole Bay Leaves, Whole Oregano

Rancher's Reserve - Rubs (Classic Steak, Cowboy Blend w/Coffee, Roast)

Safeway Brand - All Spices & Seasonings, Fajita Seasoning Mix, Meat Marinade Mix

Sharwood's - Curry Powder (Hot, Medium, Mild)

Spartan Brand - Black Pepper, Brine Salt Black Sleeve, Chili Powder, Cinnamon, Garlic Powder, Garlic Salt, Ground Nutmeg, Imitation Vanilla, Iodized Salt, Iodized Salt Crystals, Minced Onion, Oregano Leaves, Paprika, Parsley Flakes, Salt, Vanilla Extract

Spice Islands - All Food Coloring, All Liquid Extracts, All Liquid Flavorings, All Pepper Black/White, All Steak Seasonings, Allspice, Alum, Anise Seed, Apple Pie Spice, Arrowroot, Basil, Bay Leaves, Caraway Seed, Cardamom, Cayenne Pepper, Celery Flakes, Celery Seed, Chicken & Rib Rub, Chicken Seasoning, Chili Powder, Chives, Cilantro, Cinnamon, Cloves, Coriander, Crazy Dave's Lemon Pepper, Crazy Dave's Pepper & Spice, Crazy Dave's Salt & Spice, Cream Of Tartar, Crushed Red Pepper, Cumin, Curry Powder, Dill Seed/Weed, Fennel, Garlic Minced, Garlic Pepper, Garlic Powder, Garlic Salt, Ginger, Hickory Smoke Salt, Italian Seasoning, Jamaican Jerk Seasoning, Lemon & Herb, Lemon Peel, Lemon Pepper, Lime Pepper, Mace, Marjoram, Meat Tenderizer, Mint Leaves, Mr. Pepper, MSG, Mustard, Nutmeg, Onion Minced, Onion Powder, Onion Salt, Orange Peel, Oregano, Oriental 5-Spice, Paprika, Parsley, Pepper Green Bell, Pickling Spice, Pizza Seasoning, Poppy Seed, Poultry Seasoning, Pumpkin Pie Spice, Rosemary, Rosemary Garlic Seasoning, Sage, Salt Free Garden Seasoning, Salt Free Garlic & Herb, Salt Free Lemon Pepper, Salt Free Original All Purpose Seasoning, Salt Free Veg. Seasoning, Seasoned Pepper, Sesame Seed, Six Pepper Blend, Smokey Mesquite Seasoning, Spaghetti/Pasta Seasoning, Spicy Spaghetti Seasoning, Tarragon, Thyme, Turmeric

Spice Islands Grilling Gourmet & World Flavors - All Varieties

Spice Islands Salt-Free - All Varieties

Spice Islands Specialty - Beau Monde, Crystallized Ginger, Fine Herbs, Garlic Pepper Seasoning, Italian Herb Seasoning, Old Hickory Smoked Salt, Saffron, Summer Savory, Vanilla Bean

Spicely▲ - 100% Certified Organic Extracts (All Varieties) ●, Natural Spices (All Varieties) ●, Organic Spices (All Varieties) ●, Seasoning Blends (All Varieties) ●

S

Stubb's - Spice Rub (Bar BQ ●, Burger ●, Chile Lime ●, Herbal Mustard ●, Rosemary Ginger ●)

Tones - All Food Coloring, All Liquid Extracts, All Liquid Flavorings, All Pepper Black/White, All Steak Seasonings, Allspice, Alum, Anise Seed, Apple Pie Spice, Arrowroot, Basil, Bay Leaves, Buttermilk Ranch Dressing, Caraway Seed, Cardamom, Cayenne Pepper, Celery Flakes, Celery Seed, Chicken & Rib Rub, Chicken Seasoning, Chili Powder, Chives, Cilantro, Cinnamon, Cloves, Coriander, Crazy Dave's Lemon Pepper, Crazy Dave's Pepper & Spice, Crazy Dave's Salt & Spice, Cream Of Tartar, Crushed Red Pepper, Cumin, Curry Powder, Dill Seed/Weed, Fennel, Garlic Minced, Garlic Pepper, Garlic Powder, Garlic Salt, Ginger, Hickory Smoke Salt, Italian Seasoning, Jamaican Jerk Seasoning, Lemon & Herb, Lemon Peel, Lemon Pepper, Lime Pepper, Mace, Marjoram, Meat Tenderizer, Mint Leaves, Mr. Pepper, MSG, Mustard, Nutmeg, Onion Minced, Onion Powder, Onion Salt, Orange Peel, Oregano, Oriental 5-Spice, Paprika, Parsley, Pepper Green Bell, Pickling Spice, Pizza Seasoning, Poppy Seed, Poultry Seasoning, Pumpkin Pie Spice, Rosemary, Rosemary Garlic Seasoning, Sage, Salt Free Garden Seasoning, Salt Free Garlic & Herb, Salt Free Lemon Pepper, Salt Free Original All Purpose Seasoning, Salt Free Veg. Seasoning, Seasoned Pepper, Sesame Seed, Six Pepper Blend, Smokey Mesquite Seasoning, Spaghetti/Pasta Seasoning, Spicy Spaghetti Seasoning, Tarragon, Thyme, Turmeric

Trade East - Blackened, Cajun, Canadian (Chicken, Steak), Garlic Pepper, Grill (Beef, Gourmet, Smokey), Italian (Pizza, Spaghetti, Whole Herb), Jamaican Jerk, Mesquite (Herb & Fajita, w/Butter), No Salt (Garden, Garlic Herb, Herb, Vegetable, Zesty), Pepper (Lemon, Lime), Poultry, Salad w/Cheese, Salt w/No MSG, Six Pepper Blend, Spicy Taco

Trader Joe's - All Private Label Spices, Frozen Chopped Basil, Frozen Chopped Cilantro, Taco Seasoning

Victoria Gourmet - 7 Seed Crust, Brining Blend (Asian, Smoky, Spicy, Traditional), Chipotle Pepper Flakes, Cinnamon Chili

Rub, Curry, Fire Roasted Tomatoes, Ginger Citrus, Herbes De Provence, Holiday, Jalapeno Pepper Flakes, Mediterranean, Moroccan, Mulling Spices, New Orleans, Pepper (Chef's Ground Black, Cracked Black, Ground White, Lemon, Mill Mix, Shaker Ground Black), Peppercorns (Tellicherry, White), Pie Spices, Red Bell Peppers, Red Pepper Flakes, Roasted Garlic Slices, Seafood, Shallots, Sicilian, Smoky Paprika Chipotle, Texas Red, Toasted Onion Herb, Toasted Sesame Ginger, Tuscan

Watkins - Garlic Salt, Seasoning (All Purpose, Chicken, Coleslaw, Grill, Ground Beef, Omelet Souffle, Potato Salad, Poultry, Soup & Vegetable)

Weber Grill Creations - Club Pack Seasoning (Gourmet Burger, Smokey Mesquite), Grinders (Chicago Steak, Kick 'N Chicken, Roasted Garlic & Herb, Six Pepper Fusion, Twisted Citrus Garlic, Zesty Lemon Seasoning), Rub (Burgundy Beef, Classic BBQ), Seasoning (Chicago Steak, Gourmet Burger, Kick 'N Chicken, Mango Lime, N' Orleans Cajun, Seasoning Salt, Smokey Mesquite, Veggie Grill)

Wegmans Brand - Bay Leaves, Black Pepper, Cracked Pepper Blend, Fleur De Sel Sea Salt, Garlic & Sea Salt, Oregano, Parsley, Sage

Winn Dixie - All Varieties

Wright's - Liquid Smoke (Hickory Seasoning, Mesquite)

Seaweed

Eden Organic - Agar Agar Bars, Agar Agar Flakes

Nagai's - Sushi Nori Roasted Seaweed

Yaki - Sushi Nori Roasted Seaweed

Yamamotoyama - Roasted Nori, Temaki Party Toasted

Seeds

Arrowhead Mills - Flax, Mechanically Hulled Sesame, Organic Golden Flax, Sunflower, Unhulled Sesame

Durkee - Anise, Celery, Dill, Poppy, Sesame

Eden Organic - Organic Pumpkin (Dry Roasted & Salted, Spicy Dry Roasted w/Tamari)

FritoLay - Sunflower (Kernels**!!**, Seeds**!!**, Seeds Ranch**!!**)

S

Gerbs Pumpkin Seeds - Dark Chocolate Pumpkin Seed Clusters ●, Raw Kernel Pumpkin Seeds ●, Sunflower Seeds w/Sea Salt ●, Whole Roasted Pumpkin Seeds Homestyle Onion & Garlic ●

Gluty Free - Hemp ●, Organic Golden Flax Seed ●, Pumpkin Seeds (Organic No Shell ●, Raw (In Shell ●, No Shell ●), Salted (No Shell ●, Organic No Shell ●), Unsalted (In Shell ●, No Shell ●)), Raw (Chia ●, White Chia ●), Raw Organic (Chia ●, Hemp ●), Sesame (Hulled) ●, Sunflower Seeds (Chocolate ●, Raw (In Shell ●, No Shell ●), Raw Organic No Shell ●, Salted (In Shell ●, No Shell ●), Unsalted (In Shell ●, Israeli In Shell ●, No Shell ●)), Watermelon Seeds ●

Goraw▲ - Seed Mix (Simple ●, Spicy ●), Seeds (Sprouted Pumpkin ●, Sprouted Sunflower ●)

Hy-Vee - Dry Roasted Sunflower Kernels

Kaia Foods - Sprouted Sunflower Seeds (Cocoa Mole, Garlic & Sea Salt ●, Sweet Curry ●, Teriyaki ●)

Laura Lynn - Sunflower

Meijer Brand - Sunflower (Plain, Salted In Shell)

Nuchia - Original Chia

Nuts Online - Chia Seeds (Organic ●, Regular ●, White ●), Chocolate Covered Pumpkin Seeds ●, Chocolate Covered Sunflower Seeds (Blue ●, Green ●, Pink ●, Purple ●, White ●, Yellow ●), Hemp ●, Hulled Sesame Seeds ●, Organic Raw No Shell Hemp ●, Pepitas Organic Dry Roasted Salted No Shell Pumpkin Seeds ●, Organic No Shell Pumpkin Seeds ●, Raw No Shell Pumpkin Seeds ●, Roasted (Salted No Shell Pumpkin Seeds ●, Unsalted No Shell Pumpkin Seeds ●), Pumpkin Seeds (Organic Tamari Roasted No Shell ●, Raw In Shell ●, Sprouted ●), Roasted Squash Seeds Unsalted In Shell ●, Sunflower Seeds (Chocolate Covered ●, Israeli Unsalted In Shell ●, Organic Raw No Shell ●, Organic Roasted Salted No Shell ●, Organic Tamari Roasted No Shell ●, Raw (In Shell ●, No Shell ●), Roasted (Salted In Shell ●, Salted No Shell ●, Unsalted In Shell ●, Unsalted No Shell ●)), Watermelon Seeds ●

Publix - Sunflower Seeds

Pure Market Express▲ - Spicy Pepitos ●

Purely Chia▲ - White Chia Seed (Micro Milled ●, Whole ●)

Running Food▲ - Chia Seed (Milled ●, Whole ●)

Ruth's Hemp Power - Raw Goodness Chia Seed, Soft Hemp Shelled

Shiloh Farms - Black Sesame Seeds **!!**, Chia Seeds **!!**

Spice Islands - Anise, Caraway, Celery, Dill, Poppy, Sesame

Spitz - Seasoned Pumpkin **!!**, Sunflower (Chili Lime **!!**, Cracked Pepper **!!**, Dill Pickle **!!**, Salted **!!**, Seasoned **!!**, Smoky BBQ **!!**, Spicy **!!**)

Tones - Anise, Caraway, Celery, Dill, Poppy, Sesame

Trader Joe's - Pumpkin Seeds & Pepitas, Sunflower

Tropical Traditions - Whole Golden Flax Seeds

Woodstock Farms - Non Organic Seeds (Pumpkin (Regular, Roasted & Salted), Sunflower Hulled (Regular, Roasted & Salted, Roasted No Salt)), Organic Seeds (Flax, Hulled Sesame, Pumpkin Regular, Sunflower Hulled (Regular, Roasted & Salted, Roasted No Salt))

Sesame Oil... see Oil

Sesame Seeds... see Seeds

Shakes

Amazake -

Almond

Amazing Mango

Banana Appeal

Chocolate (Almond, Chimp)

Cool Coconut

Go (Go Green, Hazelnuts)

Oh So Original

Rice Nog

Tiger Chai

Vanilla (Gorilla, Pecan Pie)

Garelick Farms - Chug (Chocolate Milkshake, Cookies 'N' Cream Milkshake, Vanilla Milkshake)

Glucerna - Butter Pecan, Chocolate, Homemade Vanilla, Strawberries 'N Cream

Gluty Free - Organic Cacao Powder ●, Raw Cacao Powder ●, Raw Organic (Acai ●, Maca ●, Red Maca ●)

S

Nasoya - Silken Creations Non Dairy Starter For Smoothies & Desserts

Grainaissance - Almond Shake, Amazing Mango, Banana Appeal, Chocolate (Almond, Chimp, Cool Coconut), Gimme Green, Go (Go Green, Hazelnuts), Oh So Original, Rice Nog, Tiger Chai, Vanilla (Gorilla, Pecan Pie)

Nesquik - Milk Shake

Nuts Online - Organic Powder Acai ●, Hemp Protein ●, Lucuma ●, Maca ●, Mesquite ●, Noni ●, Pomegranate ●, Raw (Strawberry ●, VitaCherry ●), Red Maca ●, Wild Blueberry ●, Yumberry ●, Powder (Apple Cider Vinegar ●, Camu Camu ●, Chamomile ●, Chlorella ●, Dandelion Root ●, Echinacea ●, Ginkgo Leaf ●, Goji Berry ●, Gotu Kola ●, Green Tea ●, Mangosteen ●, Pumpkin Seed ●, Spirulina ●, Stevia ●, Tomato ●, Tomato ●)

Safeway Brand - Nutritional Shake/Drink Including Plus (All Flavors), Weight Loss Shake (Chocolate Royale, Milk Chocolate, Vanilla)

Worldwide Pure Protein - Banana Cream, Frosty Chocolate, Strawberry Cream, Vanilla Cream

Shortening

Albertsons

Bakers & Chefs - 100% Pure Creamy Liquid Shortening

Crisco - All Vegetable (Butter Flavor, Regular)

Earth Balance ▲ - Vegetable Shortening

Food Club Brand

Hy-Vee - Vegetable (Butter Flavor Shortening, Oil Shortening)

Kroger Value

Laura Lynn - 3 lbs. Vegetable, 42 oz. Shortening

Lowes Foods Brand - Shortening

Meijer Brand

Midwest Country Fare - Pre Creamed Shortening

Publix - Vegetable Shortening

Spartan Brand - All Vegetable, Butter Flavored Vegetable Shortening

Stop & Shop Brand - Meat Fat/Vegetable Shortening, Vegetable

Tropical Traditions - Organic Palm Shortening

Wegmans Brand - Vegetable

Winn Dixie

Shrimp
... *All Fresh Seafood Is Gluten-Free (Non-Marinated, Unseasoned)

Bumble Bee - Broken, Deveined Shrimp (Large, Medium, Small), Jumbo, Large, Small, Tiny

Captain's Choice - Cooked Tail On Shrimp

Chicken Of The Sea - All Shrimp Products

Crown Prince - Broken, Tiny

Great Value Brand (Wal-Mart) - Canned Tiny Shrimp

Henry & Lisa's - Uncooked Natural

Hy-Vee - Frozen Cooked, Platter

Kirkland Signature - Frozen (Cooked, Raw)

Port Side -
Frozen
Cooked Salad
Shrimp (Cooked Medium, Ready To Eat)

Publix - All Sizes (Cooked, Fresh)

Sweet Bay - All Frozen

Trader Joe's - Roasted Poblano Peppers w/Shrimp Rice & Cheese, Shrimp Stir Fry

Wegmans Brand - Shrimp From Belize Uncooked

Whole Catch - Cooked, Raw, Tail Off, Wild Key West Pink Shell On

Shrimp Sauce... see Cocktail Sauce

Sloppy Joe Sauce
Food Club Brand

Hannaford Brand

Heinz - Sloppy Joe Sauce

Hormel - Not So Sloppy Joe

Hy-Vee

Kroger Brand

Laura Lynn

Meijer Brand - Sloppy Joe Mix, Sloppy Joe Sauce

Safeway Brand

Spartan Brand - Mix, Sauce

Winn Dixie - Original

S Smoke

    Colgin - All Varieties

    Stop & Shop Brand - Hickory Smoke, Original

    Wright's - Liquid Smoke (Hickory Seasoning, Mesquite)

  Smoked Sausage... see Sausage

  Smoked Turkey... see Turkey

  Smoothies

    Cascade Fresh - Cascaders (Acai, Peach, Raspberry, Strawberry)

    Ella's Kitchen - Smoothie Fruits (The Green One, The Purple One, The Red One, The Yellow One)

    Hansen's Smoothie Nectar - Energy Island Blast, Guava Strawberry, Mango Pineapple, Peach Berry, Pineapple Coconut, Strawberry Banana

    Jamba - Smoothie Kits (Mango A Go Go, Razzmatazz, Strawberries Wild)

    Lucerne - All Varieties

    Pure Market Express▲ - Athena ●, Blueberry Buzz ●, Classic Green ●, Creamy Strawberry ●, Easy Like Sunday Morning ●, Greenberry Heaven ●, Happy Green ●, Hemp Love ●, Jolly Green ●, Life's A Peach ●, Mud Slide Pie ●, Om ●, Pandora's Peach ●, Perfect Pear ●, Pina Colada Song ●, Power Ranger ●, Purple Power ●, Razzle ●, Thin Mint ●, Tropical Peach ●, Vanilla Nut ●

    Silk Live Smoothies - All Varieties

    Tillamook - All Yogurt Smoothies **!**

    WholeSoy & Co. - All Varieties **!!**

    Zola - Antioxidant, Energy, Immunity

  Snacks

    AllerEnergy▲ - Soft Pretzels

    Annie's - Organic Bunny Fruit Snacks (Berry Patch **!!**, Summer Strawberry **!!**, Sunny Citrus **!!**, Tropical Treat **!!**)

    Baffles - Snack Clusters (Caramel Crunch, Cheddar Cheese, Chocolate, Cinnamon Crisp, Trail Mix)

    Baked Cheetos - Crunchy 100 Calorie Mini Bites Cheese **!!**, Crunchy Cheese **!!**, Flamin' Hot Cheese **!!**

Baken-Ets - Pork Skins (Cracklins Hot 'N Spicy **!!**, Hot 'N Spicy **!!**, Sweet 'N Tangy **!!**, Traditional **!!**)

Better Made Snack Foods - Corn Pops (All Varieties)

Betty Lou's - Krispy Bites, Nut Butter Balls (Almond, Cashew Pecan, Chocolate Walnut, Coconut Macadamia, Peanut, Spirulina Ginseng)

Caroline's Desserts - Krispette/Mmmmini (Amaretto Bianco ●, Boo Boo Bar ●, Caramel Apple ●, Cocoa Jayne ●, Eggnog ●, Mint Everest ●, Myrtle's Turtles ●, Not So Plain Jayne ●, Oh Joy ●, Peanut Casanova ●, Peppermint Spark ●, Roca Crunch ●, Sonoma Sunshine ●, Sweet Cherrity ●, Sweet Joe ●, The Great Almondo ●, Tiki Bar ●, Triple Chocolate Nirvana ●)

CheeCha ▲ - Potato Puffs (Luscious Lime, Mediterranean Ginger, Original, Sea Salt & Spiced Pepper, Sea Salt & Vinegar)

Cheeky Monkey - Peanut Butter Puffs ●

Cheetos -
Baked (Crunchy Cheese **!!**, Flamin' Hot Cheese **!!**)
Flavored Snacks
Crunchy Cheddar Jalapeno **!!**
Crunchy Cheese **!!**
Fantastix Flavored Baked Corn/Potato (Chili Cheese **!!**, Flamin Hot **!!**)
Flamin' Hot (Cheese **!!**, Limon Cheese **!!**)
Natural White Cheddar Puffs Cheese **!!**
Puffs Cheese **!!**
Twisted Cheese **!!**
Wild Habanero Cheese **!!**
Mighty Zingers (Ragin' Cajun & Tangy Ranch Cheese **!!**, Sharp Cheddar & Salsa Picante **!!**)

Chester's -
Butter Flavored Puffcorn **!!**
Cheddar Cheese Flavored Popcorn **!!**
Cheese Flavored Puffcorn **!!**
Flamin' Hot Flavored (Fries **!!**, Puffcorn **!!**)

S

Chi-Chi's - Nacho Cheese Snackers

Corn Nuts - Barbeque, Chile Picante, Nacho Cheese, Original, Ranch

Cracker Jack - Original Caramel Coated Popcorn & Peanuts **! !**

Crunchies -
  All Natural Edamame
  Freeze Dried (BBQ Corn, Blueberries, Cinnamon Apple, Corn
    Snack, Mango, Mixed Fruit, Pears, Pineapple, Raspberries,
    Roasted Veggies, Strawberries, Tropical Fruit, Very Berry)
  Organic (100% Bananas, 100% Peas, 100% Strawberries)
  Seasoned Veggie Edamame (Grilled w/Wild Rice, Salted)

Deep River Snacks - Baked Fries (Jalapeno & Cheddar, Sweet Maui
  Onion), Sharp White Cheddar Popcorn

Eat Smart - Naturals (Crispy Waffle Chips, Garden Veggie Crisps ●,
  Garden Veggie Stix, White Cheddar Cheese (Corn & Rice Puffs,
  Multi Grain Cheese Puffs ●))

Eden Organic - All Mixed Up (Regular, Too), Wild Berry Mix

Edward & Sons - Brown Rice Snaps (Black Sesame, Cheddar, Onion
  Garlic, Plain Unsalted, Salsa, Sesame (Tamari, Unsalted), Tamari
  Seaweed, Toasted Onion, Vegetable)

Enjoy Life ▲ - Not Nuts (Beach Bash ●, Mountain Mambo ●)

Food Club Brand - Potato Sticks, Yellow Popcorn

Funyuns - Onion Flavored Rings (Flamin' Hot **! !**, Regular **! !**)

Gerbs Pumpkin Seeds -
  Baked Kernel Pumpkin Seeds (Roasted Red Pepper ●, Toasted
    Onion & Garlic ●, Touch Of Sea Salt ●)
  Whole Roasted Pumpkin Seeds (Homestyle Red Pepper ●, Lightly
    Salted ●, Sea Salt N' Cracked Pepper Pumpkin Seeds In Shell ●)

Giant Brand - Corn Cakes (Butter, Caramel, White Cheddar), Corn
  Snacks (Crunchy Cheese, Puff Cheese), White Cheddar Popcorn

Gladcorn - A Maizing Corn Snack (Bar BQ, Gourmet Cheddar,
  Jalapeno, Original)

Glenny's - Brown Rice Marshmallow Treat (Chocolate **!** ●, Peanut
  Caramel **!** ●, Raspberry Jubilee **!** ●, Vanilla **!** ●)

Glutano ▲ - Snackers

Gluty Free - Raw Organic Cacao Beans ●

Goraw▲ - Flax Snax (Pizza ●, Simple ●, Spicy ●, Sunflower ●), Ginger Snaps ●, Granola (Apple Cinnamon ●, Live ●, Live Chocolate●, Simple ●), Seed Mix (Simple ●, Spicy ●), Seeds (Sprouted Pumpkin●, Sprouted Sunflower ●), Super Chips (Pumpkin ●, Spirulina ●)

Herr's - Cheese Curls (Baked, Honey, Hot), Pork Rinds (BBQ Flavored, Original)

Hy-Vee - Fruit Snacks (Dinosaurs, Peanuts, Sharks, Snoopy, Variety Pack, Veggie Tales)

Johnsonville - Summer Sausage Deli Bites (Beef, Original, Salami)

Katy Sweet▲ -
  Chewy Pralines (Coconut Pecan ●, Maple Walnut ●, Peanut Pie ●, Pecan ●)
  Cookie Cutters (Bayou Bites ●, Enchantments ●, Fleur De Lis ●, Lone Stars ●, Longhorns ●, Razorbacks ●, Sooners ●)
  Creamy Pralines (Fudge Pecan ●, Maple Walnut ●, Original Pecan ●, Original Walnut ●)
  No Sugar Added Chewy Pralines (Almond ●, Pecan ●, Walnut ●)
  Organic Chewy Pralines (Maple Walnut ●, Original Pecan ●),
  Organic Creamy Pralines (Fudge Pecan ●, Maple Walnut ●, Original Pecan ●, Original Walnut ●)

Kay's Naturals Better Balance - Protein Chips (Chili Nacho Cheese, Crispy Parmesan, Lemon Herb), White Cheddar Kruncheeze

Kroger Brand -
  Cheese (Balls, Crunch, Puffs)
  Popcorn (Butter, Cheese, Salted, White Cheddar)
  Poppers (Extreme Butter, Ultimate Cheese)
  Pork Rinds (Barbecue, Hot & Spicy)
  Potato Sticks

Kroger Value - Cheese Puffs, Gummi (Bears, Sour Neon Bears, Sour Neon Worms, Worms)

Laura Lynn - Baked Cheese Curls, Cheese Krunchy, Fruit Snacks (Aliens, Animal, Creapy, Dinosaur)

S

LesserEvil -
> Kettle Corn (Black & White‼, Classic Kettle‼, Maple Pecan‼)
> Krinkle Sticks (Classic Sea Salt‼, Sour Cream & Onion‼)

Lowes Foods Brand - Cheese Crunchy, Cheese Puffs, Pork Rinds
(BBQ, Hot, Regular)

Manischewitz - Viennese Crunch

Mareblu Naturals▲ -
> Crunch Bags (Almond ●, Cashew ●, Cashew Coconut ●,
> CranMango Cashew ●, Dark Chocolate Almond ●, Pecan
> Cinnamon ●, Pecan Cranberry Cinnamon ●)
> Crunch Bars (Almond ●, Cashew ●)
> Trail Mix Crunch Bags (Blueberry Pomegranate ●, Cranberry
> Pomegranate ●, Cranblueberry ●, Cranstrawberry ●, Pecan ●,
> Pistachio ●)
> Trail Mix Crunch Bars (BlueCran Pomegranate ●, Mango
> Pomegranate ●, Pistachio ●, Strawberry Pomegranate ●)

Mary's Gone Crackers▲ - Sticks and Twigs (Chipotle Tomato ●,
Curry ●, Sea Salt ●)

Meijer Brand -
> Fruit Rolls (Justice League Galactic Berry, Rescue Heroes,
> Strawberry (Garfield, Regular), Wildberry Rush)
> Fruit Snacks (African Safari, Curious George, Dinosaurs, Jungle
> Adventure, Justice League (Big Box, Regular))
> Mixed Fruit (Peanuts, Rescue Heroes Big Box, Sharks, Underwater
> World, Variety Pack (Big Boy, Regular), Veggie Tales)
> Cheezy Treats
> Chicago Style Popcorn
> Potato Sticks
> Purple Cow Butter Popcorn
> Snacks (Caramel Corn, Cheese (Popcorn, Pops, Puffs))
> White Cheddar (Popcorn, Puffs)
> Xtreme Snack Bars

Michael Season's -
> Baked Cheese Curls (Cheddar, Hot Chili Pepper)

Baked Cheese Puffs (Cheddar, Jalapeno)

Baked White Cheddar Pops

Ultimate (Cheddar Cheese Curls, Cheddar Cheese Puffs, White Cheddar Cheese Puffs)

Mini Pops▲ - Popped Sorghum (Baby White Cheddar ●, Hot N' Chilly Chili ●, Itsy Bitsy Chili Cheese ●, Little Lemon Pepper ●, Petite Plain ●, Subatomic Sea Salt ●)

Mrs. Crimble's -

Cheese Bites (Original Cheese, Sour Cream & Onion, Tomato Olive & Oregano)

Slightly Salted Corn Cakes

Mrs. May's Naturals - Crunch (Almond ●, Black Sesame ●, Cashew ●, Coconut Almond ●, Cran Blueberry ●, Cran Tropical ●, Pom Raspberry ●, Pumpkin ●, Strawberry Pineapple ●, Sunflower ●, Ultimate ●, Walnut ●, White Sesame ●)

Munchos - Regular Potato Crisps **! !**

Nature's Promise - Soy Crisps (BBQ, Ranch)

Nutland - Almond Crunch ●, Berries & Cherries Crunch ●, Cashew Crunch ●, Pecan Crunch ●, Pistachio Crunch ●, Trail Mix Crunch ●

Nu-World Foods - Snackers (BBQ Sweet & Sassy ●, Chili Lime ●, French Onion ●)

Nuts Online - Organic Pecan Date Rolls ●, Organic Walnut Date Rolls ●, Raw Organic Cacao Beans ●, Soy Beans (Dry Roasted Halves ●, Hickory Smoked ●, Spicy BBQ ●), Turkish Delight (Almond ●, Mixed Nut ●, Pistachio ●)

Old Dutch - Bac'N Puffs, Baked (Cheese Stix, Crunchy Curls), Puffcorn (Carmel, Cheesy, Cheesy Jalapeno, Cinnamon Caramel, Original)

Original Tings - Crunchy Corn Sticks

Oskri Organics - Honey Crunch (Almond, Cashew w/Cranberries, Pecan w/Cinnamon)

Pajeda's - Crunchy Cheese

Pirate's Booty - Popcorn (Aged White Cheddar, Barbeque, Sour Cream & Onion, Veggie)

S

Planters -
  Harvest (Almond Orchard Blend, California Almonds, Jumbo
     Cashews, Pistachio Grove Blend)
  On The Go (Cocktail Peanuts (Smoky Bacon, Stadium Roasted In
     Shell Salted))
  Kettle Roasted Extra Crunchy Classic Salt
  Peanut Bar Original
  Peanuts (Dry Roasted, Honey Roasted, Salted)
  Sunflower Kernels
  Trail Mix (Fruit & Nut, Mixed Nuts & Raisins, Nuts Seeds & Raisins)
Pro Bites - Protein On The Go (Chili Nacho ●, French Toast ●)
Publix - Chocolate Covered (Almonds, Raisins), Crunchy Cheese
  Curls, Deli Snacks Popcorn, Fruit Snacks (Dinosaurs, Rescue
  Heroes, Sharks, Snoopy, Veggie Tales), Jumbo Cheese Puffs, Mini
  Rice Cakes (Caramel, Cheddar, Ranch)
Pure Market Express▲ - Bacon Jalapeno Poppers ●, MexiWraps ●,
  Pepperoni Bites ●, Spicy Pepitos ●
Sensible Foods - Organic (Crunch Dried Soy Nuts, Crunch Dried
  Sweet Corn)
Sharkies▲ - Kids Sports Chews (Berry Blasters, Tropical Splash),
  Organic Energy Sports Chews (Berry Blasters, Citrus Squeeze,
  Fruit Splash, Watermelon Scream)
Smart Puffs - Real Wisconsin Cheddar
Smartfood - Cranberry Almond Flavored Popcorn Clusters**!!**, White
  Cheddar Cheese Flavored (Reduced Fat**!!**, Regular**!!**)
Snyder's Of Hanover - Butter Flavored Popcorn, Cheese Twists,
  Gluten Free Pretzel Sticks ●, Multigrain Puffs (Aged Cheddar,
  White Cheddar)
Spartan Brand - Cheese Popcorn, Cheese Puffs, Fruit Snacks (Build
  A Bear, Curious George, Dinosaurs, Star Wars, Variety Pack)
Stop & Shop Brand -
  Corn Cakes (Apple Cinnamon, Caramel)
  Fruit Snacks (Build A Bear, Curious George, Dinosaur,
     Justice League, Peanuts, Sharks, Tom & Jerry, Underwater World
     Fruit, Variety Pack, Veggie Tales)

Snacks (Circus Peanuts, Crunchy Cheese Corn Snacks, Puff Cheese Corn Snacks, Simply Enjoy Fruit Medley)

Sunbelt - Fruit Jammers, Gummy Bears

Trader Joe's - Buccaneer Joes White Cheddar Corn Puffs, Corn Tortilla Strips White, Cranberry Nut Clusters Popcorn, Crunchy Curls**!!**, Green Bean Snacks**!!**, Reduced Fat Cheese Crunchies**!!**, Sea Salt & Pepper Rice Crisps**!!**

UTZ - Baked Cheese Balls, Cheese Curls (Baked, Crunchy, White), Popcorn (Butter, Cheese, White Cheddar), Puff'N Corn (Caramel, Cheese, Plain)

Wegmans Brand - Cheese Puffs

Wise -

Cheez Doodles (Cheese Balls, Crunchy, Jalapeno Cheddar Crunchy, Puffed, White Cheddar Puffed)

Doodle O's

Nacho Twisters

Onion Flavored Rings

Popcorn (Hot Cheese, Original Butter Flavored, Reduced Fat Butter Flavored, Reduced Fat White Cheddar Flavored, White Cheddar Cheese Flavored)

Woodstock Farms -

Organic Snack Mixes (Campfire, Cranberry Walnut Cashew, Goji Berry Power, Tamari Delight, Trail Mix, Tropical Delight, Tropical Fruit)

Snack Mixes (California Supreme, Cape Cod Cranberry, Cascade, Choco Cranberry Crunch, Chocolate Cherry Munch, Cranberrys Cove, Enchanted Trail, Goji Berry Bliss, Gourmet Trail, In The Raw, Mocha Madness, On The Trail, Sunglow)

Soda Pop/Carbonated Beverages

7up - All Varieties

A & W - Root Beer

Albertsons - All Varieties

Aquafina - FlavorSplash (Grape, Lemon, Peach Mango, Raspberry, Strawberry Kiwi, Wild Berry)

S

Barq's Root Beer - Caffeine Free, Diet, Diet Red Crème Soda, Regular

Blue Sky - All Soda Varieties

Boylan Bottleworks -
    Birch Beer (Creamy Red, Diet, Regular)
    Black Cherry
    Creme
    Diet (Black Cherry, Cane Cola, Creme, Root Beer)
    Ginger Ale
    Grape
    Natural (Black Cherry, Cane Cola, Root Beer)
    Orange
    Orange Creme
    Root Beer
    Seltzer (Lemon, Orange, Pure)
    Sugar Cane Cola

Bunch - Grape Soda

Canada Dry -
    Club Soda (All Varieties)
    Ginger Ale (Cranberry, Diet, Regular)
    Seltzer (All Varieties)
    Tonic Water (All Varieties)

Clear American (Wal-Mart) - Sparkling Water (Black Cherry, Golden Peach, Key Lime, Lemon, Mandarin Orange, Pomegranate Blueberry Acai, Raspberry Apple, Strawberry, White Grape, Wild Cherry)

Coca-Cola -
    Cherry Coke (Diet, Regular, Zero)
    Classic Coke (Caffeine Free, Regular, Zero)
    Diet Coke (Caffeine Free, Plus, Regular, w/Lime, w/Splenda)
    Vanilla Coke (Regular, Zero)

Cott - All Varieties

Crush - Cherry, Grape, Orange, Strawberry

Diet Rite - All Varieties

Dr. Pepper - All Varieties

Enviga - Sparkling Green Tea (Berry, Regular)

soda pop/carbonated beverages

S

Fanta - Grape, Orange (Regular, Zero)

Fiesta Mirinda - Mango, Pina

Food Club Brand - Club Soda, Cola (Diet, Regular), Dr. Wow, Ginger Ale (Diet, Regular), Grape, Lemon Lime, Orange, Peach, Root Beer, Strawberry, Wild Mountain

Fresca

Great Value Brand (Wal-Mart) - Low Sodium Club Soda, Sodium Free Seltzer, Tonic Water (Calorie Free, Regular)

Hannaford Brand - All Soda Flavors, Seltzer Water

Hansen's - All Sodas

Hires - Root Beer

Hy-Vee -

Black Cherry

Cherry Cola

Club Soda

Cola (Diet, Regular)

Cream Soda

Diet Dr. Hy-Vee

Diet Tonic

Dr. Hy-Vee

Fruit Punch (Coolers, Regular)

Gingerale

Grape

Hee Haw (Diet, Regular)

Lemon Lime

Orange (Diet, Regular)

Root Beer (Diet, Regular)

Seltzer Water

Sour

Strawberry

Tonic Water

Tropical Punch Coolers

Water Cooler (Black Cherry, Key Lime, Kiwi Strawberry, Mixed Berry, Peach, Peach Melba, Raspberry, Strawberry, White Grape)

S

I.B.C. - Root Beer

Kas Mas

Kroger Brand - Big K Soft Drinks

Lowes Foods Brand - Cola (Diet, Regular), Dr. Sparkle, Fruit Punch, Ginger Ale, Grape, Kiwi Strawberry, Lemonade, Mountain Breeze, Orange, Root Beer, Seltzer Original, Sparkle Up, Tonic Water Diet

Manzanita Sol

Meijer Brand - Encore Cherry Red, Diet (Blue, Red), Red Pop

Mountain Dew - Baja Blast, Caffeine Free, Caffeine Free Diet, Code Red (Diet, Regular), Diet (Regular, Ultraviolet), Live Wire, Regular, Throwback, Voltage

Mr. Pibb - Xtra, Zero

Mug - Cream Soda (Diet, Regular), Root Beer (Diet, Regular)

O Organics - Italian Soda (Blood Orange, Cranberry Acai, Lemon, Orange Blueberry, Pink Grapefruit, Pomegranate)

Orangina - Sparkling Citrus Beverage

Patch - Strawberry Soda

Patio - Gingerale, Quinine Tonic

Pepsi -
   Caffeine Free Pepsi (Diet, Regular)
   Cherry Vanilla
   Lime (Diet, Regular)
   Max
   Natural
   One
   Pepsi (Diet, Regular)
   Throwback
   Vanilla Diet
   Wild Cherry (Diet, Regular)

Publix -
   Black Cherry Soda
   Cherry Cola
   Citrus Hit Soda

soda pop/carbonated beverages

S

   Club Soda
   Cola Regular
   Cream Soda
   Diet (Cola, Ginger Ale, Tonic Water)
   Ginger Ale
   Grape Soda
   Lemon Lime (Seltzer, Soda)
   Orange Soda
   Raspberry Seltzer
   Root Beer
   Tonic Water
RC Cola - All Varieties
Reed's - Ginger Brew (Cherry, Extra, Original, Premium, Raspberry, Spiced Apple Cider)
Rehab - Regular
Safeway Brand -
   Blackberry
   Cherry Go2 Soda
   Cream Soda
   Ditto (Diet, Regular)
   Dr. Skipper
   Ginger Ale
   Go2 Cola (Diet, Regular)
   Grape
   Grapefruit
   Mountain Breeze
   Orange (Diet, Regular)
   Punch
   Root Beer (Diet, Regular)
   Strawberry
Safeway Select - Clear Sparkling Water (Cranberry Raspberry, Grapefruit Tangerine, Key Lime, Raspberry Black Cherry, Strawberry Kiwi, Strawberry Watermelon, Tangerine Lime, Wild Cherry), Sodas (All Varieties)

S

Schweppes - All Varieties

Sierra Mist - Cranberry Splash (Diet, Regular), Free, Regular, Ruby Splash (Diet, Regular)

Slice - Grape, Orange (Diet, Regular), Red

Sprite - Regular, Zero

Squirt - All Varieties

Stewarts -
  Cream Soda
  Grape
  Key Lime
  Orange Cream (Diet, Regular)
  Root Beer (Diet, Regular)

Sun Drop - Caffeine Free, Caffeine Free Diet, Cherry Lemon, Diet, Regular

Sunkist - Cherry Limeade, Citrus Fusion, Diet Orange, Fruit Punch, Grape, Lemonade (Diet Sparkling, Sparkling), Orange, Peach, Pineapple, Solar Fusion, Strawberry

Trader Joe's - French Market Sparkling Beverages, Organic Sparkling Beverages (Grapefruit, Lemon), Refreshers (Blueberry, Pomegranate, Tangerine), Sparkling Juice Beverages (Apple Cider, Blueberry, Cranberry, Pomegranate), Sparkling Water (All Flavors)

Tropicana Twister Soda - Grape, Orange (Diet, Regular), Strawberry

Tubz - Diet Root Beer, Root Beer

Vernors - Diet, Regular

Virgil's - Cream Soda, Diet Root Beer, Root Beer

Wegmans Brand -
  Aqua Mineral Water (Lemon, Lemongrass, Lime, Mixed Berry)
  Frizzante European Soda (Blood Orange, Blueberry Lemon, Cranberry Lime, Sicilian Lemon, Sour Cherry Lemon)
  Soda
    Cherry (Black, Diet Wedge)
    Club Soda
    Cola (Caffeine Free, Caffeine Free Diet, Diet, Regular)

Cream Soda
Diet (Lime, Orange)
Diet Wedge (Cherry Grapefruit, Grapefruit, Peach)
   Dr. W Cola (Diet, Regular)
Fountain Root Beer (Diet, Regular)
Ginger Ale (Diet, Regular)
Grape Soda
Green Apple Sparkling Soda (Diet, Regular)
Mango
Mountain W
Orange (Diet, Regular)
Tonic (Diet, Regular)
W-up (Diet, Regular)
Sparkling Beverage
   Black Cherry Regular
   Cranberry Blend
   Cranberry Raspberry (Diet, Regular)
   Grape (Pink, Red, White)
   Key Lime (Diet, Regular)
   Kiwi Strawberry (Diet, Regular)
   Lemonade
   Mineral Water
   Mixed Berry (Diet, Regular)
   Peach Diet
   Peach Grapefruit (Diet, Regular)
   Sparkling Beverage w/Sweeteners (Black Cherry, Key Lime, Tangerine Lime)
   Sparkling Juice Niagara Grape
Welch's - All Varieties
Winn Dixie - All Varieties, Sparkling Water (All Varieties)

Sorghum
Shiloh Farms - Whole Sorghum**!!**

S Soup

A Taste Of Thai - Coconut Ginger Soup Base

Amy's -

  Indian Dal Golden Lentil!

  Lentil Curried!

  Organic

    Black Bean Vegetable!

    Chunky Tomato Bisque (Light In Sodium!, Regular!)

    Chunky Vegetable!

    Cream Of Tomato (Light In Sodium!, Regular!)

    Fire Roasted Southwestern Vegetable!

    Hearty (Rustic Italian Vegetable!, French Country Vegetable!)

    Lentil (Light In Sodium!, Regular!)

    Lentil Vegetable (Light In Sodium!, Regular!)

    Spanish Rice & Red Bean!

    Split Pea (Light In Sodium!, Regular!)

    Summer Corn & Vegetable!

    Tuscan Bean & Rice!

    Thai Coconut!

Baxters -

  Deli Inspired (Red Lentil Dahl & Beechwood Smoked Bacon, Roast Tomato & Parmesan w/Smoked Garlic)

  Favourites

    Chicken Broth

    Cock A Leekie

    French Onion

    Lentil & Bacon

    Pea & Ham

    Potato & Leek

    Scotch Vegetable

  Healthy Choice

    Chicken & Vegetable

  Chunky

    Chicken & Vegetable Casserole

    Country Vegetable

Smoked Bacon & Three Bean
Puy Lentil & Tomato
Spicy Tomato & Rice w/Sweetcorn
Tomato & Brown Lentil
Luxury (Beef Consomme, Lobster Bisque)
Vegetarian (Carrot & Butterbean, Country Garden,
Mediterranean Tomato, Tomato & Butterbean)
Boulder Soup Works▲ - Carrot Coconut ●, Garden Minestrone ●,
Green Pea w/Dill ●, Potato Leek ●, Red Lentil Dahl ●, Roasted
Tomato Basil ●, White Bean w/Tomato ●
Caskey's - Onion Soup Mix
Cuisine Sante▲ - Soup Mix (Sweet Corn ●, Tomato ●), Soup/Sauce
Base White Roux ●
Dinty Moore - Stew (Beef, Chicken)
Dr. McDougall's - Black Bean & Lime, Light Sodium Split Pea, Pad
Thai Noodle, Ready To Serve Soups (Black Bean, Chunky Tomato,
Roasted Pepper Tomato, Vegetable), Spring Onion Noodle, Tamale
w/Baked Chips, Tortilla w/Baked Chips
Edward & Sons - Miso Cup (Delicious Golden Vegetable, Japanese
Restaurant Style, Organic Traditional w/Tofu, Reduced Sodium,
Savory w/Seaweed)
El Peto▲ - Onion, Tomato, Tomato Vegetable, Vegetable
Fantastic World Foods - Simmer Soups (Blarney Stone Creamy
Potato, Cha Cha Chilin Bean, Split Pea Soup)
Fischer & Wieser - Mom's Limited Edition Tomato Basil
Food Club Brand - Beef Stew
Frontera - Black Bean Tomato, Classic Tortilla, Roasted Tomato,
Roasted Vegetable, Three Bean Chili
Frontier Soups - Soup Mix (Asparagus Almond !, Black Bean !,
Broccoli Cheddar !, Cincinnati Chili !, Corn Chowder !, Cranberry
Bean !, Eleven Bean !, Fisherman's Stew !, French Onion !, Garden
Gazpacho !, Golden Peanut !, Green Pea !, Jambalaya !, Potato
Leek !, Red Bean Gumbo !, Red Pepper Corn !, Sausage Lentil !,
Ski Country Chili !, Spicy Fiesta !, Tomato Rice !, Tortilla !, White
Bean Chili, Wild Rice & Mushroom, Yellow Split Pea

S

Full Flavor Foods - Soup Mix (Beef ●, Chicken ●, Cream ●)

Fungus Among Us - Organic Soup Mix (Moroccan Porcini & Green Lentil, Smoked Oyster Mushroom Chowder, Spicy Shiitake & Vegetable)

Gluten Free Cafe - Black Bean ●, Chicken Noodle ●, Cream Of Mushroom ●, Veggie Noodle ●

Gordon Food Service - Baja Chicken Enchilada, Heat & Serve (Broccoli Cheese, California Medley, Chicken Gumbo, Potato w/Bacon)

Grandma Ferdon's ▲ - Soup Mix (Cream ●, Onion ●)

Health Valley - No Salt Added Organic Tomato

Hormel - Microwave Chicken w/Vegetable & Rice

Imagine -

Organic Creamy Acorn Squash & Mango, Broccoli, Butternut Squash, Corn & Lemongrass, Portobello Mushroom, Potato Leek, Sweet Pea, Sweet Potato, Tomato, Tomato Basil

Organic Creamy Light In Sodium (Garden Broccoli, Garden Tomato & Basil, Harvest Corn, Red Bliss Potato & Roasted Garlic, Sweet Potato),

Kettle Cuisine -

Chicken w/Rice Noodles ●

New England Clam Chowder ●

Organic Mushroom & Potato ●

Roasted Vegetable ●

Southwest Chicken & Corn Chowder ●

Thai Curry Chicken ●

Tomato w/Garden Vegetables ●

Laura Lynn - Chicken And Rice Soup, Soup Mix (Beefy Onion, Onion)

Lowes Foods Brand - Chicken & Wild Rice, New England Style Clam Chowder

Manischewitz - Borscht

Medifast - Chicken & Wild Rice ●, Maryland Crab ●

Meijer Brand - Condensed Chicken w/Rice, Homestyle Chicken w/Rice

Member's Mark - Southwestern Style Chicken Tortilla Soup

Midwest Country Fare - Onion

Mixes From The Heartland▲ - Soup Mix (Beer Cheese ●, Broccoli & Cheese ●, Cajun Bean ●, Cajun Pastalaya ●, Cheeseburger Chowder ●, Chicken Veggie ●, Corn Chowder ●, Cowboy ●, Cream Of (Broccoli ●, Celery ●, Mushroom ●), Green Chili Hamburger ●, Green Chili Stew ●, Hamburger Pasta ●, Harvest Chicken & Rice ●, Italian Bean ●, Minestrone ●, Navy Bean ●, Pasta Veggie ●, Potato●, Southwest Chicken Stew ●, Tex Mex Pasta ●, Texas Sausage & Bean●, Tortilla Pasta ●, Wild Rice & Mushroom ●)

O Organics - Butternut Squash, Lentil, Southwest Blackbean

Orgran▲ - Garden Vegetable, Sweet Corn, Tomato

Pacific Natural Foods -

    Buttery Sweet Corn

    Cashew Carrot Ginger

    Creamy Roasted Carrot

    Curried Red Lentil

    Organic Creamy

        Butternut Squash

        Creamy Roasted Red Pepper & Tomato

        Creamy Tomato

        French Onion

    Organic Light Sodium

        Creamy Butternut Squash

        Creamy Tomato

        Roasted Red Pepper & Tomato

    Organic Savory

        Chicken & Wild Rice

        White Bean w/Bacon

    Organic Spicy

        Black Bean w/Chicken Sausage

        Chicken Fajita

    Organic Split Pea w/Ham & Swiss Cheese

    Spicy Black Bean

    Tuscan White Bean

S

Progresso -
Reduced Sodium Garden Vegetable
Rich & Hearty (Chicken Corn Chowder Flavored w/Bacon, New England Clam Chowder)
Traditional
99% Fat Free New England Clam Chowder
Chicken Cheese Enchilada
Chicken Rice w/Vegetables
Manhattan Clam Chowder
New England Clam Chowder
Potato Broccoli & Cheese Chowder
Southwestern Style Chicken
Split Pea w/Ham
Vegetable Classics
99% Fat Free Lentil
Creamy Mushroom
French Onion
Garden Vegetable
Hearty Black Bean w/Bacon
Lentil
Publix - Deli (Broccoli & Cheddar, Chicken Tortilla, Chili w/Beans, Spring Vegetable)
Pure Market Express▲ - Corn Chowder ●, Emerald City ●, French Onion ●, Spicy Cilantro ●, Tomato Herb ●, Tzatziki ●, Watermelon ●
Really Great Food Company▲ - Black Bean, Curry Lentil, Golden Pea, Split Pea, Sweet Corn Chowder
Safeway Brand - Condensed Chicken w/Rice, Onion Soup Mix
Safeway Select - Signature Soups (Autumn Harvest Butternut Squash, Baked Potato Soup, Fiesta Chicken Tortilla, Rosemary Chicken & White Bean)
Sharwood's - Tarka Dahl
Signature Cafe - Autumn Harvest Butternut Squash, Baked Potato w/Bacon, Roasted Red Pepper & Crab Bisque, Rosemary Chicken & White Bean

Simply Asia - Rice Noodle Soup Bowl (Garlic Sesame, Sesame Chicken, Spring Vegetable)

Spartan Brand - Chicken & Rice, Onion Soup & Dip

Stop & Shop Brand - Condensed Chicken w/Rice Soup, Ready To Serve Chunky Vegetable Soup

Thai Kitchen - Coconut Ginger, Hot & Sour, Instant Rice Noodle Soup (Bangkok Curry, Garlic & Vegetable, Lemongrass & Chili, Spring Onion, Thai Ginger), Rice Noodle Soup Bowl Mushroom

Trader Joe's -

   Organic

      Black Bean**!!**

      Creamy Corn & Roasted Red Pepper (Low Sodium, Regular)

      Creamy Tomato**!!**

      Split Pea**!!**

      Sweet Potato Bisque

      Tomato & Roasted Red Pepper**!!**

      Tomato Bisque**!!**

   Regular

      Butternut Squash**!!**

      Carrot Ginger**!!**

      Corn & Roasted Red Pepper**!!**

      Creamy (Corn Chowder Potbelly, Vegetable Medley Bisque)

      Garden Patch Veggie

      Instant Rice Noodle Soup (Mushroom, Roasted Garlic, Spring Onion)

      Latin Black Bean

      Miso 4 Pack

      Organic Lentil Soup w/Vegetables**!!**

      Sweet Potato Bisque**!!**

Wegmans Brand - Broccoli & Vermont White Cheddar, Chili Soup Vegetarian, Gazpacho, Lobster Bisque, Moroccan Lentil w/Chick Pea, Spicy Red Lentil Chili

Wolfgang Puck - Tomato Basil Bisque

S Sour Cream

Albertsons - Fat Free, Regular
Breakstone - All Natural, Fat Free, Reduced Fat
Cabot - Lite, Regular
Cascade Fresh
Coburn Farms - Regular
Daisy Brand - Fat Free, Light, Regular
Follow Your Heart - Sour Cream Alternative
Food Club Brand - Light, Non Fat, Regular
Friendship - All Varieties
Giant Brand - Lite, Non Fat
Hannaford Brand - All Varieties
Hood - All Varieties
Horizon Organic - All Varieties
Hy-Vee - Light, Regular
Kemps - All Varieties
Kroger Brand
Laura Lynn - Regular
Lowes Foods Brand - Lite, Non Fat, Regular
Lucerne - Light, Non Fat, Regular
Nancy's - All Cultured Dairy & Soy Products
Organic Valley - Low Fat, Regular
Prairie Farms - Fat Free, Light, Regular
Publix - Fat Free, Light, Regular
Pure Market Express▲ - Regular ●
Shamrock Farms - Light, Organic, Traditional
Smart Balance - Reduced Fat, Regular
Spartan Brand - Fat Free, Regular
Stop & Shop Brand - Light, Non Fat
Tillamook - All Varieties **!**
Trader Joe's - All Varieties
Wayfare - We Can't Say It's Sour Cream Original ●
Wegmans Brand - Fat Free, Light, Regular
Winn Dixie - Fat Free, Light, Regular

Soy Beverages/Soy Milk
Eden Organic - Eden Organic Soy Unsweetened, Organic EdenBlend
Full Circle - Refrigerated (Original, Vanilla), Shelf Stable (Chocolate, Original, Vanilla)
Great Value Brand (Wal-Mart) - Light (Plain, Vanilla), Original (Chocolate, Plain, Vanilla)
Kirkland Signature - Organic (Plain, Vanilla)
Laura Lynn - Soy Milk
Nature's Promise - Chocolate, Organic Vanilla, Plain
Organic Valley - Chocolate, Original, Unsweetened, Vanilla
Pacific Natural Foods - All Varieties
Private Selections - All Varieties
Publix GreenWise Market - Organic Soy Milk (Chocolate, Plain, Vanilla)
Silk Soymilk - All Varieties
Soy Dream - Enriched (Chocolate, Original, Vanilla), Refrigerated Non Dairy Soymilk Classic Original, Enriched (Original, Vanilla), Shelf Stable Non Dairy Soymilk Classic Vanilla,
Sunrise - Soya Beverage (Light Fortified Sweetened, Organic Unsweetened, Sweetened, Unsweetened)
Trader Joe's - All Refrigerated Soy Milk, All Soy Beverages **!!**
Vitasoy - Soymilk (Holly Nog, Peppermint Chocolate)
Wegmans Brand - Organic (Chocolate, Original, Vanilla), Reduced Fat (Original, Vanilla)
Westsoy - Organic Soymilk Original, Organic Unsweetened Soymilk (Almond, Chocolate, Original, Vanilla), Soymilk Lite (Plain, Vanilla), Soymilk Non Fat (Plain, Vanilla), Soymilk Plus (Plain, Vanilla)
Wild Wood Organics - All Varieties
ZenSoy - All Soy Milk & Soy On The Go Varieties
Soy Burgers... see Burgers
Soy Sauce
Eden Organic - Organic Tamari Soy Sauce *(Brewed In U.S.)*
Food Club Brand
Hannaford Brand - Light, Regular

S

Hy-Vee

Jade Dragon

Kroger Brand - Lite, Regular

Panda - Kari Out Packets

San-J - Organic Tamari Wheat Free Soy Sauce (Reduced Sodium ●, Regular ●)

Spartan Brand - Less Sodium, Original

Yin - Soy Free Sauce

Soy Yogurt... see Yogurt

Soymilk... see Soy Beverage/Soy Milk

Spaghetti... see Pasta

Spaghetti Sauce... see Sauces

Spices... see Seasonings

Spinach

*... *All Fresh Fruits & Vegetables Are Gluten-Free*

Albertsons - Canned Cut Leaf

Birds Eye - All Plain Frozen Vegetables

C & W - All Plain Frozen Vegetables

Del Monte - All Canned Vegetables

Dr. Praeger's - Spinach Littles **!**

Food Club Brand - Canned, Frozen Leaf, Spinach (Chopped, Cut Leaf)

Freshlike - Frozen Plain Vegetables

Great Value Brand (Wal-Mart) - Canned Whole Leaf Spinach, Frozen Cut Leaf Spinach

Green Giant - Frozen Vegetables Creamed Spinach w/Artificial Cream Flavor

Hannaford Brand - Whole Leaf

Hy-Vee - Canned, Frozen (Chopped, Leaf)

Laura Lynn - Canned

Lowes Foods Brand - Frozen (Chopped, Leaf)

Meijer Brand - Canned (Cut Leaf, No Salt, Regular), Frozen Spinach (Chopped, Leaf)

Nuts Online - Simply Spinach Freeze Dried Vegetables ●

O Organics - Chopped Frozen

Pictsweet - All Plain Vegetables (Frozen)

Publix - Canned, Frozen (Chopped, Cut Leaf, Leaf)

Publix GreenWise Market - Organic (Baby Spinach Salad, Spinach)

S&W - All Canned Vegetables

Safeway Brand - Canned Leaf, Frozen Chopped

Signature Cafe - Side Dish Savory Asiago Creamed Spinach

Spartan Brand - Canned Cut Leaf, Frozen (Chopped, Cut, Leaf)

Stop & Shop Brand - Chopped, Cut, Leaf, No Salt Added, Regular

Tasty Bite - Kashmir Spinach!, Spinach Dal!

Trader Joe's - Frozen Organic Chopped

Wegmans Brand - Frozen (Chopped, Cut Leaf, In Cream Sauce), Whole Leaf

Winn Dixie - Canned (No Salt Added, Regular), Frozen (Chopped, Cut Leaf)

Woodstock Farms - Organic Frozen Cut Spinach

Sports Drinks

Gatorade -

G Series Perform 02 (G Powder (Fruit Punch, Grape, Lemon Lime, Orange))

G Series Prime 01 (Berry, Fruit Punch, Orange)

G Series PRO (01 Prime, 02 Perform, 03 Recover)

G Series Recover 03 (Lemon Lime Orange, Mixed Berry)

G2 Lo Cal (Blueberry Pomegranate, Fruit Punch, Glacier Freeze, Grape, Lemon Lime, Orange)

G2 Natural (Berry, Orange Citrus)

G2 Powder Packets (Fruit Punch, Grape)

Original G (Berry, Citrus Cooler, Cool Blue, Fruit Punch, Fruit Punch & Berry, Glacier Freeze, Grape, Lemon Lime, Lemon Lime & Strawberry, Lemonade, Lime, Melon, Orange, Orange & Tropical Fruit, Orange Strawberry, Riptide Rush, Strawberry, Strawberry Kiwi, Tropical Mango)

Hy-Vee - Thunder Sports Drink (Berry, Fruit Punch, Glacial Ice, Lemon Lime, Orange)

Kirkland Signature - Sports Drink

S

    Laura Lynn - Sports Drink

    Meijer Brand - Drink Thirst Quencher (Fruit Punch, Lemon Lime, Orange)

    Powerade - Ion 4 (Fruit Punch, Grape, Lemon Lime, Mountain Berry Blast, Sour Lemon, Strawberry Lemonade, White Cherry Zero, Zero)

    Wegmans Brand - MVP Sport Drink (Blue Freeze, Fruit Punch, Grape, Green Apple, Lemon Lime, Orange, Raspberry Lemonade), Velocity Fitness Water (Berry, Black Cherry, Grape, Kiwi Strawberry, Lemon)

Spread

    Benecol - Light, Regular

    Bett's - Cheese Spread (Blue Cheese'N Herbs, Cheddar & Horseradish Spread, Chesapeake Crab, Herbs'N Spices, Hot 'N Tangy Buffalo Style, Smoked Salmon & Chives)

    Bionaturae - Organic Fruit Spread (All Varieties)

    Breakstone - Salted Whipped Butter, Unsalted Whipped Butter

    Canoleo - 100% Canola Margarine

    Cantare - Olive Tapenade (Traditional, w/Crumbled Goat Cheese Feta)

    Coburn Farms - Home Churned Spread

    Country Crock - All Spreads

    Dietz & Watson▲ - Jalapeno ●, Muffuletta Mix ●, Sandwich Spread ●

    Dorothy Lane Market - Asiago Roasted Garlic, Balsamic Parmesan, BLT, Cheddar Pimento, Danish Gouda & Nut, Emerald Pub, Scallion Cream Cheese, Smoked Salmon

    Earth Balance▲ -
        Natural Buttery Spread (Olive Oil, Original, Soy Free, Soy Garden)
        Natural Shortening
        Organic Buttery Spread Original Whipped
        Vegan Buttery Sticks

    Eden Organic - Butter (Apple, Cherry)

    Food Club Brand - Margarine (Patties, Spread)

    Fungus Among Us - Black Truffle

    Giant Brand - 48% Margarine Spread

    Gordon Food Service - Margarine (Reddies, Whipped)

S

Great Value Brand (Wal-Mart) - Buttery Spread, Margarine (Buttery Spread, Cardio Choice, Light Cardio Spread, Regular, Vegetable Oil Spread), Vegetable Oil Spread

Hy-Vee - 100% Corn Oil Margarine, Best Thing Since Butter, Soft Margarine (Regular, Rich & Creamy), Soft Spread, Vegetable Margarine Quarters

I Can't Believe It's Not Butter - All Varieties

Ian's - Soy Butter 4 ME

Kraft - Cheez Whiz, Old English, Pimento

Kroger Brand - Margarine, Sandwich, Vegetable Spreads

Kroger Value - Sticks, Tub

Land-O-Lakes - Butter w/Olive Oil, Fresh Buttery Taste, Garlic Butter, Honey Butter, Margarine, Salted Butter, Spreadable Butter w/Canola Oil, Unsalted Butter, Whipped Salted Butter, Whipped Unsalted Butter

Laura Lynn - Margarine Spread (Lite, Quarters, Squeezeable, Taste Like Butter)

Lawry's - Garlic Spread!!

Lowes Foods Brand - Patties, Quarters, Soft 1lb., Spread, Squeeze

Malone's - Ham Spread

Manischewitz - Apple Butter Spread

Maple Grove Farms Of Vermont - Blended Maple, Honey Maple, Pure Maple

Meijer Brand - Margarine Corn Oil Quarters, Margarine Soft (Sleeve, Tub), Spread (48% Crock, 70% Quarters, No Ifs Ands or Butter)

Odell's - Clarified Butter

Peloponnese - Baba Ganoush, Eggplant Meze, Eggplant Spread, Kalamata Olive Spread, Sweet Pepper Spread

Polaner▲ - All Varieties

Publix - Corn Oil Margarine Quarters, Homestyle Spread 48% Vegetable Oil, Homestyle Squeeze Spread 60% Vegetable Oil, It Tastes Just Like Butter Spread 70% Vegetable Oil, Original Spread Quarters 70% Vegetable Oil

Santa Barbara Olive Co. - Olive Muffalette

S

Shedd's Spread Country Crock - All Spreads

Simply Enjoy - Smoked Salmon Dill Sandwich Spread

Smart Balance - Buttery Spread (Extra Virgin Olive Oil, Extra Virgin Olive Oil Light, Heart Right, Heart Right Light, Omega 3, Omega 3 Light, Organic Original, Original, Original Light, Original w/Flax, Original w/Flax Light, w/Calcium, Whipped Low Sodium Lightly Salted)

So-Cheezy - Screamin Cheese Cheddar

Spartan Brand - 48% Spread, 70% Quarters Spread, Butter, Is It Butter 70% Spread, Margarine Soft Tub, Unsalted

Stop & Shop Brand - Simply Enjoy Smoked Salmon Dill Sandwich Spread

Tartex -

Cremisso (Champignon, Chardonnay Cote D'Or, Delicacy, Exquisite, Green Pepper, Herbs, Horseradish Apple, Hungarian, Mediterrana, Mexicana, Olivera, Peppers Chili, Pesto, Pomodoro D'Italia, Provence Herbs, Ratatouille, Shiitake, Tomato Basil, Truffle Champagne, Zucchini Curry)

Organic Pate In Tubes (Chilli, Classic, Green Olive, Herb, Herb & Garlic, Mushroom, Roasted Onion & Pink Peppercorn, Sundried Tomato)

Pate (Chanterelle Mushroom, Grilled Aubergine, Porcini Mushrooms & Cranberry)

Pate Creme (Basil, Italian Olives, Rocket & Mustard, Sundried Tomato & Vandouvan)

The Ginger People - Ginger Spread**!**

Trader Joe's - Artichoke Red Pepper Tapenade**!!**, Eggplant Garlic Spread, Olive Green Tapenade**!!**, Red Pepper Spread w/Garlic & Eggplant

Underwood - Deviled Ham Spread

Walden Farms - Spreads (Apple Butter, Apricot, Blueberry, Grape, Orange, Raspberry, Strawberry)

Wegmans Brand - Margarine Sticks

Willow Run - Soybean Margarine

Sprinkles... see Baking Decorations & Frostings

Squash

... *All Fresh Fruits & Vegetables Are Gluten-Free*

   C & W - All Plain Frozen Vegetables

   Meijer Brand - Frozen Squash Cooked

   Pictsweet - All Plain Vegetables (Frozen), Cracked Pepper Seasoned Okra & Squash

   Publix - Frozen (Cooked Squash, Yellow Sliced)

   Spartan Brand - Frozen Yellow

   Stop & Shop Brand

   Winn Dixie - Frozen Yellow

Starch

   AgVantage Naturals▲ - Tapioca ●

   Argo - Corn

   Augason Farms - Gluten Free (Potato ●, Tapioca ●)

   Authentic Foods▲ - Corn, Potato

   Bob's Red Mill▲ - Arrowroot, Corn, Potato

   Cause You're Special▲ - Corn, Potato

   Clabber Girl - Corn **!**

   EasyGlut - Rice

   El Peto▲ - Arrowroot, Corn, Potato, Tapioca

   Ener-G▲ - Potato

   Expandex▲ - Modified Tapioca ●

   Gifts Of Nature▲ - Potato

   Ginger Evans - Corn

   Gluty Free - Potato ●

   Grandma Ferdon's▲ - Corn ●, Potato ●, Tapioca ●

   Hannaford Brand - Corn

   Hearth Club - Corn

   Hodgson Mill - Pure

   Hy-Vee - Corn

   Kingsford - Corn

   Kinnikinnick▲ - Corn, Potato, Tapioca

   Kroger Brand - Corn

S

    Laura Lynn - Corn
    Let's Do...Organic - Corn
    Meijer Brand - Corn
    Nuts Online - Gluten Free Corn ●, Potato ●
    Really Great Food Company▲ - Potato
    Rumford - Corn
    Safeway Brand - Corn
    Spartan Brand - Corn

Steak
    ... *All Fresh Cut Meat Is Gluten-Free (Non-Marinated, Unseasoned)

Steak Sauce
    A.I. - Bold & Spicy, Cracked Peppercorn, Regular Steak Sauce, Sweet Hickory, Thick & Hearty
    Albertsons
    Fischer & Wieser - Jethro's Heapin' Helping, Steak & Grilling Sauce
    Food Club Brand - Regular
    Hannaford Brand
    Heinz - Traditional
    Hy-Vee - Classic, Vidalia Onion
    Jack Daniel's - Original, Smokey
    Kroger Brand - Bold & Spicy, Original, Sweet & Spicy
    Kurtz - Original
    Laura Lynn
    Lea & Perrins - Traditional
    Meijer Brand
    Mr. Spice Organic - Garlic Steak
    Publix
    Safeway Brand - Original
    Spartan Brand - Original
    Wegmans Brand - Bold, Regular

Stew
    Dinty Moore - Beef, Chicken, Microwave Meals Beef
    Kroger Brand - Beef

Stir Fry Sauce
  Mr. Spice Organic - Ginger Stir Fry Sauce & Marinade
Stir Fry Vegetables
  Albertsons - Stir Fry Vegetables
  Amy's - Asian Noodle **!**, Thai **!**
  C & W - The Ultimate (Asian Blend, Harvest Blend, Southwest Blend, Stir Fry)
  Lowes Foods Brand - Peking Stir Fry
  Meijer Brand - Frozen Vegetable Stir Fry
  Stop & Shop Brand - Japanese Stir Fry Blend
  Trader Joe's - Shrimp Stir Fry
  Wegmans Brand - Asian, Cleaned & Cut Vegetable Medley, Far East, Hong Kong
Stock
  Cuisine Sante▲ - Beef Flavored ●, Chicken Flavored ●, Vegetable ●
  Emeril's - Beef, Chicken, Organic Vegetable
  Full Flavor Foods - Soup Stock Mix (Beef ●, Chicken ●)
  Imagine - Organic Cooking Stock (Beef, Chicken, Low Sodium Beef, Vegetable)
  Kirkland Signature - Chicken (Organic, Regular)
  Kitchen Basics▲ - Original (Beef, Chicken, Clam, Ham, Pork, Seafood, Turkey, Veal), Unsalted (Beef, Chicken, Vegetable)
  Massel - Advantage Stock Powder (Beef Style, Chicken Style), Perfect Stock Powder (Beef Style, Chicken Style, Vegetable Style), Stock Powder (Beef, Beef Style, Chicken, Chicken Style, Vegetable)
  Swanson - Beef Carton, Chicken Carton
  Wegmans Brand - Culinary Stock (Beef Flavored, Chicken, Thai, Vegetable)
  Wolfgang Puck - All Natural Chicken Stock
Strawberries
  ... *All Fresh Fruits & Vegetables Are Gluten-Free
  Albertsons - Frozen (Sliced w/Sugar, Whole)
  Bramley's - Frozen
  C & W - All Plain Frozen Fruits

S

    Food Club Brand - Frozen (Sliced, Whole)

    Full Circle - Organic Whole Strawberries

    Giant Brand - Frozen Sliced (Plain, w/Artificial Sweetener, w/Sugar), Whole

    Gluty Free - Dried ●, Freeze Dried ●, Organic Dried ●

    Great Value Brand (Wal-Mart) - Frozen (Sliced w/Sugar, Whole)

    Hy-Vee - Frozen (Sliced, w/Sugar, Whole)

    Kirkland Signature - Frozen

    Kroger Brand - Plain Frozen Fruit

    Meijer Brand - Frozen (Organic, Sliced), Whole Individually Quick Frozen

    Nuts Online - Dried Strawberries (Dried ●, Natural Dried Juice Infused ●, Organic ●, Organic Simply ●, Simply ●, Simply Whole ●)

    Publix - Frozen (Sliced, Sweetened, Whole)

    Safeway Brand - Frozen (Sliced w/Sugar, Sliced w/Sweetener, Whole)

    Spartan Brand - Frozen (Sliced, Whole)

    Stop & Shop Brand - Sliced Strawberries (In Sugar, Regular, w/ Artificial Sweetener), Strawberries

    Trader Joe's - Frozen (Grade A Fancy, Organic)

    Wegmans Brand - Frozen Sliced w/Sugar

    Winn Dixie - Frozen (Sugar Whole, Sweetener, Whole)

    Woodstock Farms - Organic Frozen Whole Strawberries

Strudel

    Celiac Specialties▲ - Apple, Blueberry, Cherry

Stuffing

    Aleia's▲ - Plain ●, Savory ●

    Celiac Specialties▲ - Stuffing Mix

    El Peto▲ - Stuffing

    Gillian's Foods▲ - Turkey Bread Stuffing

    Grandma Ferdon's▲ - Sage Dressing ●

    Mixes From The Heartland▲ - Cornbread Stuffing Mix ●

    Mrs. Crimble's - Stuffing Mix

    The Grainless Baker▲ - Stuffing Cubes

    Whole Foods Market Gluten Free Bakehouse▲ - Stuffing Cubes

Succotash
  Giant Brand - Canned, Frozen
  Publix - Frozen Vegetable Blend
  Spartan Brand - Frozen
Sugar
  Albertsons - Dark Brown, Granulated, Light Brown, Powdered
  Bakers & Chefs - Light Brown, Powdered
  Dixie Crystals - All Varieties
  Domino - Brown, Brownulated, Confectioners, Cubes, Demerara Washed Raw Cane, Granulated, Organic, Pure D'Lite, Sugar 'N Cinnamon, Superfine, Tablets
  Food Club Brand - Granulated, Light Brown, Powdered
  Full Circle - Light Brown, Organic Cane Sugar
  Giant Brand - Granulated
  Giant Eagle Brand - Regular, Sucralose
  Gifts Of Nature▲ - Turbinado Sugar (Raw Sugar)
  Ginger Evans - Brown, Powdered, Sugar
  Gluty Free - Organic (Evaporated Cane Juice ●, Palm Sugar ●)
  Great Value Brand (Wal-Mart) - Confectioners Powdered, Extra Fine Granulated, Light Brown, Pure Cane
  Hain Pure Foods - Organic (Light Brown, Powdered, Regular), Turbinado
  Hannaford Brand - Dark Brown, Granulated, Light Brown, Powdered
  Heavenly Sugar - Premium Organic Sugar
  Hy-Vee - Confectioners Powdered, Dark Brown, Light Brown, Pure Cane
  Imperial Sugar - All Varieties
  Kinnikinnick▲ - Icing Sugar
  Kroger Brand - Dark Brown, Granulated, Light Brown, Powdered
  Kroger Value
  Laura Lynn - Brown, Confectioner, White
  Lowes Foods Brand - Granulated, Light Brown, Powdered
  Meijer Brand - Confectioners, Dark Brown, Granulated, Light Brown
  Midwest Country Fare - Granulated, Light Browned, Powdered

S

Nielsen-Massey - Madagascar Bourbon Pure Vanilla Sugar ●

Nuts Online - Organic Evaporated Cane Juice ●, Organic Palm Sugar ●

O Organics - Evaporated Cane Juice, Light Brown, Powdered, Turbinado

Phildesco - Coconut

Private Selections - Natural Cane Turbinado, Organic (Blue Agave, Light Brown, Powdered, Regular)

Publix - Dark Brown, Granulated, Light Brown, Powdered

Rapunzel - Organic Whole Cane, Powdered

Safeway Brand - Brown (Dark, Light), Granulated, Powdered

Shiloh Farms - Organic Date **!!**

Spartan Brand - Confectioners Powdered, Dark Brown, Granulated, Light Brown

Stop & Shop Brand - Granulated

Tops - Confectioner's Powdered, Light Brown, Pure Granulated

Trader Joe's - All Varieties

United Sugar Products - Crystal Sugar Products

Wegmans Brand - Cocktail Sugar Mandarin, Dark Brown, Granulated White, Light Brown Pure Cane

Wholesome Sweeteners - All Varieties

Winn Dixie - Granulated, Light Brown, Powdered

Woodstock Farms - Organic (Brown, Powdered, Pure Cane, Turbinado)

Sugar Substitute/Sweetener

Albertsons - Aspartame, Saccharin

Equal - Flavor For Water (Black Cherry, Lemon Lime, Mandarin Orange), Lemon, Packets, Peach, Spoonful, Sugar Lite, Tablets, Vanilla

Food Club Brand - Aspartame, Sugar Substitute

Giant Brand - Sucralose, Sweet Measure

Great Value Brand (Wal-Mart) - Calorie Free Sweetener, w/Aspartame

Hannaford Brand - Sweetener (Aspartame, Sweet Choice)

Hy-Vee - Aspartame Sweetener, Delecta Sugar Substitute

Kirkland Signature - Sweetener Made w/Sucralose

Krisda - Premium Stevia Extract
Kroger Brand - Apriva, Calorie Free (Liquid, Powdered)
Lowes Foods Brand - Sucralose Sweetener
NutraSweet
Publix - Aspartame
Spartan Brand
Splenda -
　　Brown Sugar Blend
　　Flavors For Coffee (French Vanilla, Hazelnut, Mocha)
　　Minis
　　No Calorie Sweetener (Granulated, Packets, w/Fiber)
　　Sugar Blend
Sweet And Low
Sweet Fiber - All Natural Sweetener ●
Wegmans Brand - Sugar Substitute w/Saccharin
Wholesome Sweeteners - All Varieties
Winn Dixie - Sugar Sweetner Substitute
Sunflower Seeds... see Seeds
Sweet & Sour Sauce
　　Contadina
　　Mr. Spice Organic - Sweet & Sour Sauce & Marinade
　　San-J - Gluten Free Sweet & Tangy ●
　　Wegmans Brand - Sweet & Sour
Sweet Potatoes
　　*... *All Fresh Fruits & Vegetables Are Gluten-Free*
　　Dr. Praeger's - Sweet Potato Littles **!**, Sweet Potato Pancake **!**
　　Giant Brand - Canned (In Light Syrup, Regular)
　　Meijer Brand - Cut Light Syrup
　　Pure Market Express ▲ - Pineapple Slaw ●
Sweetener... see Sugar Substitute/Sweetener
Swiss Chard
　　*... *All Fresh Fruits & Vegetables Are Gluten-Free*
Swordfish
　　*... *All Fresh Fish Is Gluten-Free (Non-Marinated, Unseasoned)*
　　Whole Catch - Fillet

S Syrup

Albertsons - Buttery, Chocolate, Light, Original, Strawberry

Beehive - Corn Syrup

Black Horse - Marionberry, Raspberry

Brer Rabbit - Syrup (Full, Light)

Cabot - Vermont Pure Maple Syrup

Crown - Corn Syrup (Golden, Lily White)

Dagoba - Chocolate Syrup

Food Club Brand - Butter Flavored, Chocolate Syrup (Regular, Sugar Free), Lite Corn, Maple 100% Dark Amber, Pancake Syrup (Microwaveable, Sugar Free w/Splenda)

Full Circle - Organic Maple

Giant Brand - Chocolate, Strawberry

Giant Eagle Brand - 100% Maple

Golden Griddle - Pancake Syrup

Gordon Food Service - Pancake Maple, Dessert Syrup (Butterscotch, Hot Fudge Velvet, Mallow, Pineapple, Strawberry, Wild Cherry)

Grand Selections - 100% Pure Maple

Hannaford Brand - Chocolate, Pancake (100% Pure Maple, Butter Flavored, Lite, Regular, Sugar Free), Strawberry

Hershey's - Chocolate (Lite, Regular, Special Dark)

Hy-Vee - Butter Flavor, Chocolate, Lite, Low Calorie Sugar Free, Pancake & Waffle, Strawberry

Karo▲ - All Varieties

Kirkland Signature - Maple

Kroger Brand - Butter Flavor, Chocolate, Cinnamon Maple, Light Corn, Lite, Original, Strawberry, Sugar Free

Kroger Value - Regular

Laura Lynn - Pancake & Waffle (Butter, Lite, Regular)

Log Cabin - Butter Flavored, Country Kitchen, Lite, Original

Lowes Foods Brand - 2% Maple (Lite, Regular), Butter Flavored, Chocolate, Light Corn Syrup *(Red Label)*

Lundberg▲ - Sweet Dreams Brown Rice Syrup (Eco Farmed, Organic)

Maple Grove Farms Of Vermont - Flavored Syrups (Apricot, Blueberry, Boysenberry, Red Raspberry, Strawberry), Pure & Organic Maple Syrup, Sugar Free Syrup (Butter Flavor, Maple Flavor, Vermont)

Maple Ridge - Buttery, White Corn

Maple Valley - Organic Maple Syrup

Meijer Brand - Butter, Chocolate, Lite, Lite Butter, Lite Corn, Regular

Melissa's - Organic Blue Agave

Midwest Country Fare - Chocolate, Pancake & Waffle (Butter, Original)

Morning Delight - Buttery Rich, Original

Mrs. Renfro's - Cane, Country

Nesquik - All Flavors

Nestle - Nesquik Syrup (All Flavors)

O Organics - 100% Pure Maple

Old Tyme - All Varieties

Organic Nectars - Chocagave, Vanillagave

Oskri Organics - Date

Private Selections - Pure Maple

Publix - Chocolate (Regular, Sugar Free), Pancake (Butter Flavor, Lite, Lite Butter Flavor, Original, Sugar Free)

Safeway Brand - Butter, Butter Light, Chocolate, Light, Original

Safeway Select - Pure Maple

Santa Cruz - Dessert Toppings (All Varieties)

Shiloh Farms - Maple (Agave Blend, Dark Amber Grade B, Grade A, Organic Blueberry, Organic Cranberry)

Smucker's - All Fruit Syrup, Pure Maple Syrup, Sugar Free Breakfast Syrup

Spartan Brand - 2% Real Maple, Artificial Butter, Corn Syrup, Reduced Calorie (Butter, Lite)

Taste Of Inspiration - Red Raspberry **!**

The Ginger People - Ginger Syrup **!**

Trader Joe's - All Maple Syrup

Tropical Traditions - Brown Rice Syrup

Uncle Luke's - 100% Pure Maple Syrup

Vermont Maid - All Varieties

S
T

Walden Farms -
    Fruit Syrups (Blueberry, Strawberry)
    Single Serve Packets (Chocolate, Pancake)
    Syrup (Caramel, Chocolate, Pancake)
Wegmans Brand -
    Buttery Flavor (Light, Syrup)
    Regular
        Chocolate (Flavored, Triple Chocolate)
        Creamy Caramel
        Maraschino Cherry Flavored
        Pancake (Light, Regular)
        Pure Maple (Organic Dark Amber, Regular)
        Sugar Free
Winn & Lovett - Maple Syrup (All Varieties)
Winn Dixie - Butter Flavor, Chocolate, Lite, Regular, Strawberry

T

Taco Meat
    Pure Market Express▲ - Taco Meat ●
Taco Sauce
    Chi-Chi's - Taco Sauce
    Food Club Brand - Mild
    Frontera - Taco Sauce (Chipotle Garlic, Roasted Tomato)
    Hannaford Brand
    Hy-Vee - Medium, Mild
    Kroger Brand - Hot, Mild
    La Victoria - Chipotle Medium, Green (Medium, Mild), Red
        (Medium, Mild)
    Laura Lynn - Regular
    Lowes Foods Brand - Mild
    Old El Paso - Hot, Medium, Mild
    Ortega - Green, Green, Hot, Medium, Mild
    Pace - Medium, Mild
    Spartan Brand - Fat Free (Medium, Mild)

Taco Bell - Medium, Mild, Restaurant Sauce (Hot, Mild)

Taco Seasoning... see also Seasonings

   Chi-Chi's - Fiesta Restaurante Seasoning Mix

   Hy-Vee - Regular

   Meijer Brand - Taco Seasoning

   Old El Paso - Taco Seasoning Mix (40% Less Sodium, Hot & Spicy, Mild, Original)

   Ortega - Chipotle Mix, Hot & Spicy Mix, Jalapeno & Onion Mix, Taco 40% Less Sodium Mix, Taco Seasoning Mix

   Publix - Taco Seasoning Mix

   Trader Joe's - Taco Seasoning

Taco Shells

   Food Club Brand - Taco Shells

   Garden Of Eatin' - Blue Corn Taco Shells, Yellow Corn Taco Shells

   Giant Brand - Regular

   Hy-Vee - Taco Shells

   Kroger Brand - Taco Shells

   Lowes Foods Brand - Taco Shells

   Meijer Brand - Taco Shells

   Old El Paso - Stand N' Stuff Yellow Corn Taco Shells, Taco Shells (Super Stuffer, White Corn, Yellow Corn), Tostada Shells

   Ortega - Hard Shells (White, Whole Grain, Yellow), Tostada Shells

   Safeway Brand - Taco Shells (Jumbo, White Corn)

   Senora Verde - Taco Shells

   Taco Bell - Taco Shells (12 ct., 18 ct.)

Tahini

   Arrowhead Mills - Organic Sesame Tahini

   Gluty Free - Organic ●

   Krinos - Tahini

   Lee Kum Kee - Sesame Seed Paste

   MaraNatha - Natural w/Salt (Raw, Roasted)

   Nuts Online - Organic Sesame Tahini ●

   Oskri Organics - Tahini (& Honey, & Molasses, Regular)

   Peloponnese - Tahini Paste

T

Tamales
- **Amy's** - Roasted Vegetables**!**, Verde Black Bean**!**, Verde Cheese**!**
- **Hormel** - Beef
- **Trader Joe's** - Handcrafted (Beef, Cheese & Green Chilies, Chicken & Cheese)

Tangerines
- ... *All Fresh Fruits & Vegetables Are Gluten-Free*

Tapioca
- **Let's Do...Organic** - Organic (Granules, Pearls, Starch)

Taquitos
- **Trader Joe's** - Black Bean & Cheese, Chicken

Tartar Sauce
- **Best Foods** - Regular
- **Cains** - Regular
- **Food Club Brand** - Squeeze Bottle
- **Hannaford Brand**
- **Heinz** - Regular
- **Hellmann's** - Regular
- **Kroger Brand**
- **Laura Lynn** - Squeeze Tartar
- **Legal** - Regular
- **McCormick** - Fat Free, Original
- **Old Bay**
- **Royal Food Products** - Garden Fresh, Royal Deluxe
- **Simply Delicious** - Organic Tartare Sauce
- **Spartan Brand**
- **Wegmans Brand** - Regular

Tarts
- **Crave Bakery▲** - Apple Frangipane, Apricot Frangipane, Lemon, Pumpkin
- **El Peto▲** - Butter, Lemon, Pecan, Raspberry
- **Pure Market Express▲** - Lemon ●

Tater Tots...see Potatoes

Tea

Albertsons - Bags (Decaf, Regular)

Arizona - All Varieties

Bigelow Tea - All Novus Varieties, All Organic Varieties

American Classic Pyramid Bags

Charleston (Blended Loose, Breakfast)

Governor Grey

Plantation Peach

Rockville Raspberry

American Classic Regular

Dajeerling

Decaffeinated

Constant Comment

Earl Grey

English Teatime

French Vanilla

Green Tea (Regular, w/Lemon)

Lemon Lift

Spiced Chai

Easy Mix Iced

Green w/Lemon & Honey

Green w/Pomegranate & Blueberry

Peach

Raspberry

English (Breakfast, Teatime)

Flavored Tea

Cherry Vanilla

Cinnamon Stick

Constant Comment

Earl Grey

Eggnogg'n

French Vanilla

Lemon Lift

Plantation Mint

Pumpkin Spice

Raspberry Royale

Spiced Chai

Vanilla (Almond, Caramel, Chai, Hazelnut)

White (Chocolate Kisses, Tangerine)

Green Tea

Chai Green

Constant Comment Green

Earl Grey Green

Jasmine Green

Regular

w/(Lemon, Mango, Mint, Peach, Pomegranate)

Herbal Tea

Apple Cider

Chamomile (Lemon, Mint)

Chinese Oolong

Cozy Chamomile

Cranberry Apple

Fruit & Almond

Ginger Snappish

Hibiscus & Rose Hips

I Love Lemon (Regular, w/Vitamin C)

Juice Tea (Berri Good, Pomegranate Pizzazz, Taste Of The Tropics, Tasty Tangerine)

Mint Medley

Orange & Spice

Peppermint

Perfect Peach

Red Raspberry

Sweet Dreams

Sweetheart Cinnamon

Iced Tea

Perfect Peach

Red Raspberry

Loose Tea
  Constant Comment
  Earl Grey
  English Breakfast
  Green
Ready To Drink Chai Latte (Mocha, Vanilla)
Tea In No Time
  Green Lemon & Honey
  Green Mandarine & Mango
  Original
  Peach
  Raspberry
Caribou - All Flavors
Celestial Seasonings -
  Bottled Tea Kombucha (Antioxidant Superfruit, Digestion Meyer
    Lemon Ginger, Energy Pomelo Citrus, Metabolism Berry Guava,
    Super Green Tropical Blend)
  Chai (Decaf Sweet Coconut Thai, Honey Vanilla, India Spice
    (Decaf, Regular))
  Cool Brew Iced Tea (Blueberry Ice, Peach Ice, Raspberry Ice,
    Tropical Fruit)
  Green Tea
    Antioxidant
    Authentic
    Blueberry Breeze
    Decaf
      Green
      Mandarin Orchard
      Mint Green
      Sleepytime Lemon Jasmine
    Gen Mai Cha
    Goji Berry Pomegranate
    Honey Lemon Ginseng
    Raspberry Gardens
    Tropical Acai Berry

T

Herbal Tea
    Acai Mango Zinger
    Bengal Spice
    Black Cherry Berry
    Caffeine Free
    Chamomile
    Cinnamon Apple Spice
    Country Peach Passion
    Cranberry Apple Zinger
    Fruit Tea Sampler
    Herb Tea Sampler
    Honey Vanilla Chamomile
    Lemon Zinger
    Mandarin Orange Spice
    Mint Magic
    Morning Thunder
    Peppermint
    Raspberry Zinger
    Red Zinger
    Sleepytime (Regular, Vanilla)
    Sweet Apple Chamomile
    Sweet Clementine Chamomile Organic
    Tangerine Orange Zinger
    Tension Tamer
    Tropic Of Strawberry
    True Blueberry
    Wild Berry Zinger
Holiday Tea
    Candy Cane Lane
    Nutcracker Sweet
    Rooibos Tea (African Orange Mango, Madagascar Vanilla, Moroccan Pomegranate Red, Safari Spice)
    Sweet Zinger Iced Tea (Acai Mango, Raspberry, Tangerine Orange, Wild Berry)

Wellness Tea Antioxidant Max (Blackberry Pomegranate, Blood
Orange Star Fruit, Dragon Fruit Melon, Tummy Mint)

Wellness Tea All Natural Herbal (Echinacea Complete Care,
Senna Sunrise, Sleepytime Extra, Sleepytime Sinus Soother,
Sleepytime Throat Tamer)

White Tea (Antioxidant Supplement Plum, Decaf, Imperial
White Peach, Perfectly Pear)

Choice Organic Teas - All Varieties

Food Club Brand - Tea Bags (Family Size (Regular, Tagless), Regular,
Tagless)

Full Circle - Organic Tea (Chai, Chamomile, Earl Grey, English
Breakfast, Green, Peppermint)

Fuze - Black & Green Tea, Diet Green Tea w/Orange Ginger, Diet
White Tea w/Pomegranate, Green Tea w/Honey, White Tea Agave
Gogi Berry

Garelick Farms - Diet Iced Tea w/Lemon Flavor, Sweetened Green
Tea, Sweetened Iced Tea w/Lemon Flavor

Gloria Jean's - All Varieties

Gluty Free - Hibiscus Flowers ●

Gold Peak - Iced Tea Lemon

Great Value Brand (Wal-Mart) - Refrigerated (Green, Sugar Free
Sweet Tea), Tea 100% Natural (Decaf, Regular)

Hannaford Brand - All (Bags, Instant)

Hansen's - All Varieties

Higgins & Burke - All Varieties

Honest - Assam Black, Black Forest Berry, Community Green, Green
Dragon, Half & Half, Honey Green, Jasmine Green Energy, Just
Black, Just Green, Lemon Black, Lori's Lemon, Mango Acai, Mango
Green, Moroccan Mint Green, Passion Fruit Green Tea, Peach
Oolalong, Peach White, Perfect White, Pomegranate Red w/Goji
Berry

Hy-Vee -
Bottled (Diet Green Tea w/Citrus, Green Tea w/Citrus, Green Tea
w/Pomegranate)

T

Chai Black
Chamomile Herbal
Cinammon Apple Herbal
Decaf (Green, Tea Bags)
Dream Easy Herbal
Earl Grey Black
English Breakfast Black
Family Size Tea Bags
Green Tea (Bags, Regular, w/Pomegranate)
Honey Lemon Ginseng
Instant (Jasmine Green, Orange & Spice Specialty, Peppermint
  Herbal, Rooibos Red Herbal, Strawberry Herbal Tea Bags)
Inko's White Tea - Apricot, Blueberry, Cherry Vanilla, Energy,
  Honeydew, Lemon, Lychee, Original, Unsweetened Hint O'Mint,
  Unsweetened Honeysuckle, Unsweetened Original, White Peach
Kirkland Signature - Tea Bags
Kroger Brand - Tea (Bagged, Instant)
Laura Lynn - Cold Brew, Decaf, Family, Family Decaf, Green, Tagless,
  Tea Bags
Lipton -
  Black Tea Bags (Cold Brew, Decaf, Decaf Cold Brew, Decaf
    Pitcher Sized, Hint Of Peach, Pitcher Sized, Regular)
  Bottled Iced Tea
    Chilled Green w/Peach & Mango
    Chilled Iced w/Lemon
    Diet (Green w/Citrus, Green w/Mixed Berry, Iced Green
      w/Lemon, Sparkling Green w/Strawberry Kiwi, White w/
      Raspberry)
    Green w/Citrus,
    Half & Half Tea Lemonade
    Iced Tea w/Lemon
    Pure Leaf (Extra Sweet, Green w/Honey, Iced w/Lemon,
      Iced w/Peach, Iced w/Raspberry, Sweetened, Unsweetened)
    Sparkling Green w/Berry, Sweet Iced, White w/Raspberry)

Diet Iced Tea Mix Lemon (Decaf, Decaf, Regular)
Peach
Raspberry
Unsweetened
Flavored Tea Bags (French Vanilla, Orange & Spice, Spiced Chai),
Green Tea Bags (100% Natural, 100% Natural Decaf, Cranberry
Pomegranate, Decaf Honey Lemon, Honey, Lemon Ginseng,
Mint, Mixed Berry, Orange Passionfruit & Jasmine, Purple
Acai & Blueberry, Red Goji & Raspberry, w/Citrus, White
Mangosteen & Peach)
Herbal Tea Bags (Cinnamon Apple, Ginger Twist, Lemon,
Orange, Peppermint, Quietly Chamomile)
Iced Tea Mix (Lemon, Mango, Summer Peach, Unsweetened,
Wild Raspberry)
Iced Tea To Go (Green w/Blueberry & Pomegranate, Green
w/Citrus, Green w/Honey & Lemon, Green w/Mandarin &
Mango, Regular w/Natural Lemon, White w/Raspberry)
Pyramid Tea Bags (Bavarian Wild Berry, Bedtime Story Herbal,
Black Pearl, Green w/Mandarin Orange, Red w/Strawberry &
Passionfruit, Tuscan Lemon, Vanilla Caramel Truffle, White
w/Blueberry & Pomegranate, White w/Mango & Peach)
Lowes Foods Brand - Green (Decaf, Regular), Tea Bags
(Decaf, Regular)
Medifast - Chai Latte ●, Pro Tea (Peach ●, Raspberry ●)
Meijer Brand - Iced Tea Mix, Instant, Tea Bags (Decaf, Green, Green
Decaf, Regular)
Midwest Country Fare - Tea Bags 100 Ct.
Minute Maid - Pomegranate Flavored Tea
Mother Parkers - All Tea (Black, Flavored, Green, Herbal)
Nature's Promise - Organic Fair Trade Green Tea (Decaf,
Lemon, Regular)
Newman's Own - Lemon Aided Iced Tea
Numi - All Varieties
O Organics - Bags (Green, Mint Herbal)

T

Oregon Chai - All Varieties

Orient Emporium - All Varieties

Pacific Natural Foods - Organic Iced Tea (Green, Lemon, Peach, Raspberry, Sweetened Black), Organic Simply Mate Yerba Mate (Citrus Lychee, Lemon Ginger, Peach Passion, Traditional), Organic Simply Tea (Kiwi Mango Green, Peach Green, Tangerine Green, Unsweetened Green, Wild Berry Green)

Prairie Farms - Sweetened Iced Tea

Private Selections - Organic (All Varieties), Regular All Varieties

Publix - Deli Iced Tea (Sweetened, Unsweetened), Instant (Lemon, Regular), Tea Bags All Varieties

Pura Vida - All Varieties

Red Rose - All Varieties

Republic Of Tea - Black (2010 Darjeeling First Flush ●, All Day Breakfast ●, Assam Breakfast ●, Big Bold ●, Bing Cherry Vanilla●, Blackberry Sage ●, British Breakfast ●, Calorie Free Naturally Sweet●, Cinnamon Plum ●, Comfort & Joy ●, Cranberry Blood Orange ●, Decaf (Apricot ●, Blackberry Sage ●, British Breakfast●, Earl Greyer ●, Ginger Peach ●, Mango Ceylon ●, Vanilla Almond●), Earl Greyer ●, Eat Pray Love Blood Orange Cinnamon ●, Ginger Peach ●, Golden Yunnan ●, Imperial Republic Lychee ●, Imperial Republic Pu Erh ●, Jerry Cherry ●, Lapsang Souchon ●, Lucky Irish Breakfast ●, Mango Ceylon ●, Margaret's Hope Rare Darjeeling ●, Organic Ceylon Breakfast ●, PassionFruit Papaya ●, Phoobsering Rare Darjeeling ●, Raspberry Quince ●, Republic Chai ●, Republic Darjeeling ●, Rohini Rare Pearl ●, Rose Petal ●, Tea Of Good Tidings●, Vanilla Almond ●, Wild Blueberry ●), Green (Acai ●, Acerola Cherry ●, Apple Blossom ●, Big Hojicha ●, Black Raspberry●, Blood Orange ●, Blueberry Lemon ●, Blueberry●, Decaf (Honey Ginseng ●, Kiwi Pear ●, Pomegranate ●, The People's Green ●, Wild Berry Plum ●), Dragon Well ●, Flower Of Prosperity●, Flowering (Dancing Blossom ●, Lychee Blossom●), Ginger Lemon●, Ginger Peach ●, Goji Raspberry ●, Honey Ginseng●, Jasmine Jazz ●, Kiwi Pear ●, Moroccan Mint ●, Orange Spice ●,

Organic (Dancing Leaves ●, Earl Greyer ●, Lemon w/Honey ●, Turmeric Ginger ●), Pineapple Ginger ●, Pomegranate ●, Republic Chai ●, Sea Buckthorn ●, Sky Between the Branches ●, Spring Cherry ●, Tangerine Orange ●, Tea Of Inquiry ●, The People's Green ●, Wildberry Plum ●), Herbal (Be Well Red (Get Charged No. 3 ●, Get Clean No. 7 ●, Get Gorgeous No. 1 ●, Get Happy No. 13 ●, Get Heart No. 12 ●, Get It Going No. 2 ●, Get Lost No. 6 ●, Get Maternal No. 10 ●, Get Passionate No. 17 ●, Get Relaxed No. 14 ●, Get Relief No. 9 ●, Get Smart No. 16 ●, Get Some Zzz's No. 5 ●), Cardamon Cinnamon ●, Chamomile Lemon ●, Desert Sage ●, Double Dark Chocolate Mate ●, Ginseng Peppermint ●, Hot Apple Cider ●, Imperial Republic Snow Rose ●, Lemon Wintergreen ●, Orange Ginger Mint ●, Organic (Cedarburg Red ●, Double Red Rooibos ●, Flowering Fruit ●, Mint Fields ●, Temple Of Health ●), Rainforest ●, Red (Cherry Apple ●, Cinnamon Orange ●, Dream By The Fire ●, Earl Greyer ●, Ginger Peach ●, Good Hope Vanilla ●, PassionFruit Mango ●, Republic Chai ●, Safari Sunset ●, Sip For The Cure Pomegranate Vanilla ●, Strawberry Chocolate ●, Tangerine ●, Yak The Yak Strawberry Vanilla ●), Year Of The Tiger ●, Yerba Mate Latte ●), Hibiscus Superflower (Blueberry ●, Key Lime ●, Natural ●, Pineapple Lychee ●, Vanilla Apple ●), Oolong (All Day Breakfast ●, Dragon ●, Imperial Republic Monkey Picked ●, Imperial Republic Orchid ●, Old Bush Shui Xian Rare ●, Osmanthus Rare Estate ●, Peach Blossom ●, Ti Kuan Yin ●, Wuyi ●), Organic Matcha Powder ●, Raw Green Bush Tea (Black Currant Cardamon ●, Mango Chili ●, Natural Organic ●, Plantain Coconut ●), White (Asian Jasmine ●, Emperor's ●, Ginger Peach ●, Honeydew Melon ●, Honeysuckle ●, Orange Blossom ●, Persimmon ●, Pineapple Guava ●, Silver Rain ●, Sip For The Cure Red Cherry ●, Vanilla Coconut ●)

Rishi Tea ▲ - All Varieties

Safeway Brand - Black, Iced Tea Mix (All Flavors), Tea Bags (Chamomile, Decaffeinated, Earth Grey, English Breakfast, Green, Peppermint)

Salada Tea - Decaffeinated & Regular (Green, White)

T

Santa Cruz - Bottled Tea (All Varieties)

Snapple - All Varieties

SoBe - Green

Somerset - Iced Tea Mix, Instant Tea

Spartan Brand - Instant Tea Bags, Orange Pekoe Tea Bags (Decaf, Regular)

Stash Tea - All Varieties

Summer Set - Decaffeinated Tea Bags, Sweetened Iced, Tea Bags, Unsweetened Iced

Sweet Leaf - Bottled (Citrus Green, Half & Half Tea Lemonade, Lemon, Lemon & Lime Unsweet, Mint & Honey, Peach, Raspberry, Sweet Tea), Diet Bottled (Citrus Green, Peach, Sweet)

Tazo Tea - All Varieties *(Except Green Ginger, Tazo Honeybush)*

Trader Joe's - All Tea, Green Tea Unsweetened

Twinings Tea - All Varieties

Wegmans Brand - Black Tea, Decaf (Black Tea, Green Tea), Earl Grey (Black, Black Decaf, Green, Supreme, Supreme Decaf), English Breakfast (Black, Organic), Green Tea, Ice Tea Mix Regular, w/Natural Lemon Flavor & Sugar (Decaf, Regular), Iced Tea (Diet, Lemon, Regular), Organic (Chai, Chamomile, Earl Grey, English Breakfast, Jasmine Green, Peppermint, Rooibos Strawberry Cream), Regular Bags, Sencha Pure Japanese Green

Winn Dixie - Regular & Family (Decaffeinated, Tea Bags)

Teff

Bob's Red Mill▲ - Flour, Whole Grain Teff

La Tortilla Factory - Gluten Free Teff Wraps (Dark ●, Ivory ●)

Shiloh Farms - Brown‼, Ivory‼

Tempeh

Lightlife - Flax, Garden Veggie, Organic Soy, Wild Rice

White Wave - Original Soy, Soy Rice

Wild Wood Organics - Nori Seaweed, Onion Herb, Soy Rice

Tequila

... *All Distilled Alcohol is Gluten-Free*[2]

Teriyaki Sauce
 Moore's Marinade - Teriyaki Marinade
 Organicville - Island Teriyaki ●, Sesame Teriyaki ●
 Premier Japan - Wheat Free
 San-J - Gluten Free Teriyaki Stir Fry & Marinade ●
 Simply Boulder - Truly Teriyaki Culinary Sauce ●

Tikka
 Amy's - Indian Paneer **!**
 Sharwood's - Sauce (Spicy Tikka Masala, Tikka Masala)
 Stop & Shop Brand - Simply Enjoy Tikka Masala
 Trader Joe's - Chicken Tikka, Paneer Tikka **! !**

Tilapia
 ... *All Fresh Fish Is Gluten-Free (Non-Marinated, Unseasoned)*

Tofu
 Amy's - Indian Mattar **!**
 Giant Brand - Extra Firm, Firm
 Lightlife - Tofu Pups
 Marigold - Braised
 Melissa's - Extra Firm, Firm, Soft
 Mori-Nu - All Silken Tofu
 Nasoya - Cubed, Extra Firm, Firm, Lite Firm, Lite Silken, Silken, Soft,
  Tofu Plus (Extra Firm, Firm)
 Sunrise - Chinese Puff, Extra Firm, Firm, Fried, Homemade Style
  Fried, Medium Firm, Premium (Extra Soft, Medium Firm, Soft),
  Pressed, Silken Tube, Soft, Tofu Desserts (Almond, Banana,
  Coconut, Custard Flavor, Ginger, Original, Peach Mango), Tofu Puff
 Trader Joe's - Organic Extra Firm, Organic Firm
 Wegmans Brand - Asian Classic, Organic (Extra Firm, Firm)
 White Wave - Extra Firm Tofu, Fat Reduced Tofu, Organic Tofu (Extra
  Firm Vacuumed Pack, Firm Water Pack, Soft Water Pack)
 Wild Wood - SprouTofu (Extra Firm, High Protein Super Firm, Silken)
 Woodstock Farms - Organic Tofu (Extra Firm, Firm)

Tomatillos
 ... *All Fresh Fruits & Vegetables Are Gluten-Free*
 Las Palmas - Crushed Tomatillos

T

Tomato Paste
  Albertsons - Regular
  Bionaturae - Organic
  Contadina - Regular, w/Roasted Garlic, w/Tomato Pesto
  Del Monte - All Tomato Products *(Except Spaghetti Sauce Flavor)*
  Food Club Brand - Regular
  Full Circle - Organic
  Giant Brand - Canned
  Gordon Food Service - California
  Hannaford Brand
  Hy-Vee - Regular Tomato
  Lowes Foods Brand - Tomato
  Meijer Brand - Domestic, Organic
  Nature's Basket - Tomato Paste
  Nature's Promise - Organic
  Publix - Regular
  Publix GreenWise Market - Organic
  S&W - All Canned Vegetables
  Spartan Brand
  Wegmans Brand - Tomato
  Winn Dixie - Regular
Tomato Puree
  Contadina - Regular
  Dei Fratelli - Regular
  Full Circle - Organic
  Meijer Brand - Regular
  S&W - All Canned Vegetables
  Wegmans Brand - Regular
  Winn Dixie - Regular
Tomato Sauce... see Sauces
Tomatoes
  *... *All Fresh Fruits & Vegetables Are Gluten-Free*
  Albertsons - Diced Italian Style, Diced Tomatoes & Green Chilies,
    Stewed Italian, Whole (No Salt, Regular)

Bionaturae - Organic (Strained, Whole Peeled & Diced, Whole Peeled Diced & Crushed)

Cara Mia - Sun Dried

Contadina - All Crushed, All Stewed, Diced (Petite Cut, Regular, w/ Burgandy Wine & Olive Oil, w/Italian Herbs, w/Roasted Garlic, w/ Roasted Red Pepper, w/Zucchini Bell Pepper & Carrots)

Dei Fratelli - Canned (Chili Ready Diced, Chopped (Italian, Mexican Tomatoes & Jalapenos, w/Onions & Garlic), Crushed (Regular, w/ Basil & Herbs), Diced (In Hearty Sauce, Low Sodium, Seasoned), No Salt Whole, Petite Diced (Regular, w/Onion & Celery & Pepper), Pizza Sauce, Stewed, Whole (In Puree, Regular))

Del Monte - All Tomato Products *(Except Spaghetti Sauce Flavor)*

Diane's Garden - Canned (Diced w/Basil, Garlic, & Oregano, Sliced Stewed, Tomato Juice, Tomato Paste, Tomato Sauce, Whole Peeled)

Eden Organic - Crushed (Regular, w/Basil, w/Onion & Garlic), Diced (Regular, w/Basil, w/Green Chilies, w/Roasted Onion), Whole Tomatoes (Regular, w/Basil)

Food Club Brand -
Canned
    Crushed (In Puree, Regular)
    Diced (& Green Chiles, In Juice, In Juice No Salt, Italian, Mexican, Regular, w/Garlic & Onion)
    Diced Chili Ready (Regular, w/Onions)
    Diced Petite (Peeled w/Green Chilies, Regular, Smoked Chipotle, Southwestern, w/Sweet Onion)
    Hearty Cuts & Strips
    Petite Diced
    Puree
    Stewed (Italian Style, Mexican Style, Regular)
    Whole Peeled (No Salt, Regular)

Full Circle - Organic (Crushed Tomatoes w/Basil, Diced)

Gluty Free - Sun Dried ●

Gordon Food Service - Crushed, Diced (California, w/Juice, Petite), Puree (California, Regular), Stewed Sliced, Whole Peeled California

T

Great Value Brand (Wal-Mart) - Fire Roasted Diced, Fire Roasted Tex Mex Style

Hannaford Brand - Diced (Crushed, Italian, Kitchen Ready Crushed In Heavy Puree, No Salt, Puree, Regular, w/Green Chilies, w/ Roasted Garlic & Onion, Whole Peeled), Stewed (Italian, Mexican, No Salt, Regular)

Hy-Vee - Diced (Chili Ready, Regular, w/Chilies, w/Garlic & Onion), Italian Style (Crushed, Diced, Stewed), Original Diced & Green Chilies, Petite Diced, Stewed, Tomato Paste, Whole Peeled

Kroger Value - Diced, Fire Roasted, Whole

Laura Lynn - Tomato Products

Lowes Foods Brand - Crushed, Diced, Diced No Salt, Diced Petite, Diced w/Green Chilies, Italian, Paste, Sauce, Stewed, Whole

Meijer Brand -
Crushed In Puree, Diced (Chili Ready, In Italian, In Juice, Organic, Petite, w/Green Chilies)
Stewed (Italian, Mexican, Regular)
Whole (Organic, Peeled, Peeled No Salt, w/Basil Organic)

Melissa's - Sun-Dried**!**

Mezzetta - Sun Ripened Dried (Julienne Cut In Olive Oil, Tomatoes, Tomatoes In Olive Oil)

Midwest Country Fare - Diced, Stewed, Whole Peeled

Nature's Basket - Diced, Whole Peeled

Nature's Promise - Canned Organic (Crushed w/Basil, Diced, Whole Peeled)

Nuts Online - Dried Tomatoes (Julienne ●, Organic Sun Dried ●, Sun Dried ●, Sun Dried w/Olive Oil ●)

O Organics - Diced (No Salt Added, Regular, w/Basil Garlic & Oregano), Whole Peeled

Pictsweet - All Plain Vegetables (Frozen)

Private Selections - Organic Diced (No Salt, w/Salt), Sun Dried

Publix - Crushed, Diced (Italian Style, w/Green Chilies, w/Roasted Garlic & Onion), Paste, Peeled Whole, Sauce, Sliced & Stewed

Publix GreenWise Market - Organic (Crushed, Diced, Diced w/ Basil Garlic & Oregano, Paste, Sauce)

S&W - All Canned Vegetables

Safeway Brand - Crushed, Diced (Fire Roasted, Peeled, Peeled No Salt, Petite), Italian Style Stewed, Mexican Style Stewed, Whole Peeled

Senora Verde - Diced Tomatoes

Spartan Brand - Crushed, Diced (For Chili, Italian, Mexican, No Salt Added, Regular, w/Green Chilies, w/Roasted Garlic & Onion), Italian Stewed, Stewed, Whole

Stop & Shop Brand - Crushed (Italian Seasonings, No Added Salt, Regular), Diced (Italian Seasonings, No Added Salt, Regular), Stewed (Italian Seasonings, Mexican Style, No Added Salt, Regular), Whole Peeled (No Added Salt, Regular)

Trader Joe's - All Sun Dried Tomatoes, Whole Peeled Tomatoes w/Basil

Wegmans Brand -
Crushed
Diced (Chili Style, Italian Style Stewed, Petite, Regular, Roasted Garlic & Onion)
Italian Classics (Course Ground, Crushed w/Herb, Kitchen Cut w/Basil, San Marzano Tomatoes Whole Peeled)
Italian Style (Diced Tomatoes, Stewed, Whole w/Basil)
Organic (Diced, Diced In Juice)
Peeled Whole
Petite Diced Tomatoes w/Garlic Olive Oil & Seasoning
Puree
Stewed
Whole Peeled

Winn Dixie - Canned (Crushed, Diced, Diced w/Chilies, Italian Style (Diced, Stewed), Paste, Petite Diced, Petite Diced w/Onion Celery Green Peppers, Puree, Sauce, Stewed, Whole Peeled)

Woodstock Farms - Organic Crushed (Original, w/Basil), Organic Diced (Basil & Garlic, Italian Herbs, No Salt, Original), Organic Sauce No Salt Added, Organic Tomato Paste, Organic Whole Peeled (In Juice, w/Basil)

Tonic... see Soda Pop/Carbonated Beverages

T Tortilla Chips... see Chips

Tortillas

    Charras - Tostadas (Corn, Jalapeno)

    Don Pancho - Gluten Free Flour Tortillas

    Food For Life - Brown Rice

    French Meadow Bakery - Gluten Free Tortillas ●

    La Tortilla Factory - Gluten Free Teff Wraps (Dark ●, Ivory ●)

    Laura Lynn - Ole Corn Tortillas

    Manny's - Corn Tortillas

    Maria & Ricardo's - Gluten Free Tortillas ●

    Mission - Corn Tortillas (Extra Thin **!**, Super Size White **!**, Super Size Yellow **!**, White **!**, Yellow **!**)

    Nuevo Leon - White Corn Tortillas

    Que Pasa ▲ - Corn Tortillas

    San Carlos - Masa Lista

    Trader Joe's - Corn Tortillas (Handmade **! !**, Original **! !**)

Trail Mix... see also Nuts

    Back To Nature - Harvest Blend, Nantucket Blend, Red Rock Blend, Sonoma Blend

    Baffles - Snack Clusters Trail Mix

    Eden Organic - All Mixed Up, All Mixed Up Too

    Enjoy Life ▲ - Not Nuts (Beach Bash ●, Mountain Mambo ●)

    FritoLay - Nut & Chocolate **! !**, Nut & Fruit **! !**, Original **! !**

    Mareblu Naturals ▲ -

        Crunch Bags (Almond ●, Cashew ●, Cashew Coconut ●, CranMango Cashew ●, Dark Chocolate Almond ●, Pecan Cinnamon ●, Pecan Cranberry Cinnamon ●)

        Trail Mix Crunch Bags (Blueberry Pomegranate ●, Cranberry Pomegranate ●, Cranblueberry ●, Cranstrawberry ●, Pecan ●, Pistachio ●)

    NoNuttin' Foods ▲ - Trail Mix Energy Explosion ●

    Nuts Online - Mango Goji Fire Sprouted ●, Wild Berry Sprouted ●

    Oskri Organics - Honey Crunch (Almond, Cashew w/Cranberries, Pecan w/Cinnamon)

Pure Market Express▲ - The Goji Trail ●
Trader Joe's -
  Go Raw Trek Mix
  Nutty American Trek Mix
  Pumpkin Seeds & Pepitas
  Rainbows End Trail Mix
  Simply Almonds Cashews & Cranberries Trek Mix
  Simply The Best Trek Mix
  Sweet Savory & Tart Trek Mix
  Tempting Trail Mix
Wild Garden - Raisin & Nut Mix, Sweet & Nutty, Tropical Mix
Trek Mix... see Trail Mix
Tuna... see also Fish
*... *All Fresh Fish Is Gluten-Free (Non-Marinated, Unseasoned)*
  Albertsons - Canned Tuna (Albacore, Chunk Light)
  Bumble Bee -
    Chunk Light Tuna Touch Of Lemon Water
    Chunk White Albacore (In Oil, In Water)
    Premium Albacore Tuna In Water Pouch
    Prime Fillet Albacore Steak Entrees (Lemon & Cracked Pepper,
      Mesquite Grilled)
    Sensations Seasoned Tuna Medley (Lemon & Cracked Pepper,
      Sundried Tomato & Basil)
    Solid White Albacore In Water
    Tonno In Olive Oil
  Chicken Of The Sea - All Products
  Coral - Chunk Light Tuna (In Oil, In Water)
  Crown Prince - Natural Albacore (Solid White, Solid White
    No Salt Added)
  Food Club Brand - Tuna Light Chunk In Water, Tuna Light
    Chunk In Oil
  Great Value Brand (Wal-Mart) - Pouch w/Water, Premium Chunk
    Light Tuna In Water, Sold White Albacore Tuna In Water
  Henry & Lisa's - Canned Solid White Albacore

T

Hy-Vee - Chunk Light Tuna In (Oil, Water)
Kirkland Signature - Albacore, Fresh Ahi
Kroger Brand - Canned In Oil (Chunk, Solid), Canned In Water
    Solid, Chunk Canned In Water, Pouched
Laura Lynn - Chunk, Solid White Albacore
Lowes Foods Brand - Chunk Lite
Member's Mark - Highest Quality Solid White Albacore Tuna In Water
Midwest Country Fare - Chunk Light Tuna Packed In Water
Port Side - Chunk Light Tuna In Water
Publix - Tuna Fillets
Safeway Brand - Chunk Light
Safeway Select
Spartan Brand - Chunk Light, Solid White Albacore
StarKist -
    Canned
        Classics (All Varieties)
        Creations (Hickory Smoked, Sweet Spicy, Zesty Lemon Pepper),
        Gourmet Choice (Albacore Tuna Fillet, Low Sodium, Solid Light
            Tuna Fillet In Olive Oil, Solid Light Tuna Fillet In Water, Very Low
            Sodium, Yellowfin Marinated Tuna Fillet w/Roasted Garlic)
    Pouch
        Albacore White (Low Sodium, Regular)
        Chunk Light (Low Sodium, In Vegetable Oil)
        Yellowfin Tuna In Extra Virgin Olive Oil
Trader Joe's - All Canned Tuna, Marinated Ahi Tuna Steaks
Wegmans Brand - Albacore In Water, Yellowfin Light In Water
Winn Dixie - Albacore, Chunk Light
Turkey... see also Deli Meat
    ... *All Fresh Meat Is Gluten-Free (Non-Marinated, Unseasoned)
    Always Tender - Fresh Flavored Turkey Honey Mustard
    Applegate Farms -
        Natural
            Herb Turkey Breast
            Honey & Maple
        Turkey Breast (Roasted, Smoked)

Turkey Bologna
Turkey Salami
Uncured Turkey Hot Dogs
Organic (Herb Turkey Breast, Smoked Turkey Breast)
Organic Turkey Burgers
Organic Uncured Turkey Hot Dogs

Armour - Deli (Oven Roasted, Oven Roasted w/Broth, Smoked)

Boar's Head - All Varieties

Bowman & Landes - All Turkeys

Butcher's Cut - Ground Turkey, Jumbo Turkey Franks, Oven Roasted
Turkey Breast (97% Fat Free, Deli Style 98% Fat Free)

Butterball -
All Natural Turkey (Cutlets, Filets, Strips, Tenders)
Burgers Fresh (All Natural, Seasoned)
Fresh Fully Cooked Turkey (Oven Baked, Smoked)
Fresh Turkey (Li'l Butterball, Whole)
Frozen Boneless Roast (Ready To Roast Classic, Turkey, Turkey
Breast)
Frozen Fully Cooked Turkey (Li'l Butterball Baked, Baked, Smoked)
Frozen Turkey (Li'l Butterball, Whole *(Except Stuffed Turkeys)*)
Fully Cooked Turkey Breast Roast (Cherrywood Smoked, Deep
Fried, Honey Smoked, Oven Roasted)
Ground Turkey (Italian Style, Regular, Seasoned, Turkey Breast,
White)
Ground Turkey Chub (All Natural (85/15, 93/7), Seasoned)
Lunch Meat
Extra Thin Sliced Deep Fried Turkey Breast (Buttery Herb,
Cajun Style, Original, Thanksgiving Style)
Extra Thin Turkey Breast (Honey Roasted, Oven Roasted,
Rotisserie Seasoned, Smoked)
Lean Family Size (Honey Roasted Turkey Breast, Oven Roasted
Turkey Breast, Smoked Turkey Breast, Turkey Bologna, Turkey
Ham)
Thick Sliced (Honey Roasted, Oven Roasted, Smoked)

Thick Sliced Deep Fried Turkey Breast (Cajun Style, Original, Thanksgiving Style)

Thin Sliced (Honey Roasted, Oven Roasted, Rotisserie Seasoned, Smoked)

Tenderloins Herb Roasted

Turkey Bacon (Lower Sodium, Regular, Thin & Crispy)

Turkey Breast (Fresh Whole, Frozen Whole, Ready To Roast Classic Bone In)

Turkey Breast Fully Cooked Whole (Baked, Smoked)

Turkey Breast Strips Oven Roasted

Turkey Drumsticks

Turkey Mignons

Turkey Sausage (Fresh Bratwurst, Fresh Breakfast, Fresh Hot Italian, Fresh Sweet Italian, Polska Kielbasa Dinner, Smoked, Smoked Cheddar, Smoked Dinner, Smoked Hot)

Turkey Thighs

Turkey Wings

Carl Buddig - Deli Cuts (Honey Roasted Turkey, Oven Roasted Turkey, Smoked Turkey), Extra Thin Original (Honey Roasted Turkey, Mesquite Turkey, Oven Roasted Turkey, Regular), Fix Quix Turkey, Original (Honey Roasted Turkey, Mesquite Turkey, Oven Roasted Turkey, Regular)

Carolina Turkey - Ground Turkey

Castle Wood Reserve - Deli Meat (Herb Roasted Turkey Breast, Hickory Smoked Turkey, Oven Roasted Turkey, Turkey Pastrami)

Columbus Salame - Deli Meat (All Varieties)

Dietz & Watson ▲ - Applewood Smoked ●, Bacon Lover's Turkey ●, Black Forest Chef Carved Smoked ●, Black Forest Turkey ●, Butter Basted ●, Cajun Style ●, Carving Ready ●, Chipotle Pepper ●, Fire Roasted Breast Of Turkey ●, Glazed Honey Cured Turkey Breast●, Gourmet Gold'n Brown ●, Gourmet Lite No Salt ●, Gourmet Lite Turkey ●, Herb Lemon Butter ●, Herbed ●, Homestyle Black Pepper●, Honey Mustard ●, Italian Style ●, London Broil ●, Maple

& Honey Cured ●, Mesquite Smoked ●, Oven Classic ●, Oven Roasted ●, Pepper & Garlic ●, Roasted ●, Santa Fe Brand ●, Slow Roasted ●, Smoked Breast Fillets ●, Smoked Julienne Strips ●, Smoked Peppercorn ●, Turkey Ham ●

Eckrich - Deli Meat (Fried Skinless, Mesquite Smoked, Oven Roasted, Smoked)

Empire Kosher -

Fresh Chill Pack Turkey

Frozen Whole Turkey & Turkey Breasts

Fully Cooked Barbecue Turkey (Fresh, Frozen)

Ground Turkey (Fresh, Frozen)

Premiere Signature Edition (All Natural Turkey Breast (Skinless, w/Skin), Breast Pastrami Skinless, Pastrami Skinless)

Smoked Turkey Breast Skinless

Roll (Turkey Bologna, Turkey Salami, White Turkey)

Signature Edition Turkey Breast (Oven Prepared, Smoked), Skinless Honey Smoked Turkey Breast

Slices (Smoked Turkey Breast, Turkey Bologna, Turkey Breast, Turkey Pastrami)

Turkey Franks

Farmer John - Lunch Meat Premium Oven Roasted Turkey Breast

Garrett County Farms - Frozen Turkey Maple Breakfast Links!, Turkey Andouille!, Turkey Breast Sliced (Roasted!, Smoked!), Turkey Ham!, Turkey Ham Steak!), Turkey Franks!, Turkey Kielbasa!, Turkey Tom Tom Snack Sticks!

Giant Brand - Deli Meat (97% Fat Free Honey, 97% Fat Free Oven Roasted, Smoked)

Gordon Food Service - Deli Meat (Sliced Breast, Smoked Sliced Breast), Cooked Turkey Burgers, Cooked (Cook In Bag (Breast, Thigh), Cooked Breast)

Hillshire Farms - Deli Select Thin Sliced Turkey Breast (Honey Roasted, Oven Roasted, Smoked), Deli Select Ultra Thin Turkey Breast (Honey Roasted, Oven Roasted)

T

Honeysuckle White -
Estate Recipe Turkey Deli Meat
Buffalo Style
Canadian Brand Maple
Dry Roasted
Hickory Smoked (Honey Pepper, Original, Sun Dried Tomato),
Honey Smoked
Mesquite Smoked
Fresh
Bone In Turkey Breast
Breast (Boneless Skinless, Cutlets, Roast, Strips, Tenderloins,
Thin Cut Slices Scallopini & Milanesa)
Drumsticks
Neck Pieces
Split Breast
Thighs
Wing (Drumettes, Portions)
Frozen
Bone In Turkey Breast
Boneless Turkey
Breast w/Gravy Packet, Turkey Burgers)
Fully Cooked Hickory Smoked Bone In Turkey Breast
Fully Cooked Smoked Sausage (Chipotle Links, Original Links)
Ground Turkey (85/15, 93/7, 97% Fat Free, 99% Fat Free, Italian Style
Seasoned, Patties, Roll (93/7, 99% Fat Free), Rolls, Taco
Seasoned)
Hardwood Smoked (Bacon, Franks)
Hickory Smoked Deli Meat (Cooked Turkey Salami, Turkey
Ham, Turkey Pastrami)
Lunch Meat Deli Sliced (Hickory Smoked Honey Turkey Breast,
Hickory Smoked Turkey Breast, Oven Roasted Turkey Breast,
Turkey Pastrami)
Marinated Turkey Selections (Bacon Ranch Turkey Breast
Tenderloins, Balsamic Rosemary Turkey Breast Tenderloins,

Basil Pesto Turkey Breast Tenderloins, Cracked Pepper Turkey Breast Tenderloins, Creamy Dijon Mustard Breast Tenderloins, Homestyle Breast Tenderloins, Lemon Garlic Breast Tenderloins, Rotisserie Turkey Breast Tenderloins, Zesty Italian Herb Breast Tenderloins)

Ready To Roast Turkey Breast

Sausage
    Links (Breakfast, Chipotle Seasoned, Hot Italian, Original Smoked, Poblano Pepper, Sweet Italian, Tomato & Garlic)
    Patties Breakfast
    Roll (Breakfast, Mild Italian)
    Traditional Bratwurst

Turkey Bologna

Turkey Breast Deli Meats
    Cajun Style Hickory Smoked
    Golden Roasted
    Hickory Smoked (Peppered, Regular)
    Honey Mesquite Smoked
    Oil Browned
    Original Rotisserie
    Oven Prepared

Whole Young Turkey Fresh
    Fresh All Natural
    Frozen All Natural
    Fully Cooked (Hickory Smoked, Oven Roasted)

Hormel - Bread Ready (Oven Roasted, Smoked), Chunk Meats Turkey, Deli Meat Natural Choice (Honey, Oven Roasted, Smoked), Natural Choice Deli Counter (Honey Mesquite, Oil Browned, Oven Roasted), Turkey Pepperoni, Turkey Stroganoff Fully Cooked Entrée

Hy-Vee - All Natural (Fresh, Frozen), Cubed, Deli Thin Slices Turkey Breast (Honey Roasted, Oven Roasted), Thin Sliced (Honey Turkey, Turkey)

Isaly's - All Deli Meat

T Jennie-O Turkey Store -

Breakfast Lover's Turkey Sausage

Deli Meat

Apple Cinnamon

Grand Champion Turkey Breast (Hickory Smoked, Homestyle Pan Roasted, Honey Cured, Mesquite Smoked, Oven Roasted, Tender Browned)

Hickory Smoked Turkey Breast (Cracked Pepper, Garlic Pesto, Honey Cured, Sun Dried Tomato)

Honey (Maple, Mesquite)

Hot Red Peppered

Italian Style

Maple Spiced

Mesquite Smoked

Natural Choice Turkey Breast (Oven Roasted, Peppered, Tender Browned)

Northwestern (Hickory Smoked, Oven Roasted Turkey Breast) Peppered, Smoked)

Extra Lean Smoked Turkey Sausage (Kielbasa, Regular)

Flavored Tenderloins (Applewood Smoked, Balsamic Herb & Olive Oil, Lemon Garlic, Roast Turkey Flavor, Smoky SW Style, Tequila Lime, Tomato Basil)

Fresh Deli Meat

Breakfast Sausage (Maple Links, Mild Links, Mild Patties)

Dinner Sausage (Hot Italian, Lean Turkey Bratwurst, Sweet Italian)

Ground Turkey (Extra Lean, Italian, Lean, Taco Seasoned)

Tray (Breast Slices, Breast Strips, Tenderloins)

Frozen

Fully Cooked Sausage (Links, Patties)

Ground Turkey (Regular, Seasoned, Turkey Burgers)

Oven Ready Turkey (Garlic & Herb *(Except Gravy Packet)*, Homestyle *(Except Gravy Packet)*)

Oven Ready Turkey Breast *(Except Gravy Packet)*

Pan Roasts w/Gravy (White, White/Dark Combo)

Prime Young Turkey Fresh or Frozen *(Except Gravy Packet)*

Refrigerated (Honey Cured Ham, Turkey Ham)

Refrigerated Quarter Turkey Breasts (Cajun Style, Cracked Pepper, Hickory Smoked, Honey Cured, Oven Roasted, Sun Dried Tomato)

Smoked (Tender Browned, Tomato Basil)

Smoked Turkey Breast (Hickory, Honey Cured, Mesquite)

Smoked Turkey Wings & Drumsticks

So Easy Slow Roasted Turkey Breast

Turkey Franks

Johnsonville - Tenderloins Lemon Pepper

Jones Dairy Farm - Golden Brown All Natural Fully Cooked Turkey Sausage Links ●

Kayem - Deli Meat Buffalo Style Breast, Turkey Breast (Homestyle, Homestyle w/Skin On)

Kirkland Signature - Deli Meat Oven Roasted Breast

Manor House - Frozen Enhanced Turkey

Meijer Brand - Frozen (Breast Tenders, Duckling, Split Breast, Young), Gold Turkey (Hen, Tom), Hen Turkey, Regular Turkey Breast, Tom Turkey, Turkey Basted w/Timer, Turkey Breast (Fresh, Fresh Natural, Hickory Smoked, Honey Roasted, Zipper 97% Fat Free)

Member's Mark - Premium Chunk Turkey Breast In Water

Organic Prairie - Fresh Organic (Hardwood Smoked Turkey Bacon, Sliced Roast Turkey Breast, Sliced Smoked Turkey Breast, Turkey Hot Dogs), Frozen Organic (Ground Turkey 12 oz., Whole Young Turkey (10-14 lbs., 14-18 lbs.))

Oscar Mayer -

Deli Fresh Meats (Oven Roasted, Smoked Turkey Breast)

Deli Meat (Lean White Honey Smoked, Oven Roasted White Turkey, Smoked White Turkey)

Shaved Deli Fresh Meats (Cracked Black Peppered Turkey Breast, Honey Smoked Turkey Breast, Mesquite Turkey Breast, Oven Roasted Turkey Breast, Smoked Turkey Breast)

Thin Sliced Deli Fresh (Honey Smoked Turkey Breast, Mesquite Turkey Breast, Oven Roasted Turkey Breast, Smoked Turkey Breast)

T

Perdue -
  Carving Classics Pan Roasted Turkey Breast (Cracked Pepper, Honey Smoked, Original)
  Carving Turkey (Ham Honey Smoked, Whole)
  Carving Turkey Breast (Hickory Smoked, Honey Smoked, Mesquite Smoked, Oven Roasted)
  Deli Dark Turkey Pastrami Hickory Smoked
  Deli Pick Ups Sliced Turkey (Golden Browned, Honey Smoked, Mesquite Smoked, Oven Roasted, Smoked)
  Deli Pick Ups Sliced Turkey Ham Honey Smoked
  Deli Turkey (Bologna, Breast Oil Browned, Ham Hickory Smoked, Salami)
  Gound Turkey Burgers
  Ground Turkey (Fresh Breast, Fresh Lean)
  Healthsense Turkey Breast Oven Roasted Fat Free & Reduced Sodium
  Rotisserie Turkey Breast
  Short Cuts Carved Turkey Breast Oven Roasted
  Slicing Turkey Ham
  Turkey Sausage Seasoned Fresh Lean (Hot Italian, Sweet Italian), Whole Turkey Seasoned w/Broth
Primo Taglio - Turkey Breast (Dinner Roast, Honey Maple, Mesquite Smoked, Natural Hickory Smoked, Natural Hickory Smoked Peppered, Pan Roasted)
Private Selections - Frozen Seasoned Burgers (Lean, Regular)
Publix - Deli Fully Cooked Turkey Breast, Deli Pre-Pack Lunch Meats (Extra Thin Sliced Oven Roasted Turkey Breast, Extra Thin Sliced Smoked Turkey Breast, Smoked Turkey, Turkey Breast), Fully Cooked Breast, Ground Turkey (Breast, Regular)
Sara Lee - Deli Meat Slices (Cracked Pepper Turkey Breast, Hardwood Smoked Turkey Breast, Honey Roasted Turkey Breast, Oven Roasted Turkey Breast)
Shelton's -
  Free Range Ground Turkey (#1 Chub Pack, #3 Chub Pack)
  Free Range Ground White Turkey #1 Chub Pack

Free Range Whole Turkey (16-26 lbs., 8-15 lbs.)
Organic (Large, Small)
Turkey Burgers
SPAM - Oven Roasted Turkey
Stop & Shop Brand - Turkey Breast (Oven Roasted Fat Free, Smoked)
Thumann's - All Varieties ●
Trader Joe's - Deli Meat (Oven Roasted Turkey Breast, Smoked
    Turkey Breast Sliced), Fresh All Natural
Tropical Traditions - Pastured Whole Turkey
Valley Fresh - All Varieties
Wegmans Brand - Lean Ground Turkey (94%, 99%), Organic Turkey
    Breast (Honey Roasted, Oven Roasted), Sliced Turkey Breast
    (Oven Browned, Smoked), Split Turkey Breast, Turkey (Drumsticks,
    London Broil, Thighs, Wings)
Wellshire Farms -
    Morning Maple Turkey Breakfast Link Sausage **! !**
    Sliced (Oven Roasted Turkey Breast **! !**, Smoked Turkey Breast **! !**,
        Turkey Bologna **! !**, Turkey Ham **! !**)
    Turkey (Andouille Sausage **! !**, Franks **! !**, Kielbasa **! !**)
    Turkey Dinner Link Sausage Mild Italian Style **! !**
    Turkey Ham (Ham Steak **! !**, Nuggets **! !**, Whole **! !**)
    Turkey Tom Toms (Hot & Spicy **! !**, Original **! !**)
Wellshire Organic - Organic Turkey Bacon
Winn Dixie - Frozen Whole
Turkey Bacon... see Bacon
Turkey Burgers... see Burgers and/or Turkey
Turkey Ham... see also Ham and/or Turkey
    Honeysuckle White - Hickory Smoked Turkey Ham
    Perdue - Deli Produce
Turkey Jerky... see Jerky/Beef Sticks
Turkey Lunch Meat... see Deli Meat
Turnips
    *... *All Fresh Fruits & Vegetables Are Gluten-Free*
    Laura Lynn - Canned Turnip Greens w/Diced Turnips

T
U
V

Lowes Foods Brand - Turnip Greens w/Diced Turnips
Pictsweet - All Plain Vegetables (Frozen)
Safeway Brand - Frozen Chopped
Winn Dixie - Frozen (Chopped, w/Turnips)

U

V

Vanilla Extract... see Extract
Vanilla Powder
    Authentic Foods▲
    Gifts Of Nature▲ - Cooks Vanilla Powder
    Mixes From The Heartland▲ - Powdered Vanilla ●
    Really Great Food Company▲
Vegetable Juice... see Juice/Drinks
Vegetable Oil... see Oil
Vinegar
    Albertsons - Apple Cider, Red Wine, White Distilled
    Bakers & Chefs - White Distilled
    Bionaturae - Organic Balsamic
    Bragg - Apple Cider
    Dave's Gourmet - Precocious Pepper
    Eden Organic - Organic (Apple Cider, Brown Rice, Red Wine,
        Ume Plum)
    Food Club Brand - Balsamic, Cider, Italian (Red Wine,
        White Wine), White
    Full Circle - Organic Balsamic Vinegar
    Giant Brand - Cider, Red Wine, White Distilled
    Grand Selections - Balsamic Of Modena, Red Wine, White Wine
    Great Value Brand (Wal-Mart) - Apple Cider, Balsamic, Distilled
        White, Premium (Garlic Flavored Red Wine, Red Wine)
    Hannaford Brand - Apple Cider, Balsamic, Red Wine, White

Heinz - Apple Cider, Distilled White, Garlic Wine, Red Wine

Holland House - All Vinegars *(Except Malt Vinegar)*

Hy-Vee - Apple Cider Flavored Distilled, White Distilled

Kirkland Signature - Balsamic

Kroger Brand - All Varieties

Kurtz - Apple Cider, Distilled White

Lowes Foods Brand - Cider, White

Meijer Brand - Balsamic Aged (12 Yr., 4 Yr.), Cider, Red Wine, White Distilled, White Wine

Musselman's - Apple Cider, White Distilled

Newman's Own Organics - Balsamic

O Organics - Balsamic

Publix - Red Wine, White Distilled

Regina - All Varieties

Safeway Brand

Safeway Select - Balsamic, Red Wine, Rice, White Wine

Santa Barbara Olive Co. - Basil, Garlic & Pepper, Oregano, Tarragon

Simply Enjoy - Balsamic Of Modena, White Balsamic

Spartan Brand - Apple Cider, White

Spectrum - Balsamic, Organic (Balsamic, Brown Rice, Distilled White, Filtered Apple Cider, Golden Balsamic, Red Wine, Seasoned Brown Rice, Unfiltered Apple Cider, White Wine)

Star - Balsamic, Garlic Wine, Golden Balsamic, Italian Kitchen (Garlic Wine, Red Wine, White Wine), Natural Rice, Seasoned Rice

Stop & Shop Brand - Cider, Simply Enjoy (Balsamic Of Modena, White Balsamic), White, Wine

Trader Joe's - Orange Muscat Champagne

Tropical Traditions - Coconut Water Vinegar

Wegmans Brand - Apple Cider, Asian Classic Rice, Balsamic, Chianti Red Wine, Red Wine, Tuscan White Wine, White Distilled

Westcott - Apple Cider, White

Winn Dixie - Apple Cider, White

Vitamins... see Gluten-Free OTC Pharmacy Guide Rx

WW

Wafers... see Cookies

Waffles/Waffle Mix... see Pancakes/Pancake Mix

Walnuts... see Nuts

Wasabi

    Eden Organic - Wasabi Powder

    Hime - Powdered Sushi Wasabi

    S & B - Prepared Wasabi In Tube

    Spectrum - Organic Wasabi Mayonnaise

    Sushi Sonic - Real Wasabi

    Trader Joe's - Wasabi Mayo

Water

    Acqua Panna - Natural Spring

    Albertsons - All Varieties

    Aquafina - Flavor Splash (Grape, Lemon, Peach Mango, Raspberry, Strawberry Kiwi, Wild Berry), Purified Drinking Water, Sparkling Water (Berry Burst, Citrus Twist)

    Aquarius Spring! - Natural Spring Water

    Arrowhead - Mountain Spring

    Calistoga - Sparkling Mineral Water (All Flavors)

    Crystal Geyser - Alpine Spring, Sparkling Mineral Water

    Dasani - Essence (Black Cherry, Lime, Strawberry Kiwi), Lemon, Plus Cleanse And Restore, Plus Refresh And Restore, Purified

    Deer Park - Natural Spring

    Deja Blue - Purified Drinking Water

    Evian

    Fiji - Natural Artesian

    Food Club Brand - Distilled, Spring (Flavored, Regular), Tonic Water

    Fruit2O - All Varieties

    Gordon Food Service - Lemon (Honey, Nectar)

    Hannaford Brand - Natural Spring, Seltzer Water, Sparkling (Black Cherry, Key Lime, Kiwi Strawberry, Peach, Raspberry, Tropical Punch, White Grape)

W

Hy-Vee - 10 oz. Fun Pack (Flavored, Regular), 10 oz. Kids Size Purified Water w/Fluoride, Mother's Choice Infant Water (w/Fluoride, Regular), Natural Spring, Premium Distilled, Purified, Spring, Tonic

Ice Mountain

Kirkland Signature - Vita Rain

Kroger Brand - Crystal Clear Flavored Water

Lowes Foods Brand - Diet Tonic, Drinking, Spring

Meijer Brand - Calcium, Distilled, Flavored Crystal Quencher (Black Cherry, Key Lime, Kiwi Strawberry, Peach, Raspberry, Tangerine Lime), White Grape, Natural Calcium, Spring

Nestle Pure Life - Purified

Ozarka - Natural Spring

Perrier - Carbonated Natural Spring

Poland Spring - Natural Spring

Publix - Spring Water

Safeway Brand - Drinking, Purified Drinking, Spring

San Pellegrino - Sparkling Water

Smart Water (Glaceau)

Snapple - All Varieties

SoBe -

Lifewater

Agave Lemonade

Blackberry Grape

Orange Tangerine

Pomegranate Cherry

Strawberry Kiwi

w/Purevia (Acai Fruit Punch, B Energy Black Cherry Dragonfruit, B Energy Strawberry Apricot, Black and Blue Berry, Cherimoya Punch, Fuji Apple Pear, Mango Melon, Strawberry Dragonfruit, Strawberry Kiwi Lemonade, Syrah Grape Berry, Yumberry Pomegranate)

Spartan Brand - Water (Distilled, Drinking, Natural Spring, Spring)

Sweet Bay - Distilled, Drinking Water w/Minerals, Natural Spring Water Sodium Free

W

Trader Joe's - All Sparkling

Vitaminwater (Glaceau) - All Varieties

WaterPlus

Wegmans Brand - Aqua Mineral Water (Italian, Lemon, Lemongrass, Lime, Mixed Berry), Sparkling Water (Lemon, Lime, Mandarin Orange, Mineral, Mixed Berry, Natural, Raspberry, Tangerine Lime)

Winn Dixie - Distilled, Drinking, Purified, Sparkling Water (All Flavors), Spring

Zephyrhills - Natural Spring

Water Chestnuts

Ka-Me - Sliced/Peeled !, Whole/Peeled !

Reese - Diced, Sliced, Whole

Spartan Brand - Canned (Sliced, Whole)

Watermelon

... *All Fresh Fruits & Vegetables Are Gluten-Free*

Whipping Cream

Albertsons - Aerosol (Extra Creamy, Original), Frozen (Fat Free, Light, Regular), Heavy

Cabot - Whipped Cream Aerosol

Coburn Farms - Creamy Whip Light

Cool Whip - Aerosol (Extra Creamy, Lite, Regular), Topping (Extra Creamy, Free, Lite, Original, Sugar Free)

Food Club Brand - Aerosol Whipped Topping (Extra Creamy, Original), Frozen Whipped Topping (Extra Creamy, Fat Free, Light, Original)

Garelick Farms - Ultra Pasteurized Whipping Cream

Giant Brand - 20% Light, Frozen Whipped Topping (Fat Free, Lite, Non Dairy, Regular, Vanilla), Heavy, Sweetened Light

Giant Eagle Brand - Light Whipping Cream

Gordon Food Service - Heavy (36%, 40%), Light Real Aerosol, Mixed Whipped Cream

Great Value Brand (Wal-Mart) - Heavy Whipping Cream, Sweetened Whipped Cream Ultra Pasteurized Aerosol (Extra Creamy, Regular)

Hannaford Brand - All (Aerosol, Frozen)

W

Hood - Instant Whipped Cream (Light, Original)

Horizon Organic - All Varieties

Hy-Vee - Aerosol (Extra Creamy, Light), Frozen Lite Whipped, Frozen Whipped Topping (Extra Creamy, Fat Free, Regular), Real Whipped Cream (Lite, Regular)

Kraft - Cool Whip Topping (Chocolate, French Vanilla), Dips (Chocolate, Strawberry Crème)

Kroger Brand - All Varieties, Whipped Topping Mix

Laura Lynn - Frozen Whipped Topping, Whipping Cream

Lowes Foods Brand - Frozen Whipped Topping (Fat Free, Lite, Regular), Whipping Cream (Heavy, Light, Regular)

Lucerne - Aerosol Whipping Cream (Extra Creamy, Light French Vanilla)

Meijer Brand - Frozen Whipped Topping (Fat Free, Lite, Original), Ultra Pasteurized Heavy Whipping Cream, Whipped Cream Aerosol (Non Dairy, Regular)

MimicCreme - Almond & Cashew Cream (Sugar Free Sweetened, Sweetened, Unsweetened), Healthy Top Cream

Organic Valley - Heavy Whipping Cream (Pasteurized, Ultra Pasteurized)

Prairie Farms - Half & Half (Fat Free, Heavy Whipping, Regular, Ultra Pasteurized), Ultra Pasteurized Heavy Whipping Cream

Publix - Aerosol Whipped Cream (Heavy, Light), Aerosol Whipped Topping Fat Free, Heavy Whipping Cream, Whipping Cream

Safeway Brand - Light, Non Dairy, Regular, Whipped Topping

Shamrock Farms - Fresh Whipping, Heavy Cream

Soyatoo - Rice Whip, Soy Whip (Whippable Soy Topping, Whipped Topping)

Spartan Brand - Frozen Whipped Topping (Light, Regular)

Stop & Shop Brand - Whipped Topping (Fat Free, French Vanilla, Lite, Non Dairy, Regular), Ultra Pasteurized Cream (Heavy Whipping, Sweetened Whipping Light)

Wegmans Brand - Fat Free, Fresh (Extra Creamy, Fat Free, Light, Regular), Frozen Whipped Topping (Regular, Lite)

Winn Dixie - Aerosol (Extra Creamy, Original), Frozen

W Whiskey
... *All Distilled Alcohol Is Gluten-Free[2]*

Wine
... *All Wine Made In The USA Is Gluten-Free[2]*

Wing Sauce
Di Lusso - Buffalo Wing Sauce
Frank's RedHot - Buffalo (Hot, Regular), Sweet Heat BBQ
Ken's Steak House - Buffalo Wing Sauce
Moore's Marinade - Buffalo Wing, Honey BBQ Wing
Mr. Spice Organic - Salt Free Hot Wing Sauce & Marinade
Texas Pete - Buffalo Wing
Wingo - Wing Sauce

Wings
... *All Fresh Chicken Is Gluten-Free (Non-Marinated, Unseasoned)*
Giant Brand - Buffalo, Honey BBQ
Great Value Brand (Wal-Mart) - Frozen Wing Sections
Honeysuckle White - Chicken (Barbecue Glazed, Buffalo Style, Oven Roasted)
Jennie-O Turkey Store - Smoked Turkey Wings & Drumsticks
Stop & Shop Brand - Wings (Buffalo Style, Honey BBQ)
Trader Joe's - Chicken Wings
Wegmans Brand - Chicken Wings, Jumbo Buffalo Style Chicken

Worcestershire Sauce
Food Club Brand
French's
Great Value Brand (Wal-Mart) - Worcestershire Sauce
Hannaford Brand
Heinz
Hy-Vee - Light, Original
Kroger Brand
Kurtz
Lea & Perrins - Low Sodium, Original, Thick Original
Lowes Foods Brand
Meijer Brand

W
X
Y

Publix
Safeway Brand
Spartan Brand
The Wizard's - Organic GF/CF Vegan Worcestershire

X

Xanthan Gum
    Augason Farms
    Authentic Foods▲
    Bob's Red Mill▲
    Cause You're Special▲
    Ener-G▲
    Gifts Of Nature▲
    Gluten-Free Essentials▲
    Hodgson Mill▲
    Kinnikinnick▲
    Mixes From The Heartland▲
    Nuts Online ●
    Really Great Food Company▲

Y

Yams
    ... *All Fresh Fruits & Vegetables Are Gluten-Free
    Food Club Brand - Canned Sweet Cut
    Kroger Brand - Candied
    S&W - All Canned Vegetables
    Spartan Brand - Yams Cut
Yeast
    Bakipan - Active Dry, Bread Machine, Fast Rising Instant
    Bob's Red Mill▲ - Active Dry
    Bragg - Nutritional Yeast
    Fleischmann's - All Varieties
    Gaylord Hauser - 100% Natural Brewer's Yeast (Flake Form,
        Tablet Form)

Y

Hodgson Mill▲ - Active Dry, Fast Rise

Kroger Brand - Yeast Packets

Nuts Online - Gluten Free (Nutritional Yeast ●, Yeast ◉)

Really Great Food Company▲ - Yeast

Red Star - Active Dry, Bread Machine, Cake, Quick Rise

SAF - Bread Machine, Gold Instant, Gourmet Perfect Rise, Red Instant, Traditional Active Dry

Yogurt

Albertsons - All Flavors (Blended, Fruit On Bottom, Light, Low Fat, Non Fat)

Brown Cow Yogurt - Low Fat (Black Cherry ●, Blueberry ●, Boysenberry ●, Lemon Twist ●, Maple ●, Peach ●, Plain 32 ●, Strawberry ●, Vanilla 32 ●, Vanilla Bean ●), Non Fat (Apricot Mango ●, Blueberry ●, Chocolate ●, Lemon ●, Plain ●, Raspberry ●, Strawberry ●, Vanilla ●, Vanilla 32 ●), Whole Milk Yogurt (Apricot/ Mango ●, Blueberry Cream Top ●, Blueberry ●, Cherry/Vanilla ●, Chocolate ●, Coffee ●, Maple ●, Maple 32 ●, Peach ●, Plain ●, Plain 32●, Raspberry ●, Strawberry ●, Vanilla ●, Vanilla 32 ●)

Cabot - Flavored (Banana, Blueberry, Cherry, Lemon, Peach, Raspberry, Strawberry, Vanilla, Very Berry), Greek Style (2% Plain, 2% Vanilla Bean, Plain), Plain

Cascade Fresh - All Varieties

Chobani - Champions (Chocolate ●, Honeynana ●, Strawnana ●, Verryberry ●), Low Fat (Pineapple ●, Plain ●, Strawberry Banana ●), Non Fat (Blueberry ●, Honey ●, Peach ●, Plain ●, Pomegranate ●, Raspberry ●, Vanilla ●)

Coburn Farms - Lite, Low Fat

Dannon - Plain (Activia 24 oz. Container, Low Fat, Natural, Non Fat)

Fage - All Flavors ●

Friendship - All Varieties

Giant Eagle Brand -

Low Fat Plain

Non Fat (Plain, Vanilla)

Blended (Blackberry, Blueberry, Mixed Berry, Peach, Raspberry, Red Cherry, Strawberry, Strawberry Banana, Vanilla)

Y

Fruit On The Bottom (Black Cherry, Blueberry, Mixed Berry, Peach, Raspberry, Strawberry)

Light (Banana Creme, Blackberry, Blueberry, Key Lime, Lemon Chiffon, Mixed Berry, Orange Creme, Peach, Raspberry, Raspberry Lemonade, Strawberry, Strawberry Banana, Vanilla)

Great Value Brand (Wal-Mart) - Light Yogurt (Banana Cream Pie, Black Cherry, Blueberry, Key Lime Pie, Orange Cream, Peach, Raspberry, Strawberry, Strawberry Banana, Vanilla)

Hannaford Brand - All Flavors

Horizon Organic - All Varieties

Hy-Vee -

Fat Free Plain

Hy Active (Blueberry, Peach, Strawberry, Vanilla)

Light (Banana Cream, Blueberry, Cherry, Lemon Chiffon, Peach, Raspberry, Strawberry, Strawberry Banana, Vanilla)

Low Fat (Black Cherry, Blueberry, Cherry Vanilla, Lemon, Mixed Berry, Plain, Raspberry, Strawberry, Strawberry Banana)

Kemps - All Varieties

Kirkland Signature - Low Fat

Laura Lynn - Low Fat, Non Fat

Lifeway▲ - Lassi Yogurt Drink (All Varieties)

Lowes Foods Brand - Drinkable Yogurts (Mixed Berry, Strawberry, Strawberry Banana), Lite (Black Cherry, Blueberry, Key Lime, Lemon Chiffon, Peach, Raspberry, Strawberry, Vanilla), Low Fat Vanilla, Non Fat Plain, Regular (Blueberry, Mixed Berry, Peach, Strawberry, Strawberry Banana)

Lucerne - All Varieties (Fat Free, Pre Stirred Low Fat)

Meijer Brand -

Blended (Boysenberry, Strawberry, Strawberry Banana, Tropical Fruit)

Fruit On The Bottom (Blueberry, Peach, Raspberry, Strawberry),

Lite (Banana Crème, Black Cherry, Blueberry, Cherry Vanilla, Coconut Cream, Lemon Chiffon, Mint Chocolate, Peach, Raspberry, Strawberry, Strawberry Banana, Vanilla)

Y

   Low Fat Blended (Blueberry, Cherry, Mixed Berry, Peach, Pina
     Colada, Raspberry)

   Low Fat Vanilla

   Tube Yo Lar (Strawberry Banana, Strawberry Blueberry, Tropical
     Punch Raspberry)

Nancy's - All Cultured Dairy & Soy Varieties

Nature's Basket - Low Fat *(6 oz. Only)* (Blueberry, Peach, Raspberry,
   Strawberry, Vanilla)

Nogurt - Organic (Banana Cinnamon ●, Blueberry ●, Chocolate ●,
   Orange ●, Pomegranate ●)

O Organics - All Flavors

Oikos - Organic Greek (Blueberry ●, Caramel ●, Chocolate ●,
   Honey ●, Plain ●, Strawberry ●, Vanilla ●)

Prairie Farms -

   Fat Free (Banana Crème Pie, Black Cherry, Blueberry, Cherry
     Vanilla, Keylime Pie, Mixed Berry, Orange Crème, Peach,
     Raspberry, Strawberry, Vanilla)

   Low Fat (Apricot, Black Cherry, Blackberry, Blueberry, Cherry
     Vanilla, Peach, Pineapple, Raspberry)

Publix -

   Creamy Blends (Black Cherry, Blueberry, Peach, Regular,
     Strawberry, Vanilla)

   Fat Free Active (Peach, Strawberry, Vanilla)

   Fat Free Light (Apple Pie, Banana Crème Pie, Blueberry,
     Cappuccino, Caramel Crème, Cherry, Cherry Vanilla, Coconut
     Crème Pie, Honey Almond, Key Lime Pie, Lemon Chiffon,
     Mandarin Orange, Peach, Pina Colada, Raspberry, Strawberry,
     Strawberry Banana, Vanilla, Wild Berry Crumb Cake)

   Fat Free Plain

   Fruit On The Bottom (Banana, Black Cherry, Blackberry, Blueberry,
     Cherry, Guava, Mango, Mixed Berry, Peach, Pineapple,
     Raspberry, Strawberry, Strawberry Banana, Tropical Blend)

   Just 4 Kidz (Blue Raspberry & Cotton Candy, Strawberry &
     Blueberry, Strawberry Banana & Cherry)

Limited Edition (Black Cherry w/Chocolate, Egg Nog, Pumpkin
Pie, Strawberry w/Chocolate)
Multi Packs Creamy Blends (Black Cherry & Mixed Berry,
Blueberry & Strawberry Banana, Peach & Strawberry)
No Sugar Added (Blueberry, Cranberry Raspberry, Peach,
Strawberry, Vanilla)
Smoothies Fat Free Light (Mixed Berry, Strawberry)
Pure Market Express▲ - Cocogurt ●, Strawberry Cocogurt Parfait ●
Siggi's▲ - Acai ●, Blueberry ●, Grapefruit ●, Orange & Ginger ●, Plain ●,
Pomegranate & Passion Fruit ●, Vanilla ●
Silk Live - All Varieties
So Delicious - Coconut Milk (Blueberry ●, Chocolate ●, Passionate
Mango ●, Pina Colada ●, Plain ●, Raspberry ●, Strawberry ●,
Strawberry Banana ●, Vanilla ●)
Sol Cuisine - Organic Solgurt (Low Fat Blueberry, Low Fat Strawberry,
Low Fat Vanilla, Unsweetened Natural)
Spartan Brand - Banana Cream, Black Cherry, Blueberry, Cherry
Vanilla, Mango, Mixed Berry, Peach, Raspberry, Strawberry,
Strawberry Banana, Vanilla
Stonyfield Organic - All Frozen Yogurts ●, All Smoothies ●, All Soy
Yogurts ●, YoBaby *(All Varieties Except YoBaby Plus Fruit &
Cereal)* ●, YoKids (All Varieties) ●, YoToddler (All Varieties) ●
Stop & Shop Brand -
Grab'ums Yogurt To Go (Cotton Candy Melon, Strawberry
Blueberry, Tropical Punch Raspberry)
Low Fat Blended (Blueberry, Peach, Raspberry, Strawberry,
Strawberry Banana)
Low Fat Fruit On The Bottom (Blueberry, Peach, Raspberry,
Strawberry, Strawberry Banana)
Non Fat Plain Yogurt
Non Fat Light (Banana, Blueberry, Cherry, Cherry Vanilla, Coffee,
Peach, Raspberry, Strawberry, Strawberry Vanilla, Vanilla)
Tillamook - Yogurt & Yogurt Smoothies**!**
Trader Joe's - All Varieties, Soy Yogurt (All Varieties)

Y **Wegmans Brand -**

> Blended Low Fat (Blueberry, Cherry, Coffee, Key Lime, Lemon, Mixed Berry, Orange Cream, Peach, Raspberry, Strawberry, Strawberry Banana)
>
> Fruit On The Bottom
>> Light (Black Cherry, Blueberry, Mixed Berry, Peach)
>> Low Fat (Apricot Mango, Blueberry, Blueberry, Cherry Vanilla, Mixed Berry, Peach, Pina Colada, Pineapple, Raspberry, Strawberry, Strawberry Banana)
>
> Light Blended Non Fat (Blueberry, Key Lime, Mixed Berry, Orange Cream, Peach, Raspberry, Strawberry, Vanilla)
>
> Low Fat Vanilla
>
> Organic Super Yogurt (Blueberry, Peach, Plain, Raspberry, Strawberry, Vanilla)
>
> Plain (Low Fat, Non Fat)

WholeSoy & Co. - All Products (Frozen Yogurts, Smoothies, Yogurts)

Wild Wood - Probiotic Soyogurt (All Varieties)

Winn Dixie - All Varieties

Yo-J - All Varieties

Yoplait -

> All Natural Plain Fat Free (16 oz., 32 oz.)
>
> Delights Parfait (Chocolate Raspberry, Creme Caramel, Lemon Torte, Triple Berry Creme)
>
> Fiber One (Key Lime Pie, Peach, Strawberry, Vanilla)
>
> Fridge Pack (Light Key Lime Pie/Vanilla, Light Strawberry/Light Blueberry Patch, Light Strawberry/Light Harvest Peach, Original Strawberry, Original Strawberry/Original Harvest Peach, Original Strawberry/Strawberry Banana)
>
> Go-Gurt (Banana Split/Strawberry Milkshake, Berry Blue Blast/ Chill Out Cherry 16 ct., Carly Rad Raspberry/Paradise Punch, Cool Cotton Candy/Burstin' Melon Berry, Ro Gurt Shaggy's Like Cool Punch & Rawberry, Simply...Go Gurt Strawberry, Sponge Bob Strawberry Riptide/Bikini Bottom Berry,

Strawberry Banana Burst/Watermelon Meltdown, Strawberry
Kiwi Kick/Chill Out Cherry, Strawberry Splash/Berry Blue Blast,
Strawberry Splash/Cool Cotton Candy 16 ct.)
Greek Yogurt (Blueberry, Honey Vanilla, Plain, Strawberry)
Kids (Strawberry Banana/Peach, Strawberry/Strawberry Vanilla,
Vanilla/Banana)
Large Size (99% Fat Free (Creamy Harvest Peach, Creamy
Strawberry, Creamy Strawberry Banana)
Light Fat Free (Creamy Strawberry, Creamy Vanilla)
Light (Apple Turnover, Apricot Mango, Banana Cream Pie,
Blackberry, Blueberry Patch, Boston Cream Pie, Harvest Peach,
Key Lime Pie, Lemon Cream Pie, Orange Crème, Pineapple
Upside Down Cake, Raspberry Cheesecake, Red Raspberry,
Strawberries 'N Bananas, Strawberry, Strawberry Shortcake, Very
Cherry, Very Vanilla, White Chocolate Strawberry)
Light Thick & Creamy (Orange Creme, French Vanilla, Key Lime
Pie, Lemon Meringue, Mixed Berry, Strawberry)
Original
Banana Creme, Blackberry Harvest, Boysenberry, Cherry
Orchard, Coffee, French Vanilla, Harvest Peach, Key Lime Pie,
Lemon Burst, Mango, Mixed Berry, Mountain Blueberry, Orange
Crème, Pear, Pina Colada, Pineapple, Red Raspberry, Strawberry
(Banana, Cheesecake, Kiwi, Mango, Regular)
Smoothie Triple Berry (Club Pack)
Splitz (Rainbow Sherbet, Strawberry Banana Split, Strawberry
Sundae)
Thick & Creamy (Blackberry Harvest, Key Lime Pie,
Peaches 'N Cream, Royal Raspberry, Strawberry, Strawberry
Banana, Vanilla)
Trix Yogurt (Strawberry Banana Bash/Raspberry Rainbow,
Strawberry Kiwi/Cotton Candy, Strawberry Punch/
Watermelon Burst, Triple Cherry/Wildberry Blue, Very Berry
Watermelon/Berry Bolt)

Y

Z

Whips (Chocolate, Chocolate Raspberry, Key Lime Pie, Lemon Burst, Orange Creme, Peaches 'N Cream, Raspberry, Strawberry Mist, Vanilla Creme)

Yoplus (Blackberry Pomegranate, Blueberry Acai, Cherry, Peach, Strawberry, Vanilla)

Z

Zucchini

... *All Fresh Fruits & Vegetables Are Gluten-Free*

C & W - All Plain Frozen Vegetables

Del Monte - Zucchini w/Italian Style Tomato Sauce

Giant Brand - Frozen

Nuts Online - Simply Zucchini Freeze Dried Vegetables ●

Trader Joe's - Frozen Misto Alla Grigio ❗❗

Gluten-Free
Over The Counter (OTC)
Pharmacy Guide

Rx

After Shave/Shaving Gel

Arbonne - RE9 Advanced For Men Shave Gel
Surya Brasil - Sapien Mens After Shave

Allergy/Sinus/Cold/Flu Relief

Actifed - Tablets
Afrin - Nasal Spray
Airborne - Lemon Lime, On The Go Lemon Lime, Original, Pink Grapefruit, Very Berry
Albertsons - Allergy Relief, Children's (Cold, Allergy)
Children's Motrin - Cold Suspension (Berry)
Claritin - Child Chews, Child Grape Syrup, D, Liquid Gels, Original Tablets
Cold-Eeze - Cold Remedy Lozenges (All Flavors)
Dayquil - All Varieties
Diabetic - Diabetic Tussin (All Varieties)
Halls -
> Cough Drops Regular (Cherry, Honey Lemon, Ice Blue, Mentho Lyptus, Spearmint, Strawberry, Tropical Fruit)
> Cough Drops Sugar Free (Cherry, Citrus Blend, Fresh Mint, Honey Berry, Honey Lemon, Mountain Menthol, Peppermint, Spearmint)
> Halls Breezers (Cool Berry, Cool Creamy Strawberry, Sugar Free Cool Berry Tropical Chill)
> Halls Defense (Assorted Citrus, Harvest Cherry, Strawberry, Sugar Free, Watermelon)
> Halls Naturals (Harvest Peach w/Soothing Honey Center, Honey Lemon Chamomile, Mountain Berry w/Soothing Honey Center, Wild Cherry)
> Halls Plus (Cherry, Honey Lemon, Icy Lemon, Icy Strawberry, Menthol Lyptus)

Rx

Halls Refresh (Juicy Strawberry, Lemon Raspberry, Refreshing Mint, Tropical Wave)

Hannaford Brand - Allergy (All), Children's (Cold, Allergy), Children's Chewables, Cold & Flu

Kirkland Signature - AllerClear, Allergy Medicine, Allergy Tec, Children's Allergy Tec

Meijer -

Apap

Cold Child Suspension Grape

Cough Cold (Child Suspension Cherry, Infant Drops Cherry)

Daytime 6hr (Liquid, Liquid Gels)

Dibromm (DM Grape Elixir, Grape Elixir)

Diphedryl (Capsules, Cherry Elixir, Tablets)

Effervescent Cold Tablets

Ibuprofen Sinus (Brown Caplets)

Loratadine (QD Tablets, D 24hr Tablets)

Naproxen Sodium Sinus Cold Caplets

Nasal Spray (Extra Moist Liquid, Liquid, No Drip Pump Liquid)

Nitetime 6 hr (Cherry Liquid, Liquid Gels, Original Liquid)

Nitetime Cough 6 hr (Cherry Liquid)

PE Allergy Sinus Caplets

PE Cold Flu Day Cool Caplets

PE Cold Severe Congestion Caplets

Pedia Cough Decongestion Drops

Tri Acting Nitetime Grape Liquid

Tussin (CF Liquid, CS Liquid, Cough Cold Softgels, DM Clear Liquid, DM Liquid, Pedia Cough Cold Liquid)

Nyquil - All Varieties

Olbas -

Aromatherapy Massage Oil & Inhalant

Cough Syrup

Inhaler

PediaCare-

Allergy (Cherry)

Rx
    Allergy & Cold (Grape)
    Children's Plus w/Acetaminophen
    Children's w/o Acetaminophen
    Cough & Congestion (Cherry)
    Cough & Runny Nose (Cherry)
    Cough & Sore Throat (Cherry)
    Decongestant (Raspberry)
    Fever Reducer Pain Reliever (Cherry, Cherry & Grape, Dye Free)
    Flu (Bubblegum)
    Gentle Vapors
    Multi Symptom & Cold (Grape)

Primatene - Mist

St. Claire's Organics - Cough Calming Syrup, Decongest Inhaler, Herbal Throat Spray, Infection Formula, Throat Soothers

Theraflu -
    Hot Liquids (Cold & Cough, Cold & Sore Throat, Daytime Severe Cold & Cough, Flu & Sore Throat, Nighttime Severe Cold & Cough, Sugar Free Nighttime Severe Cold & Cough)
    Warming Relief Syrups (Cold & Chest Congestion, Flu & Sore Throat)

Tylenol -
    Cold Severe Congestion Caplets
    Sinus Severe Congestion

Walgreens -
    Allergy Multi Symptom (Day/Night Caplet Combo Pack, Day Caplets, Day Quick Gels, Night Caplets)
    Allergy Sinus Decongestant Daytime Caplets
    Apap Junior Strength Rapid Tab (Bubble Gum, Grape)
    Chest Congestion Caplets
    Children's (Multi Symptom, Plus Cold, Plus Flu Bubble Gum)
    Cold (Decongestant Multi Symptom (Day, Night), Head Congestion (Day, Day Severe, Night), Liquid Caplet (Day, Night), Liquid Caplet Sinus (Day, Night), Multi Symptom (Day/Night

Rx

Combo, Day Caplets, Day Quick Gel, Day Severe Capsules, Night Caplets), Tablets)

Cold & Flu Nighttime Relief Liquicaps

Cough & Sore Throat Cherry

Extended Cough Relief Adult Grape

Flu Relief Maximum Strength Tablets

Mucus Relief Tablets (DM Expectorant, PE Expectorant, Regular)

Runny Rhino Cold Relief Pops

Severe Allergy Caplets

Sinex (Long Acting Spray, Ultra Fine Mist)

Sinus D Daytime Caplets

Sinus Congestion & Pain (Day Night Caplet Combo, Day (Caplets, Gelcaps, Quick Gels, Severe Caplets))

Wal-Act Tablets

Wal-Born Effervescent Tablets (Lemon Lime, Orange, Grape)

Wal-Dryl (Capsules, D Allergy Sinus, Dye Free Liquigels, Minitabs, Severe Allergy & Sinus,)

Wal-Finate (Allergy Tablets, D Tablets)

Wal-Flu Warming Relief Severe Cold (Daytime Cherry, Nighttime Cherry)

Walgreens Child Plus Cough Nose Cherry

Walgreens Comfort Gel Supreme Cherry

Walgreens Soothe (Cherry, Original)

Walgreens Cola Syrup

Walgreens Throat Lozenge Cherry

Wal-Mucil Smooth Sugar Free Berry

Wal-Phed (Cold Cough Caplets, D Tablets, PE (Nighttime Cold, Non Drying Sinus, Severe Cold, Sinus Headache, Tablets), Sinus & Allergy)

Wal-Tap DM Children's Cold Cough Elixir Red Grape

Wal-Tussin Cough (Long Acting Orange, Softgels)

Vicks - All Products *(Except Sore Throat Lozenges)*

Rx

Antacids

Children's Mylanta - Tablets Bubblegum

Digestive Advantage - Crohn's & Colitis, Irritable Bowel
  Syndrome, Lactose Intolerance

Kirkland Signature - Antacid

Lactaid - Dietary Supplement (Fast Act Caplets, Fast Act Chewables,
  Original Strength Caplets)

Meijer -
  Antacid Calcium (Peppermint Chewables, Ultra Fruit Chewables,
    XS Berry Chewables, XS Chewables, XS Fruit Chewables, XS
    Tropical Chewables, XS Wintergreen Chewables)
  Antacid Fast Acting Liquid (Maximum Strength Cherry, Regular
    Strength Original)
  Cimetidine Tablets
  Dairy Digestive (Regular Strength, Ultra Caplets)
  Effervescent Antacid Pain Tablets
  Milk Of Magnesia (Cherry Liquid, Mint Liquid, Original Liquid)
  Pink Bismuth (Chewables, Maximum Strength Liquid, Regular
    Strength Liquid)
  Ranitidine

Mylanta - Maximum Strength Liquid Original Flavor, Regular
  Strength Liquid Original Flavor,

Pepcid AC - 10 mg Tablets, Complete Chewable Mint Tablets

Pepto Bismol - All Varieties

St. Claire's Organics - Tummy Soothers

Tagamet HB

Tums -
  Extra 750 (Assorted Berries, Assorted Fruit, Assorted Tropical Fruit,
    Wintergreen)
  Extra 750 Sugar Free (Orange Cream)
  Kids (Cherry Blast)
  Regular Strength (Assorted Fruit, Peppermint)

Rx

Smoothies (Assorted Fruit, Assorted Tropical Fruit, Peppermint)
(Cocoa & Crème Are NOT Gluten Free)
Ultra 1000 (Assorted (Berries, Fruit, Tropical Fruit), Peppermint)
Walgreens-
Antacid Chewable Tablets (Assorted, Original Mint, Maximum
Strength Lemon, Peppermint, Ultra Tabs (Berry, Fruit, Mint),
Wintergreen)
Lactose Relief

Antibiotic/Analgesic Ointment & Spray

Cortaid - All Varieties
Walgreens - Hydrogen Peroxide

Anti-Diarrhea

Digestive Advantage - Crohn's & Colitis, Irritable Bowel Syndrome,
Lactose Intolerance
Imodium - AD Caplets, Advanced Chewable Tablets
Lactaid - Dietary Supplement (Fast Act Caplets, Fast Act Chewables,
Original Strength)
Meijer -
Loperamide (Caplets, Liquid)
Pink Bismuth (Chewables, Maximum Strength Liquid, Regular
Strength Liquid)
Pepto Bismol - All Varieties
St. Claire's Organics - Tummy Soothers
Walgreens - Anti Diarrheal Caplets, Lactose Relief

Rx

Anti-Fungal

AZO - Yeast Tablet (Maximum Strength, Standard)
Meijer -
  Miconazole Cream (3 Day Preapp. Combo, 3 Day Disapp. Combo, 7 Day Disapp., 7 Day Reapp.)
  Tioconazole 1 Day Ointment (Disapp.)
Walgreens - Tioconazole 1 Day Ointment (Disapp.)

Anti-Gas

Digestive Advantage - Crohn's & Colitis, Irritable Bowel Syndrome, Lactose Intolerance
Infant's Mylicon - Drops Non Staining
Lactaid - Dietary Supplement (Fast Act Caplets, Fast Act Chewables, Original Strength)
Meijer - Gas Relief Ultra Softgels, Simethicone Nonstaining Drops
Mylanta - Maximum Strength Gas Mint Tablets
Phazyme ▲ - Ultra Strength Softgels
St. Claire's Organics - Tummy Soothers
Walgreens - Cherry Gas Relief Tablets, Lactose Relief

Cosmetics

Afterglow Cosmetics ▲ - All Products
Arbonne-
  Blusher
  Cream Concealer
  Eye Liner
  Eye Shadow
  Lip Liner

Loose Translucent Powder
Mineral Powder Foundation SPF 15
Wipe Out Eye Makeup Remover

Rx

Cough Drops/Sore Throat Spray/Lozenges

Albertsons - Mouth Rinse, Sore Throat Spray

Best Sweet - Bee M.D (Organic Honey Lemon Throat Drop (Natural Honey, Regular))

Cold-Eeze - Cold Remedy Lozenges (All Flavors)

Halls -

Cough Drops Regular (Cherry, Honey Lemon, Ice Blue, Mentho Lyptus, Spearmint, Strawberry, Tropical Fruit)

Cough Drops Sugar Free (Cherry, Citrus Blend, Fresh Mint, Honey Berry, Honey Lemon, Mountain Menthol, Peppermint, Spearmint)

Halls Breezers (Cool Berry, Cool Creamy Strawberry, Tropical Chill, Sugar Free Cool Berry)

Halls Defense (Assorted Citrus, Harvest Cherry, Strawberry, Sugar Free, Watermelon)

Halls Naturals (Harvest Peach w/Soothing Honey Center, Honey Lemon Chamomile, Mountain Berry w/Soothing Honey Center, Wild Cherry)

Halls Plus (Cherry, Honey Lemon, Icy Lemon, Icy Strawberry, Menthol Lyptus)

Halls Refresh (Juicy Strawberry, Lemon Raspberry, Refreshing Mint, Tropical Wave)

Hannaford Brand - Cough Drops (All)

Meijer - Cherry Sore Throat Spray

Organix - Organic Cough & Sore Throat Drops (Dark Chocolate Mint, Golden Honey Lemon, Orchard Cherry)

Rx Vicks - Formula 44 Sore Throat Spray
    Walgreens -
        Cola Syrup
        Comfort Gel Supreme Cherry
        Cough & Sore Throat Cherry
        Soothe (Cherry, Original)
        Throat Lozenge Cherry

Deodorant

Crystal -
    All Deodorants
    All Crystal Essence
Dakota Free - Solid Stick Deodorant
Naturally Fresh Deodorant Crystal -
    Clear Twist Up Stick w/Aloe Vera
    Roll On
Tom's Of Maine -
    Crystal Confidence Roll On Deodorant (Citrus Zest, Fragrance
        Free, Wild Garden)
    Natural Long Lasting Deodorant (Roll On, Stick)
    Natural Original Deodorant Stick
    Natural Sensitive Care Deodorant Stick

Detox

Renew Life -
    Cleansing (Candi Gone, Cleanse More, Cleanse Smart, Daily
        Multi Detox, Diet Start Cleanse, First Cleanse, Heavy Metal
        Cleanse, Liver Detox, Merc Free Cleanse, Organic Total Body
        Cleanse, Power Cleanse, Total Kidney Detox, Total Body Rapid
        Cleanse)

Diabetic Products

Rx

Albertsons - Tussin (All)
Diabetic - Diabetic Tussin (All Varieties)
Diachrome - Nutritional Supplements
Enterex - All Products
Glucerna - Shakes (All Varieties), Snack Shakes (All Varieties)
Glucoburst - Vanilla Drink, Gel, Glucose Tablets
Hannaford Brand - Tussin (All)
Scot-Tussin -
  Cough
  Cough Suppressant & Cold Relief
  Multi Action Cold & Allergy
Walgreens -
  Glucose Tablets (Assorted, Grape, Orange, Raspberry, Sour Apple)
  Glucoshot (Lemon Lime, Mixed Berry)

Eye Care

Hy-Vee Health Market - Healthy (Eyes Extra, Super Vision)
Visine - A, AC, Advanced Relief, All Day Eye Itch Relief, Dry Eye
  Relief, Long Lasting Dry Eye Relief, Long Lasting Redness Relief,
  Maximum Redness Relief, Multi Symptom Relief, Original
  Redness, Tired Eye Relief, Total Eye Soothing Wipes

Hair Care

Arbonne - Sea Source Detox Spa Fortifying Hair Mask
California Baby -
  Calendula (Hair Conditioner, Shampoo & Body Wash)
  Calming (Hair Conditioner, Hair Detangler, Shampoo & Body
    Wash)

Rx

Super Sensitive (Hair Conditioner, Shampoo & Body Wash)

Swimmer's Defense (Conditioner, Shampoo & Body Wash)

Tea Tree & Lavender (Conditioner, Shampoo & Body Wash)

Dessert Essence Organics -

Conditioner (Fragrance Free, Green Apple & Ginger, Italian Red Grape, Lemon Tea Tree, Red Raspberry)

Shampoo (Fragrance Free, Green Apple & Ginger, Italian Red Grape, Lemon Tea Tree, Red Raspberry)

Dove -

Damage Therapy Shampoo (Daily Moisture, Frizz Control, Heat Defense, Intensive Repair, Shine Boost, Volume Boost)

Damage Therapy Conditioner (Daily Moisture Treatment, Frizz Control, Intensive Repair Daily Treatment, Intensive Repair, Volume Boost)

EO-

Conditioner (Rose Geranium & Citrus ●, Rosemary & Mint ●)

French Lavender Detangler Spray ●

Rosemary & Cedarwood Pre Shampoo Treatment●

Shampoo (Chamomile & Honey ●, French Lavender ●, Rose & Chamomile ●, Rosemary & Mint ●, Sweet Orange ●)

Wild Lime & Ginger Hair Repair ●

Wild Rose & Coconut Conditioning Serum ●

Fleurish Beauty - Premium Conditioner, Premium Shampoo

Full Circle - Dry Hair Conditioner, Shampoo (Dry Hair, Normal Hair)

Gluten-Free Savonnerie▲ - All Products

Head & Shoulders – All Varieties

Johnson's - Baby Shampoo

Keys ▲- All Products

Kroger Brand - Comforts For Baby (Baby Wash, Shampoo)

Meijer - Minoxidil 5% Liquid (30 Day, 90 Day)

Surface - All Hair Products

Laxatives/Hemorrhoidal Relief Rx

Citrucel -
 Caplets
 Fiber Therapy Powder (Orange Regular, Orange Sugar Free)
Ensure - All Shakes
Fiber Choice -
 Assorted Berry Plus Calcium, Orange, Strawberry Weight
  Management, Sugar Free (Assorted, Orange)
Fleet - Fiber Gummies
Kirkland Signature - Fiber Tabs
Konsyl - All Fiber Products
Meijer -
 Fiber Therapy Caplets
 Hemorrhoidal (Cream, Ointment, Suppository)
 Laxative Tablets (Natural MS, Senna, Womens)
 NVP (Capsules, Original Orange Powder, Original Regular Powder,
  Smooth Orange Powder, Sugar Free Smooth Orange Powder)
Metamucil - All Capsules, All Powders
Pedia-Lax - All Varieties
Tucks - Hydrocortisone Anti Itch Ointment, Medicated Pads,
 Hemorrhoidal Ointment, Take Alongs Medicated Pads
Walgreens -
 Castor Oil
 Fiber (Berry Chewable Tablets, Caplets (Laxative, Plus Calcium,
  Regular), Soluble Powder)
 Laxative Tablets (Maximum Strength, Regular Strength)
 Women's Laxative

Rx
Lip Care

Arbonne -
  Before Sun Lip Saver SPF 30
  Bio Nutria Herbal Lip Ointment
  Bio Nutria Lip Service Dietary Supplement
Blistex -
  Complete Moisture
  DCT SPF 20
  Deep Renewal
  Fruit Smoothies (Berry Explosion, Melon Medley, Triple Tropical)
  Lip Infusions (Cherry Splash, Moisture Splash)
  Lip Ointment
  Lip Revitalizer
  Raspberry Lemonade Blast
Desert Essence Organics - Lip Tints (Coconut, Italian Red Grape,
  Red Raspberry, Vanilla Chai)

Misc. Products

Band-Aid - Flexible Fabric
Elmer's - All Products *(Except Finger Paints)*
Nature's Baby Organics - All Purpose Deodorizer

Motion Sickness

Meijer - Anti Nausea Liquid
Wal-Dram - Tablets (Less Drowsy, Motion Sickness, Motion Sickness
  Chewable, Travel Sickness)

Oral Hygiene

3M - All Dental Materials *(at the dentist)*
Aquafresh - All Toothpaste Varieties
Biotene Oral Balance - All Products
Crest - All Products
Dentsply Caulk - All Dental Materials *(at the dentist)*
Efferdent - Denture Cleanser
Effergrip - Denture Adhesive Cream
Enamel Pro -
    Fluoride Topical Gel (Bubblegum, Cherry, Orange, Strawberry)
        (at the dentist)
    Fluoride Varnish *(at the dentist)*
    Prophy Paste (All Flavors) *(at the dentist)*
Glide - Floss
Glitter - Prophy Paste (All Flavors) *(at the dentist)*
Hannaford Brand - Mouth Rinses (All)
Jason - All Toothpaste
Kolorz - Prophy Paste (All Flavors) *(at the dentist)*
Listerine -
    Agent Cool Blue Tinting Rinse
    Antiseptic Mouthwash (All Varieties)
    Pocket Paks Oral Care Strips (All Varieties)
    Totalcare Anticavity Mouthwash (All Varieties)
    Whitening Pen
    Whitening Pre Brush Rinse
    Whitening Quick Dissolving Strips
    Whitening Vibrant White Rinse
    ZERO Mouthwash
Nupro -
    Fluoride *(at the dentist)*
    Prophy Paste *(at the dentist)*

Rx
    Oasis - Moisturizing Mouthwash, Moisturizing Mouth Spray

    Peridex - Chlorhexidine Gluconate Oral Rinse

    Plax - Advanced Formula Plaque Loosening Rinse
       (Original, Soft Mint)

    Polident - Denture Cleanser

    Scope - Mouthwash (All Varieties)

    Sensodyne - Pronamel Toothpaste

    Sparkle - Prophy Paste (All Flavors) *(at the dentist)*

    Sparkle Free - Prophy Paste (All Flavors) *(at the dentist)*

    St. Claire's Organics - Icy Mint Herbal Mouthwash

    Tom's Of Maine -

       Children's Natural Anticavity Fluoride Toothpaste

       Children's Natural Fluoride Free Toothpaste

       Floss Antiplaque Flat (Original, Spearmint)

       Floss Antiplaque Round

       Maximum Strength Sensitive Fluoride Toothpaste

       Natural Anticavity Fluoride Toothpaste

       Natural Antiplaque Fluoride Free Toothpaste w/Propolis & Myrrh

       Natural Antiplaque Plus Whitening Gel Fluoride Free Toothpaste

       Natural Antiplaque Tartar Control & Whitening Fluoride Free
          Toothpaste

       Natural Cleansing Mouthwash

       Natural Sensitive Toothpaste Fluoride

       Natural Whole Care Toothpaste

       Natural Whole Care Toothpaste Gel

    Walgreens -

       Antiseptic Mouthwash (Amber, Blue Mint, Spring Mint)

         Toothpaste (Herbal Mint, Minty Fresh, Sensitive (Mint,
         Whitening Paste), Total)

       Denture Cream (Mint, Original)

    Ziroxide - Prophy Paste *(at the dentist)*

Pain Relief

Rx

Children's Motrin - Suspension Berry, Suspension Bubblegum, Suspension Dye Free, Suspension Grape

Children's Tylenol - Meltaways (Bubblegum Burst, Cherry Blast, Grape Punch)

Hannaford Brand - Aspirin, Ibuprofen

Infant's Motrin - Drops (Dye Free, Regular)

Infant's Tylenol - Drops (Cherry, Grape)

Junior Tylenol - Meltaways (Bubblegum Burst, Grape Punch)

Kirkland Signature - Aspirin, Children's Pain Reliever, Extra Strength Rapid Release Pain Reliever, Ibuprofen, Low Dose, Naproxen Sodium

Meijer -

Apap (Caplet, Cool Caplet, ER Caplet Red, ER Caplet White, ETS Tablet, Gelcap, Geltab, Tablet)

Apap Child (Bubblegum Suspension, Cherry Suspension, Grape Suspension)

Apap Infant Cherry Suspension

Aspirin (Adult Orange Chewables, Child Orange Chewables, Coated Tablets, Coated Yellow Tablets)

Aspirin Enteric Coated (Tablet, Yellow Tablet)

Headache Tablets

Ibuprofen (Caplets Brown, Caplets Orange, Child Suspension Bubblegum, Junior Caplets, Junior Chewables Orange, Tablets Brown, Tablets Orange)

Migraine Caplets

Naproxen Sodium (Caplets, NCRC Caplets, Tablets)

Motrin IB - Caplets, Tablets

St. Joseph - Aspirin (Adult Chewable Tablets, Enteric Coated Tablets)

Tylenol - 8hr Caplets, Arthritis Pain Caplets, Extra Strength Caplets, Regular Strength Tablets

Rx

Walgreens -

Adult Low Strength Aspirin (Enteric, Chewable)

Aspirin Tablets (Box, Bottle, Chewable Low Dose (Cherry, Orange), Yellow Label)

Backache Relief Caplets

Extra Strong Headache Relief Tablets

Extra Strong Pain Reliever Caplets (Easy Open, Quick Gels (PM, Regular), Regular, Twin)

Extra Strong Women's Menstrual Caplets

Headache Relief PM Tablets

Ibuprofen Tablets (Brown (Caplets, Tablets), Dye & Color Free, Dye Free, Orange (Caplets, Tablets))

Knee Pain Relief Ortho (For Men, For Women)

Menstrual Relief (Caplets, Gelcaps)

Tri Buffered Aspirin Tablets

Urinary Pain Relief

Pet Food

IAMS -

Healthy Naturals Dry Cat Food Adult (Weight Control)

Premium Protection Dry Cat Food (Adult Cat, Kitten, Senior Cat)

Premium Protection Dry Dog Food (Puppy)

ProActive Health Dry Cat Food (Adult Active Maturity, Adult Active Maturity Hairball Care, Adult Digestive Care, Adult Hairball Care, Adult Indoor Weight & Hairball Care, Adult Multi Cat w/ Chicken, Adult Original Chicken, Adult Original Ocean Fish w/Rice, Adult Original w/Lamb & Rice, Adult Original w/Tuna, Adult Weight Control, Kitten)

ProActive Health Dry Dog Food (Adult Active Maturity Small & Toy Breed, Adult Chunks, Adult Mini Chunks, Smart Puppy Large Breed, Smart Puppy Original, Smart Puppy Small & Toy Breeds)

ProActive Health Canned Cat Food (Adult Filets w/Chicken In

pet food **Rx**

Gravy, Adult Filets w/Salmon In Sauce, Adult Filets w/Skipjack
Tuna In Sauce, Adult Pate w/Chicken & Liver, Adult Pate w/
Pacific Salmon, Adult Pate w/Seafood Sampler, Adult Premium
w/(Country Style Turkey & Giblets, Gourmet Chicken, Lamb &
Rice, Select Oceanfish, Tender Beef), Kitten Premium Pate w/
Gourmet Chicken)

ProActive Health Canned Dog Food (Adult Ground Dinner w/
(Beef & Rice, Chicken & Rice, Lamb & Rice, Turkey & Rice),
Adult Ground Mixed Grill w/Chicken & Beef), Puppy Ground
Dinner with Chicken & Rice)

Veterinary Formula Canned Cat Food (Intestinal Low Residue
Feline, Maximum Calorie Canine & Feline, Renal Multi Stage
Feline, Skin & Coat Response LB Feline, Urinary S Low Ph/S
Feline, Weigh Loss Restricted Calorie Feline)

Veterinary Formula Canned Dog Food Canine Formula (Intestinal
Low Residue, Skin & Coat Response FP)

Veterinary Formula Dry Dog Food (Early Stage Canine, Intestinal
Low Residue Canine, Intestinal Low Residue Puppy)

Joint Canine

Skin & Coat Response FP Canine

Weight Control D Optimum Weight Control Canine

Nutro -

Natural Choice Dry Food Adult Dog (High Energy, Lamb Meal &
Rice, Lite)

Natural Choice Dry Food Adult Dog Large Breed (Lamb & Rice
Meal)

Natural Choice Dry Food Puppy (Lamb Meal & Rice)

Natural Choice Dry Food Puppy Large Breed (Lamb & Rice Meal)

Purina One -

Adult Cat (Hairball & Healthy Weight Formula, Healthy Weight
Formula, Salmon & Tuna Flavor)

Royal Canin -

Adult Cat Indoor Intense Hairball 34

Baby Cat 34

Rx

Veterinary Diets Canine (Hypoallergenic, Potato & Duck, Potato & Rabbit, Potato & Venison, Potato & Whitefish)

Veterinary Diets Feline (Hypoallergenic, Green Peas & Duck, Green Peas & Lamb, Green Peas & Rabbit, Green Peas & Venison)

Science Diet -

Adult Cat (Hairball Control, Hairball Control Light, Indoor, Light, Optimal Care (Oceanfish & Rice, Original), Oral Care, Sensitive Skin)

Adult Dog (Active, Hi Energy, Large Breed, Light (Large Breed, Regular, Small & Toy Breed, Small Bites), Oral Care, Sensitive Skin)

Kitten (Healthy Development (Oceanfish & Rice, Original), Indoor)

Mature Adult Cat (Active Longevity, Hairball Control, Indoor)

Mature Adult Dog (Active Longevity, Large Breed, Small Bites, Small & Toy Breed)

Puppy (Healthy Development Original, Large Breed, Small Bites, Small & Toy Breed)

Play Dough

Aroma Dough - All Natural Playing Dough
BlueDominoes - Organic Activity Dough ●
Crayola - Air Dry Clay, Model Magic, Model Magic Fusion, Modeling Clay *(Crayola Play Dough is NOT Gluten Free)*
Max's Mud - Organic Sculpting Dough ●

Skin Care

Arbonne -

ABC Baby Care (Body Oil, Herbal Diaper Rash Cream)

Aromassentials

Awaken Sea Salt Scrub 16 oz.

Unwind (Bath Salts, Massage Oil)

Rx

Bio Nutria
  Herbal (Muscle Massage Gel, Vapor Rub)
  Leg Vein Formula
Clear Advantage
  Acne Lotion
  Skin Support Supplement
  Spot Treatment
FC5
  Exfoliating New Cell Scrub
  Hydrating Eye Crème
  Moisturizing Night Crème
  Nurturing Day Lotion w/SPF 20
  Oil Absorbing Day Lotion w/SPF 20
  Purifying Cleanser + Toner
  Skin Conditioning Oil
  Ultra Hydrating Hand Crème
NutriMinC RE9
  Retaliate Wrinkle Filler
SeaSource Detox Spa
  5 In 1 Essential Massage Oil
  Foaming Sea Salt Scrub
  Purifying Sea Soak
  Remineralizing Body Lotion 24 Hr.
  Renewing Body Gelée
  Sea Mud Face and Body Mask
California Baby -
  Aloe Vera Cream
  Calendula (Cream, Everyday Lotion)
  Calming (Botanical Moisturizing Cream, Everyday Lotion, Diaper
    Rash Cream, Massage Oil, Non Talc Powder, Soothing & Healing
    Spray)
  Citronella (SPF 30+ Sunscreen Lotion, Summer Lotion)
  Colds & Flu Massage Oil
  Everyday/Year Round SPF 30 (Sunblock Stick, Sunscreen Lotion)

Rx

I Love You Aromatherapy Massage Oil
No Fragrance Sunblock Stick (SPF 30+)
No Fragrance Sunscreen Lotion (SPF 18, SPF 30+)
Overtired & Cranky Massage Oil
Sunblock Stick SPF 30 (No Fragrance)
Sunscreen SPF 30 (Citronella, No Fragrance)
Super Sensitive (Everyday Lotion, Massage Oil)

Clean & Clear - Foaming Facial Cleaner (Oil Free, Sensitive Skin)

Coppertone - All Varieties (Oil Free, Pure & Simple, Sensitive, Sport, Ultra Guard, Water Babies)

Dessert Essence Organics -

Age Reversal Pomegranate (Eye Serum, Face Serum)
Age Reversal SPF 30 Mineral Sunscreen
Almond Hand & Body Lotion
Bulgarian Lavender Hand & Body Lotion
Coconut Hand & Body Lotion
Pistachio Foot Repair Cream
Pumpkin Hand Repair Cream
Spicy Citrus Hand & Body Lotion
Vanilla Chai Hand & Body Lotion

Fleurish Beauty - Luxe Lotion

Gluten-Free Savonnerie ▲ - All Products

Johnson's - Head To Toe Fragrance Free Baby Lotion

Keys ▲ - All Products

Kroger Brand - Comforts For Baby (Lotion, Powder)

Lubriderm -

Advanced Therapy (Hand Cream, w/SPF 30, Moisturizing Cream, Original Lotion, Soothing Lotion)
Daily Moisture Lotion (Fragrance Free, Sensitive Skin, Original, w/SPF 15, w/Shea & Cocoa Butter)
Intense Skin Repair (Body Lotion, Calming Relief Lotion, Ointment)

Rx

Nature's Baby Organics - Ah Choo Chest Rub, Baby Oil, Diaper
Ointment, Face & Body Moisturizer, Silky Dusting Powder,
Soothing Stick
NutraBeautiful - Lotion
Oil Of Olay - All Professional ProX Products
St. Claire's Organics - Athletic Recovery Oil
Walgreens -
Callus Reducing Ointment
Callus Remover (Regular, Extra Thick)

Sleep Aids

Meijer - Sleep Aid Nitetime (Caplets, Tablets)
Simply Sleep - Caplets
Sominex - Caplets
Tylenol - PM Caplets
Walgreens - Nightime Sleep Aid

Soap

Arbonne -
Aromassentials
Awaken Sea Salt Scrub 16 oz.
Bio Nutria Herbal Vapor Soak
Clear Advantage Acne Wash
Unwind Bath Salts
FC5
Exfoliating New Cell Scrub
Purifying Cleanser + Toner
SeaSource Detox Spa
Detoxifying Rescue Wash
Foaming Sea Salt Scrub
Purifying Sea Soak

Rx California Baby -
  Bubble Bath (Calendula, Calming, Chamomile & Herbs, Colds
    & Flu, I Love You, Light & Happy, Overtired & Cranky, Party, Super
    Sensitive)
  Calendula Shampoo & Body Wash
  Calming Shampoo & Body Wash
  Diaper Area Wash
  Hand Wash (First Aid Moisturizing, Super Sensitive)
  Swimmer's Defense Shampoo & Body Wash
  Tea Tree & Lavender Shampoo & Body Wash
Dessert Essence Organics -
  Age Reversal Pomegranate Facial Cleansing Gel
  Almond Body Wash
  Bulgarian Lavender Body Wash
  Coconut Body Wash
  Fragrance Free Body Wash
  Grapefruit Hand Wash
  Green Apple & Ginger Body Wash
  Italian Red Grape Body Wash
  Red Raspberry Body Wash
  Vanilla Chai Body Wash
EO -
  Liquid Hand Soap (Chocolate & Mint ●, French Lavender ●,
    Lemon & Eucalyptus ●, Peppermint & Tea Tree ●, Rose
    Geranium & Citrus ●, Rosemary & Mint ●, Unscented w/
    Coconut Milk ●)
  Shower Gel (Chocolate & Peppermint ●, Grapefruit & Mint ●,
    Lavender ●, Orange Fusion ●, Rose & Chamomile ●)
Fleurish Beauty - Aloe & Shea Body Wash, Bar Soap (Ambrosia,
  Cassia Clove, Lavender, Lemongrass, Patchouli, Peppermint,
  Sandalwood)
Full Circle - Shower Gel (Tangerine, Melon & Ginger)
Gillette - Mens Body Wash (All Varieties)
Gluten-Free Savonnerie ▲ - All Products

Rx

Keys ▲ - All Products
Kiss My Face -
   Peace Soap
      100% Natural All Purpose Castille Soap (Grassy Mint, Lavender
         Mandarin, Lemongrass Clary Sage, Pomegranate Acai)
      100% Natural Foaming Castille Soap (Grassy Mint, Lavender
         Mandarin, Lemongrass Clary Sage, Pomegranate Acai)
Nature's Baby Organics - Bubble Bath (Lovely Lavender,
   Tangy Tangerine)
Oil Of Olay - Sensitive Moisturizing Bar
Tom's Of Maine - Body Bar (Natural Deodorant, Natural
   Moisturizing)

Stay Awake

Meijer - Stay Awake Tablets
Vivarin - Tablets
Walgreens - Awake Caffeine Caplets

Supplements

Arbonne - Smart Nutritional Hybrids Daily Nutritional Chews For
   Teens, Smart Nutritional Hybrids Daily
Carlson - All Supplements
Country Life - All Supplements ●
Ensure - All Shakes
Flex A Min - Complete, Triple Strength
Freeda - All Supplements ●
Giant Eagle Brand -
   ABC Senior w/Lutein
   Acidophilus
   Beta Carotene

Rx
Biotin
Calcium (Magnesium, Magnesium & Zinc, w/Vitamin D)
Chondroitin Complex
Cod Liver Oil
Co Q10 15mg
Cranberry
Echinacea
Echinacea/Goldenseal
EPA Fish Oil
Ferrous Sulfate
Fish Oil (1000mg, 1200mg)
Flaxseed
Folic Acid
Garlic Odorless
Ginkgo Biloba
Ginseng
Ginseng w/Royal Jelly
Green Tea
Lecithin 1200mg
Lysine
Magnesium
Maximum Strength Glucosamine/Chondroitin
Melatonin
Milk Thistle
Multi Day (Calcium Iron & Zinc, Vitamin)
Niacin
Oystercal 500
Potassium
St. John's Wort
Stress Tablets
Triple Strength Glucosamine/Chondroitin
Zinc
Ginkoba - Memory
Ginsana - Energy

supplements

GlutaSolve - Powdered Glutamine Supplement (Packets)   **Rx**

Hannaford Brand –
  Acetaminophen
  Acidophilus
  Beta Carotene
  Biotin
  Calcium (600, 600 w/Vitamin D)
  Calcium Magnesium Zinc
  Chromium Picolinate (200, 500)
  Co Q10 (50, 100, 200, 300)
  Cranberry
  Echinacea
  Evening Primrose Oil
  Ferrous Sulfate
  Fish Oil (1200, 1000)
  Flaxseed Oil (1000, 1200)
  Folic Acid ((400, 800) For Women, For Women +50)
  Garlic
  Ginkgo Biloba
  Glucosamine
  Glucosamine Chondroitin
  Green Tea
  Korean Ginseng
  L Lysine
  Lutein (6mg, 20mg)
  MSM
  Magnesium (250, 500)
  Melatonin
  Norwegian Cod Liver Oil
  Potassium Gluconate
  Prenatal
  Saw Palmetto
  Soya Lecithin
  St. John's Wort
  Xliacin

Rx Hy-Vee Health Market -
   Acidophilus
   Enteric Coated Fish Oil 1000mg Omega 3
   Enteric Coated Triple Omega Complex 3 6 9
   Evening Primrose Oil 500mg
   Fish Oil 1000mg Omega 3
   Fish Oil 1200mg Softgels
   Hair Skin & Nails
   Natural Garlic Oil Softgels
   Norwegian Cod Liver Oil
   Omega 3 1000mg Softgels
   Omega 3 Fish Oil 1000mg Enteric Coated
   Water Soluble E 400

Iceland Health -
   Advanced Memory Formula w/Omega 3
   Bone Health
   Co Q10 Softgels
   Glucose Control Formula
   Immunity Plus
   Joint Relief w/Omega 3 (Cream, Softgels)
   Maximum Strength Omega 3 Softgels
   Omega 3 Regular Strength + Vitamin D3

Kirkland Signature -
   Co Q10 300mg
   Daily Multi Pack w/Asian Ginseng
   Glucosamine HCl w/MSM 1500mg
   Glucosamine HCl 1500mg w/Chondroitin Sulfate 1200mg
   Omega 3 Fish Oil

Kirkman -
   Acetyl L Carnitine
   Acidophilus Powder
   Alpha Ketoglutaric Acid
   Alpha Lipoic Acid
   Amino Support (Capsules, Powder)

Rx

Beta Glucan

Bifido Complex (Advanced Formula, Regular)

Bio Core Dairy

Buffered Magnesium (Glycinate Bio Max Series Powder, Oxide)

Carb Digest w/Isogest

Chromium

Cod Liver Oil (Lemon Lime Liquid, Regular Liquid, w/Vitamins A & D)

Coenzyme Q10 (Capsules, Chewable Tablets, Tablets)

Colostrum Gold (Flavored, Unflavored)

Creatine (Capsules)

DMAE (Capsules, Chewable Wafers)

DMG (Capsules, Capsules w/Folic Acid & B12, Capsules w/Folinic Acid & B12, Liquid, Maximum Strength, w/B12 & Folinic Acid Liquid)

DPP IV Forte

DRN (Detoxification Booster Capsules, Lithium, Vitamin/Mineral Basic Supplement Powder, Vitamin/Mineral LDA Basic Supplement)

Detox Aid Advanced Formula

Detoxification Aid Pro Support II

EFA Powder

EnZym Complete DPP IV II (Regular, w/Isogest)

EnZymAid Multi Enzyme Complex

Everyday Multi Vitamin (Regular, w/o Vitamins A & D)

Folic Acid (Chewable Tablets, w/B12 Capsules, w/B12 Liquid)

Folinic Acid (Capsules, w/B12 Liquid)

GABA (Plain, w/Niacinamide & Inositol)

Gastro Support

Gastromune AI Support

Ginkgo Biloba

Glucosamine Sulfate

Glycine

Grape Extract

Rx

Grapefruit Seed Extract

Idebenone

Immuno Aid

Inositol Pure Soluble Powder

Iron Bio Max Series (Capsules, Liquid)

L Glutamine

L Taurine

Lactobacillus Acidophilus

Lactobacillus Duo

Magnesium (Citrate Soluble Powder, Glycinate Bio Max Series, Magnesium, Malate, Sulfate Cream)

Maximum Spectrum Enzyme Complete/DPP IV Fruit Free w/Isogest

Melatonin (Chewables, Plus Magnesium, Slow Release Tablets)

Methylcobalamin Concentrated Powder

Milk Thistle

Mito Cell Support

Molybdenum

Multi (Enzyme Formula, Flora Spectrum)

N Acetyl Cysteine

Nordic Naturals (Arctic Cod Liver Oil Liquid (Orange, Peach, Regular), Balanced Omega Combination, Cod Liver Oil Soft Gels, DHA Junior Strawberry, ProDHA, ProEFA Capsules, ProEFA Soft Gels, ProEPA, ProOmega Soft Gels)

Nu Thera (Everyday, Everyday Companion, w/P5P, w/o Vitamins A & D)

P 5 P (Regular, w/Magnesium Glycinate)

Peptidase Complete

Phenol Assist (Companion, Regular)

Pro Bio (Chewable Wafers, Defense, Gold, Inulin Free)

Pro Culture Gold

Pro Immune Support

Reduced L Glatathione (Capsules, Lotion)

Saccharomyces Boulardii

Selenium

supplements

Rx

Spectrum Complete (Capsules, Powder Flavored, Powder Regular)

Super Cranberry Extract (Capsules, Chewables)

Super NuThera (Caplets, Capsules, Challenge Powders, Lemon Lime Liquid, New Improved Powder, Powder, Raspberry Flavored Concentrate, Tropical Fruit Liquid, w/P5P Caplets, w/P5P Lemon Lime Flavored Concentrate, w/P5P Liquid, w/P5P New Improved Powder, w/P5P Powder, w/o Vitamins A & D (Cherry Liquid, Regular, Tropical Fruit Liquid))

Super Pro Bio (Bio Max Series)

TMG (Capsules, Capsules w/Folic Acid & B12, Liquid w/Folinic Acid & B12, Powder w/Folic Acid & B12, w/Folic Acid & B12, w/Folinic Acid & B12, w/Folinic Acid & Methyl B12)

Thera Response

Threelac

Vanadium

Yeast Aid (Capsules, Powder)

Meijer -

Acidophilus Bifido RS

Antioxidant (Natural Caplets, Regular, w/Zinc Tablets)

Astaxanthin

Beta Carotene Natural Softgels

Biocosinol

CLA (Conjugated Linolenic Acid)

Chromium Picolinate

Cinnamon Capsules

Cod Liver Oil

Co Q10 (Capsules, Softgels)

Cranberry Caplets

Cranmax

DHA

EPA (Eicosapentaenoic Acid)

Echinacea Caplets

Estroplus Extra Strength

Rx

Evening Primrose Oil Softgels

Ferrous Gluconate Tablets

Fish Oil (Concentrate, Enteric Coated, Enteric Softgels, Extra
Strength, Extra Strength Enteric Coated, Hi Potency Softgels,
Softgels, w/Co Q10)

Flax Seed Oil Softgels

Focus Smart

Folic Natural Tablets

GLA (Gamma Linolenic Acid)

Garlic Hi Potency Odorless Tablets

Ginkgo Biloba Caplets

Ginseng Softgels

Glucosamine & Collagen & HA

Glucosamine Chondroitin (3X, All Day Double Strength Tablets,
Extra Strength, Plus MSM, Regular, Regular Strength Caplets,
SOD Free Caplets, w/HA Tablets, w/MSM Double Strength
Caplets, w/MSM HLA Caplets)

Glucosamine Complex Caplets

Glucosamine Sulfate Caplets

Green Tea

Hair Skin Nail

Lecithin Softgels

Lutein (Capsules, Softgels)

Lycopene Capsules

Memory & Mood Supplement

Menopause Complex AM PM

Odorfree Garlic

Omega Super Softgels

Panax Ginseng

Papaya Enzyme

Phytosterol Esters

Policosanol Capsules

Potassium Natural Caplets

Saw Palmetto Softgels

supplements

Rx

Soy Isoflavones
St. John's Wort Caplets
Super Omega
Vision Formula w/Lutein
Vitamin Mineral Herb Menopause Supplement

Member's Mark -
Cranberry
Co Q 10 (200 mg, 400 mg)
Fish Oil (1000 mg, 1200 mg)
Flaxseed Oil
Garlic 1000 mg
Gingko Biloba
Glucosamine +MSM
Glucosamine
Green Tea
Lutein
Omega 3 6 9
Probiotic Formula Acidophilus
Red Yeast Rice

Natrol - All Products *(EXCEPT Acai Berry Diet, Broccoli Festiv, Carb Intercept Sprinkles, Digest Support, Juice Festiv, Melatonin Liquid, MFM Original, MFM Prime, Oat Bran Tablets, Papaya Enzyme, Probiotic Intestinal Max Care, Resveratrol Diet, Resveratrol Plus)*

Nature's Basket -
100% Organic Spirulina Tablets
Acidophilus Bifidus
Advanced Antioxidant Complex Veg Caps
Alpha Lipoic Acid
Amino Acid Complex Tabs
Beta Carotene 25000 IU
Biotin (5 mg, 500 mg)
Brain Formula
Cardio Formula

Rx

Chelated Cal Mag
Chewable (Calcium, Peppermint Enzyme)
Cholesterol Complex
Chromium Picolinate
Co Q 10 (30mg, 60 mg, 100mg)
Cod Liver Oil
Complete Omega Complex
Concentrated Omega 3
Echinacea 400mg
Enzyme Complex w/Herbs
EPA & DHA Softgels
Evening Primrose Oil (500 mg Softgels)
Eye Formula
Flax Seed Oil 1000mg
Folic Acid 800
Garlic 500mg
Gingko Biloba 80mg
Glucosamine (Chondroitin, Sulfate)
Green Tea Extract 250 mg
Kidfit Tigers
L Carnitine 500mg
L Glutamine 500 mg
L Lysine 500 mg
Lecithin 1200mg
Liver Detox Complex
Lutein 20 mg Softgels
Maximum One
Mega Magnesium
Melatonin 3mg
Mens 45+
Mens Multi Food Rich
Milk Thistle 175mg
Niacin 100mg
No Flush Niacin 500mg

Rx

Non GMO Soy Protein Powder
Ocu Complete
One Daily Multiple 60
Organic Greens N' Things Vegan Powder
Organic Reds N' Things Vegan Powder
Organic Soy Protein Powder (Chocolate, Vanilla)
Potassium 99mg
Prenatal Complete
Probiotic Quattro
Prostate Formula
Psyllium Husk
Saw Palmetto 160mg
Whey Protein Powder (Chocolate, Original)
Novasource - Renal High Calorie Supplement Pack (Vanilla)
Nutrition Now - All Varieties
Os-Cal - Calcium Supplement (500+ D, 500 + Extra D, 500 +
Extra D Chewable, Ultra)
Pioneer - All Supplements
Publix -
Acidophilus
Adult Cold Relief
Balanced Nutritional Drink (Chocolate, Chocolate Plus,
Strawberry, Strawberry Plus, Vanilla, Vanilla Plus)
Beta-Carotene
Calcium (Citrate Caplets, Oyster Shell w/Vitamin D Tablets,
Tablets, w/Vitamin D Tablets)
Children's Cough Cold Allergy
Cough Drops
Cranberry Caplets
Echinacea Caplets
Evening Primrose Oil Softgels
Fish Oil Softgels
Folic 400mcg Natural Tablets
Ginkgo Biloba Caplets

Rx
    Glucosamine Chondroitin
    L Lysine Natural Tablets
    Lutein
    Magnesium Natural Tablets
    Mouth Rinses
    Niacin Time-Release Tablets
    Potassium Gluconate
    Saw Palmetto Softgels
    Selenium Tablets
    St. John's Wort
    Tussins
    Zinc Natural Caplets

Renew Life -
    Probiotics (Ultimate Flora (Adult Formula, Critical Care, Senior
        Formula))
    Enzymes (Candi Zyme, Constipation Stop, Digest More, Digest
        More Ultra, Gas Stop, Heartburn Prevention, Indigestion Stop,
        Paragone)

Schiff - Probiotics Acidophilus (Tablets)

Schiff Move Free - Advanced (Plus MSM Tablets, Regular)

Simplexity Health -
    Acidophilus
    Alpha Sun (Capsules, Tablets)
    Bifidus
    ImmuSun
    Omega Sun (Capsules, Tablets)
    OsteoSun
    Simply SBGA
    StemPlex
    Super Q10
    Super Sun Smoothie

Walgreens -
    3 In 1 Mens
    3 In 1 Womens

supplements

Rx

5 HTP Fast Acting Capsules Maximum Strength
Absorbable Calcium Softgels
Acetyl L Carnitine
Acidophilus (Bifidus Regularis Beads, Capsules, Chewable,
   Chewable Wafers w/Bifidus, Gold Capsules, Ultimate Probiotic)
Apple Cider Vinegar Tablets
Biotin Super Strength Tablets
Black Cohosh Root
Breast Solutions Complex Tablet
Cholesterol Health Caplets
Cinnamon (Capsules, Plus Chromium Capsules)
Citrate Of Magnesium (Low Sodium Cherry, Regular)
CoQ 10 Softgels
Cod Liver Oil Softgels
Collagen w/Vitamin C Tablets
Cranberry (Extract Tablets, Triple Strength Softgels (Regular,
   w/C&E))
Echinacea
Estronatural Caplets
Evening Primrose Oil
Bilberry Softgels Extra Strength
Ferrous Tablets (Gluconate, Sulfate)
Finest Naturals
   DHA Omega 3 Softgels
   Coenzyme Q10 Chewable Tablets
   Cranberry Tablets
   Echinacea (Tablets, w/Vitamin C Capsules)
   Estronatural Caplets (Regular, Extra Strength)
   Flaxseed Oil Softgels
   Fish Oil Enteric Softgels
   Ginkgo (Tablets, Capsules)
   Ginseng Capsules
   Grapeseed Tablets
   Green Tea Capsules

Rx

Iron

L Carnitine Capsule

Milk Thistle Caspules

Natural DHA Complete

Pomegranate Capsules

Primrose Oil Softgels

Resveratrol Capsules

Saw Palmetto Softgels

Soy Isoflavonoid Capsules

St. John's Wort Tablets

Fish Oil Softgels (Cholesterol Free, EPA Bonus, Highly Concentrated Omega 3, High Potency, Odorless (Double Strength, Regular), Regular, w/Co Q 10)

Flax Seed Oil (Fish Borage, Liquid, Softgels)

Flush Free Niacin

Garlic (High Potency Odorless, Odorless, Regular)

Ginger Root Capsules

Gingko Biloba

Ginsana

Ginseng (Complex Plus Royal Jelly, Softgels)

Glucosamine (& Condroitin (DS Caplets, MSM Advanced, Triple Strength), Sulfate)

Grapeseed Extract Tablets

Green Tea Extract w/EGCG

Gripe Water

Horny Goat Weed

L Arginine Tablets

L Carnitine Caplets

Lecithin Softgels

Lutein (Plus Billberry, Softgels)

Magnesium Tablets (Oxide, Natural, Regular)

Melatonin Tablets

Milk Thistle Softgels

Natural Woman Menopause Supplement

Rx

    Omega Super Softgels (Cholesterol Health, Regular)
    Papaya Enzyme Natural Tablet
    Pomegranate
    Red Yeast Rice
    Resveratrol
    Saw Palmetto (Capsules, Softgels)
    Sea Thin
    Shark Cartilage Caplets
    Skin Hair & Nails Formula
    St John's Wort (Extract, Tablets)
    Super Goat Weed
    Super Strength Enzyme Formula Tablets
    Tea Tree Oil Liquid
    Theragran M Glucosamine & Condroitin Tablets (DS, TS)
    Turmeric Curcumin Capsules
    Valerian Root (Extra Strength, Plus Calming Blend)
    Zinc Natural Caplets
Viactiv - All Soft Multivitamin Chews

Vitamins & Minerals

Carlson - All Vitamins
Country Life - All Vitamins ●
Freeda - All Vitamins ●
Geritol - Multi Vitamin
Giant Eagle Brand-
    B 50 Tablets
    Vitamin A 10,000 IU
    Vitamin ABC w/Lutein & Lycopene
    Vitamin B 6
    Vitamin B 12
    Vitamin B Complex w/Vitamin C
    Vitamin C (250mg, 500mg, 500mg w/Rose Hips, 1000 mg,
        1000mg w/Rose Hips, Time Release)

Rx   Vitamin D 400
Vitamin E (200IU, 400IU, 400IU Natural, 400 Water Dispersible,
  1000IU)
Hannaford Brand –
  B 6 (100, 200)
  B 12 (100, 250, 500, 2000)
  B 50
  B Complex (& Vitamin C, w/Folic Acid & Vitamin C)
  One Daily (Multi Vitamin Daily, For Men, For Men +50)
  Vitamin A 8000 IU
  Vitamin C (500, 1000, w/Rose Hips 500, w/Rose Hips 1000)
  Vitamin D (400, 1000)
  Vitamin E (200, 400, 1000)
Hy-Vee Health Market –
  Calcium 600 Plus D
  Natural B Complex w/Vitamin C
  Natural Vitamin E (200, 400, 1000)
  Vitamin A 10,000 IU
  Vitamin E (200, 400, 1000)
Kirkland Signature -
  Calcium 600mg Plus D3
  Calcium Citrate w/500mg Calcium
  Mature Multi Vitamin
  Premium Performance Multi Vitamin
  Vitamin B 100
  Vitamin C 500mg
  Vitamin C 1000mg
  Vitamin D 3 2000IU
  Vitamin E 400 IU
Kirkman -
  Advanced Adult Multi Vitamin
  Advanced Mineral Support
  B Complex w/CoEnzymes Pro Support (Capsules, Powder)
  Buffered Vitamin C Powder

vitamins & minerals

Rx

Calcium Bio Max Series
Calcium Magnesium Liquid
Calcium w/o Vitamin D Bio Max Series
Calcium w/Vitamin D (Chewable Tablets, Powder Unflavored)
Children's Chewable Multi Vitamin/Mineral (Capsules, Wafers)
D Biotin
Multi Mineral Complex Pro Support
Multi Vitamin Pro Support
Mycellized Vitamin A Liquid
Perry Prenatal
Vitamin B6 (Magnesium Vitamin/Mineral Chewable Wafers,
    Regular)
Vitamin C (Bio Max Series Buffered Powder Flavored, Bio Max
    Series Buffered Powder Unflavored, Capsules, Chewables,
    Tablets)
Vitamin D
Vitamin D 3
Vitamin E
Zinc (Bio Max Series, Liquid, Sulfate, w/Vitamin C & Slippery Elm
    Lozenges)
Meijer -
50 Plus w/Ester C
A Shaped (Gummy Chewables, w/Iron Chewables)
Advanced Formula w/Ester C
Calcium (All Day w/Vitamin D, Citrate Chewable, Citrate w/
    Vitamin D Caplets, Coral, Magnesium Zinc Caplets, Natural
    Oyster Shell Tablets, Phosphorus Plus D, Tablets, w/D
    Chewables, w/D Mineral Tablets, w/Soy Tablets)
Central Vitamin Select
Daily Energy Multi Caplets
Ester C
Ferrous Sulfate (Green Tablets, TR Tablets)
Multivitamin (Bone Health, Cardio Caplets, Century Advantage,
    Century Mature Tablets, Century Tablets, Hi Potency Men, Hi

Rx Potency Women, Inov., Inov. Complete, Inov. Prenatal, Prenatal
Tablets, RDI Cholesterol Caplets, RDI Diet Tablets, RDI Men
Tablets, RDI Tablets, SNR Tablets, Super Kid Chewables, Thera
M Caplets)

Niacin Tablets

One Daily Plus (Mens Tablets, Womens Tablets)

Slow Release Iron

Teen Multi Caplets

Vitamin A

Vitamin B (Complex w/Iron, Natural Tablets, Regular Tablets,
Synthetic Tablets, Time Release Tablets)

Vitamin B12 Tablets

Vitamin C (Caplets, Fruit Chewables, Natural w/Rosehips Caplets,
Synthetic Orange Chewables, Synthetic Tablets)

Vitamin E (Blended Softgels, Natural Softgels, Oil, Synthetic
Softgels, Regular, w/Fish Oil, w/Vitamin C)

Zinc Natural Caplets

Member's Mark -

Calcium Liquigels 600mg

Calcium Plus Vitamin D & Plus Vitamins

Chewable Vitamin C

Complete Multivitamin

Niacin

Potassium

Slow Release Iron

Vitamin B12

Vitamin B Complex w/Vitamin C

Vitamin C w/Natural Rose Hips

Vitamin D3

Vitamin E

Natrol - All Products *(EXCEPT Acai Berry Diet, Broccoli Festiv,
Carb Intercept Sprinkles, Digest Support, Juice Festiv,
Melatonin Liquid, MFM Original, MFM Prime, Oat Bran Tablets,
Papaya Enzyme, Probiotic Intestinal Max Care, Resveratrol
Diet, Resveratrol Plus)*

vitamins & minerals

Rx

Nature's Basket -
- All Day C 500mg
- B 12 Lozengiant Eagle
- B Complex (50mg, 100mg)
- B Complex w/Vitamin C
- B Complex 100mg
- Cal Mag (Regular, Zinc)
- Calcium 600mg w/Vitamin D
- Calcium Citrate w/Vitamin D
- Softgels Multi
- Supreme Stress B Cap
- Vegetarian Multi
- Vitamin A
- Vitamin A & D
- Vitamin B 12
- Vitamin C (500mg, 1000mg)
- Vitamin C Chewable 500mg
- Vitamin D (Regular, Oil)
- Vitamin E (200IU, E 400IU)
- Womens 45
- Womens Multi Food Rich
- Zinc 50mg
- Zinc Lozengiant Eaglecool LMN

Nutrition Now - All Varieties

Ocuvite - Adult 50+ Lutein & Omega 3 Formula, Ocuvite, Ocuvite Lutein

Pioneer - All Vitamins

Publix -
- Vitamin B (6, 12)
- Vitamin C (Fruit Chewables, Tablets, Time Release Tablets
- Vitamin E (400IU, 1000IU)

Schiff - Niacin Flush Free (Tablets)

Slice of Life - Gummy Vitamins For Adults (All Varieties)

Viactiv - All Soft Multivitamin Chews

Rx Walgreens -

Alpha Lipoic Acid Capsules

B 12 (Oral, Sublingual (Liquid, Tablet))

B Complex + C T/R Tablets

Biotin Tablets

Calcium (Chewable (Caramel, Chocolate)

Creamies (Fruit , Neapolitan, Softgels, w/Vitamin D Chews)

Disney Princess Gummies Multivitamin

Finest Naturals Vitamin D 3 Softgels

L'il Critters (Gummy Vitamins, Immune C Plus Zinc & Echinacea,
Omega 3 Gummy Fish)

Multi Vitamin (50 Plus, Century Advantage Tablets, High Potency
Men's, Mature Tablets, Prenatal, RDI Tablet, RDI w/Iron)

Niacin (EP Plain, SLO, Softgels)

Theragran Multi Vitamin (50 Plus, Mature Caplets, Inov. Caplets)

Prenatal Complete Plus DHA (Softgels, Tablet)

Potassium Natural Tablets

Super B Maxi Complex Caplets

Vitamin C (Regular, w/Rose Hips)

Vitamin D

Vitamin E 400 Natural D Alpha Softgels

Vitamin E Oil

Yummi Bears - All Varieties (Organic, Regular)

Weight Loss

Alli

Arbonne - Figure 8 On The Go Weight Loss Chocolate Chews

CLA Tonalin - Softgels

Hoodia - Day Slim, Hoodia Max, Night Slim

Natrol- CitriMax Plus, Pure Citrimax

Index

index

index

index

U

V

W

X

Y

Z

Gluten-Free OTC Pharmacy Rx

index

Gluten-Free Sponsors

NOTES

NOTES

NOTES

NOTES

Making Gluten-Free Living Easy!

Cecelia's Marketplace
Kalamazoo, Michigan

www.CeceliasMarketplace.com

Mail In Order Form

Quick Order Form

Online Orders: www.CeceliasMarketplace.com

✉ Mail Orders: Kal-Haven Publishing
P.O. Box 20383
Kalamazoo, MI 49019
U.S.A.

Cecelia's Marketplace	Quantity	Price	Total
Gluten-Free Grocery Shopping Guide	_____	(x $24.95) =	_____
Gluten/Casein Free Grocery Shopping Guide	_____	(x $24.95) =	_____
Gluten/Casein/Soy Free Grocery Shopping Guide	_____	(x $24.95) =	_____
Gluten-Free Mexican Cookbook	_____	(x $14.95) =	_____

Sales Tax: Michigan residents please add 6% sales tax _____

Sub Total: _____

Shipping: (quantities 1-2 add $5.95)
(quantities 3-6 add $11.95) _____

Total: _____

*Please make check or money order payable to Kal-Haven Publishing

Name: _____

Address: _____

City: _____ State: _____ Zip: _____

Email address: _____

Making Gluten-Free Living Easy!

Cecelia's Marketplace
Kalamazoo, Michigan

www.CeceliasMarketplace.com

Mail In Order Form

Quick Order Form

 Online Orders: www.CeceliasMarketplace.com

✉ Mail Orders: Kal-Haven Publishing
P.O. Box 20383
Kalamazoo, MI 49019
U.S.A.

Cecelia's Marketplace	Quantity	Price	Total
Gluten-Free Grocery Shopping Guide	_____	(x $24.95) =	_____
Gluten/Casein Free Grocery Shopping Guide	_____	(x $24.95) =	_____
Gluten/Casein/Soy Free Grocery Shopping Guide	_____	(x $24.95) =	_____
Gluten-Free Mexican Cookbook	_____	(x $14.95) =	_____

Sales Tax: Michigan residents please add 6% sales tax _____

Sub Total: _____

Shipping: (quantities 1-2 add $5.95)
(quantities 3-6 add $11.95) _____

Total: _____

*Please make check or money order payable to Kal-Haven Publishing

Name: _____

Address:_____

City:_____State:_____Zip:_____

Email address:_____

Making Gluten-Free Living Easy!

Cecelia's Marketplace
Kalamazoo, Michigan

www.CeceliasMarketplace.com

Mail In Order Form

Quick Order Form

 Online Orders: www.CeceliasMarketplace.com

✉ Mail Orders: Kal-Haven Publishing
P.O. Box 20383
Kalamazoo, MI 49019
U.S.A.

Cecelia's Marketplace	Quantity	Price	Total
Gluten-Free Grocery Shopping Guide	_____	(x $24.95) =	_____
Gluten/Casein Free Grocery Shopping Guide	_____	(x $24.95) =	_____
Gluten/Casein/Soy Free Grocery Shopping Guide	_____	(x $24.95) =	_____
Gluten-Free Mexican Cookbook	_____	(x $14.95) =	_____

Sales Tax: Michigan residents please add 6% sales tax _____

Sub Total: _____

Shipping: (quantities 1-2 add $5.95)
(quantities 3-6 add $11.95) _____

Total: _____

*Please make check or money order payable to Kal-Haven Publishing

Name: _____

Address: _____

City: _____ State: _____ Zip: _____

Email address: _____

Making Gluten-Free Living Easy!

Cecelia's Marketplace
Kalamazoo, Michigan

www.CeceliasMarketplace.com

Mail In Order Form

Quick Order Form

 Online Orders: www.CeceliasMarketplace.com

✉ **Mail Orders:** Kal-Haven Publishing
P.O. Box 20383
Kalamazoo, MI 49019
U.S.A.

Cecelia's Marketplace	Quantity	Price	Total
Gluten-Free Grocery Shopping Guide	_____	(x $24.95) =	_____
Gluten/Casein Free Grocery Shopping Guide	_____	(x $24.95) =	_____
Gluten/Casein/Soy Free Grocery Shopping Guide	_____	(x $24.95) =	_____
Gluten-Free Mexican Cookbook	_____	(x $14.95) =	_____

Sales Tax: Michigan residents please add 6% sales tax _____

Sub Total: _____

Shipping: (quantities 1-2 add $5.95)
(quantities 3-6 add $11.95) _____

Total: _____

*Please make check or money order payable to Kal-Haven Publishing

Name: _____

Address:_____

City:_____ State:_____ Zip:_____

Email address:_____